iWrite Math

Foundations of Mathematics and Pre-Calculus 10 Book

- ***Number***
- ***Exponents***
- ***Measurement***
- ***Trigonometry***
- ***Polynomial Operations***
- ***Factoring Polynomial Expressions***
- ***Relations and Functions***
- ***Characteristics of Linear Relations***
- ***Equations of Linear Relations***
- ***Systems of Linear Equations***

Publisher: Absolute Value Publications

Authors: Alan Appleby, Greg Ranieri

Printed in Canada.

ISBN 978-0-9780872-5-8

For information contact:

Absolute Value Publications Inc.
P.O. Box 71096
8060 Silver Springs Blvd. N.W.
Calgary, Alberta
T3B 5K1

Bus: (403) 313-1442
Fax: (403) 313-2042

e-mail: avp@avpbooks.com
avp@absolutevaluepublications.com

web site: www.avpbooks.com
www.absolutevaluepublications.com

About this FPC 10 Math Workbook

The iWrite Math Foundations of Mathematics and Pre-Calculus 10 Book is a complete resource for the combined Western and Northern Canadian mathematics curriculum.

Each curricular unit is subdivided into individual lessons. The last lesson in each unit is a practice test containing 15 multiple choice questions, 5 numeric response questions, and 1 extended response question.

Most lessons can be covered in one hour (plus homework time), but some may require more time to complete. Most lessons are composed of four parts:

- ***Investigations, Explorations, or Review*** - Inquiry based learning that can be teacher led, student led, or a combination of both.
- ***Class Examples*** - intended to be instructor led.
- ***Assignments*** - short response, extended response, multiple choice and numeric response questions provided for student practice.
- ***Answer Key*** - answers to the assignment questions.

The **Teacher Solution Manual** is a complete copy of the book with detailed solutions to all the Investigations/Explorations/Review, Class Examples, and Assignments included.

The **Student Solution Manual** provides detailed solutions to all the Investigations/Explorations/Review, Class Examples, and Assignment questions. It does not include the actual questions.

Acknowledgments

We would like to acknowledge the following people for their contributions in the production of this book:

- Jason Crawford, Tony Audia, Susan Appleby, and Rose Ranieri for their help in proofreading, editing, and reviewing the material.

- Our students for their suggestions, opinions, and encouragement.

- Robert Letal and Darryl Marchand for their advice and support.

Advantages for Students

- Students write **in** the book so that the math theory, worked examples, and assignments are all in one place for easy review.
- Students can write on the diagrams and graphs.
- Provides class examples and assignments so that students can use their time more efficiently. By focusing on solving problems and making their own notes, students improve their study skills.
- For independent learners, the book plus solution manual fosters self-paced learning.
- Encourages inquiry-based learning, group learning, and peer tutoring.
- The design of the book ensures that students are fully aware of the course expectations.
- The iWrite Math book is also available as an app at the Apple iTunes Store.
- We hope you enjoy using this book and that with the help of your teacher you realize the success that thousands of students each year are achieving using the book series.

Advantages for Teachers

- Written by teachers experienced in preparing students for success in high school and diploma examinations.
- Comprehensively covers the Western and Northern Canadian curriculum.
- Can be used as the main resource, or in conjunction with a textbook, or for extra assignments, or review.
- Reduces school photocopying costs and time.
- Allows for easy lesson planning in the case of teacher or student absence.
- The iWrite Math series is available in the following fromats:
    - Book
    - App form for tablets
    - Promethean Flipchart
    - One Note
    - Smart Notebook
    - Windows Journal

Student, teacher, and parent responses to the iWrite Math book series have been very positive. We welcome your feedback. It enables us to produce a high quality resource meeting our goal of success for both students and teachers.

iWrite Math Foundations of Mathematics and Pre-Calculus 10 Book
Table of Contents

Factoring Polynomial Expressions

Relations and Functions

Characteristics of Linear Relations

Equations of Linear Relations

Systems of Linear Equations

Notes Pages

Number Lesson #1:
Prime Factors

Overview

In this unit we look at prime factors of whole numbers and applications: including, greatest common factor, least common multiple, square root and cube root.
We also look at the real number system with particular emphasis on rational and irrational numbers and on the relationship between mixed and entire radicals.

Factors

The whole number 6 is exactly divisible by 1, 2, 3, and 6 and by no other whole numbers.

The numbers 1, 2, 3, and 6 are the **factors** of the whole number 6.

The number 6 has four factors.

State the factors of the following:

a) 15   **b)** 24

1, 15, 3, 5   12, 2, 6, 4, 8, 3, 1, 24

In each case, determine the number of factors of the given whole number.

a) 3   **b)** 10   **c)** 1   **d)** 7   **e)** 18

3, 1   10, 1, 2, 5   1   7, 1   3, 6, 18, 1, 9, 2

two #   four #   one #   two #   six #

Prime and Composite Numbers

A **prime number** is defined as a whole number which has exactly two factors.
The two factors are always 1 and the number itself, e.g. 3, 7.

A **composite number** is a whole number which has more than two factors, e.g. 10, 18.

The number 1 has only one factor and is neither prime nor composite.

In this course the number 0 is defined to have no factors.

Complete the list of the first ten prime numbers;

2, 3, 5, 7, 11, 13, 17, 19, 23, 29, ...

Classify the following whole numbers as prime or composite.

a) 46 **b)** 37 **c)** 39 **d)** 101 **e)** 103

Composite *prime* *composite* *prime* *prime*

Prime Factors

The **prime factors** of a whole number are the factors of the number which are prime.

For example The factors of 6 are 1, 2, 3, and 6.

The prime factors of 6 are 2 and 3.

a) State the factors of 12.

12, 1, 2, 6, 3, 4

b) State the prime factors of 12.

2, 3

c) Express 12 as a product of prime factors.

2 × 2 × 3

$2^2 \times 3$

Prime Factorization

Every composite number can be expressed as a product of prime factors. Expressing a whole number as a product of prime factors is called the prime factorization of the number.

The prime factorization of small numbers like 12 can probably be done mentally, but, for larger numbers, a division table or a tree diagram can be used.

The diagrams below illustrate these techniques for the prime factorization of 48.

division table tree diagram

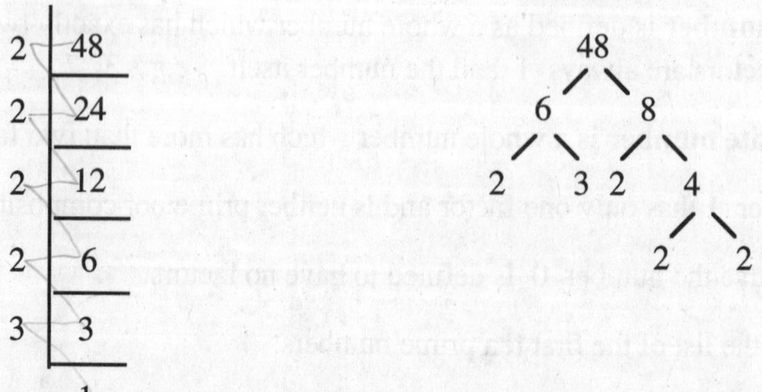

$48 = 2 \times 2 \times 2 \times 2 \times 3$ or $2^4 \times 3$

Class Ex. #5

Use a division table to determine the prime factorization of 2 772.

$2^2 \cdot 3^2 \cdot 11$

2	2772
2	1386
3	693
3	231
11	77
1	7
	1

Class Ex. #6

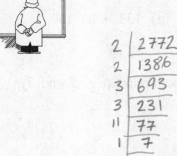

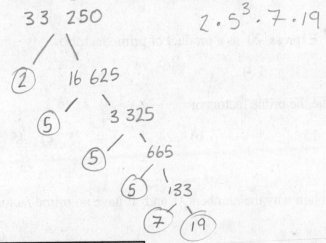

Use a tree diagram to determine the prime factorization of 33 250.

33 250

(2) 16 625

(5) 3 325

(5) 665

(5) 133

(7) (19)

$2 \cdot 5^3 \cdot 7 \cdot 19$

Complete Assignment Questions #1 - #16

Assignment

1. State the factors of the following:

a) 21 3, 7, 21, 1 **b)** 22 11, 2, 22, 1

c) 25 25, 1, 5, **d)** 36 6, 36, 1, 2, 18

2. In each case, determine the number of factors of the given whole number.

a) 8 — 8, 1, 4, 2 — four # **b)** 11 — 11, 1 — two # **c)** 17 — 17, 1 — two # **d)** 33 — 3, 11, 1, 33 — four # **e)** 45 — 15, 9, 5, 45, 1, 3 — six #

3. State the numbers in question #2 which are

a) prime 11, 17 **b)** composite 8, 33, 45

4. Classify the following whole numbers as prime or composite.

a) 30 **b)** 41 **c)** 43 **d)** 57 **e)** 59 **f)** 121 **g)** 133 **h)** 169

composite prime prime composite prime composite composite composite

5. Twin primes are defined to be consecutive odd numbers that are both prime (e.g. 5 and 7). List the seven other twin primes less than 80.

6. a) State the factors of 20.

10, 20, 1, 2, 5, 4

b) State the prime factors of 20.

2, 5

c) Express 20 as a product of prime factors.

2 × 5 × 2

7. State the prime factors of

a) 15 **b)** 24 **c)** 45 **d)** 66

3, 5 3 5, 3 11, 3, 2

8. Explain why the numbers 0 and 1 have no prime factors.

0 does not contain at least 2 factors

1 only contains 1 factor

Prime # contain 2 factors that are 1 and itself.

9. Use a division table to determine the prime factorization of

a) 140 **b)** 330 **c)** 1 911 **d)** 1 925

a)		b)		c)		d)	
2	140	2	330	3	1911	5	1925
2	70	5	165	7	637	5	385
5	35	11	33	7	91	11	77
7	7	3	3	13	13	7	7
	1		1		1		1

10. Use a tree diagram to determine the prime factorization of the following:

 a) 390 **b)** 546 **c)** 3 705 **d)** 6 762

390
2 195
39 5
3 13

546
2 273
91 3
7 13

3705
2 741
247 3
13 19

6762
2 3381
1127 3
7 161
7 23

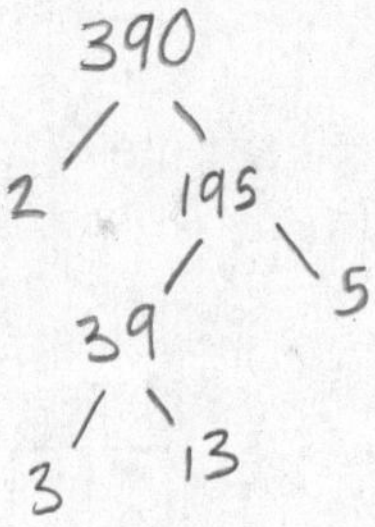

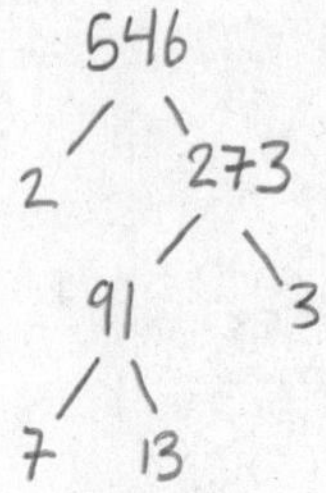

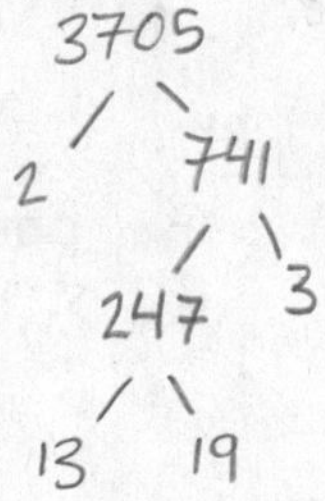

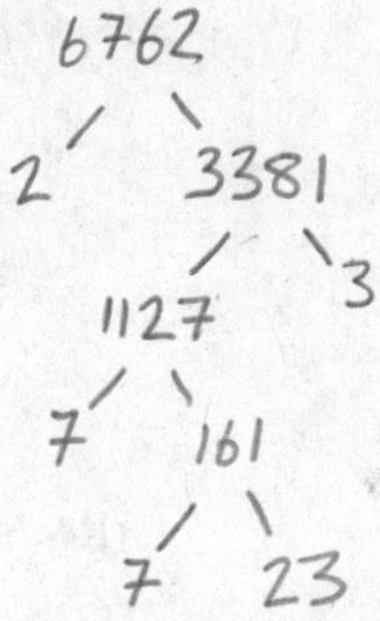

11. In each case write the number as a product of prime factors.

 a) 189 **b)** 685 **c)** 4 235 **d)** 7 980

$3 \times 7 \times 7$ 137×5 $11 \times 11 \times (5 \times 7)$ $19 \times 3 \times 7 \times 2 \times 5 \times 2$

Multiple Choice **12.** Which of the following numbers is not a prime factor of 1 925?

 A. 5
 B. 7
 C. 11
 D. 13

13. How many of the numbers in the list 2, 3, 9, 13 are not prime factors of 2 592?

 A. 4
 B. 3
 C. 2
 D. 1

Numerical Response

14. The sum of all of the prime factors of 373 065 is <u>6</u>.

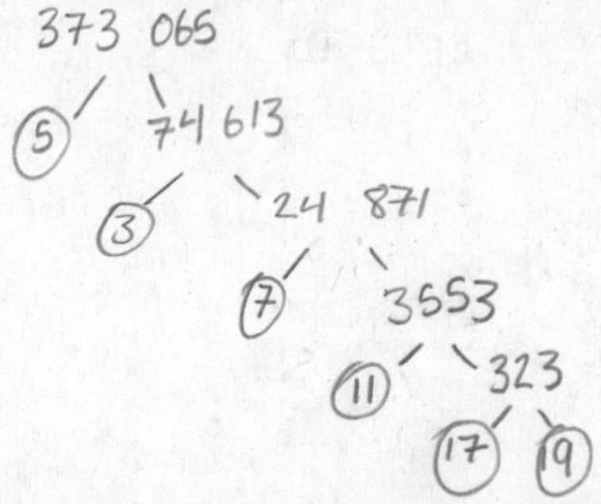

(Record your answer in the numerical response box from left to right)

15. There is only one set of prime triplets: three consecutive odd numbers which are all prime. If the prime triplets are a, b, and c, then the value of abc is ______.

(Record your answer in the numerical response box from left to right)

16. The number 686 can be expressed as a product of prime factors in the form $p \times q^r$. The value of $p + q + r$ is ______.

(Record your answer in the numerical response box from left to right)

Answer Key

1.a) 1, 3, 7, 21 **b)** 1, 2, 11, 22 **c)** 1, 5, 25 **d)** 1, 2, 3, 4, 6, 9, 12, 18, 36

2.a) 4 **b)** 2 **c)** 2 **d)** 4 **e)** 6 **3. a)** 11, 17 **b)** 8, 33, 45

4.a) composite **b)** prime **c)** prime **d)** composite **e)** prime **f)** composite **g)** composite **h)** composite

5. 3 and 5, 11 and 13, 17 and 19, 29 and 31, 41 and 43, 59 and 61, 71 and 73.

6.a) 1, 2, 4, 5, 10, 20 **b)** 2, 5 **c)** $2 \times 2 \times 5$ **7. a)** 3, 5 **b)** 2, 3 **c)** 3, 5 **d)** 2, 3, 11

8. 0 is defined to have no factors and 1 has only one factor. Since a prime number has exactly two factors there cannot be any prime numbers which are factors of 0 or 1.

9.a) $2 \times 2 \times 5 \times 7$ **b)** $2 \times 3 \times 5 \times 11$ **c)** $3 \times 7 \times 7 \times 13$ **d)** $5 \times 5 \times 7 \times 11$

10.a) $2 \times 3 \times 5 \times 13$ **b)** $2 \times 3 \times 7 \times 13$ **c)** $3 \times 5 \times 13 \times 19$ **d)** $2 \times 3 \times 7 \times 7 \times 23$

11.a) $3 \times 3 \times 3 \times 7$ **b)** 5×137 **c)** $5 \times 7 \times 11 \times 11$ **d)** $2 \times 2 \times 3 \times 5 \times 7 \times 19$

12. D **13.** C **14.** | 6 | 2 | | | **15.** | 1 | 0 | 5 | | **16.** | 1 | 2 | | |

Number Lesson #2:
Applications of Prime Factors

Review

Express the numbers 48 and 72 as products of prime factors.

$48 = 2 \times 2 \times 2 \times 2 \times 3 \rightarrow 48 = 2^4 \cdot 3$

$72 = 2 \times 2 \times 3 \times 2 \times 3 \rightarrow 72 = 2^3 \cdot 3^2$

Greatest Common Factor

The **greatest common factor** (GCF) of a set of whole numbers is the largest whole number which divides exactly into each of the members of the set.

For example, the GCF of 8, 16, and 20 is 4.

State the greatest common factor of

a) 15, 25, and 35 5 **b)** 18 and 20 2 **c)** 36 and 54

In the example above, parts a) and b) were fairly simple to do, but part c) was more complicated because each number had a large number of factors.

In cases like this we can use prime factorization to determine the GCF.

From the warm-up $48 = 2 \times 2 \times 2 \times 2 \times 3$ and $72 = 2 \times 2 \times 2 \times 3 \times 3$.

To determine the greatest common factor of 48 and 72 we find the product of each prime factor (including repeats) which is common to each prime factorization.

GCF of 48 and 72 is $2 \times 2 \times 2 \times 3 =$ ____.

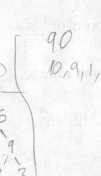

Use prime factorization to determine the greatest common factor of the given whole numbers.

a) 90 and 225 **b)** 154 and 198

90

10, 9, 1,

90 → 2, 45 → 5, 9 → 3, 3

Class Ex. #3 Use prime factorization to determine the greatest common factor of the given whole numbers.

a) 245, 315, and 770 **b)** 171, 285, 399, and 1 140

$5 \cdot 7^2$ $3^2 \cdot 5 \cdot 7$ $2 \cdot 5 \cdot 7 \cdot 11$

$$2^6 \cdot 3^6 \cdot 5^1 \cdot 7^1 \cdot 11^0$$
$$= 35$$

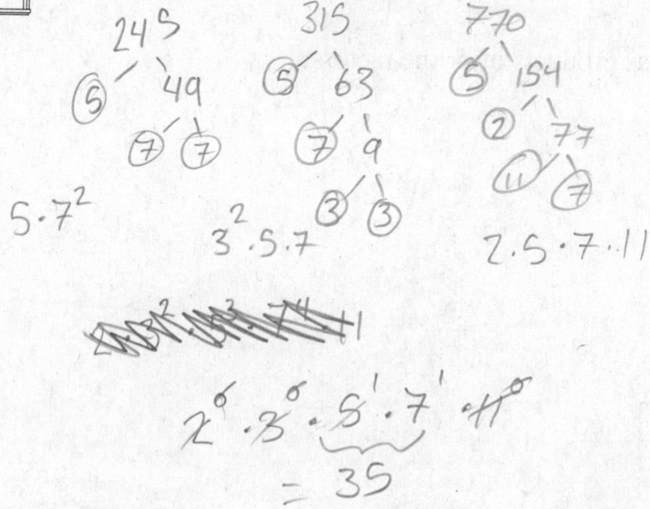

Lowest Common Multiple

Multiples of 6 are 6, 12, 18, 24, 30, 36, 42, 48,

Multiples of 8 are 8, 16, 24, 32, 40, 48, 5,

Common multiples of 6 and 8 are 24, 48,

The **lowest common multiple** (LCM) of 6 and 8 is ____ .

Class Ex. #4 State the lowest common multiple of the following:

a) 5 and 7 **b)** 10, 15, and 20 **b)** 10, 12, and 14

In the example above, parts a) and b) were fairly simple to do, but part c) was more complicated. Prime factors can be used to simplify the solution.

$10 = \mathbf{2 \times 5}$ To determine the LCM, take all the prime factors of one of the numbers and multiply by any additional factors in the other numbers.

$12 = \mathbf{2 \times 2 \times 3}$

$14 = \mathbf{2 \times 7}$ Take **2** and **5** from 10, another **2** and **3** from 12, and **7** from 14.

$\mathbf{2 \times 5 \times 2 \times 3 \times 7} =$ _____ , the LCM of 10, 12, and 14.

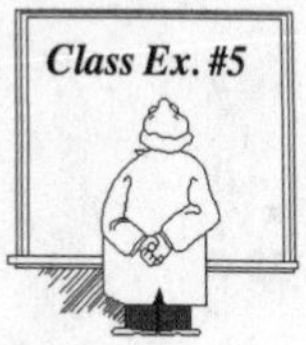

Use prime factorization to determine the lowest common multiple of

a) 15 and 35 **b)** 126 and 441 **c)** 22, 154, and 198

Complete Assignment Questions #1 - #7

Prime Factorization of a Perfect Square

Perfect squares of whole numbers include 1, 4, 9, 16, 25, 36, 49, etc.

Every perfect square has two **square roots**: one positive and one negative. The square root which is positive is called the **principal square root.**

The principal square root of each number above is 1, 2, 3, 4, 5, 6, 7, etc.

In this lesson, where we are dealing only with whole numbers, we will use the term square root to mean the principal square root.

Complete the prime factorization of the following perfect squares: 9, 36, 49, and 64.

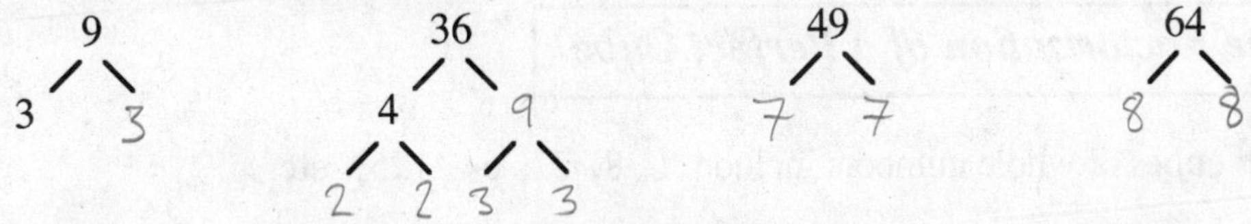

$9 = 3 \times 3$ The square root of 9 is 3

$36 = 2 \times 2 \times \quad \times$ The square root of 36 is $2 \times 3 =$

$49 =$ The square root of 49 is

$64 =$ The square root of 64 is $2 \times \quad \times \quad =$

The prime factorization of a perfect square will involve factors which occur in pairs.

If the prime factorization of a number does not result in pairs of factors, then we can say that the number is not a perfect square.

Class Ex. #6

Consider the number 44 100.

a) Use a calculator to find the square root of 44 100.

b) **Explain** how we can use the prime factorization of 44 100 to show that 44 100 is a perfect square. Verify your calculator answer by this method.

Class Ex. #7

In each case use prime factorization to determine if the number is a perfect square. If the number is a perfect square, state the square root of the number.

a) 1 225 **b)** 3 042

Prime Factorization of a Perfect Cube

Perfect cubes of whole numbers include 1, 8, 27, 64, 125, etc.

The **cube root** of each number above is 1, 2, 3, 4, 5, etc.

Complete the prime factorization of the following perfect cubes: 27, 216, and 3 375.

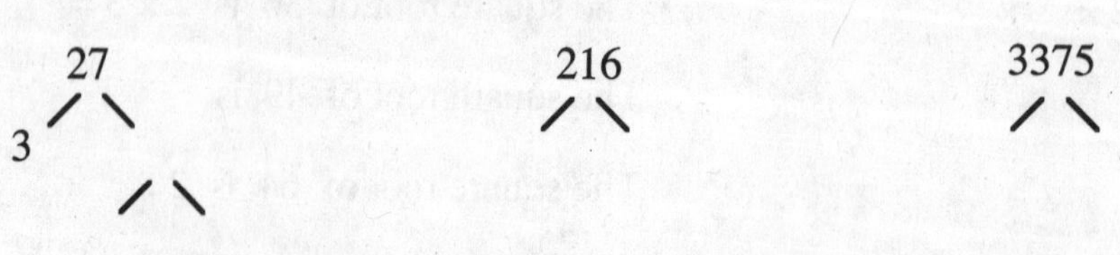

The prime factorization of a perfect cube will involve sets of factors which each occur three times (or a multiple of three times).

If the prime factorization of a number does not result in factors which each occur three times (or a multiple of three times), then we can say that the number is not a perfect cube.

In each case use prime factorization (division table) to determine whether the number is a perfect cube.
If the number is a perfect cube, state the cube root of the number.

a) 6 912 **b)** 970 299

Complete Assignment Questions #8 - #15

Assignment

1. State the greatest common factor of

a) 14 and 21 **b)** 30 and 40 **c)** 12, 30, and 54

7 10 6

2. Use prime factorization to determine the greatest common factor of

a) 150 and 420 **b)** 126 and 189 **c)** 294 and 385

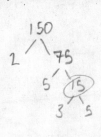

15 63

3. Use prime factorization to determine the greatest common factor of

a) 483 and 575 **b)** 180 and 504 **c)** 1 700 and 1 938

d) 663 and 910 **e)** 84 and 231 **f)** 525 and 850

4. Determine the greatest common factor of

a) 66, 495, and 2 541 **b)** 128, 984, 1 496, and 3 080

5. State the lowest common multiple of

 a) 4 and 6 **b)** 3 and 9 **c)** 9 and 15 **d)** 40, 60, and 100

4,8,(12) 6,(12) 9, 18, 27, 36, (45)

(12) 15, 30, (45) (45)

6. Use prime factorization to determine the lowest common multiple of

 a) 14 and 30 **b)** 28 and 60 **c)** 10 and 115

14 30 10, 20, 30, 40, 50, 60, 70, 80, 90, 100, 110,

2 7 2 15 120, 130, 140, 150, 160, 170, 180, 190, 200, 210,

? 3 5 220, (230)

115, (230)

14, 28, 42, 56, 70, 84, 98, 102, 126, 140, 154, 168, 182, 196, (210)

30, 60, 90, 120, 150, 180, (210)

 d) 18 and 63 **e)** 55 and 143 **f)** 72 and 252

 g) 125 and 175 **h)** 39 and 52 **i)** 58 and 124

7. Determine the lowest common multiple of

a) 6, 10, and 42

b) 12, 30, and 105

c) 3, 5, 7, and 13

d) 3, 14, 70, and 150

8. In each case use prime factorization to determine whether the number is a perfect square.
If the number is a perfect square, state the square root of the number.
Verify your answer by using a calculator to determine the square root.

a) 216

b) 11 025

c) 882

d) 1 225

not

$\sqrt[2]{11\,025} = 105$

105^2

Not

$\sqrt{1225}$

$= 35$

35^2

9. Consider the number 74 088.

 a) Use a calculator to find the cube root of 74 088. $\sqrt[3]{74088} = 42$

 b) **Explain** how we can use the prime factorization of 74 088 to show that 74 088 is a perfect cube. Verify your calculator answer by this method.

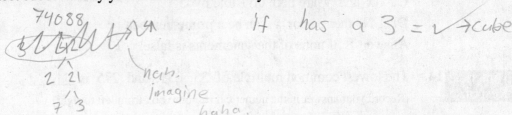

If has a 3, = √cube

74088

2 21

7 3

nah.
imagine
haha.

10. In each case use prime factorization to determine whether the number is a perfect cube. Verify your answer by using a calculator to determine the cube root.

 a) 216 **b)** 11 025 **c)** 27 783 **d)** 421 875

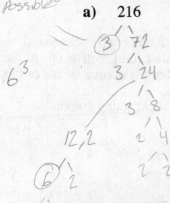

possible (3)

6^3

3 72

3 24

3 8

12,2 2 4

6 2 2 2

3 3

11. **Explain** how you could use prime factorization to determine if a particular whole number is both a perfect square and a perfect cube.

Multiple Choice

12. The greatest common factor of 399 and 462 is

 A. 3
 B. 7
 C. 19
 D. 21

13. The greatest common factor of two whole numbers x and y is 10. Which of the statements A, B, C, or D below is false?

A. x and y must be even numbers.
B. The product xy must be divisible by 100.
C. x and y are both divisible by 5.
D. Neither x nor y can be a prime number.

Answer **E** if none of the statements is false.

Numerical Response

14. The lowest common multiple of 35, 231, and 275 is _______.

(Record your answer in the numerical response box from left to right)

15. A new children's encyclopedia has 950 pages. Each page contains two background colours for illustrations. Page 8 and every 8th page thereafter has green as one of the background colours. Page 18 and every 18th page thereafter has orange as one of the background colours.
How many pages in the book have both green and orange as background colours?

(Record your answer in the numerical response box from left to right)

Answer Key

1a) 7 **b)** 10 **c)** 6 **2a)** 30 **b)** 63 **c)** 7 **3a)** 23 **b)** 36 **c)** 34 **d)** 13

e) 21 **f)** 25 **4a)** 33 **b)** 8 **5a)** 12 **b)** 9 **c)** 45 **d)** 600

6a) 210 **b)** 420 **c)** 230 **d)** 126 **e)** 715 **f)** 504 **g)** 875 **h)** 156 **i)** 3596

7a) 210 **b)** 420 **c)** 1365 **d)** 1050 **8a)** no **b)** yes, 105 **c)** no **d)** yes, 35

9a) 42 **b)** If the prime factorization of 74 088 has factors which each appear three times, then 74 088 is a perfect cube.

10a) yes, 6 **b)** no **c)** no **d)** yes, 75

11. If the prime factorization of the number has factors which each appear six times, then the number will be both a perfect square and a perfect cube.

12. D **13.** E **14.** | 5 | 7 | 7 | 5 | **15.** | 1 | 3 | | |

Number Lesson #3:
Rational and Irrational Numbers

Review

a) * Convert $\frac{28}{11}$ to a decimal. $28 \div 11 = 2.5\overline{454}$

 * Circle the correct alternatives in the following statement.

The decimal representing $\frac{28}{11}$ has a (*repeating* / non-repeating) pattern and (terminates / *does not terminate*).

b) * Convert $\frac{28}{8}$ to a decimal. 3.5

 * Circle the correct alternatives in the following statement.

The decimal representing $\frac{28}{8}$ has a (repeating / *non-repeating*) pattern and (*terminates* / does not terminate).

stop *not stop*

c) * Convert $\sqrt{2}$ to a decimal. $\sqrt{2} = 1.414213562\ldots$

 * Circle the correct alternatives in the following statement.

The decimal representing $\sqrt{2}$ has a (repeating / *non-repeating*) pattern and (terminates / *does not terminate*).

no pattern

$3.\overline{55}$
stops
3.10
pie π

Terminology

Repeating Decimals - decimals which have a recurring pattern of digits.

Non-Repeating Decimals - decimals which have no recurring pattern of digits.

Terminating Decimals - decimals with a finite number of digits.

Non-Terminating Decimals - decimals with an infinite number of digits.

Class Ex. #1 State whether the decimal equivalent of each number is repeating or non-repeating. Also state whether it is terminating or non-terminating.

a) $\frac{1}{8} = 0.125$ b) $\frac{2}{11}$ c) $\frac{9}{7}$

non-repeat
terminates

d) $0.9\overline{4}$ e) $\sqrt{8}$ f) $\sqrt{0.16}$

Rational and Irrational Numbers

- Decimal numbers which repeat or terminate can be converted into fractions. These numbers are called **rational numbers**, since they can be written as the ratio of two integers.
- Decimal numbers which are both non-repeating and non-terminating cannot be converted into fractions and are called **irrational numbers**.

Class Ex. #2

Identify each of the following numbers as rational or irrational. Give a reason in each case. Use a calculator to convert the rational numbers to improper fractions in simplest form.

a) 1.493 **b)** $\sqrt{5}$ **c)** 2.347 347 347 347...

d) $-\sqrt{81}$ **e)** $\sqrt{4.41}$ **f)** –8.1122111222111 ...

Class Ex. #3

Order the following irrational numbers on the number line.

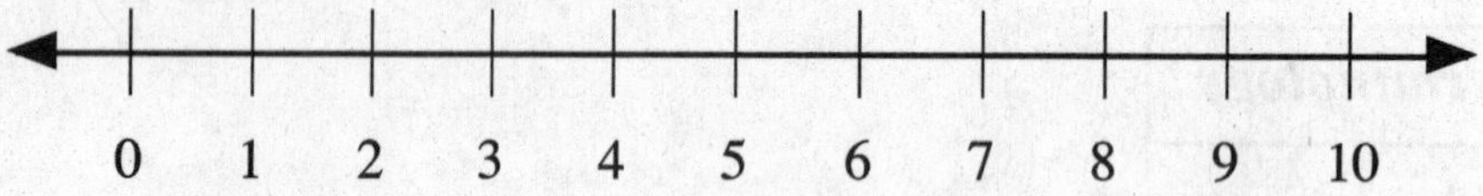

a) $\sqrt{14}$ **b)** π **c)** $\sqrt{80}$ **d)** $2\sqrt{15}$ **e)** $\sqrt{0.1}$

Complete Assignment Questions #1 - #5

Converting a Repeating Decimal to a Fraction using a Graphing Calculator

Class Ex. #4

Use a graphing calculator to convert each of the following to an improper fraction in simplest form.

a) $0.\overline{36}$ **b)** $3.9\overline{5}$

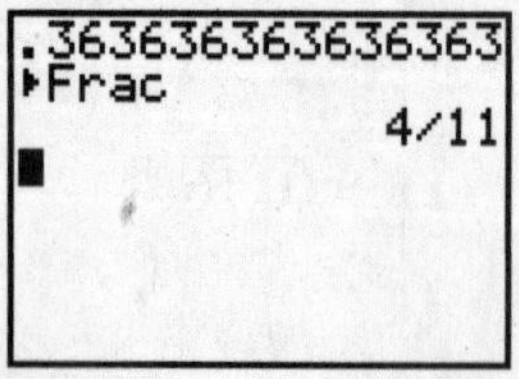

Converting a Repeating Decimal to a Fraction Algebraically

The following method can be used to convert a repeating decimal to a fraction algebraically.

Step 1. Let x be the original number.

Step 2. Identify the digit(s) which repeat.

Step 3. Multiply both sides in step 1 by a power of 10 which moves the repeating part to the **left** of the decimal point.

Step 4. If necessary, multiply both sides in step 1 by a power of 10 which moves the repeating part immediately to the **right** of the decimal point.

Step 5. Subtract the equation in step 4 from the equation in step 3, and solve for x. If there is no step 4, subtract the equation in step 1 from the equation in step 3 and solve for x.

A student is using the above procedure to convert $2.0\overline{51}$ to a fraction. Follow the procedure, and complete the last step.

Step 1. Let $x = 2.0\overline{51}$.
Step 2. The repeating digits are 51.
Step 3. To move the 51 to the left of the decimal point multiply both sides in step 1 by 10^3 or 1000.

$$1000x = 2051.\overline{51}$$

Step 4. To move the 51 to the immediate right of the decimal point multiply both sides in step 1 by 10.

$$10x = 20.\overline{51}$$

Step 5.

$$1000x = 2051.\overline{51}$$
$$\underline{10x = 20.\overline{51}}$$

subtract

Use an algebraic procedure to convert each of the following to a fraction in simplest form.

a) $0.\overline{36}$

b) $3.9\overline{5}$

Complete Assignment Question #6 - #12

Assignment

1. State whether the decimal equivalent of each number is repeating or non-repeating. Also state whether it is terminating or non-terminating.

a) $\frac{1}{2}$ **b)** 0.123 123 123 ... **c)** $-\frac{3}{7}$ **d)** $\sqrt{\frac{49}{81}}$

terminate
non-repeating

non-termanite
repeating

non-term
non-repeat

non-term
repeating

e) $-\sqrt{17}$ **f)** $\sqrt{0.64}$ **g)** $-4\frac{3}{8}$ **h)** π

non term
non-repeat

2. Classify the following statements as true or false.

a) Decimals which are terminating can be converted to fraction form.

b) Repeating decimals cannot be converted to fraction form.

c) Only decimal numbers which terminate can be converted to fraction form.

d) Rational numbers are either repeating decimals or terminating decimals.

e) A decimal number can be repeating and non-repeating at the same time.

f) π is an irrational number.

3. Determine whether the following numbers are rational or irrational. Explain your reasoning.

a) $-\frac{7}{5}$ **b)** $0.\overline{234}$ **c)** $\sqrt{144}$ **d)** 0.23223222322223222223...

4. Order the following irrational numbers on the number line.

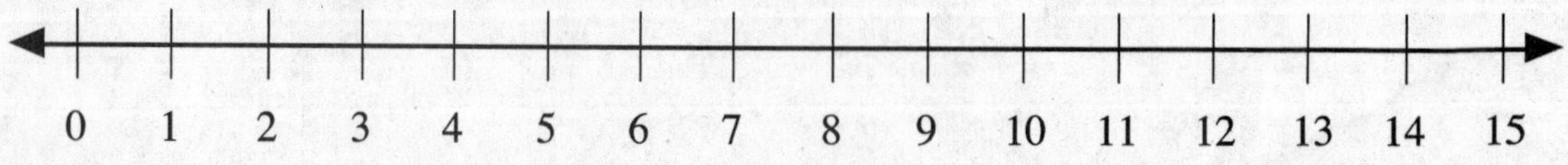

a) $\sqrt{10}$ **b)** $\sqrt{\pi}$ **c)** $\sqrt{0.2}$ **d)** $\sqrt{60}$ **e)** $2\sqrt{30}$ **f)** $3\sqrt{20}$

5. Identify each of the following numbers as rational or irrational.
Use a calculator to convert the rational numbers to fractions in simplest form.

a) 0.8 **b)** $\sqrt{\frac{1}{9}}$ **c)** $\sqrt{0.0064}$ **d)** $-\sqrt{79}$ **e)** −0.555

f) $-\sqrt{1\frac{9}{16}}$ **g)** 4.102 102 102 ... **h)** 5.724 734 744 ... **i)** $\sqrt{\sqrt{\frac{81}{256}}}$

6. Use a graphing calculator to convert each of the following to an improper fraction in simplest form.

a) $0.\overline{6}$ **b)** $0.\overline{21}$ **c)** $1.0\overline{8}$ **d)** $0.\overline{123}$ **e)** $-3.24\overline{70}$

7. Use an algebraic procedure to convert each of the following to a fraction in simplest form.

a) $0.\overline{2}$ **b)** $0.\overline{61}$ **c)** $0.9\overline{8}$

8. Use an algebraic procedure to convert each of the following to an improper fraction in simplest form.

a) $2.\overline{005}$ **b)** $-1.\overline{234}$ **c)** $4.47\overline{3}$

Multiple Choice

9. The decimal number representing $\frac{4}{9}$ is

A. terminating and repeating
B. terminating and non-repeating
C. non-terminating and repeating
D. non-terminating and non-repeating

10. Which of the following is an irrational number?

A. $\sqrt{169}$ **B.** $\sqrt{0.025}$ **C.** $\frac{5}{6}$ **D.** 3.14

11. $9.\overline{9}$ is equal to

A. $\frac{99}{10}$ **B.** $\frac{999}{100}$ **C.** 9.9 **D.** 10

Numerical Response

12. When the repeating decimal $0.\overline{476}$ is converted to a rational number in simplest form $\frac{a}{b}$ the value of $b - a$ is ______.

(Record your answer in the numerical response box from left to right)

Answer Key

1. a) non-repeating, terminating **b)** repeating, non-terminating **c)** repeating, non-terminating
d) repeating, non-terminating **e)** non-repeating, non-terminating **f)** non-repeating, terminating
g) non-repeating, terminating **h)** non-repeating, non-terminating

2. a) true **b)** false **c)** false **d)** true **e)** false **f)** true

3. a) rational since it is a terminating decimal **b)** rational since it is a repeating decimal
c) rational since it is a terminating decimal
d) irrational since it is a non-repeating and non-terminating decimal

4.

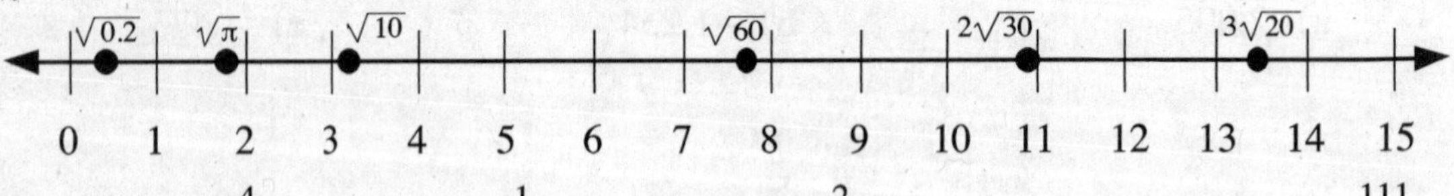

4. a) rational, $\frac{4}{5}$ **b)** rational, $\frac{1}{3}$ **c)** rational, $\frac{2}{25}$ **d)** irrational **e)** rational, $-\frac{111}{200}$
f) rational, $-\frac{5}{4}$ **g)** rational, $\frac{1366}{333}$ **h)** irrational **i)** rational, $\frac{3}{4}$

6. a) $\frac{2}{3}$ **b)** $\frac{7}{33}$ **c)** $\frac{49}{45}$ **d)** $\frac{41}{333}$ **e)** $-\frac{16073}{4950}$

7. a) $\frac{2}{9}$ **b)** $\frac{61}{99}$ **c)** $\frac{89}{90}$ **8. a)** $\frac{397}{198}$ **b)** $-\frac{137}{111}$ **c)** $\frac{671}{150}$

9. C **10.** B **11.** D **12.**

2	5	9	

Number Lesson #4:
Number Systems

The Real Number System

Recall from Lesson 3 the definitions of rational numbers and irrational numbers.

- Decimal numbers which repeat or terminate can be converted into fractions and are called **rational numbers**, since they can be written as the ratio of two integers.

- Decimal numbers which are both non-repeating and non-terminating cannot be converted into fractions and are called **irrational numbers**.

The set of all rational numbers and the set of all irrational numbers, when combined, form the set of **real numbers**. These numbers can be represented on a number line.

The following sets of numbers are within the real number system:

Natural Numbers

$N = \{ 1, 2, 3, ... \}$

Nitro engine:
ex. Natural # = Tune top
Whole # = Mid tune
Integers = Bottom tune.

Whole Numbers

$W = \{ 0, 1, 2, 3, ... \}$

Integers

$I = \{ ..., -3, -2, -1, 0, 1, 2, 3, ... \}$

Rational Numbers

$Q = \left\{ \frac{a}{b}, \text{ where } a, b \in I,\ b \neq 0 \right\}$

Irrational Numbers

$\overline{Q} = \{\text{non-terminating and non-repeating decimals}\}$

Real Numbers

$R = \{Q \text{ and } \overline{Q}\}$

The interrelationship between the sets can be shown in the following diagram. It illustrates how the number sets are nested within the real number system. Complete the diagram.

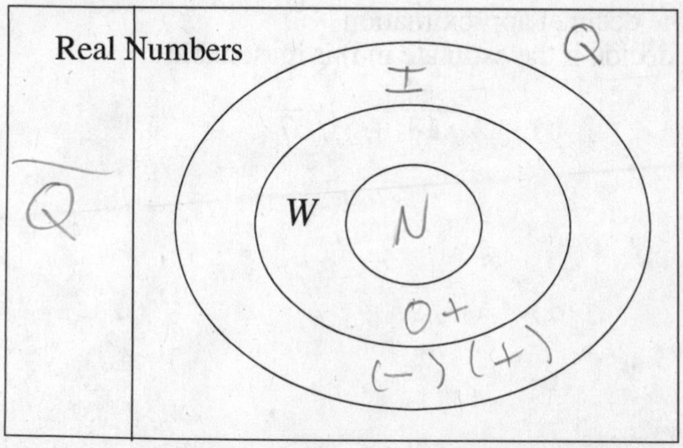

Note that the area of each region bears no relation to the number of members in each set.

everything is real

Error = non-real

Class Ex. #1

a) For each of the following write all the sets of numbers to which the given number belongs. Write the answers from the largest set to the smallest set.

i) 9 **ii)** $\dfrac{11}{7}$ **iii)** $\sqrt{5}$ **iv)** -7

N = natural #
W
I
Q R

1.57....
Q

FRACTION = Q (rat). Q = also Rea

b) Explain why 9 belongs to five number sets, but -9 belongs to only three number sets.

Complete Assignment Questions #1 - #7

Square Roots

All positive numbers have two square roots: one a positive number and the other a negative number. The positive square root is called the **principal square root** and is denoted by the symbol $\sqrt{}$.

The square roots of a perfect square are rational numbers.
 e.g. the square roots of 16 are 4 and –4. **NOTE:** $\sqrt{16} = 4$ <u>only</u>.

The square roots of a non-perfect square are irrational numbers.
 e.g. the square roots of 17 are $\sqrt{17}$ and $-\sqrt{17}$.

The ability to estimate mentally the square root of a non-perfect square is important when checking a calculator calculation for possible error.
A knowledge of some common perfect squares enables us to make such estimates to the nearest whole number.

1^2	= 1
2^2	= 4
3^2	= 9
4^2	= 16
5^2	= 25
6^2	= 36
7^2	= 49
8^2	= 64
9^2	= 81
10^2	= 100
11^2	= 121
12^2	= 144
13^2	= 169
14^2	= 196
15^2	= 225

Class Ex. #2

In each of the following:

i) estimate the value mentally (use whole numbers)
ii) use a calculator to find the decimal approximation
 to the nearest tenth, and decide if the estimate in i) is reasonable

a) $\sqrt{46}$ **b)** $2\sqrt{18} + 5\sqrt{37}$

c) $-\sqrt{5}$ **d)** $\sqrt{\sqrt{95}}$

To estimate square roots of large numbers or of positive numbers less than 1, divide the number into groups of 2 digits starting from the decimal point.

Class Ex. #3

Estimate to one significant digit.

a) $\sqrt{6\,210}$ **b)** $\sqrt{82\,147.3}$ **c)** $\sqrt{0.002\,43}$ **d)** $\sqrt{0.024\,3}$

Cube Roots

All numbers (positive and negative) have one cube root, denoted by the symbol $\sqrt[3]{}$.

The cube root of a perfect cube is a rational number.

e.g. the cube root of 1 000 is 10, i.e. $\sqrt[3]{1\,000} = 10$

the cube root of -27 is -3, i.e. $\sqrt[3]{-27} = -3$

The cube root of a non-perfect cube is an irrational number.

e.g. the cube root of 9 is $\sqrt[3]{9}$, which is irrational.

Class Ex. #4

In each of the following:

i) estimate the value mentally (use whole numbers)

ii) use a calculator to find the decimal approximation to the nearest tenth, and decide if the estimate in i) is reasonable

a) $\sqrt[3]{11}$ **b)** $\sqrt[3]{120}$

c) $4\sqrt{70} - 4\sqrt[3]{70}$

1^3	= 1
2^3	= 8
3^3	= 27
4^3	= 64
5^3	= 125
6^3	= 216
7^3	= 343
8^3	= 512
9^3	= 729
10^3	= 1000

Complete Assignment Questions #8 - #18

Extension - Absolute Value

The **absolute value** of a real number can be defined as the principal square root of the square of the number.

e.g. the absolute value of 6 = $\sqrt{(6)^2} = \sqrt{36} = 6$

the absolute value of −6 = $\sqrt{(-6)^2} = \sqrt{36} = 6$

For a real number, a, the absolute value of a is written $|a|$. e.g. $|6| = 6$ and $|-6| = 6$.

The absolute value of a real number can be regarded as the distance of the number from zero on a number line.

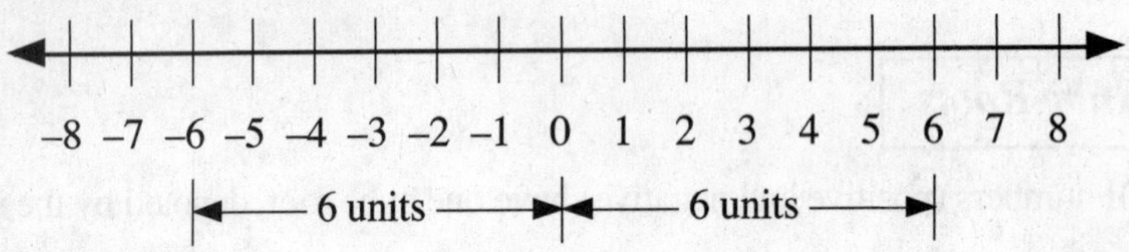

To graph the inequality, $|a| < 4,\ a \in R$, we know that the distance from 0 must be less than 4 units.

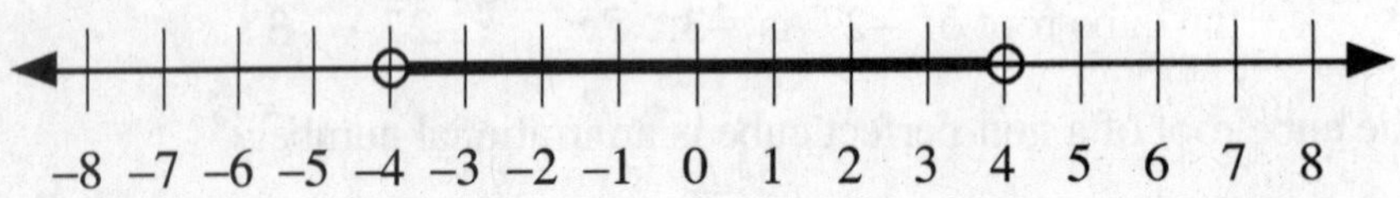

Class Ex. #5

Evaluate:

a) $|-7| + |7|$ **b)** $|1 - 5|$ **c)** $-|-\sqrt{81}|$

Class Ex. #6

In each case state the absolute value inequality represented by the graph.

a)

b)

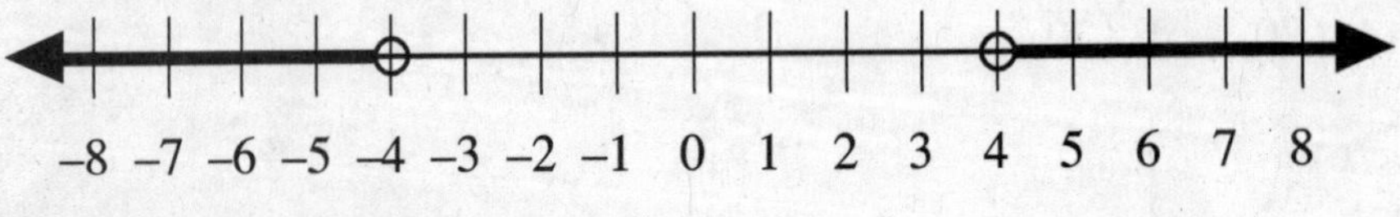

Complete Assignment Questions #19 - #21

Assignment

1. Complete the Venn Diagram to show the interrelationship between the sets of numbers in the real number system.

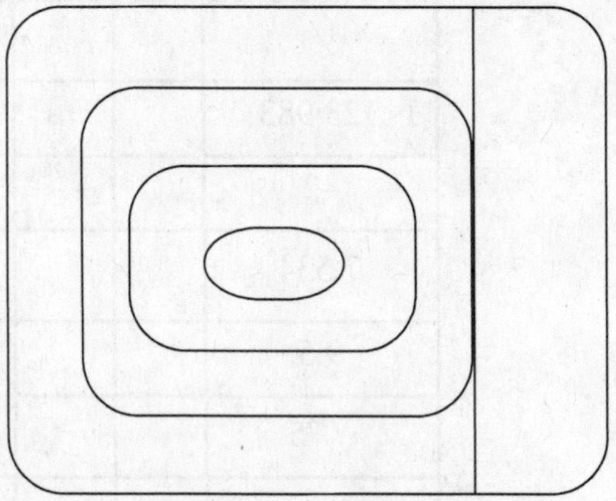

2. For each of the following write all the sets of numbers to which the given number belongs. Write the answers from the largest set to the smallest set.

a) -2 **b)** $\sqrt{36}$ **c)** 3.14159265 **d)** $-\frac{7}{5}$

e) 0 **f)** $\sqrt{7}$ **g)** $-2.1345218...$ **h)** π

3. Explain why -7 belongs to more number sets than $-\frac{7}{2}$.

4. Use check marks to indicate all the sets to which each number belongs.

	N	W	I	Q	$\overline{Q}$	R
$\frac{1}{3}$						
123 983						
−2						
$7.53\overline{4}$						
9.5						
$\sqrt{75}$						
$-\pi$						
$-\frac{355}{113}$						
$-\sqrt{49}$						
0.000005						
2.232425...						
$\sqrt{0.16}$						

5. Find one number which satisfies each condition.

a) An integer, but not a whole number.

b) A rational number, but not an integer.

c) A real number, but not a rational number

d) A whole number, but not a natural number.

6. Complete the following statements using *always*, *sometimes*, or *never*.

a) A whole number is ____________ a natural number.

b) The quotient of two integers is ____________ an integer.

c) A whole number is ____________ a rational number.

d) The difference between two integers is ____________ an integer.

e) The square root of a number is ____________ in set $\overline{Q}$.

f) A negative number is ____________ in set W.

g) A number in set N is ____________ a number in set R.

7. Determine whether each statement is true (T) or false (F). Answer in the space provided.

a) ___ All natural numbers are integers.

b) ___ Real numbers consist of rational numbers and irrational numbers.

c) ___ The set of integers is nested within the set of rational numbers.

d) ___ All integers are rational numbers.

e) ___ All irrational numbers are real.

f) ___ The set R is nested within the set N.

g) ___ The set Q is nested within the set W.

h) ___ There is only one number in set W which is not also in set N.

8. Determine whether each statement is true or false.

a) ___ Every positive number has two square roots, but only one cube root.

b) ___ Every negative number has one cube root, but no square roots.

9. a) Use estimates to explain why $\sqrt{8} + \sqrt{17}$ is not equal to $\sqrt{25}$.

b) Use estimates to explain why $\sqrt{2} + \sqrt{3} + \sqrt{4}$ is not equal to $\sqrt{9}$.

10. Determine whether each statement is true or false.

a) ___ $\sqrt{9} + \sqrt{4}$ is equal to $\sqrt{9 + 4}$.

b) ___ $\sqrt{9} - \sqrt{4}$ is equal to $\sqrt{9 - 4}$.

c) ___ $\sqrt{9} \times \sqrt{4}$ is equal to $\sqrt{9 \times 4}$.

d) ___ $\sqrt{9} \div \sqrt{4}$ is equal to $\sqrt{9 \div 4}$.

11. In each of the following:

i) estimate the value mentally (use whole numbers)
ii) use a calculator to find the decimal approximation to the nearest tenth, and decide if the estimate in i) is reasonable

a) $\sqrt{19}$ **b)** $\sqrt{26.4}$ **c)** $4\sqrt{50} - 3\sqrt{60}$ **d)** $\frac{3}{4}\sqrt{13.9} + \frac{1}{2}\sqrt{3}$

e) $\sqrt{119}$ **f)** $\sqrt{\sqrt{80}}$ **g)** $\sqrt{\sqrt{10} + \sqrt{23.9}}$ **h)** $\sqrt{\sqrt{2501}}$

12. Estimate to one significant digit.

a) $\sqrt{507.1}$ **b)** $\sqrt{7\,991}$ **c)** $\sqrt{10\,389}$ **d)** $\sqrt{823\,775}$

e) $\sqrt{0.501}$ **f)** $\sqrt{0.050\,1}$ **g)** $\sqrt{0.087\,6}$ **h)** $\sqrt{0.000\,397\,2}$

13. In each of the following:

i) estimate the value mentally (use whole numbers)
ii) use a calculator to find the decimal approximation to the nearest tenth, and decide if the estimate in i) is reasonable

a) $\sqrt[3]{25}$ **b)** $\sqrt[3]{2}$ **c)** $\sqrt[3]{202}$ **d)** $\sqrt[3]{999.9}$

e) $2\sqrt[3]{58.7} - 3\sqrt[3]{7.62}$ **f)** $\frac{2}{3}\sqrt{40} - \frac{1}{2}\sqrt[3]{60}$ **g)** $\sqrt[3]{3\sqrt{10}}$

14. Order the following rational numbers on the number line.

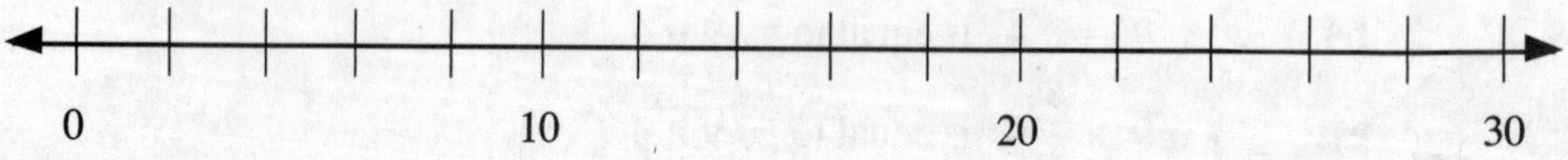

a) $\sqrt{50}$ **b)** $\sqrt[3]{50}$ **c)** $5\sqrt{10}$ **d)** $5\sqrt[3]{10}$ **e)** $10\sqrt{5}$ **f)** $10\sqrt[3]{5}$

Multiple Choice

15. Consider the following statements.

i) The set of irrational numbers is nested within the set of rational numbers.
ii) The set of integers contains the set of rational numbers.
iii) The set of whole numbers is nested within the set of natural numbers.
iv) The set of real numbers contains the set of irrational numbers.

Which of the above statements is false?

A. i), ii), and iii) only **B.** i), ii), and iv) only **C.** ii), iii), and iv) only

Answer **D** if all the above statements are false.

16. How many of the numbers $-\sqrt{6}$, $\sqrt{-6}$, $-\sqrt[3]{6}$, $\sqrt[3]{-6}$, do not belong to the real number system?

A. 0 **B.** 1 **C.** 2 **D.** 3

17. How many of the numbers $\sqrt{49}$, $\sqrt{4.9}$, $\sqrt{0.49}$, $\sqrt{\frac{4}{9}}$, can be expressed in the form $\frac{a}{b}$ where $a, b \in N$?

A. 1 **B.** 2 **C.** 3 **D.** 4

Numerical Response

18. To the nearest hundredth, the value of $5\sqrt[3]{7}$ is _____.

(Record your answer in the numerical response box from left to right)

Extension Questions.

19. Evaluate:

a) $|-4|$ **b)** $|13|$ **c)** $|3-9|$ **d)** $|3|-|9|$

e) $||3|-|9||$ **f)** $-|\sqrt[3]{27}|$ **g)** $|-\sqrt[3]{27}|$ **h)** $|\sqrt[3]{-27}|$

20. Decide whether each statement is true or false.

a) $|x| = x$ if $x > 0$ **b)** $|x| = -x$ if $x < 0$

21. In each case draw a graph to represent the absolute value inequality. The variables are defined on the set of real numbers.

a) $|x| < 5$ **b)** $|a| \geq 3$

Answer Key

1.

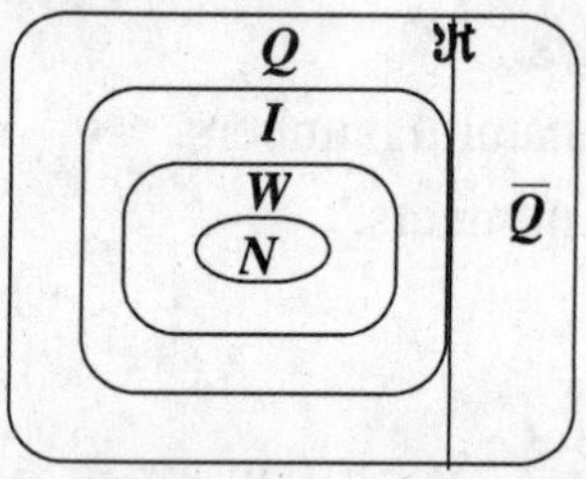

2.a) real numbers, rational numbers, integers
b) real numbers, rational numbers, integers, whole numbers, natural numbers
c) real numbers, rational numbers
d) real numbers, rational numbers
e) real numbers, rational numbers, integers, whole numbers
f) real numbers, irrational numbers
g) real numbers, irrational numbers
h) real numbers, irrational numbers

3. –7 is a real number, rational number and integer whereas $-\frac{7}{2}$ is a real number and a rational number but not an integer.

4.

	N	W	I	Q	$\overline{Q}$	R
$1/8$				√		√
123 983	√	√	√	√		√
–2			√	√		√
$7.53\overline{4}$				√		√
9.5				√		√
$\sqrt{75}$					√	√
$-\pi$					√	√
$-355/113$				√		√
$-\sqrt{49}$			√	√		√
0.000005				√		√
2.232425...					√	√
$\sqrt{0.16}$				√		√

5. a) –3 **b)** $\frac{4}{5}$ **c)** $\sqrt{3}$ **d)** 0

6. a) sometimes **b)** sometimes **c)** always
d) always **e)** sometimes **f)** never **g)** always

7. a) true **b)** true **c)** true **d)** true
e) true **f)** false **g)** false **h)** true

8. a) true **b)** true

9. a) $3 + 4 \neq 5$ **b)** $1 + 2 + 2 \neq 3$

10.a) false **b)** false **c)** true **d)** true

11.a)i) 4 **ii)** 4.4 **b)i)** 5 **ii)** 5.1 **c)i)** 4 **ii)** 5.0 **d)i)** 4 **ii)** 3.7
e)i) 11 **ii)** 10.9 **f)i)** 3 **ii)** 3.0 **g)i)** 3 **ii)** 2.8 **h)i)** 7 **ii)** 7.1

12.a) 20 **b)** 90 **c)** 100 **d)** 900 **e)** 0.7 **f)** 0.2 **g)** 0.3 **h)** 0.02

13.a)i) 3 **ii)** 2.9 **b)i)** 1 **ii)** 1.3 **c)i)** 6 **ii)** 5.9 **d)i)** 10 **ii)** 10.0
e)i) 2 **ii)** 1.9 **f)i)** 2 **ii)** 2.3 **g)i)** 2 **ii)** 2.1

14.

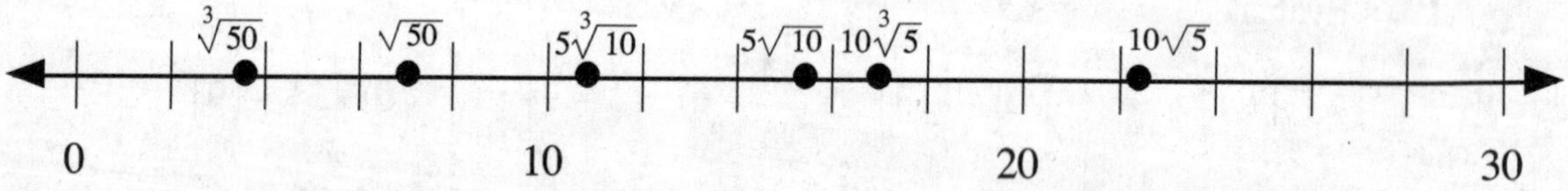

15. A **16.** B **17.** C

18.

9	.	5	6

19.a) 4 **b)** 13 **c)** 6 **d)** –6
e) 6 **f)** –3 **g)** 3 **h)** 3

20.a) true **b)** true

21.a)

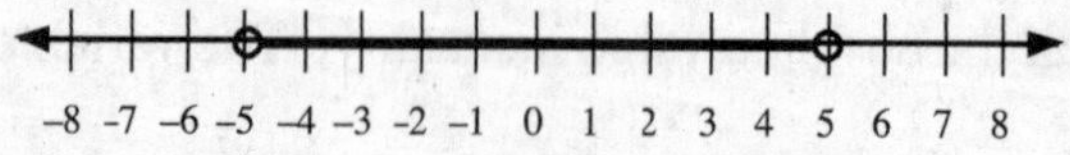

b)

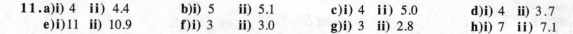

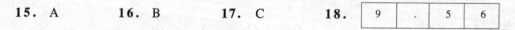

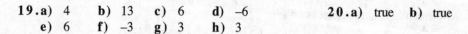

Number Lesson #5:
Radicals

Review

Square Roots : All positive numbers have two square roots: one a positive number and the other a negative number. The positive square root is called the **principal square root** and is denoted by the symbol $\sqrt{\ }$.

The square roots of a perfect square are rational numbers.

e.g. the square roots of 16 are 4 and –4. **NOTE:** $\sqrt{16} = 4$ only.

The square roots of a non-perfect square are irrational numbers.

e.g. the square roots of 17 are $\sqrt{17}$ and $-\sqrt{17}$.

Cube Roots: All numbers (positive and negative) have one cube root, denoted by the symbol $\sqrt[3]{\ }$.

The cube root of a perfect cube is a rational number. 10·10·10=1000

e.g. the cube root of 1 000 is 10, i.e. $\sqrt[3]{1\,000} = 10$

the cube root of –27 is –3, i.e. $\sqrt[3]{-27} = -3$

The cube root of a non-perfect cube is an irrational number.

e.g. the cube root of 49 is $\sqrt[3]{49}$, which is irrational.

Other Roots

Complete the following statements:

$4 \times 4 = 16$ so a square root of 16 is 4 or $\sqrt{16} =$ 4

$5 \times 5 \times 5 = 125$ so the cube root of 125 is 5 or $\sqrt[3]{125} =$ 5

$2 \times 2 \times 2 \times 2 = 16$ so a fourth root of 16 is 2 or $\sqrt[4]{16} =$ 2

$10 \times 10 \times 10 \times 10 \times 10 \times 10 = 1\,000\,000$ so ____________________

= NO calculator

Class Ex. #1

Mentally evaluate, where possible, using the real number system.

a) $\sqrt{49}$ = 7 **b)** $\sqrt[3]{-64}$ = – **c)** $\sqrt[4]{10\,000}$

d) $\sqrt[5]{\dfrac{1}{32}}$ = $\frac{1}{2}$ **e)** $\sqrt[4]{-16}$ **f)** $2\sqrt[3]{125}$

(even roots ≠ (–))

Complete Assignment Question #1

Using the $\sqrt[x]{}$ Feature of a Calculator

Use the following procedure to determine $\sqrt[4]{10\,000}$ on a calculator.

1. Press [4]. **2.** Press [MATH]. **3.** Choose 5: $\sqrt[x]{}$.

4. Press 10 000 . **5.** Press [ENTER] . The answer will be 10.

Class Ex. #2

Use a calculator to evaluate.

a) $\sqrt[5]{1\,024}$ **b)** $\sqrt[7]{-2\,187}$ **c)** $-3\sqrt[4]{50\,625}$ **d)** $\sqrt[3]{\dfrac{216}{125}}$

Class Ex. #3

Evaluate to the nearest hundredth.

a) $\sqrt[5]{125}$ **b)** $\sqrt[6]{0.5}$ **c)** $\dfrac{2}{3}\sqrt[4]{1\,000}$

Radicals

Numbers like $\sqrt{30}$, $\sqrt[3]{125}$, $\sqrt[4]{15}$, $\sqrt[6]{1\,000\,000}$ etc. are examples of **radicals.**

In fact, any expression of the form $\sqrt[n]{x}$, where $n \in N$, is called a radical.
n is called the **index**. In a number like $\sqrt{30}$ the index is 2.
x is called the **radicand** and $\sqrt{}$ is called the **radical sign**.
If the index in a radical is even, then the radicand must be positive.

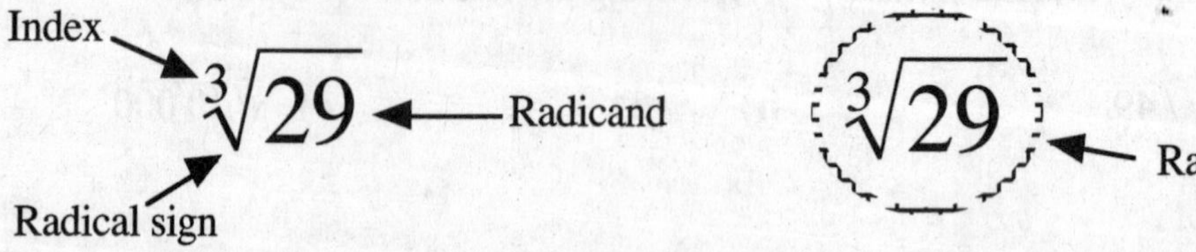

- When the index is not written in the radical, as in square root, it is assumed to be 2.
- The index is the number of times the radical must be multiplied by itself to equal the radicand.

Class Ex. #4

Identify the index and the radicand in each of the following.

a) $\sqrt[5]{75}$ **b)** $\sqrt{50}$ **c)** $5\sqrt[3]{-\frac{1}{10}}$ (coefficient)

index: 5 index: 2 index: 3

radicand: 75 radicand: 50 radicand: $-\frac{1}{10}$

Review

Recall the following results from Lesson #4, assignment question 10.

$\sqrt{9} \times \sqrt{4}$ is equal to $\sqrt{9 \times 4}$ $\sqrt{9} + \sqrt{4}$ is **not** equal to $\sqrt{9 + 4}$

$\sqrt{9} \div \sqrt{4}$ is equal to $\sqrt{9 \div 4}$ $\sqrt{9} - \sqrt{4}$ is **not** equal to $\sqrt{9 - 4}$

The calculations above are examples of some general rules involving radicals.

Note

i) **The product(quotient) of the roots of two numbers is equal to the root of the product(quotient) of the two numbers.**

ii) **The sum (difference) of the roots of two numbers is NOT equal to the root of the sum (difference) of the two numbers.**

In general $\sqrt{a} \times \sqrt{b} = \sqrt{ab}$ where $a, b \geq 0$ and $\frac{\sqrt{a}}{\sqrt{b}} = \sqrt{\frac{a}{b}}$ where $a \geq 0$, $b > 0$.

Class Ex. #5

State whether each statement is true or false.

a) $\sqrt{3} \times \sqrt{6} = \sqrt{18}$ **b)** $\frac{\sqrt{20}}{\sqrt{10}} = \sqrt{2}$ **c)** $\sqrt{16 + 9} = \sqrt{16} + \sqrt{9}$

Class Ex. #6

Write the following as a single radical in the form $\sqrt{x}$.

a) $\sqrt{8} \times \sqrt{3}$ → $\sqrt{8 \times 3}$ → $\sqrt{24}$ **b)** $\sqrt{7 \times 3}$ → $\sqrt{21}$ **c)** $\frac{\sqrt{50}}{\sqrt{10}}$ → $\sqrt{5}$ **d)** $\frac{\sqrt{\sqrt{100}}}{\sqrt{2}}$ → $\frac{\sqrt{10}}{\sqrt{2}}$ → $\sqrt{\frac{10}{2}}$

(★ Treat like a bracket.)

Class Ex. #7

Express as a product of radicals.

a) $\sqrt{77}$ → $\sqrt{7 \times 11}$ **b)** $\sqrt{27}$ → $\sqrt{3 \times 9}$ **c)** $\sqrt{40}$ → $\sqrt{4 \times 10}$

Complete Assignment Questions #2 - #13

Assignment

1. Mentally evaluate, where possible, using the real number system.

a) $\sqrt{81} = 9$

b) $\sqrt[4]{81} = 3$

c) $5\sqrt[3]{27} = 15$
5×3

d) $\sqrt[5]{100\,000} = 20\,000$

e) $\sqrt{\dfrac{16}{25}} = \dfrac{4}{5}$

f) $\sqrt[4]{\dfrac{1}{16}} = \dfrac{1}{2} = 0.5$

g) $4\sqrt{\dfrac{1}{16}}$
$\dfrac{1}{2} \times 4$
$= 4/8 \to 0.5$

h) $-\sqrt{1} =$

i) $\sqrt{-1} =$

j) $\sqrt[5]{-1} =$

k) $7\sqrt[3]{-125} = -35$
7×-5

l) $\sqrt[4]{-\dfrac{1}{16}} = -0.5$
$-\dfrac{1}{2} \to 0.5$

m) $3\sqrt{144}$

n) $\dfrac{1}{2}\sqrt[5]{32}$

o) $-\sqrt[11]{-1}$

p) $\sqrt[3]{-\dfrac{8}{27}}$
$-\dfrac{2}{3}$

2. State whether the following are true or false.

T F

a) The square roots of 25 are ±5. and -5 T

b) $\sqrt{25} = \pm 5$ T

c) If $x^2 = 25, x \in R$, then $x = \pm 5$. T

3. Use a calculator to evaluate.

a) $\sqrt[4]{4\,096} = 8$

b) $\sqrt[5]{-243} = -3$

c) $-\sqrt[4]{2401} = -7$

d) $-\sqrt[3]{729}$

e) $\sqrt[3]{-729}$

f) $-8\sqrt[4]{\dfrac{1}{256}}$

g) $4\sqrt[6]{0.015\,625}$

h) $\sqrt[4]{-6\,561}$

i) $\dfrac{3}{2}\sqrt[4]{\dfrac{16}{81}}$

4. Evaluate to the nearest hundredth.

a) $\sqrt{10}$

b) $\sqrt[8]{29}$

c) $-\dfrac{3}{2}\sqrt[9]{-527}$

5. Evaluate to the nearest tenth.

a) $\sqrt[5]{-25}$

b) $-5\sqrt[4]{169}$

c) $\dfrac{1}{2}\sqrt[3]{-81}$

6. Identify the index and the radicand in each of the following.

a) $\sqrt[3]{42}$

index: ___3___

radicand: ___42___

b) $\sqrt[4]{36}$

index: ___4___

radicand: ___36___

c) $5\sqrt{17}$

index: ~~5~~ 2

radicand: ___17___

7. Explain the meaning of the index 4 in the radical $\sqrt[4]{36}$.

 x^4 $\sqrt[4]{36} = x \rightarrow x^{4'}$ $\sqrt{6-4|2}$ $\sqrt{6}-2$

8. Determine whether each statement is true or false.

a) $\sqrt{30} = \sqrt{5}\sqrt{6}$ T

b) $\sqrt{6-4} = \sqrt{6} - \sqrt{4}$ F

c) $\sqrt{3} = \dfrac{\sqrt{45}}{\sqrt{15}}$

d) $\dfrac{\sqrt{20}}{\sqrt{10}} = \sqrt{10}$ T

e) $\sqrt{2} + \sqrt{2} = \sqrt{4}$ F

f) $\sqrt{2} \times \sqrt{2} = \sqrt{4}$ T

g) $\sqrt{\dfrac{1}{2} \times 30} = \sqrt{15}$ T

h) $\dfrac{1}{2}\sqrt{30} = \sqrt{15}$ F

 $\sqrt{6} \cdot \sqrt{11}$

9. Write the following as a single radical in the form \sqrt{x}.

a) $\sqrt{5} \times \sqrt{7}$

$\sqrt{35}$

b) $\sqrt{14 \times 2}$

$\sqrt{28}$

c) $\sqrt{3} \cdot \sqrt{8}$

$\sqrt{24}$

d) $\sqrt{6 \cdot 11}$

$\sqrt{66}$

 $\sqrt[1]{3} = \sqrt{3} \cdot \sqrt{3}$

e) $\dfrac{\sqrt{20}}{\sqrt{10}}$

$\sqrt{10}$

f) $\dfrac{\sqrt{25}}{\sqrt{5}}$

$\sqrt{5}$

g) $\dfrac{\sqrt{10}\sqrt{6}}{\sqrt{2}}$

$\sqrt{30}$

h) $\dfrac{\sqrt{\sqrt{81}}}{\sqrt{\sqrt{9}}}$

10. Express as a product of radicals.

a) $\sqrt{35}$

 $\sqrt{5 \cdot 7}$

 $\sqrt{5} \cdot \sqrt{7}$

b) $\sqrt{33}$

 $\sqrt{3} \cdot \sqrt{11}$

c) $\sqrt{65}$

 $\sqrt{5} \cdot \sqrt{13}$

d) $\sqrt{49}$

 $\sqrt{7} \cdot \sqrt{7}$

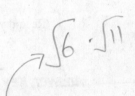

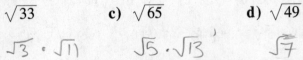

Multiple Choice

11. Consider the following statements.

I. The cube roots of −27 are ±3. **II.** The fourth roots of 81 are ±3.

III. $-\sqrt[3]{1000} = \sqrt[3]{-1000}$ **IV.** $-\sqrt[4]{16} = \sqrt[4]{-16}$

Which of the statements above are true?

A. **II** and **III** only
B. **I, II** and **III** only
C. **I, II, III,** and **IV**
D. some other combination of **I, II, III,** and **IV**

12. In the radical $\sqrt{18}$,

A. the index is 2 and the radicand is $\sqrt{18}$
B. the index is 1 and the radicand is 1
C. the index is 18 and the radicand is 1
D. the index is 2 and the radicand is 18

Numerical Response

13. To the nearest hundredth, the value of $\sqrt[5]{-\frac{7}{8}} + 2\sqrt[4]{\frac{7}{8}}$ is ______ .

(Record your answer in the numerical response box from left to right)

Answer Key

1. **a)** 9 **b)** 3 **c)** 15 **d)** 10 **e)** $\frac{4}{5}$ **f)** $\frac{1}{2}$ **g)** 1 **h)** −1 **i)** not possible

j) −1 **k)** −35 **l)** not possible **m)** 36 **n)** 1 **o)** 1 **p)** $-\frac{2}{3}$

2. **a)** true **b)** false **c)** true

3. **a)** 8 **b)** −3 **c)** −7 **d)** −9 **e)** −9 **f)** −2 **g)** 2 **h)** not possible **i)** 1

4. **a)** 3.16 **b)** 1.52 **c)** 3.01 **5.** **a)** −1.9 **b)** −18.0 **c)** −2.2

6. **a)** index 3, radicand 42 **b)** index 4, radicand 36 **c)** index 2, radicand 17

7. The index 4 refers to the number of times the value of the $\sqrt[4]{36}$ must be multiplied by itself to give a product of 36.

8. **a)** true **b)** false **c)** true **d)** false **e)** false **f)** true **g)** true **h)** false

9. **a)** $\sqrt{35}$ **b)** $\sqrt{28}$ **c)** $\sqrt{24}$ **d)** $\sqrt{66}$ **e)** $\sqrt{2}$ **f)** $\sqrt{5}$ **g)** $\sqrt{30}$ **h)** $\sqrt{3}$

10. **a)** $\sqrt{5}\sqrt{7}$ **b)** $\sqrt{3}\sqrt{11}$ **c)** $\sqrt{5}\sqrt{13}$ **d)** $\sqrt{7}\sqrt{7}$

11. A **12.** D **13.**

0	.	9	6

Number Lesson #6:
Entire Radicals and Mixed Radicals - Part One

Recall the following from Lesson #5.

i) **The product(quotient) of the roots of two numbers is equal to the root of the product (quotient) of the two numbers.**

ii) **The sum (difference) of the roots of two numbers is NOT equal to the root of the sum (difference) of the two numbers.**

In general $\sqrt{a} \times \sqrt{b} = \sqrt{ab}$ where $a, b \geq 0$ and $\dfrac{\sqrt{a}}{\sqrt{b}} = \sqrt{\dfrac{a}{b}}$ where $a \geq 0, b > 0$.

In this lesson we use the above rules in reverse:

$$\sqrt{ab} = \sqrt{a} \times \sqrt{b} \text{ where } a, b \geq 0 \text{ and } \sqrt{\frac{a}{b}} = \frac{\sqrt{a}}{\sqrt{b}} \text{ where } a \geq 0, b > 0.$$

Write the following as a product or quotient of radicals.

a) $\sqrt{24} = \sqrt{4 \times 6} = \sqrt{4} \times \sqrt{6}$

b) $\sqrt{18} = \sqrt{9 \times 2} = \sqrt{9} \times \sqrt{2}$
$= 3\sqrt{2}$

c) $\sqrt{\dfrac{11}{4}} = \dfrac{\sqrt{}}{\sqrt{}}$

Entire Radicals and Mixed Radicals

Use a calculator to approximate the value of each radical to 5 decimal places.

i) $\sqrt{80}$ = 8.94427 ii) $2\sqrt{20}$ = 1.1 iii) $4\sqrt{5}$ = 1

What do you notice about the answers? Same

Complete the following to explain why the three radicals are equivalent.

$\sqrt{80} = \sqrt{4 \times 20} = \sqrt{4} \times \sqrt{20} = 2\sqrt{20}$

$\sqrt{80} = \sqrt{16 \times 5} = \sqrt{16} \times \sqrt{5} = 4\sqrt{5}$

$\sqrt{80}$ is an example of an **entire radical**; the number is entirely under the root symbol.

$2\sqrt{20}$ and $4\sqrt{5}$ are examples of **mixed radicals.**

Entire/Pure Radicals

- Radicals expressed in the form $\sqrt[n]{b}$ are called entire (or pure) radicals.
- For example, $\sqrt{25}$, $\sqrt{80}$, $\sqrt[3]{17}$

Mixed Radicals

- Radicals expressed in the form $a\sqrt[n]{b}$ are called mixed radicals.
- For example $\frac{2}{3}\sqrt{5}$, $8\sqrt{7}$, $-9\sqrt[3]{17}$

pairs & primes

Every mixed radical can be expressed as an entire radical.

To determine if an entire radical (with an index of 2) can be expressed as a mixed radical, we need to check if the number has a factor which is a perfect square.

Converting Entire Radicals (with an index of 2) to Mixed Radicals

An entire radical of index 2 may be expressed as a mixed radical when the highest perfect square has been factored out of the entire radical.

Complete the following to convert $\sqrt{108}$ to a mixed radical.

Entire Radical ⇒ *Mixed Radical*

$\sqrt{108} = \sqrt{36 \times 3}$

$= \sqrt{36} \times \sqrt{3}$

$= 6 \times \sqrt{3}$

$\sqrt{108} = 6\sqrt{3}$

1^2	= 1
2^2	= 4
3^2	= 9
4^2	= 16
5^2	= 25
6^2	= 36
7^2	= 49
8^2	= 64
9^2	= 81
10^2	= 100
11^2	= 121
12^2	= 144
13^2	= 169
14^2	= 196
15^2	= 225

If a perfect square is factored out which is not the highest perfect square, then the process will require more than one step to obtain the mixed radical in simplest form. When converting an entire radical to a mixed radical it is expected that the answer will be in simplest form.

Convert the following radicals to mixed radicals in simplest form.

a) $\sqrt{50}$

$\sqrt{2 \times 25}$

b) $\sqrt{45}$

$3\sqrt{5}$

$\sqrt{9} \times \sqrt{5}$

c) $\sqrt{320}$

$\sqrt{64 \times 5}$

↓

$8\sqrt{5}$

Class Ex. #3

Convert the following radicals to mixed radicals in simplest form.

a) $2\sqrt{192}$ **b)** $\frac{3}{4}\sqrt{160}$ **c)** $\sqrt{\frac{7}{9}}$

$\sqrt{64 \times 3}$ $2 \cdot 8 = 16$

$2\ \sqrt{64}\sqrt{3}$ $\rightarrow 16\sqrt{3}$

$2 \cdot 8\sqrt{3}$

$\frac{3}{4}\ \sqrt{16}\ \sqrt{10}$

$\frac{3}{4}\ 4\sqrt{10}$

$3\sqrt{10}$

$\frac{\sqrt{7}}{\sqrt{9}}$ $\frac{\sqrt{7}}{3}$

Complete Assignment Questions #1 - #4

Converting Mixed Radicals *(with an index of 2)* to Entire Radicals

A mixed radical of index 2 may be expressed as an entire radical by converting the number outside the radical symbol into a radical and then multiplying it by the radicand.

The number outside the radical symbol can be converted into a radical by raising it to the power of 2.

Complete the following to convert $3\sqrt{14}$ to an entire radical.

$$\textit{Mixed Radical} \Rightarrow \textit{Entire Radical}$$

$$3\sqrt{14} = \sqrt{9} \times \sqrt{14}$$

$$= \sqrt{9 \times 14}$$

$$3\sqrt{14} = \sqrt{3} \cdot \sqrt{14}$$

Class Ex. #4

Convert the following mixed radicals to entire radicals.

a) $2\sqrt{5}$ **b)** $4\sqrt{7}$ **c)** $10\sqrt{6}$

$\sqrt{4}\sqrt{5}$
$=\sqrt{20}$

$\sqrt{16}\sqrt{7}$
$=\sqrt{112}$

$\sqrt{100}\sqrt{6}$
$=\sqrt{600}$

Class Ex. #5

Convert the following mixed radicals to entire radicals.

a) $\frac{3}{2}\sqrt{8}$ **b)** $0.4\sqrt{50}$ **c)** $-5\sqrt{7}$

$8 \cdot \left(\frac{3}{2}\right)^2$

$\sqrt{18}$

$\sqrt{\frac{9}{4}} \times \sqrt{8}$ $=\frac{72}{4}$

$0.4 = \sqrt{0.4^2}$

$\sqrt{0.16 \times \sqrt{50}}$ $\sqrt{8}$

$-\sqrt{+5^2}\sqrt{7}$
$-\sqrt{25}\sqrt{7}$

outside only

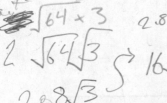

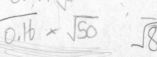

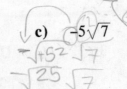

Class Ex. #6

Without using a calculator, arrange the following mixed radicals in order from greatest to least.

i) $3\sqrt{5}$ ii) $5\sqrt{3}$ iii) $\sqrt{15}$ iv) $2\sqrt{8}$ v) $8\sqrt{2}$

$\sqrt{5\cdot9}$ $\sqrt{5\cdot25}$ $\sqrt{8\cdot4}$ $\sqrt{64\cdot2}$
$\sqrt{45}$ $\sqrt{75}$ $\sqrt{5}$ $\sqrt{32}$ $\sqrt{128}$

$\sqrt{15}$ $\sqrt{32}$ $\sqrt{45}$ $\sqrt{75}$ $\sqrt{128}$

Class Ex. #7

Use the Pythagorean Theorem to determine the exact length of *AB*. Express the answer as
a) an exact value in simplest mixed radical form
b) as a decimal to the nearest hundredth

$\sqrt{116}$
$\sqrt{4\cdot29}$
$2\sqrt{29}$

$a^2+b^2=c^2$

10.77

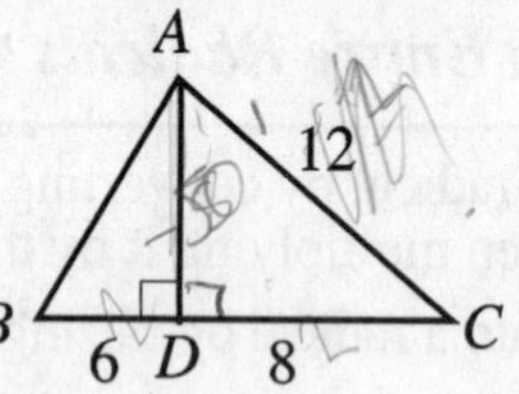

Complete Assignment Questions #5 - #16

Assignment

1. Identify whether each radical is written as a mixed radical or an entire radical.

 a) $\sqrt{35}$ **b)** $2\sqrt{7}$ **c)** $\sqrt{81}$ **d)** $0.3\sqrt{6}$

 En Mi En Mi

2. Convert the following radicals to mixed radicals in simplest form.

 a) $\sqrt{8}$ **b)** $\sqrt{20}$ **c)** $\sqrt{75}$ **d)** $\sqrt{98}$

 $\sqrt{4}\cdot\sqrt{2}$ $\sqrt{4}\cdot\sqrt{5}$ $\sqrt{25}\cdot\sqrt{3}$ imposter
 $2\sqrt{2}$ $2\sqrt{5}$ $5\sqrt{3}$ $-8\sqrt{12}$
 $-8\sqrt{2}\sqrt{2}$

 e) $3\sqrt{32}$ **f)** $-5\sqrt{45}$ **g)** $2\sqrt{54}$ **h)** $-4\sqrt{48}$

 $3\sqrt{2}\cdot\sqrt{16}$ $-5\sqrt{9}\cdot\sqrt{5}$ $2\sqrt{9}\cdot\sqrt{6}$ $-4\sqrt{6}\cdot\sqrt{8}$ $-8\sqrt{3}\cdot\sqrt{4}$
 $3\sqrt{2}\cdot4$ $12\sqrt{2}$ $-15\sqrt{5}$ $2\cdot3\sqrt{6}$ $-4\sqrt{6}\cdot\sqrt{2}\cdot\sqrt{4}$ $-16\sqrt{3}$

3. Convert the following radicals to mixed radicals in simplest form.
There are two which cannot be converted. Identify them and explain why they cannot be converted to mixed radicals.

a) $\sqrt{96}$ **b)** $\sqrt{242}$ **c)** $-\frac{2}{3}\sqrt{180}$ **d)** $\frac{1}{8}\sqrt{320}$

e) $\sqrt{245}$ **f)** $4\sqrt{338}$ **g)** $\sqrt{1\,250}$ **h)** $\sqrt{66}$

impossible → no perfect square factors

i) $-\frac{5}{6}\sqrt{304}$ **j)** $\sqrt{980}$ **k)** $4\sqrt{272}$ **l)** $-3\sqrt{288}$

m) $2\sqrt{369}$ **n)** $\sqrt{364}$ **o)** $\frac{2}{5}\sqrt{450}$ im **p)** $\frac{7}{11}\sqrt{341}$

$\frac{2}{5}\sqrt{18}\cdot\sqrt{25}$

$2\sqrt{18}$ $\sqrt{2}\cdot\sqrt{9}$

$2\sqrt{3}\cdot\sqrt{6}$ $6\sqrt{2}$

4. Convert the following radicals to mixed radicals where the radicand is a whole number.

a) $\sqrt{\frac{2}{9}}$ **b)** $\sqrt{\frac{5}{4}}$ **c)** $\sqrt{\frac{18}{25}}$ **d)** $7\sqrt{\frac{20}{49}}$

$\frac{\sqrt{2}}{\sqrt{9}} \to \frac{\sqrt{2}}{3} = \frac{1}{3}\sqrt{2}$ $\frac{\sqrt{5}}{\sqrt{4}} \to \frac{\sqrt{5}}{2} = \frac{1}{2}\sqrt{5}$ $\frac{\sqrt{18}}{\sqrt{25}} \to \frac{\sqrt{18}}{5} = \frac{1}{5}\sqrt{18}$ $\frac{\sqrt{20}}{\sqrt{49}} \to \frac{\sqrt{20}}{7} = \frac{1}{7}\sqrt{20}$

5. Convert the following to entire radical form.

 a) $2\sqrt{6}$ **b)** $3\sqrt{7}$ **c)** $5\sqrt{15}$ **d)** $12\sqrt{2}$

 $\sqrt{24}$ $\sqrt{63}$ $\sqrt{375}$ $\sqrt{288}$

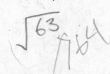

 e) $3\sqrt{25}$ **f)** $-8\sqrt{3}$ **g)** $9\sqrt{10}$ **h)** $-4\sqrt{5}$

 $\sqrt{225}$ $-\sqrt{192}$

6. Convert the following to entire radical form.

 a) $\dfrac{1}{3}\sqrt{27}$ **b)** $15^2 \to \sqrt{}$ **c)** $\dfrac{3}{2}\sqrt{8}$ **d)** $3^2\sqrt{21}$

$\dfrac{1}{3}\sqrt{3\cdot 9^2}$ $\sqrt{3\cdot 9^3}$ $9\sqrt{3}$ $\sqrt{3\cdot 5}$ $\sqrt{15^2}$ $\sqrt{225}$ $\sqrt{\dfrac{9\cdot 8\cdot 2}{}}$ $\sqrt{8}$ $9^2\sqrt{81\cdot 21}$ $\sqrt{1701}$ DIS DIS DATA

Do not use a calculator to answer question #7 or #8.

7. Given that $\sqrt{6}$ is approximately equal to 2.45, and $\sqrt{60}$ is approximately equal to 7.75, then find the approximate value of

 a) $\sqrt{600}$ **b)** $\sqrt{6\,000}$ **c)** $\sqrt{600\,000}$ **d)** $\sqrt{0.06}$

 $\sqrt{100\cdot 6}$ $\sqrt{100\cdot 60}$ $\sqrt{10000\cdot 60}$ $\sqrt{\dfrac{1}{100}\cdot 6}$

 $10\sqrt{6}$ $10\sqrt{60}$ $100\sqrt{60}$ $\dfrac{1}{10}\sqrt{6}$

 2.45 24.5 77.5 775 $\dfrac{2.45}{10}$ 0.245

 e) $\sqrt{0.6}$ **f)** $\sqrt{24}$ **g)** $\sqrt{540}$ **h)** $\sqrt{\dfrac{6}{25}}$

 $\sqrt{0.01\cdot 60}$ $\sqrt{4}\cdot\sqrt{6}$ $\dfrac{2.45}{\sqrt{25}}$ $\dfrac{2.45}{5}$

 $\sqrt{\dfrac{1}{100}\cdot 60}$ $2\sqrt{6}$ $2(2.45)$

$\dfrac{1}{10}\cdot 7.75 \to 0.775$ 4.9

8. Arrange the following radicals in order from greatest to least.

 $3\sqrt{7}\,,\ 5\sqrt{3}\,,\ \sqrt{60}\,,\ 2\sqrt{11}\,,\ \dfrac{1}{2}\sqrt{200}$

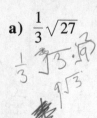

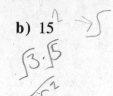

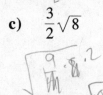

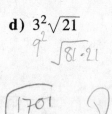

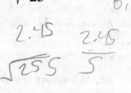

9. Consider $\triangle PQR$ as shown. Students are trying to determine the length of PQ using the Pythagorean Formula.

Louis expresses each side to the nearest hundredth and calculates the length of PQ to the nearest hundredth.

Asia uses the entire radical form for each side and expresses her answer to the nearest hundredth.

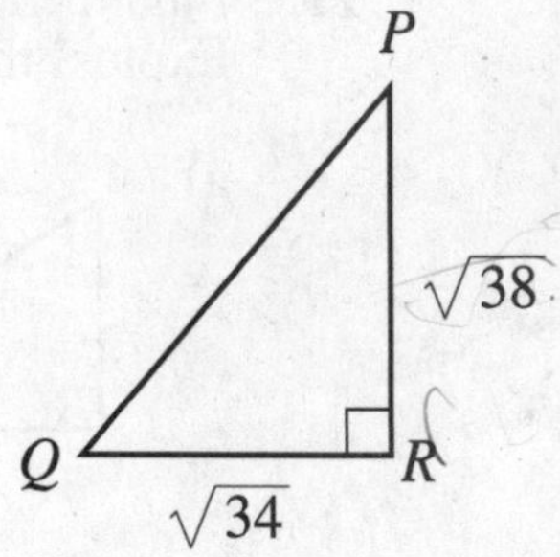

a) Complete each student's work.

Louis	Asia
$(PQ)^2 = (QR)^2 + (PR)^2$	$(PQ)^2 = (QR)^2 + (PR)^2$
$= 5.83^2 +$ 6.16^2	$= (\sqrt{34})^2 + \sqrt{38}^2$
$=$ 8.48	$= 34 +$ 38
	$\sqrt{72}$
	$\sqrt{36}\sqrt{2} = 6\sqrt{2}$
	8.49

b) Which student's answer is more accurate? Explain.

Asia, cause lois is dumb.

c) State the **exact** answer as a mixed radical.

10. Use the Pythagorean formula, $c^2 = a^2 + b^2$, in the given triangle to calculate the length of XY. Express the answer as:

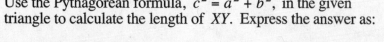

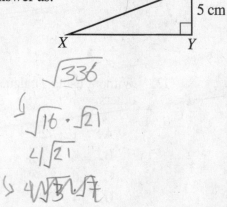

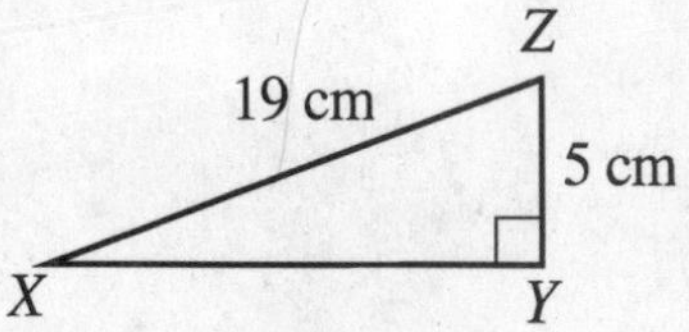

i) an entire radical
ii) a mixed radical
iii) a decimal to the nearest hundredth

$19^2 - 5^2$

$361 - 25 = 336 \Rightarrow \sqrt{336}$

i) $\sqrt{336}$
ii) $4\sqrt{21}$
iii) 18.33

$\sqrt{336}$
$\sqrt{16}\cdot\sqrt{21}$
$4\sqrt{21}$

11. Find the lengths of the missing sides.
Express the answers in simplest mixed radical form.

a)

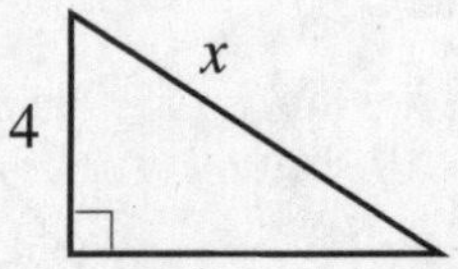

b)

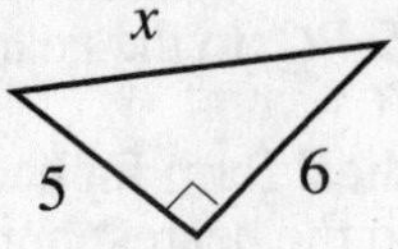

c)

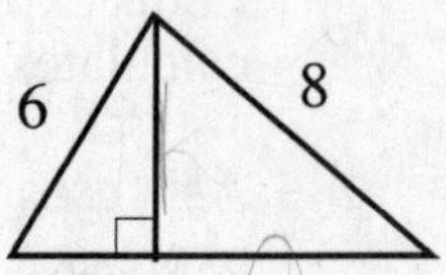

Multiple Choice **12.** The length of *KL* can be represented by which of the following?

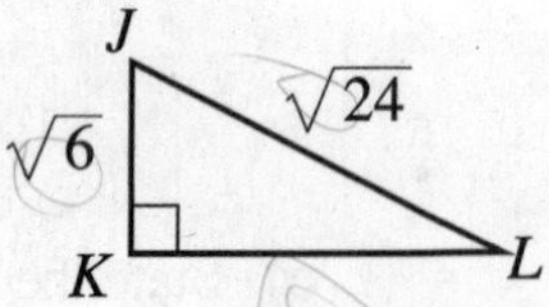

A. $\sqrt{540}$
B. $3\sqrt{2}$
C. $\sqrt{30}$
D. $9\sqrt{2}$

13. Without using a calculator, determine which of the following radicals is not equal to the others.

A. $12\sqrt{2}$
B. $\sqrt{288}$
C. $6\sqrt{8}$
D. $4\sqrt{72}$

Use the following information to answer question 14.

Devon read in his physics book that the distance, d kilometres, a person can see to the horizon on a clear day can be approximated by the formula $d = \sqrt{13h}$, where h is the person's eye level distance above the ground in metres. When standing on the ground, Devon's eye level distance is 1.8 m above the ground.

Numerical Response

14. The distance Devon can see to the horizon when he is standing on the roof of a building 698.2 m high can be represented in simplest form by the expression $a\sqrt{b}$.

The value of $a + b$ is _____ .

(Record your answer in the numerical response box from left to right)

698.2

Use the following information to answer question #15.

In Ancient Greece a formula was developed which could be used to calculate the area of a triangle. The formula, known as Heron's Formula, is shown below.

$$A = \sqrt{s(s-a)(s-b)(s-c)}$$

where a, b, and c are the lengths of the sides of a triangle,

and $s = \dfrac{a+b+c}{2}$.

15. The area of a triangle whose sides measure 14, 15, and 25 can be written in simplest form as $p\sqrt{26}$, where $a \in N$. The value of p is _____.

(Record your answer in the numerical response box from left to right)

16. The smaller square has side length 8 cm. The side length of the larger square can be written in simplest form as $p\sqrt{q}$, where $p, q \in N$. The value of pq is _____.

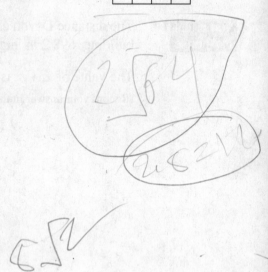

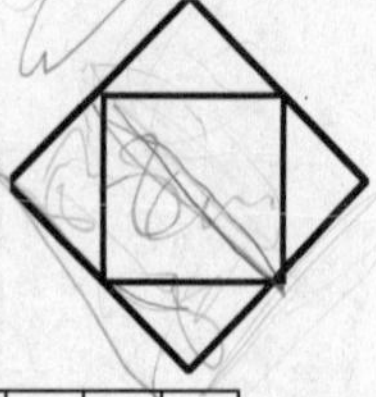

(Record your answer in the numerical response box from left to right)

Answer Key

1. a) entire b) mixed c) entire d) mixed

2. a) $2\sqrt{2}$ b) $2\sqrt{5}$ c) $5\sqrt{3}$ d) $7\sqrt{2}$ e) $12\sqrt{2}$ f) $-15\sqrt{5}$ g) $6\sqrt{6}$ h) $-16\sqrt{3}$

3. a) $4\sqrt{6}$ b) $11\sqrt{2}$ c) $-4\sqrt{5}$ d) $\sqrt{5}$ e) $7\sqrt{5}$ f) $52\sqrt{2}$ g) $25\sqrt{2}$
h) cannot be converted because 66 does not have a factor which is a perfect square.
i) $-\frac{10}{3}\sqrt{19}$ j) $14\sqrt{5}$ k) $16\sqrt{17}$ l) $-36\sqrt{2}$ m) $6\sqrt{41}$ n) $2\sqrt{91}$ o) $6\sqrt{2}$
p) cannot be converted because 341 does not have a factor which is a perfect square.

4. a) $\frac{1}{3}\sqrt{2}$ b) $\frac{1}{2}\sqrt{5}$ c) $\frac{3}{5}\sqrt{2}$ d) $2\sqrt{5}$

5. a) $\sqrt{24}$ b) $\sqrt{63}$ c) $\sqrt{375}$ d) $\sqrt{288}$ e) $\sqrt{225}$ f) $-\sqrt{192}$ g) $\sqrt{810}$ h) $-\sqrt{80}$

6. a) $\sqrt{3}$ b) $\sqrt{225}$ c) $\sqrt{18}$ d) $\sqrt{1701}$

7. a) 24.5 b) 77.5 c) 775 d) 0.245 e) 0.775 f) 4.9 g) 23.25 h) 0.49

8. $5\sqrt{3}$, $3\sqrt{7}$, $\sqrt{60}$, $\frac{1}{2}\sqrt{200}$, $2\sqrt{11}$

9. a) Louis 8.48, Asia 8.49
b) Asia because she used exact values rather than rounded values in her calculation. c) $6\sqrt{2}$

10. i) $\sqrt{336}$ cm ii) $4\sqrt{21}$ cm iii) 18.33 cm

11. a) $4\sqrt{5}$ b) $\sqrt{61}$ c) $2\sqrt{11}$

12. B

13. D

14. | 1 | 0 | 1 | | **15.** | 1 | 8 | | | **16.** | 1 | 6 | | |

Number Lesson #7:
Entire Radicals and Mixed Radicals - Part Two

Converting Entire Radicals *(with an index of 3 or greater)* to Mixed Radicals

An entire radical of index 3 may be expressed as a mixed radical when the highest perfect cube has been factored out of the entire radical.

1^3	= 1
2^3	= 8
3^3	= 27
4^3	= 64
5^3	= 125
6^3	= 216
7^3	= 343
8^3	= 512
9^3	= 729
10^3	= 1000

Complete the following to convert $\sqrt[3]{54}$ to a mixed radical.

Entire Radical ⇒ *Mixed Radical*

$$\sqrt[3]{54} = \sqrt[3]{27 \times 2}$$

$$= \sqrt[3]{27} \times \sqrt[3]{2}$$

$$= 3 \times \sqrt[3]{2}$$

$$\sqrt[3]{54} = 3\sqrt[3]{2}$$

A similar process is involved for indices greater than 3.
Questions at this level will involve simple perfect cubes, etc.

Class Ex. #1

Convert the following radicals to mixed radicals in simplest form.

a) $\sqrt[3]{6\,000}$ **b)** $\sqrt[5]{320}$ **c)** $\sqrt[3]{-16}$

$\sqrt[3]{1000 \times 6}$ $\sqrt[3]{-8 \times 2}$

$\sqrt[3]{1000}\,\sqrt[3]{6}$ $\sqrt[3]{-8}\,\sqrt[3]{2}$

$10\sqrt[3]{6}$ $-2\sqrt[3]{2}$

Converting Mixed Radicals *(with an index of 3 or greater)* to Entire Radicals

A mixed radical of index 3 may be expressed as an entire radical by converting the number outside the radical symbol into a radical and then multiplying it by the radicand.

The number outside the radical symbol can be converted into a radical by raising it to the power of 3.

Complete the following to convert $\frac{1}{2}\sqrt[3]{80}$ to an entire radical.

Mixed Radical ⇒ *Entire Radical*

$$\frac{1}{2}\sqrt[3]{80} = \sqrt[3]{\quad} \times \sqrt[3]{80}$$

$$= \sqrt[3]{\quad \times 80}$$

$$\frac{1}{2}\sqrt[3]{80} =$$

Class Ex. #2

Convert the following mixed radicals to entire radicals.

a) $2\sqrt[4]{3}$ **b)** $-4\sqrt[3]{7}$ **c)** $\frac{2}{5}\sqrt[3]{100}$ **d)** $-3\sqrt[4]{2}$

Complete Assignment Questions #1 - #7

Extension: Radicals involving Variables

Since $x^3 \times x^3 = x^6$ then $\sqrt{x^6}$ = ___ . Also, since $x^5 \times x^5 \times x^5 = x^{15}$ then $\sqrt[3]{x^{15}}$ = ___.

So $\sqrt{x^4}$ = ___. $\sqrt{y^{10}}$ = ___. $\sqrt{a^8b^6}$ = ___. $\sqrt[3]{x^{24}}$ = ___. $\sqrt[3]{y^6}$ = ___.

Complete the following to convert $\sqrt{x^5}$ to a mixed radical.

Entire Radical ⇒ *Mixed Radical*

$\sqrt{x^5} = \sqrt{x^4 \times x}$

$= \sqrt{\quad} \times \sqrt{x}$

$=$ ___ $\times \sqrt{x}$

$\sqrt{x^5} =$

Class Ex. #3

Convert the following entire radicals to mixed radicals in simplest form.

a) $\sqrt{a^7}$ **b)** $\sqrt{t^9}$ **c)** $\sqrt[3]{x^5}$ **d)** $\sqrt[3]{x^7}$

Class Ex. #4

Convert the following entire radicals to mixed radicals in simplest form.

a) $\sqrt{x^6y^5}$ **b)** $\sqrt{18x^3}$ **c)** $\sqrt{32y^7z^8}$ **d)** $\sqrt[3]{40x^4y^9}$

Class Ex. #5

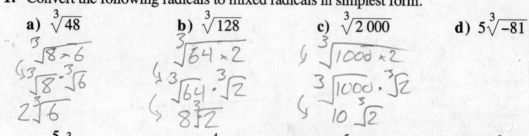

Convert the following mixed radicals to entire radicals.

a) $2\sqrt{x^3}$ **b)** $a^2\sqrt{a}$ **c)** $x^5\sqrt{xy}$ **d)** $3xy^3\sqrt[3]{2z^4}$

Complete Assignment Questions #8 - #12

Assignment

1. Convert the following radicals to mixed radicals in simplest form.

a) $\sqrt[3]{48}$ **b)** $\sqrt[3]{128}$ **c)** $\sqrt[3]{2\,000}$ **d)** $5\sqrt[3]{-81}$

$\sqrt[3]{8\times 6}$ → $\sqrt[3]{8}\cdot\sqrt[3]{6}$ → $2\sqrt[3]{6}$

$\sqrt[3]{64\times 2}$ → $\sqrt[3]{64}\cdot\sqrt[3]{2}$ → $8\sqrt[3]{2}$

$\sqrt[3]{1000\times 2}$ → $\sqrt[3]{1000}\cdot\sqrt[3]{2}$ → $10\sqrt[3]{2}$

e) $\frac{5}{6}\sqrt[3]{108}$ **f)** $5\sqrt[4]{162}$ **g)** $\sqrt[5]{-192}$ **h)** $-2\sqrt[3]{625}$

2. Convert the following mixed radicals to entire radicals.

a) $2\sqrt[4]{2}$ **b)** $3\sqrt[3]{4}$ **c)** $-3\sqrt[4]{3}$ **d)** $-10\sqrt[3]{5}$

e) $2\sqrt[5]{6}$ **f)** $\frac{1}{2}\sqrt[3]{16}$ **g)** $\frac{3}{10}\sqrt[4]{100\,000}$ **h)** $-5\sqrt[3]{9}$

Do not use a calculator to answer question #3 or #4.

3. Arrange the following radicals in order from least to greatest.

$7\sqrt[6]{1}$, $-3\sqrt[3]{-27}$, $\frac{5}{2}\sqrt[4]{16}$, $3\sqrt{\sqrt[3]{64}}$

4. Consider the following radicals $2\sqrt[3]{11}$, $3\sqrt[3]{3}$, $4\sqrt[3]{2}$, $2\sqrt[3]{6}$.

a) **Explain** how to arrange the radicals in order from least to greatest without using a calculator.

b) Arrange the radicals in order from least to greatest.

Multiple Choice

5. $\sqrt[3]{240}$ is equivalent to

A. $2\sqrt[3]{40}$ **B.** $4\sqrt[3]{15}$

C. $2\sqrt[3]{30}$ **D.** $8\sqrt[3]{30}$

6. Consider the following two statements:

Statement 1: $-3\sqrt[4]{8} = 3\sqrt[4]{-8}$. **Statement 2:** $-2\sqrt[3]{7} = 2\sqrt[3]{-7}$.

Which of the following is correct?

A. Both statements are true.
B. Both statements are false.
C. Statement 1 is true, and statement 2 is false.
D. Statement 1 is false, and statement 2 is true.

Numerical Response

7. The mixed radical $\frac{1}{12}\sqrt[3]{128}$ can be converted to a mixed radical in simplest form $a\sqrt[3]{b}$.
The value of $a + b$, to the nearest tenth, is _____.
(Record your answer in the numerical response box from left to right)

Extension Assignment

8. Express as an entire radical.

a) $6\sqrt{y}$ **b)** $8\sqrt{c^2}$ **c)** $10\sqrt{2yz^3}$ **d)** $-3\sqrt[3]{x^2}$

e) $c\sqrt{c}$ **f)** $x\sqrt{3y^3}$ **g)** $11c^2\sqrt{c^2d}$ **h)** $5a^3b\sqrt{3a^2b}$

i) $4\sqrt{3}\ a^2b$ **j)** $2p^2q\sqrt[3]{5pq^2}$ **k)** $7p^8q^9\sqrt{p^2r}$ **l)** $2xy^3\sqrt[4]{9x}$

9. Express each as a mixed radical in simplest form.

a) $\sqrt{a^5}$ **b)** $\sqrt{t^3}$ **c)** $\sqrt{x^{11}}$ **d)** $\sqrt[3]{x^4}$ **e)** $\sqrt[3]{b^8}$ **f)** $\sqrt[4]{x^6}$

10. Express each as a mixed radical in simplest form.

a) $\sqrt{8y^2}$ **b)** $\sqrt{16p^3}$ **c)** $\sqrt{75y^3z^4}$

d) $\sqrt{300a^9w^7}$ **e)** $5\sqrt{28c^4d^3}$ **f)** $-6\sqrt{29a^4b^8}$

g) $7p^3q^2\sqrt{27p^5q^6}$ **h)** $\frac{2}{3}c\sqrt{81c^3d^{12}}$ **i)** $11x^7y^{15}\sqrt{242x^9y^{10}}$

j) $\sqrt[3]{2000x^7}$ **k)** $4\sqrt[3]{250b^{13}}$ **l)** $\sqrt[4]{32x^9}$

Multiple Choice

11. $\sqrt{3x}\ \sqrt{2x}$ is equivalent to

A. $\sqrt{6x}$ **B.** $\sqrt{36x^2}$ **C.** $6\sqrt{x}$ **D.** $x\sqrt{6}$

Answer Key

1. a) $2\sqrt[3]{6}$ b) $4\sqrt[3]{2}$ c) $10\sqrt[3]{2}$ d) $-15\sqrt[3]{3}$ e) $\frac{5}{2}\sqrt[3]{4}$ f) $15\sqrt[4]{2}$ g) $-2\sqrt[5]{6}$ h) $-10\sqrt[3]{5}$

2. a) $\sqrt[4]{32}$ b) $\sqrt[3]{108}$ c) $-\sqrt[4]{243}$ d) $-\sqrt[3]{5000}$ or $\sqrt[3]{-5000}$ e) $\sqrt[5]{192}$ f) $\sqrt[3]{2}$ g) $\sqrt[4]{810}$
h) $-\sqrt[3]{1125}$ or $\sqrt[3]{-1125}$

3. $\frac{5}{2}\sqrt[4]{16}$, $3\sqrt{\sqrt[3]{64}}$, $7\sqrt[6]{1}$, $-3\sqrt[3]{-27}$

4. a) Convert the mixed radicals to entire form and compare the radicands.
b) $2\sqrt[3]{6}$, $3\sqrt[3]{3}$, $2\sqrt[3]{11}$, $4\sqrt[3]{2}$

5. C **6.** D **7.**

2	.	3	

8. a) $\sqrt{36y}$ b) $\sqrt{64c^2}$ c) $\sqrt{200yz^3}$ d) $-\sqrt[3]{27x^2}$ or $\sqrt[3]{-27x^2}$
e) $\sqrt{c^3}$ f) $\sqrt{3x^2y^3}$ g) $\sqrt{121c^6d}$ h) $\sqrt{75a^8b^3}$
i) $\sqrt{48a^4b^2}$ j) $\sqrt[3]{40p^7q^5}$ k) $\sqrt{49p^{18}q^{18}r}$ l) $\sqrt[4]{144x^5y^{12}}$

9. a) $a^2\sqrt{a}$ b) $t\sqrt{t}$ c) $x^5\sqrt{x}$ d) $x\sqrt[3]{x}$ e) $b^2\sqrt[3]{b^2}$ f) $x\sqrt[4]{x^2}$

10. a) $2y\sqrt{2}$ b) $4p\sqrt{p}$ c) $5yz^2\sqrt{3y}$ d) $10a^4w^3\sqrt{3aw}$
e) $10c^2d\sqrt{7d}$ f) $-6a^2b^4\sqrt{29}$ g) $21p^5q^5\sqrt{3p}$ h) $6c^2d^6\sqrt{c}$
i) $121x^{11}y^{20}\sqrt{2x}$ j) $10x^2\sqrt[3]{2x}$ k) $20b^4\sqrt[3]{2b}$ l) $2x^2\sqrt[4]{2x}$

11. D

Number Lesson #8:
Practice Test

Use the space beside the question for your rough work.

1. Which of the following numbers is not a prime factor of 14 014?

A. 7
B. 11
C. 13
D. 17

2. How many numbers in the list 7, 11, 17, 21, are prime factors of 3 234?

A. 1
B. 2
C. 3
D. 4

Numerical Response **1.** The sum of all of the prime factors of 160 797 is ______.

(Record your answer in the numerical response box from left to right)

3. The lowest common multiple of 33 and 110 can be written as a product of prime factors in the form $a \times b \times c \times d$ where a, b, c, and d are prime numbers with $a < b < c < d$. The value of c is

A. 3

B. 5

C. 11

D. 1 100

Numerical Response **2.** The greatest common factor of 6 699 and 8 265 is ______.

(Record your answer in the numerical response box from left to right)

4. The lowest common multiple of 14 and 105 is equal to the greatest common factor of the numbers P and Q. Which of the following statements must be false?

A. P is a multiple of 7.

B. Q is a multiple of 21.

C. P could be less than 200.

D. Q could be greater than 2 000.

Use the following information to answer the next two questions.

The partial prime factorization of a number x is shown in the tree diagram.

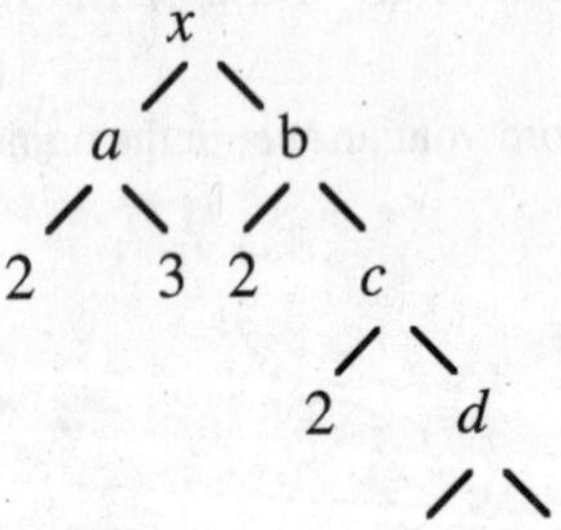

5. If x is a perfect square, then the minimum value of d is

A. 2 **B.** 3 **C.** 6 **D.** 9

Numerical Response **3.** If x is a perfect cube, then the minimum value of x is ______.

(Record your answer in the numerical response box from left to right)

6. The number represented by ⊗ is irrational. The decimal representation of ⊗ is

A. terminating and repeating **B.** terminating and non-repeating
C. non-terminating and repeating **D.** non-terminating and non-repeating

7. Which of the following are rational numbers?

I 1.01001000100001...... **II** $\sqrt[3]{\frac{8}{27}}$ **III** $\sqrt{0.04}$ **IV** $0.\overline{29}$

A. **III** and **IV** only **B.** **II, III** and **IV** only **C.** **I, II, III** and **IV**

D. some other combination of **I, II, III** and **IV**

8. The rational number $1.\overline{54}$ can be written as an improper fraction in simplest form $\frac{c}{d}$.
The value of c is

A. 17 **B.** 11

C. 6 **D.** 4

9. M and N are fixed irrational numbers satisfying $30 < M < 40$ and $3 < N < 4$.
The value of $\sqrt{M} + \sqrt{N}$ is best represented on the number line by

A. P

B. Q

C. R

D. S

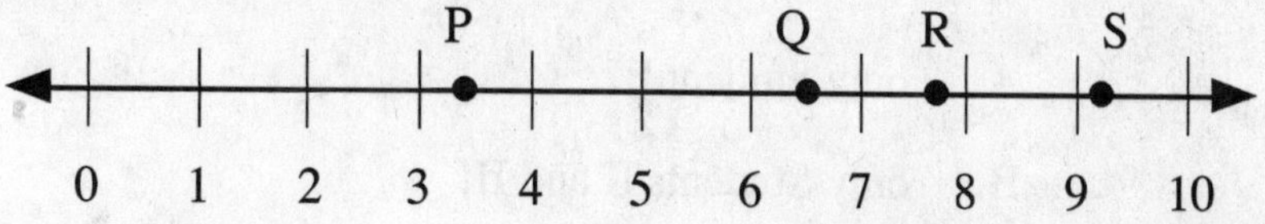

10. Consider the following numbers. $\sqrt[3]{67}$, $\sqrt[4]{98}$, $\sqrt{19}$, $\sqrt[5]{201}$.
The largest of these numbers is

A. $\sqrt{19}$ **B.** $\sqrt[4]{98}$ **C.** $\sqrt[3]{67}$ **D.** $\sqrt[5]{201}$

11. The length of a soccer field is $12\sqrt[4]{4\,000}$ metres. In the number $12\sqrt[4]{4\,000}$, the index and the radicand are respectively

A. 4 and 4 000 **B.** 12 and 4 000 **C.** 4 and 12 **D.** 4 000 and 4

Numerical Response

4. When $7\sqrt[3]{6}$ is written as an entire radical, the value of the radicand is ____.

(Record your answer in the numerical response box from left to right)

12. Three statements are given below.

***Statement* 1** : $35 = 7\sqrt{5}$

***Statement* 2** : $\sqrt{28} = 2\sqrt{7}$

***Statement* 3** : $4\sqrt{3} = 48$

Which of the statements above is/are true?

A. 1 only **B.** 2 only **C.** 1 and 2 only **D.** 2 and 3 only

13. Three students were asked to write the radical $\sqrt{4\,050}$ in another form. The answers given were:

Student I $405\sqrt{10}$ Student II $15\sqrt{18}$ Student III $45\sqrt{2}$.

A correct answer was given by

A. only Student III

B. only Students II and III

C. all three students

D. some other combination of students not given above

14. The area of a circle of radius, r, is given by the formula $A = \pi r^2$.
A circle of radius 6 cm has an area of 36π cm^2.
If a circle has an area of 120π cm^2, then the exact length of its radius in cm is

A. 60

B. $12\sqrt{10}$

C. $2\sqrt{30}$

D. $2\sqrt{15}$

Numerical Response

5. The volume of a cube of edge length x cm is given by the formula $V = x^3$. A die has a volume of $720\ \text{mm}^3$.

A student determined that the exact length of each edge of the die could be written in the form $a\sqrt[3]{b}$ where a and b are whole numbers.

The value of $a + b$ is ______.

(Record your answer in the numerical response box from left to right)

15. Consider the following three equations.

$$4\sqrt[3]{3} = \sqrt[3]{x} \qquad 5\sqrt{x} = y\sqrt{3} \qquad 16\sqrt{y} = z\sqrt{10}$$

Which of the statements below is correct?

A. $x < y < z$ **B.** $z < x < y$

C. $y < z < x$ **D.** $z < y < x$

Written Response - 5 marks

Use the following information to answer the next question.

1. A group of students have invented a simple card game based on the real number system. There are 50 cards in the deck and each card has a number written on it.

Points are awarded as follows.

Natural Number → 4 points
Whole number → 5 points
Integer → 6 points
Rational Number → 3 points
Irrational Number → 10 points
Non-real Number → 1 point

- A student selects a card. The number on the card is 7. Explain why this card is valued at 18 points.

- A second student selects a card which has the number -5 on it. How many points are awarded for this card?

- In the game each student is dealt three cards and the student with the most points wins.

  Which of the following three students wins the game?

  Student A with the following cards: $\frac{3}{4}$, $\sqrt{15}$, and 0.

  Student B with the following cards: -3, $\sqrt{\frac{4}{9}}$, and π.

  Student C with the following cards: $-\sqrt{36}$, $\sqrt{-36}$, and 36.

Answer Key

1. D **2.** B **3.** B **4.** C **5.** C **6.** D **7.** B **8.** A

9. C **10.** A **11.** A **12.** B **13.** B **14.** C **15.** D

1.

7	3		

2.

8	7		

3.

2	1	6	

4.

2	0	5	8

5.

9	2		

1. • The number 7 is a natural number, a whole number, an integer, and a rational number. The point value is $4 + 5 + 6 + 3 = 18$.

- The number -5 is an integer, and a rational number. The point value is $6 + 3 = 9$.

- Student A: $3/4 \rightarrow$ 3 points, $\sqrt{15} \rightarrow$ 10 points, $0 \rightarrow$ 14 points, for a total of 27 points.
- Student B: $-3 \rightarrow$ 9 points, $\sqrt{\frac{4}{9}} \rightarrow$ 3 points, $\pi \rightarrow$ 10 points, for a total of 22 points.
- Student C: $-\sqrt{36} \rightarrow$ 9 points, $\sqrt{-36} \rightarrow$ 1 point, $36 \rightarrow$ 18 points, for a total of 28 points.

  Student C wins the game.

Exponents Lesson #1:
Powers with Whole Number Exponents

Overview of Unit

In this unit we review powers with whole number exponents where the base is numerical. We extend these concepts into powers where the base is variable and to where the exponents are integral and rational. We learn how to write powers with rational exponents as radicals and vice versa and how to solve problems involving the exponent laws.

In this lesson we review numbers written as powers and the exponent laws applied to powers with numerical bases and whole number exponents.
We extend the work to consider bases which are variable.

Exponents

In mathematics exponents are used as a short way to write repeated multiplication.

The number of small cubes in the diagram can be calculated by the **repeated multiplication** $2 \times 2 \times 2$.
This can be written in **exponential form** as 2^3.

Exponents can also be used with variables.

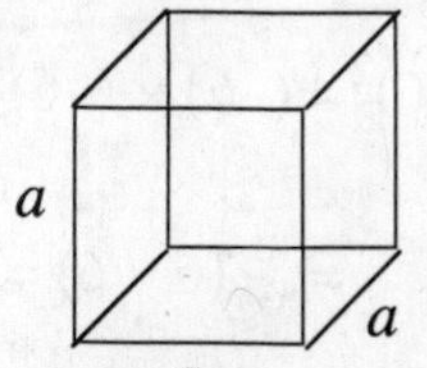

The volume of the cube to the left can be determined by repeated multiplication $a \times a \times a$ or in exponential form a^3.

Powers

A **power** is a number written in exponential form.

It consists of a **base** and an **exponent**.

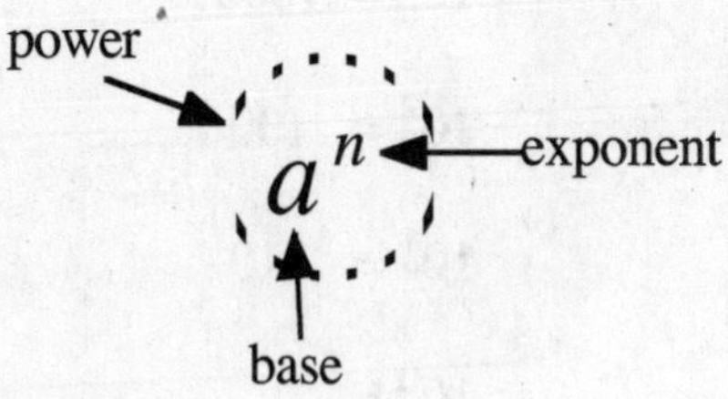

State the base and the exponent in each of the following powers.

a) 4^5 **b)** $(-3)^6$ **c)** x^y

A number that multiplies a variable is called a **coefficient**.
In the expression $7p^3$ the coefficient is 7.

Class Ex. #2

State the coefficient in each of the of the following.

a) $8x^2$ **b)** $-3z^9$ **c)** $\frac{a^8}{7}$

Note that written as a repeated multiplication $7p^3 = 7 \times p \times p \times p$,
whereas $(7p)^3 = 7p \times 7p \times 7p = 7 \times p \times 7 \times p \times 7 \times p = 7 \times 7 \times 7 \times p \times p \times p = 343p^3$.

Class Ex. #3

Write each of the following as a repeated multiplication.

a) $3a^4b$ **c)** $3(ab)^4$

b) $3ab^4$ **d)** $(3ab)^4$

Evaluating Powers

$10^3 = 10 \times 10 \times 10 =$ $3^4 = 3 \times 3 \times 3 \times 3 =$ $(-6)^2 = (-6) \times (-6) =$

$-6^2 = -(6 \times 6) =$

The Zero Exponent

Complete the patterns below by adding one more row.

$10^4 = 10000$ $3^4 = 81$

$10^3 = 1000$ $3^3 = 27$

$10^2 = 100$ $3^2 = 9$

$10^1 = 10$ $3^1 = 3$

$10^0 =$

The results above are examples of a general rule when a base is raised to the exponent zero.
Complete: $a^0 =$ ____ .

Class Ex. #4

Evaluate the following. **a)** 6^0 **b)** $(-9)^0$ **c)** -9^0 **d)** $2(6^2)^0$

Complete Assignment Questions #1 - #7

The Exponent Laws

The exponent laws with whole number exponents and numerical bases were covered in previous math courses.

The chart below extends this to bases which are variables.

Complete the table as a review of the exponent laws.

Numerical Bases	Variable Bases	Exponent Laws
$8^3 \times 8^2 = (8 \cdot 8 \cdot 8)(8 \cdot 8)$ $= 8^5$ or 8^{3+2}	$a^3 \times a^2 = (a \cdot a \cdot a)(a \cdot a)$ $= a$ or $a^{\ \ +\ \ }$	**Product Law** $(a^m)(a^n) =$
$8^3 \div 8^2 = \dfrac{8 \cdot 8 \cdot 8}{8 \cdot 8}$ $= 8^1$ or $8^{\ \ -\ \ }$	$a^3 \div a^2 = \dfrac{a \cdot a \cdot a}{a \cdot a}$ $= a$ or $a^{\ \ -\ \ }$	**Quotient Law** $a^m \div a^n = \dfrac{a^m}{a^n} =$ $(a \neq 0)$
$(8 \cdot 7)^3 = (8 \cdot 7)(8 \cdot 7)(8 \cdot 7)$ $= (8 \cdot 8 \cdot 8)(\qquad)$ $= 8^3 \cdot 7^3$	$(a \cdot b)^3 = (a \cdot b)(a \cdot b)(a \cdot b)$ $= (a \cdot a \cdot a)(\qquad)$ $= a\ b$	**Power of a Product Law** $(ab)^m =$
$\left(\dfrac{8}{7}\right)^3 = \left(\dfrac{}{}\right)\left(\dfrac{}{}\right)\left(\dfrac{}{}\right)$ $= \dfrac{8^3}{7^3}$	$\left(\dfrac{a}{b}\right)^3 = \left(\dfrac{}{}\right)\left(\dfrac{}{}\right)\left(\dfrac{}{}\right)$ $= \dfrac{a}{b}$	**Power of a Quotient Law** $\left(\dfrac{a}{b}\right)^n =$ $(b \neq 0)$
$(8^3)^2 = (8^3)(8^3)$ $= (\qquad)(\qquad)$ $= 8^6$ or $8^{\ \ \times\ \ }$	$(a^3)^2 = (a^3)(a^3)$ $= (\qquad)(\qquad)$ $= a$ or $a^{\ \ \times\ \ }$	**Power of a Power Law** $(a^m)^n =$

Class Ex. #5

Use the exponent laws to simplify and then evaluate.

a) $3^4 \cdot 3^2$ **b)** $\dfrac{(-2)^5}{(-2)^3}$ **c)** $(5^2)^3$

Class Ex. #6

Use the exponent laws to simplify.

a) $(a)^4(a)^3$ **b)** x^6x **c)** $b^7 \times b^0 \times b^4$ **d)** $\dfrac{x^8}{x^4}$ **e)** $\dfrac{y^{10}}{y^2}$ **f)** $(a^4)^3$

g) $(y^5)^5$ **h)** $\left(\dfrac{x}{y}\right)^9$ **i)** $\left(\dfrac{c}{4}\right)^2$ **j)** $(st)^6$ **k)** $(2a)^5$ **l)** $(-3pq)^4$

Complete Assignment Questions #8 - #22

Assignment

1. State the base and the exponent in each of the following powers.

a) 8^3 **b)** k^{15} **c)** 2^x **d)** $(-x)^4$ **e)** $\left(\dfrac{3}{4}\right)^6$

2. State the coefficient in each of the following.

a) $5x^7$ **b)** $-6z^2$ **c)** a^3 **d)** $\dfrac{y^3}{4}$ **e)** $\dfrac{5y^9}{8}$

3. Write each of the following as a repeated multiplication.

a) c^4 **b)** $5x^3$ **c)** $(ab)^2$ **d)** $(-5)^3$ **e)** s^2t

f) $2\left(\dfrac{5}{4}\right)^3$ **g)** $(4a)^3$ **h)** $3cd^2$ **i)** $3(cd)^2$ **j)** $(3cd)^2$

4. Evaluate.

a) 3^8 **b)** -5^2 **c)** $(-5)^2$

d) $(-5)^3$ **e)** -5^3 **f)** $\left(\frac{3}{5}\right)^3$

5. Evaluate without using a calculator.

a) -10^2 **b)** $(-10)^2$ **c)** -10^3 **d)** $(-10)^3$

6. Explain why -8^0 and $(-8)^0$ have different values.

7. Evaluate without using a calculator.

a) 32^0 **b)** -1^0 **c)** $\left(-\frac{1}{2}\right)^0$ **d)** $\frac{1}{2}(4)^0$ **e)** $\frac{1}{2}(4^2)^0$

8. Write in a simpler form and evaluate.

a) $9^3 \cdot 9^6$ **b)** $(7^2)^3$ **c)** $\frac{8^{15}}{8^{13}}$ **d)** $\left(\frac{2}{3}\right)\left(\frac{2}{3}\right)^3$

e) $\frac{1.5^7}{1.5^5}$ **f)** $(-3^3)^2$ **g)** $(-5)^6 \times (-5)^2$ **h)** $4^3 \cdot 4^4 \cdot 4^2$

9. Explain using factors why $(x^2)(x^3) \neq (x^2)^3$.

10. Use the Product Law to simplify.

a) $a^4 \times a^2$ **b)** $m^6 \cdot m^3$ **c)** $(s^5)(s^5)$ **d)** x^6x^5 **e)** $y^{10} \times y^2$

11. Use the Quotient Law to simplify.

a) $\frac{t^8}{t^2}$ **b)** $x^6 \div x^4$ **c)** $\frac{p^{10}}{p^9}$ **d)** $d^{18} \div d^9$ **e)** $p^8 \div p$

12. Use the Power of a Product Law to simplify.

a) $(xy)^5$ **b)** $(mn)^4$ **c)** $(3x)^3$ **d)** $(10z)^3$ **e)** $\left(\frac{1}{2}c\right)^2$

f) $(2b)^4$ **g)** $(-x)^3$ **h)** $(-3y)^4$ **i)** $(-4pq)^2$ **j)** $(-4pq)^3$

13. Use the Power of a Quotient Law to simplify.

a) $\left(\frac{x}{y}\right)^2$ **b)** $\left(\frac{a}{b}\right)^6$ **c)** $\left(\frac{5}{c}\right)^4$ **d)** $\left(\frac{b}{5}\right)^3$ **e)** $\left(\frac{z}{y}\right)^{10}$

14. Use the Power of a Power law to simplify.

a) $(p^2)^2$ **b)** $(h^4)^5$ **c)** $(b^4)^3$ **d)** $(s^9)^{10}$ **e)** $(z^7)^3$

15. State the value of x in each of the following.

a) $(a^3)(a^x) = a^9$ **b)** $b^x \cdot b^4 = b^8$ **c)** $c^x \div c^4 = c^{12}$

d) $\frac{d^{10}}{d^x} = d^2$ **e)** $(e^x)^5 = e^{15}$ **f)** $(f^7)^x = f^7$

16. Use the exponent laws to simplify.

a) $\frac{x^{12}}{x^3}$ **b)** $(xy)^7$ **c)** $(t^3)^3$ **d)** t^3t^3

e) $y^4 \times y^8$ **f)** $\left(\frac{a}{b}\right)^{11}$ **g)** $\left(\frac{d}{2}\right)^3$ **h)** $(2st)^6$

17. Simplify.

a) $g^{12}g^3$ **b)** $\frac{a^7}{a^5}$ **c)** $(3bc)^4$ **d)** $\left(\frac{5}{y}\right)^2$

e) $(-a)^4$ **f)** $\left(-\frac{1}{3}pq\right)^4$ **g)** $(a^3)(a^4)(a^5)$ **h)** $\frac{x^6}{x^0}$

18. Simplify.

a) $\dfrac{y^7}{y^7}$ **b)** $(-ab)^5$ **c)** $(m^6)(m^6)$ **d)** $(r^0)^3$

e) $c^3c^4c^5c^6$ **f)** $(-ab)^6$ **g)** $\dfrac{1}{a^3a^5}$ **h)** $2(xy)^3$

19. After marking an exponents quiz a teacher recorded the most common errors made by students. In each case, identify the error made by the students and, where possible, provide the correct simplification.

a) $2^3 \times 2^4 = 2^{12}$ **b)** $(4^3)^2 = 4^9$

c) $3^4 \times 3^5 = 9^9$ **d)** $3^2 \times 2^3 = 6^5$

e) $(-5a^2b)^3 = -5a^6b^3$ **f)** $\left(\frac{1}{2}pq\right)\left(\frac{1}{2}pq\right) = p^2q^2$

Matching **20.** Match each item in column 1 on the left with the equivalent item in column 2 on the right. Each item in column 2 may be used once, more than once, or not at all.

Column 1	Column 2
i) $(-a^2)^3$	**A.** a^4
ii) $(-a^3)^2$	**B.** a^5
iii) $a^3 \times a^2$	**C.** a^6
iv) $a^8 \div a^2$	**D.** a^{24}
v) $a^{30} \div a^6$	**E.** $-a^5$
vi) $-(a^2)^3$	**F.** $-a^6$
vii) $-(a^3)^2$	

Use the following information to answer the next question.

$$(2^3)^p = 2^{12} \qquad \frac{4^{10}}{4^q} = 4^2$$

$$2^r \cdot 2^r = 2^{16} \qquad (3^s)^2 = 1$$

Numerical Response **21.** Write the value of p in the first box.
Write the value of q in the second box.
Write the value of r in the third box.
Write the value of s in the fourth box.

(Record your answer in the numerical response box from left to right)

22. If $(a^n)(a^n)(a^n) = a^{27}$, where n is a whole number, then the value of n is ______ .

(Record your answer in the numerical response box from left to right)

Answer Key

1. a) base 8, exponent 3 b) base k, exponent 15 c) base 2, exponent x
d) base $-x$, exponent 4 e) base $\frac{3}{4}$, exponent 6

2. a) 5 b) -6 c) 1 d) $\frac{1}{4}$ e) $\frac{5}{8}$

3. a) $c \times c \times c \times c$ b) $5 \times x \times x \times x$ c) $a \times a \times b \times b$ d) $(-5) \times (-5) \times (-5)$
e) $s \times s \times t$ f) $2 \times \frac{5}{4} \times \frac{5}{4} \times \frac{5}{4}$ g) $4 \times 4 \times 4 \times a \times a \times a$
h) $3 \times c \times d \times d$ i) $3 \times c \times c \times d \times d$ j) $3 \times 3 \times c \times c \times d \times d$

4. a) 6561 b) -25 c) 25 d) -125 e) -125 f) $\frac{27}{125}$

5. a) -100 b) 100 c) -1000 d) -1000

6. $-8^0 = -1$ since the exponent applies only to the base 8.
$(-8)^0 = 1$ since the exponent applies to the base -8.

7. a) 1 b) -1 c) 1 d) $\frac{1}{2}$ e) $\frac{1}{2}$

8. a) $9^9 = 387\,420\,489$ b) $7^6 = 117\,649$ c) $8^2 = 64$ d) $\left(\frac{2}{3}\right)^4 = \frac{16}{81}$
e) $1.5^2 = 2.25$ f) $3^6 = 729$ g) $(-5)^8 = 390\,625$ h) $4^9 = 262\,144$

9. $(x^2)(x^3) = (x \times x)(x \times x \times x) = (x \times x \times x \times x \times x) = x^5$
$(x^2)^3 = x^2 \times x^2 \times x^2 = x \times x \times x \times x \times x \times x = x^6$

10. a) a^6 b) m^9 c) s^{10} d) x^{11} e) y^{12}

11. a) t^6 b) x^2 c) p d) d^9 e) p^7

12. a) x^5y^5 b) m^4n^4 c) $27x^3$ d) $1000z^3$ e) $\frac{1}{4}c^2$
f) $16b^4$ g) $-x^3$ h) $81y^4$ i) $16p^2q^2$ j) $-64p^3q^3$

13. a) $\frac{x^2}{y^2}$ b) $\frac{a^6}{b^6}$ c) $\frac{625}{c^4}$ d) $\frac{b^3}{125}$ e) $\frac{z^{10}}{y^{10}}$

14. a) p^4 b) h^{20} c) b^{12} d) s^{90} e) z^{21}

15. a) 6 b) 4 c) 16 d) 8 e) 3 f) 1

16. a) x^9 b) x^7y^7 c) t^9 d) t^6 e) y^{12} f) $\frac{a^{11}}{b^{11}}$ g) $\frac{d^3}{8}$ h) $64s^6t^6$

17. a) g^{15} b) a^2 c) $81b^4c^4$ d) $\frac{25}{y^2}$ e) a^4 f) $\frac{1}{81}p^4q^4$ g) a^{12} h) x^6

18. a) $y^0 = 1$ b) $-a^5b^5$ c) m^{12} d) $r^0 = 1$ e) c^{18} f) a^6b^6 g) $\frac{1}{a^8}$ h) $2x^3y^3$

19. **a)** The student multiplied 3 and 4, instead of adding 3 and 4. The correct simplification is $2^{3+4} = 2^7$.
b) The student squared 3 instead of multiplying 3 and 2. The correct simplification r is $4^{3\times 2} = 4^6$.
c) The student multiplied the bases together. The correct simplification is 3^9.
d) The student multiplied the bases together. The exponent laws are only valid when the bases are the same. No simplification.
e) The student did not cube the 5. The correct simplification is $-125a^6b^3$.
f) The student added $\frac{1}{2}$ and $\frac{1}{2}$ instead of multiplying $\frac{1}{2}$ and $\frac{1}{2}$. The correct simplification is $\frac{1}{4}p^2q^2$.

20. **i)** F **ii)** C **iii)** B **iv)** C **v)** D **vi)** F **vii)** F

21.

4	8	8	0

22.

9			

Exponents Lesson #2:
Combining the Exponent Laws

Using Factors To Combine the Exponent Laws

Part One:

Three students are attempting to simplify the following expression:

$$3x^2 \times 5x^3$$

Their answers are shown below.

Harry $\Rightarrow$ $8x^5$ Janet $\Rightarrow$ $15x^6$ Laura $\Rightarrow$ $15x^5$

Explain using factors which student is correct.

Part Two:

Use factors to explain why $6a^6 \div 3a^2 = 2a^4$.

State the simplified form of the following.

a) $4x^5 \times 2x^3$ **b)** $(-7a^8)(6a^{12})$ **c)** $\dfrac{20y^{20}}{5y^5}$ **d)** $\dfrac{30b^{14}}{45b^{10}}$

e) $(3a^4)(a^5)(6a^3)$ **f)** $(-16n^5) \div (-2n)$

Simplify the following.

a) $x^5y^8x^3y^4$ **b)** $\dfrac{x^5y^8}{x^3y^4}$ **c)** $(-3bc)(b^3c^2)(-4b^2c)$ **d)** $\dfrac{10e^8f^{12}}{4e^4f^7}$

Complete Assignment Questions #1 - #4

Combining the Exponent Laws

The following examples use two or more of the exponent laws in their solution.

Simplify.

a) $(3x^2)^3$ **b)** $(-2a^2b^3)^2$ **c)** $\dfrac{x^3x^5}{x^2x}$ **d)** $\left(-\dfrac{2a}{y^3}\right)^3$

Simplify the following.

a) $-(-n^2)^5$ **b)** $\left(\dfrac{4y^3 \times 3x^6}{6x^5}\right)^4$ **c)** $\dfrac{16(x^3y^5)^2}{(2x^2)^3}$ **d)** $(5ab^6)^2\,(4a^2b)$

Write in simplest form.

a) $(-a)^6 \div (-a)^4$ **b)** $-a^6 \div (-a)^4$ **c)** $-a^7 \div (-a)^3$

Simplify the following.

a) $(-2a^2b^3)^3(4a^5b^7)$ **b)** $\dfrac{72x^4y^{10}(-z^2)^4}{6(2xy^2)^3z^8y^3}$

Complete Assignment Questions #5 - #12

Extension

In higher level mathematics courses, you may meet variable bases and variable exponents, including binomial exponents.

Use the exponent laws to simplify the following.

a) $\dfrac{b^{4x+y}}{b^{x-2y}}$ **b)** $\dfrac{x^{5a+7b} \cdot x^{3a+b}}{x^{a} \cdot x^{2a-7b}}$

Complete Assignment Question #13

Assignment

1. Simplify the following.

a) $3a^3 \times 3a^4$ **b)** $(10b^7)(3b^8)$ **c)** $3a^3 \cdot 5a^3$

d) $(-2x^4)(12x^9)$ **e)** $\left(-\frac{1}{2}e^7\right)(-14e^8)$ **f)** $0.4c^3 \times 0.5c$

2. Simplify.

a) $12x^4 \div 6x^2$ **b)** $(81e^9) \div (9e^8)$ **c)** $\dfrac{21d^6}{7d^2}$

d) $\dfrac{-80d^{80}}{8d^8}$ **e)** $(-10e^{10}) \div (-5e^5)$ **f)** $\dfrac{12f^6}{12f^5}$

3. Write in simplest form.

a) $(3a^2b^3)(5a^4b^8)$ **b)** $x^9y^0x^2y^4$ **c)** $\dfrac{6x^4y^7}{2x^3y^2}$

d) $\dfrac{5x^4y^7}{x^3y^2}$ **e)** $\dfrac{4f^{12}d^3}{12f^4d}$ **f)** $(7b^4c)(bc^2)(-2b^2c^6)$

4. Simplify.

a) $\dfrac{10e^8f^8}{15\,e^4f^2}$ b) $(2p^3)(4p^7)(-2p)$ c) $(-2xy)(x^2y^3)(-3xy)$

$6x^4y^5$

d) $(-8b^6c) \div (2b^3c)$ e) $(-10t^8y^6) \div (-2t^7y^3)$ f) $(4x^5z^7) \div (-16xz^6)$

5. Write in simplest form.

a) $(-a^2b^3)^4$ b) $(-a^2b^3)^5$ c) $\left(\dfrac{b^4}{a^3}\right)^3$ d) $\dfrac{c^5 \times c^2}{c^4 \times c}$

6. Simplify.

a) $(3ab^2)^4$ b) $(-4a^5c^2)^4$ c) $(-2m^3n^4)^5(m^2n^3)$

d) $(-4x^2y^3)^3(8xy^8)$ e) $(a^3b^4c^5)(3abc^2)^3$

7. Write each expression in simplest form without brackets.

a) $\left(\dfrac{2d^5 \times d^4}{4d^3}\right)^3$ b) $\left(\dfrac{-16a^5b^3 \cdot 2a^2b^6}{8ab^7}\right)^3$ c) $\left(\dfrac{-5k^3 \cdot k^2}{k}\right)^2\left(\dfrac{(-k)^5 \cdot k^2}{5k^2}\right)$

8. Write in a simpler form and evaluate.

a) $\dfrac{6^6 \times 6}{6^4}$ **b)** $(-3^3)^2$ **c)** $\left(\dfrac{2^{10}}{2^5}\right)^3$ **d)** $\dfrac{(0.7)^8}{(0.7)^4 \times (0.7)^2}$

e) $-5^6 \times 5^2$ **f)** $(-5)^6 \times (-5)^2$ **g)** $-10^{10} \div (-10)^8$ **h)** $\dfrac{-10^{10}}{-10^8}$

9. Write each expression in simplest form without brackets.

a) $(-x)^{12} \div (-x)^6$ **b)** $(-a)^6 \div (-a^4)$ **c)** $-p^{10} \div (-p)^2$

d) $c^5 \div (-c)^2$ **e)** $-(-t)^4 \div (-t)^3$ **f)** $-(-t^4) \div (-(t)^3)$

Multiple Choice

10. The simplified form of $\dfrac{1}{36}(2x^3)^2(-3yx^2)$ is

A. x^8y^2
B. $-\dfrac{1}{3}x^8y$
C. $-\dfrac{1}{3}x^7y$
D. $-\dfrac{1}{6}x^6y$

11. The expression $\dfrac{6(x^3y^5)^2}{(3xy)^4}$ is equivalent to the expression

A. $\dfrac{4}{9}x^2y^6$
B. $2x^5y^6$
C. $2x^2y^6$
D. $\dfrac{2}{27}x^2y^6$

Numerical Response **12.** The expression $(-3m^2n^3)^2(-2m^3n)^3\left(\frac{1}{72m^2n^3}\right)$ can be simplified to the form am^bn^c where a, b, c, are integers. The value of $a + b + c$ is ______.

(Record your answer in the numerical response box from left to right)

Extension **13.** Simplify each expression.

a) $a^{x+y}a^{2x+3y}$

b) $\frac{m^{x+9}}{m^3}$

c) $\frac{a^{3m+2}}{a^{m-3}}$

d) $\frac{x^{2y+7} \cdot x^{3y+2}}{x^{y+8}}$

Answer Key

1. **a)** $9a^7$ **b)** $30b^{15}$ **c)** $15a^6$ **d)** $-24x^{13}$ **e)** $7e^{15}$ **f)** $0.2c^4$

2. **a)** $2x^2$ **b)** $9e$ **c)** $3d^4$ **d)** $-10d^{72}$ **e)** $2e^5$ **f)** f

3. **a)** $15a^6b^{11}$ **b)** $x^{11}y^4$ **c)** $3xy^5$ **d)** $5xy^5$ **e)** $\frac{1}{3}f^8d^2$ **f)** $-14b^7c^9$

4. **a)** $\frac{2}{3}e^4f^6$ **b)** $-16p^{11}$ **c)** $6x^4y^5$ **d)** $-4b^3$ **e)** $5ty^3$ **f)** $-\frac{1}{4}x^4z$

5. **a)** a^8b^{12} **b)** $-a^{10}b^{15}$ **c)** $\frac{b^{12}}{a^9}$ **d)** c^2

6. **a)** $81a^4b^8$ **b)** $256a^{20}c^8$ **c)** $-32m^{17}n^{23}$ **d)** $-512x^7y^{17}$ **e)** $27a^6b^7c^{11}$

7. **a)** $\frac{d^{18}}{8}$ **b)** $-64a^{18}b^6$ **c)** $-5k^{13}$

8. **a)** $6^3 = 216$ **b)** $3^6 = 729$ **c)** $2^{15} = 32768$ **d)** $(0.7)^2 = 0.49$
e) $-5^8 = -390625$ **f)** $(-5)^8 = 390625$ **g)** $-10^2 = -100$ **h)** $10^2 = 100$

9. **a)** x^6 **b)** $-a^2$ **c)** $-p^8$ **d)** c^3 **e)** t **f)** $-t$

10. B **11.** D **12.**

1	6		

13. **a)** a^{3x+4y} **b)** m^{x+6} **c)** a^{2m+5} **d)** x^{4y+1}

Exponents Lesson #3:
Integral Exponents

The Negative Exponent

a) Complete the patterns below.

$10^3 = 1000$ $\quad$ $3^3 = 27$

$10^2 = 100$ $\quad$ $3^2 = 9$

$10^1 = 10$ $\quad$ $3^1 = 3$

$10^0 =$ $\quad$ $3^0 = 1$ $\quad$ $a^0 = 1$

$10^{-1} = \frac{1}{10} = \frac{1}{10^1}$ $\quad$ $3^{-1} = \frac{1}{3}$ $\quad$ $a^{-1} = \frac{1}{a}$

$10^{-2} =$ $\quad$ $3^{-2} = \frac{1}{3^2} \rightarrow \frac{1}{9}$ $\quad$ $a^{-2} = \frac{1}{a^2}$

$10^{-3} =$ $\quad$ $3^{-3} = \frac{1}{3^3} \rightarrow \frac{1}{27}$ $\quad$ $a^{-3} = \frac{1}{a^3}$

b) Write the following with positive exponents.

i) 10^{-7} $\quad$ **ii)** 3^{-5} $\quad$ **iii)** a^{-n}

Using the Exponent Laws to Define the Negative Exponent

Consider the expression $5^4 \div 5^7$.

a) Evaluate the expression as an exact value using a calculator.

b) Complete the following to evaluate the expression.

$$5^4 \div 5^7 = \frac{5 \cdot 5 \cdot 5 \cdot 5}{\qquad} = \frac{1}{5^{\square}} =$$

c) Use the quotient law to complete the following.

$$5^4 \div 5^7 = 5^{\square - \square} = 5^{\square}$$

d) The results in a) to c) are examples of a general rule when a base is raised to a negative exponent. Complete: $a^{-p} = \frac{1}{a^p}$

e) Write the following with positive exponents and evaluate.

i) 2^{-1} $\quad$ **ii)** 3^{-2} $\quad$ **iii)** 4^{-3}

The Negative Exponent in the Denominator

Use the rule for division of fractions to show that $\dfrac{1}{4^{-3}} = 4^3$. Use a calculator to confirm.

Negative Exponent Law

A base (not including zero) raised to a negative exponent has the following properties:

$$a^{-n} = \frac{1}{a^n},\ a \neq 0 \quad \text{and} \quad \frac{1}{a^{-n}} = a^n,\ a \neq 0$$

Simplify, express with positive exponents, and evaluate without using a calculator.

a) $4^5 \times 4^{-3}$ **b)** $3^2 \times 3^{-5}$ **c)** $\dfrac{1}{2^{-5}}$ **d)** $\dfrac{6^{-7}}{6^{-5}}$ **e)** $(2^3)^{-1}$

Identify the following as true or false.

a) $\dfrac{8^3}{8^{-1}} = 8^4$ **b)** $\dfrac{8^3}{4^{-1}} = 2^4$ **c)** $a^{-3} = \dfrac{1}{a^3}$ **d)** $9a^{-3} = \dfrac{1}{9a^3}$

Simplify and write the answer with positive exponents.

a) $a^{-4} \times a^{-3}$ **b)** $6x^2 \div 2x^7$ **c)** $\dfrac{y^6}{2y^{-5}}$

d) $(-2x)^{-3}$ **e)** $\dfrac{8a^{-5}}{4b^{-3}}$ **f)** $\dfrac{(5p)^{-2}}{5q^4}$

Class Ex. #4

Simplify and write the answer with positive exponents.

$$5x^3y^{-8}z^{-2} \div \frac{15x^8y^3z^{-1}}{x^5y^{-3}z^2}$$

$$15x^3y^6z^{-2}$$

$$\frac{5x^3y^{-8}z^{-2}}{15x^3y^6z^{-2}} =$$

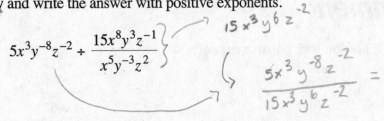

Class Ex. #5

Explain why $2p^{-3} \neq \dfrac{1}{2p^3}$.

Simplifying a Fractional Base with a Negative Exponent

Consider the expression $\left(\dfrac{2}{3}\right)^{-4}$.

a) Complete the following $\left(\dfrac{2}{3}\right)^{-4} = \dfrac{1}{\left(\dfrac{2}{3}\right)^{\square}} = \dfrac{1}{} = 1 \times =$

b) Evaluate $\left(\dfrac{3}{2}\right)^{4}$.

c) Classify the following statement as true or false. $\left(\dfrac{2}{3}\right)^{-4} = \left(\dfrac{3}{2}\right)^{4}$

d) Suggest a quick method for evaluating $\left(\dfrac{5}{2}\right)^{-3}$ without using a calculator.

$$\text{In general, } \left(\frac{a}{b}\right)^{-n} = \left(\frac{b}{a}\right)^{n} \quad a, b \neq 0.$$

Complete Assignment Questions #1 - #17

Assignment

1. Write the following with positive exponents.

a) x^{-3} **b)** y^{-9} **c)** 4^{-1} **d)** $\dfrac{1}{a^{-5}}$ **e)** $\dfrac{1}{6^{-2}}$

2. Without using a calculator show that $\dfrac{3}{5^{-2}} = 75$.

3. Simplify, express with positive exponents, and evaluate without using a calculator.

a) $4^3 \times 4^{-4}$ **b)** $3^0 \times 3^{-3}$ **c)** $\dfrac{1}{7^{-2}}$ **d)** $\dfrac{10^{-3}}{10}$ **e)** $(3^2)^{-2}$

4. Express with positive exponents.

a) n^2m^{-5} **b)** $c^{-2}x^{-5}$ **c)** $16h^{-1}$ **d)** $\dfrac{2}{3}b^{-8}$ **e)** $(y^{-4})^{-2}$

f) $\dfrac{t^{-5}}{4}$ **g)** $\dfrac{1}{4x^{-9}}$ **h)** $\dfrac{4}{x^{-9}}$ **i)** $\dfrac{a^2}{b^{-7}}$ **j)** $\dfrac{a^{-2}}{b^7}$

5. Evaluate the following without using a calculator.

a) -3^{-2} **b)** $(-3)^{-2}$ **c)** $-7^2 \cdot 8^{-2}$ **d)** $(-8.3)^0$ **e)** $[-(3.9)^0]^{-2}$

6. Use a calculator to find the exact value of the following.

a) -4^{-4} **b)** $(-7)^{-3}$ **c)** $(0.75)^{-3}$ **d)** $(-0.025)^{-2}$ **e)** $\left(\dfrac{4}{7}\right)^{-3}$

7. State whether the following are true or false.

a) $6x^{-3} = \frac{6}{x^3}$ **b)** $5a^{-4} = \frac{1}{5a^4}$ **c)** $\frac{4}{b^{-6}} = 4b^6$ **d)** $\frac{x^{-3}}{2} = \frac{2}{x^3}$

e) $\frac{1}{5y^{-1}} = 5y$ **f)** $\frac{1}{\frac{1}{4}p} = \frac{1}{4}p^{-1}$ **g)** $(3x)^5 = \frac{1}{(3x)^{-5}}$ **h)** $\frac{1}{\left(\frac{1}{7}a\right)^{-2}} = 49a^2$

8. Simplify and write the answer with positive exponents.

a) $x^{10} \cdot x^{-5}$ **b)** $m^5 \div m^8$ **c)** $b^{-1} \cdot b^{-3}$ **d)** $-w^0 \div w^5$

9. Simplify and write the answer with positive exponents.

a) $a^8 \times a^{-10}$ **b)** $10x^2 \div 2x^{-1}$ **c)** $\frac{6y^{-6}}{2y^{-4}}$ **d)** $\frac{2a^{-5}}{4b^6}$

e) $-7x^{-2}$ **f)** $-(7x)^{-2}$ **g)** $(-7x)^{-2}$ **h)** $\frac{(-7x)^{-2}}{-7x^{-2}}$

10. Simplify each expression, writing the answer with positive exponents.

a) $a^{-3}a^{-3}$ **b)** $(5b^8b^{-12})(-10b^3b^{-12})$ **c)** $(-7x^3x^{-5})(x^2x^{-3})$

d) $(-2a^3)^{-3} \cdot 3a^{12}$ **e)** $\frac{16a^6b^{-3}}{-4a^6b^3}$ **f)** $(-3a^5b^{-3}c^0)^{-2}$

11. Simplify. Write the final answer with positive exponents.

a) $\dfrac{32a^2b^{-4}}{4a^{-8}b^{-2}} \times \dfrac{-8a^{-2}}{-3b^{-3}}$ **b)** $\dfrac{10(p^3q^2r^0)^{-3}}{(8p^{-3}q^5r^3)^{-2}}$

c) $(-2x^5y^3z^8)^{-2}(-2x^2y^{-8}z^{12})^3$ **d)** $(5a^3b^2)(-2a^{-2}b)^{-3} \div (-5a^8b^{-9})^{-2}$

12. Evaluate the following without using a calculator.

a) $\left(\dfrac{2}{3}\right)^{-3}$ **b)** $\left(\dfrac{1}{5}\right)^{-2}$ **c)** $\left(\dfrac{8}{5}\right)^{-1}$ **d)** $\left(\dfrac{3}{2}\right)^{-4}$

13. Simplify. Write the final answers with positive exponents.

a) $\left(\dfrac{c}{d}\right)^{-3}$ **b)** $\left(\dfrac{x}{4}\right)^{-3}$ **c)** $\left(\dfrac{p^2}{r^4}\right)^{-3}$ **d)** $\left(\dfrac{a^{-2}}{b^{-5}}\right)^{-3}$

e) $\left(\dfrac{-12x^{-3}}{6y^{-8}}\right)^{-1}$ **f)** $\left(\dfrac{12x^3y^{-1}}{-8x^{-1}y^5}\right)^{-2}$

14. Simplify. Write the final answers with positive exponents.

a) $\left(\dfrac{-x^3}{y}\right)^{-2} \div \left(\dfrac{y^3}{x^5}\right)^2$

b) $49\left(\dfrac{7w^3x^{-5}z^4}{w^{-3}z}\right)^{-2} \times \dfrac{14(x^4z^8)^0}{x^{-8}z^8}$

Multiple Choice

15. The value of $\dfrac{1^{-3} + 3^0}{2^{-1}}$ is

A. 1
B. 4
C. 8
D. 12

16. $p = 6 \times 10^{-7}$ and $q = 2 \times 10^8$. If $r = 3 \times 10^n$ and $\dfrac{pq}{r} = 4 \times 10^6$ then n is equal to

A. –5
B. –4
C. 5
D. 4

17. Which of the following statements are true?

i) $3a^{-3} = \dfrac{1}{3a^3}$ ii) $8x^4 \div 4x^7 = \dfrac{1}{2x^3}$ iii) $\dfrac{1}{2a} = 2a^{-1}$

A. i) only
B. ii) only
C. iii) only
D. none of the statements are true

Answer Key

1. a) $\frac{1}{x^3}$ b) $\frac{1}{y^9}$ c) $\frac{1}{4}$ d) a^5 e) 6^2

2. $\frac{3}{5^{-2}} = 3 \times 5^2 = 3 \times 25 = 75$

3. a) $\frac{1}{4^1} = \frac{1}{4}$ b) $\frac{1}{3^3} = \frac{1}{27}$ c) $7^2 = 49$ d) $\frac{1}{10^4} = \frac{1}{10\,000}$ e) $\frac{1}{3^4} = \frac{1}{81}$

4. a) $\frac{n^2}{m^5}$ b) $\frac{1}{c^2x^5}$ c) $\frac{16}{h}$ d) $\frac{2}{3b^8}$ e) y^8
f) $\frac{1}{4t^5}$ g) $\frac{x^9}{4}$ h) $4x^9$ i) a^2b^7 j) $\frac{1}{a^2b^7}$

5. a) $-\frac{1}{9}$ b) $\frac{1}{9}$ c) $-\frac{49}{64}$ d) 1 e) 1

6. a) $-\frac{1}{256}$ b) $-\frac{1}{343}$ c) $\frac{64}{27}$ d) 1600 e) $\frac{343}{64}$

7. a) T b) F c) T d) F e) F f) F g) T h) F

8. a) x^5 b) $\frac{1}{m^3}$ c) $\frac{1}{b^4}$ d) $-\frac{1}{w^5}$

9. a) $\frac{1}{a^2}$ b) $5x^3$ c) $\frac{3}{y^2}$ d) $\frac{1}{2a^5b^6}$
e) $-\frac{7}{x^2}$ f) $-\frac{1}{49x^2}$ g) $\frac{1}{49x^2}$ h) $-\frac{1}{343}$

10. a) $\frac{1}{a^6}$ b) $-\frac{50}{b^{13}}$ c) $-\frac{7}{x^3}$ d) $-\frac{3}{8}a^3$ e) $-\frac{4}{b^6}$ f) $\frac{b^6}{9a^{10}}$

11. a) $\frac{64}{3}a^8b$ b) $\frac{640q^4r^6}{p^{15}}$ c) $-\frac{2z^{20}}{x^4y^{30}}$ d) $-\frac{125a^{25}}{8b^{19}}$

12. a) $\frac{27}{8}$ b) 25 c) $\frac{5}{8}$ d) $\frac{16}{81}$

13. a) $\frac{d^3}{c^3}$ b) $\frac{64}{x^3}$ c) $\frac{r^{12}}{p^6}$ d) $\frac{a^6}{b^{15}}$ e) $-\frac{x^3}{2y^8}$ f) $\frac{4y^{12}}{9x^8}$

14. a) $\frac{x^4}{y^4}$ b) $\frac{14x^{18}}{w^{12}z^{14}}$

15. B **16.** A **17.** D

Exponents Lesson #4:
Scientific Notation

Scientific Notation - Large Numbers

The distance from Earth to the sun is approximately 93 000 000 miles.

9.3×10^6

The speed of light is approximately 300 000 000 metres/second.

123456

The number of molecules of a gas per m³ is approximately 27 000 000 000 000 000 000 000.

2.7×10^{19}

123 456 789 10 11 12 13 14 15 16 17 18 19

All these large numbers are written in standard decimal notation and it would be easy when writing out these numbers to make a mistake with the number of zeros.

Scientific Notation is a way of writing numbers that are too large or too small to be conveniently written in standard decimal notation. Scientists, engineers and mathematicians often use scientific notation to represent numbers and use the properties of exponents to simplify calculations.

For this math course, we write numbers in scientific notation in the form $a \times 10^n$, where the **exponent**, n, is an integer and the **coefficient**, a, is greater than or equal to 1 but less than 10. i.e. $1 \leq a < 10$. *In further courses, significant digits will play an important role in writing numbers in scientific notation.*

The number 32 000 in standard decimal notation can be written in product form as $3.2 \times 10 \times 10 \times 10 \times 10$ or in scientific notation as 3.2×10^4.

Class Ex. #1 Complete the following table.

Standard Notation	Expanded Form	Scientific Notation
61 500	$6.15 \times 10 \times 10 \times 10 \times 10$	6.15×10^4
500 000	$5 \times 10 \times 10 \times 10 \times 10 \times 10$	5×10^5
46.3	4.63×10	4.63×10^1 or 10
281	$2.81 \times 10 \times 10$	2.81×10^2
700 000	$7 \times 10 \times 10 \times 10 \times 10 \times 10$	7×10^5
920	$9.2 \times 10 \times 10$	9.2×10^2
1 400 000	$1.4 \times 10 \times 10 \times 10 \times 10 \times 10 \times 10$	1.4×10^6

every decimal place = ×10

Class Ex. #2 Complete the following statements from the top of the page using scientific notation.

a) The distance from Earth to the sun is approximately _____ miles.

b) The speed of light is approximately _____ metres/second.

c) The number of molecules of a gas per cubic metre is approximately _____.

Convert the following numbers from scientific notation to standard notation.

a) 3.8×10^7 **b)** 2.51×10^{12} **c)** 2.9×10^3

Simplify and write in scientific notation.

a) $7.1 \times 10^2 \times 1000$ **b)** $6.98 \times 10^7 \times 10$ **c)** $\dfrac{5 \times 10^6}{1000}$

Complete Assignment Questions #1 - #5

Scientific Notation - Small Numbers

An inch is about 0.000 025 4 kilometres.
The mass of a particle of dust is about 0.000 000 000 75 kg.
The mass of an electron is about 0.000 000 000 000 000 000 000 000 000 9 g.

All these small numbers are written in standard decimal notation, and again it would be easy when writing out these numbers to make a mistake with the number of zeros.

The number 0. 000 63 in standard decimal notation can be written in the form

$$\frac{6.3}{10 \times 10 \times 10 \times 10} \text{ or } \frac{6.3}{10^4} \text{ which is equivalent to } 6.3 \times 10^{-4}.$$

Complete the following table.

Standard Notation	Expanded Form	Scientific Notation
0.000 53	5.3 / 10×10×10×10	5.3×10^{-4}
0.000 000 07	7 / 10×10×10×10×10×10 ×10×10	7×10^{-8}
0.0029	$\dfrac{2.9}{10 \times 10 \times 10}$	2.9×10^{-3}
0.0000071	$\dfrac{7.1}{10 \times 10 \times 10 \times 10 \times 10 \times 10}$	7.1×10^{-6}
0.0031	3.1 / 10×10×10	3.1×10^{-3}
0.000085	8.5 / 10×10×10×10×10	8.5×10^{-5}

Complete the following statements from the beginning of this section using scientific notation.

a) An inch is about __________ kilometres.

b) The mass of a particle of dust is about __________ kg.

c) The mass of an electron is about __________ g.

a) Explain why 0.4×10^{-8} is not written in scientific notation.

0.4 → 4 = 0.000000004

b) Write 0.4×10^{-8} in scientific notation.

4×10^{-9}

Complete Assignment Questions #6 - #10

Scientific Notation on a Calculator

Using the Sci Mode

The `Sci` mode of a graphing calculator may be used to express numbers in scientific notation.

For example, to convert the approximate average distance that Neptune is from the sun (4 506 000 000 km), use the following procedure:

1. Press MODE, scroll right to "`Sci`", and press ENTER.

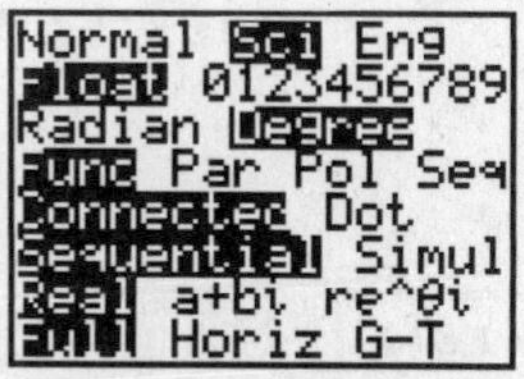

2. Then "`QUIT`" by pressing 2nd MODE.

3. Enter the number 4 506 000 000 and press ENTER.

The number `4.506E9` is to be written 4.506×10^9 as an answer.

To convert back to standard notation, set the graphing calculator back to "`Normal`" mode, input the number 4.506×10^9, and press ENTER.

Using the EE feature

The `EE` feature represents "$\times 10^n$" on the calculator.
This feature may be useful in saving time.

Example: Use the following procedure to write the product $(4.25 \times 10^6) \times (3.65 \times 10^{-4})$ in scientific notation and in standard notation.

1. Place the calculator into scientific mode (`Sci`).

2. • Access the `EE` feature by pressing [2nd] [,] (the display will only show one `E`).

• Press 4.25 [2nd] [,] 6 [×] 3.65 [2nd] [,] [(-)] 4 [ENTER]. The answer 1.55125×10^3 is displayed.

```
4.25E6*3.65E-4
        1.55125E3
```

3. To give the answer in standard notation, place the calculator in normal mode (`Normal`) and repeat steps 1 and 2 above.

```
4.25E6*3.65E-4
          1551.25
```

• Sometimes a calculation is so large or small that the calculator automatically displays the answer in scientific notation, regardless of the mode it is in. To convert back to standard notation you will have to convert back manually.

```
0.0000005*0.0000
0045
         2.25E-13
```

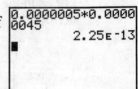

Use a calculator to:

a) Write the product $(3.5 \times 10^5) \times (2.6 \times 10^9)$ in scientific notation.

b) Write the quotient $\dfrac{7.5 \times 10^{-17}}{5 \times 10^{-9}}$ in standard notation.

Complete Assignment Questions #11 - #15

Assignment

1. Complete the following table.

Standard Notation	Expanded Form	Scientific Notation
151 000	$1.51 \times 10 \times 10 \times 10 \times 10 \times 10$	1.51×10^5
23.4	2.34×10	2.34×10^1
32 000	$3.2 \times 10 \times 10 \times 10 \times 10$	3.2×10^4
830 000	$8.3 \times 10 \times 10 \times 10 \times 10 \times 10$	8.3×10^5
730	$7.3 \times 10 \times 10$	7.3×10^2
840	$8.4 \times 10 \times 10$	8.4×10^2
6200	$6.2 \times 10 \times 10 \times 10$	6.2×10^3

2. Express each number in scientific notation.

a) 2 300
2.3×10^3

b) 7 580 000
7.58×10^6

c) 41 000 000 000
4.1×10^{10}

d) 53.1
5.31×10

e) 4 320 000 000 000
4.32×10^{12}

f) 7.6

3. Express the number of kilometres in scientific notation.

a) Mercury has an approximate average distance of 57.9 million km from the sun.

b) Saturn has an approximate average distance of 1.4 billion km from the sun.

4. Express each number in standard notation.

a) 1.8×10^{12}

b) 6.73×10^5

c) 9.99×10^7

d) Mars has an approximate average distance of 2.2794×10^8 km from the sun.

e) Neptune has an approximate average distance of 4.5×10^9 km from the sun.

5. Simplify and write in scientific notation.

a) $5.7 \times 10^3 \times 10\,000$

b) $9.843 \times 10^8 \times 10$

c) $\dfrac{6.1 \times 10^8}{10\,000}$

c) $\dfrac{20\,000}{4 \times 10^2}$

6. Complete the following table.

Standard Notation	Expanded Form	Scientific Notation
0.000 000 9	9 / (10×10×10×10×10 ×10×10)	9×10^-7
0.000 001	1 / (10×10×10×10×10×10)	1 ×10^-6
0.000035	$\dfrac{3.5}{10 \times 10 \times 10 \times 10 \times 10}$	3.5×10^-5
0.99	$\dfrac{9.9}{10}$	9.9×10^-1
0.069	6.9/ 10×10	6.9×10^{-2}
0.00085	8.5/ 10×10×10×10	8.5×10^{-4}

7. Determine the direction, and how many places the decimal point should be moved, to change the following numbers so that the number is between 1 and 10.

a) 15 **b)** 275 000 **c)** 0.009 8 **d)** 0.58 **e)** 997 123 784

8. Express each number in scientific notation.

a) 0.000 023
2.3 ×10^-5

b) 0.005
5 ×10^-3

c) 0.000 000 872 5
8.725 ×10^-7

d) 79 300
7.93 ×10^4

e) 0.6
6 × 10^-1

f) 789 000 000
7.89 ×10^8

g) 0.000 005 94
5.94 × 10^-6

h) 0.025 1
2.51 × 10^-2

i) 81 300 000
8.13 ×10^7

9. Express each number in standard notation.

a) 2.7×10^{-3} **b)** 4.51×10^{-9} **c)** 1.28×10^{-4}

d) 5.67×10^{6} **e)** 8.9×10

10. Express each of the following in scientific notation.

a) 23.2×10^{5} **b)** 0.7×10^{3} **c)** 0.089×10^{-7}

d) 45.6×10^{-9} **e)** 0.0032×10^{12}

11. Using your calculator answer the following in scientific notation.

a) $(3.6 \times 10^{8})(4.2 \times 10^{-5})$ **b)** $(1.8 \times 10^{5}) \div (3.2 \times 10^{2})$

c) $(0.089 \times 10^{-3})(0.1 \times 10^{-8})$ **d)** $(23.1) \div (0.5 \times 10^{8})$

12. Using your calculator answer the following in standard notation.

a) $(4.3\times 10^{2})(2.4 \times 10^{-7})$ **b)** $(8.1 \times 10^{2}) \div (0.75 \times 10^{-2})$

430 × 0.00000024

c) $(0.05 \times 10^{-3})(2.5 \times 10^{-3})$ **d)** $(6.8) \div (0.85 \times 10^{7})$

Multiple Choice

13. The length of the River Nile in Africa, is approximately 6 695 000 m. When this number is written in scientific notation in the form $a \times 10^{n}$, the value of n is

A. –6
B. 3
C. 6
D. 7

14. In January 2009, the highest grossing movie of all time was "Titanic", with world-wide takings of approximately 1 850 million dollars. In scientific notation, the number of dollars grossed by this movie is

A. 1.85×10^{10}
B. 1.85×10^{9}
C. 1.85×10^{6}
D. 1.85×10^{3}

Numerical Response **15.** The speed of light is 3×10^8 metres/second. The sun is 1.5×10^{11} metres from the earth. If the number of seconds it takes for light to reach the earth is expressed in scientific notation in the form $a \times 10^n$, the value of $a + n$ is _____.

(Record your answer in the numerical response box from left to right)

Answer Key

1.

Standard Notation	Expanded Form	Scientific Notation
151 000	$1.5 \times 10 \times 10 \times 10 \times 10 \times 10$	1.51×10^5
23.4	2.34×10	2.34×10^1
32 000	$3.2 \times 10 \times 10 \times 10 \times 10$	3.2×10^4
830 000	$8.3 \times 10 \times 10 \times 10 \times 10 \times 10$	8.3×10^5
730	$7.3 \times 10 \times 10$	7.3×10^2
840	$8.4 \times 10 \times 10$	8.4×10^2
6 200	$6.2 \times 10 \times 10 \times 10$	6.2×10^3

6.

Standard Notation	Expanded Form	Scientific Notation
0.000 000 9	$\frac{9}{10 \times 10 \times 10 \times 10 \times 10 \times 10 \times 10}$	9×10^{-7}
0.000 001	$\frac{1}{10 \times 10 \times 10 \times 10 \times 10 \times 10}$	1×10^{-6}
0.000 035	$\frac{3.5}{10 \times 10 \times 10 \times 10 \times 10}$	3.5×10^{-5}
0.99	$\frac{9.9}{10}$	9.9×10^{-1}
0.069	$\frac{6.9}{10 \times 10}$	6.9×10^{-2}
0.000 85	$\frac{8.5}{10 \times 10 \times 10 \times 10}$	8.5×10^{-4}

2. a) 2.3×10^3 **b)** 7.6×10^6 **c)** 4.1×10^{10}
d) 5.3×10^1 **e)** 4.3×10^{12} **f)** 7.6×10^0

3. a) 5.8×10^7 km **b)** 1.4×10^9 km

4. a) 1 800 000 000 000 **b)** 673 000 **c)** 99 900 000
d) 227 940 000 **e)** 4 500 000 000

5. a) 5.7×10^7 **b)** 9.8×10^9 **c)** 6.1×10^4 **d)** 5×10^1

6. See table above

7. a) 1 to the left **b)** 5 to the left **c)** 3 to the right **d)** 1 to the right **e)** 8 to the left

8. a) 2.3×10^{-5} **b)** 5×10^{-3} **c)** 8.7×10^{-7} **d)** 7.9×10^4 **e)** 6×10^{-1}
f) 7.9×10^8 **g)** 5.9×10^{-6} **h)** 2.5×10^{-2} **i)** 8.1×10^7

9. a) 0.002 7 **b)** 0.000 000 004 51 **c)** 0.000 128 **d)** 5 670 000 **e)** 89

10. a) 2.32×10^6 **b)** 7×10^2 **c)** 8.9×10^{-9} **d)** 4.6×10^{-8} **e)** 3.2×10^9

11. a) 1.5×10^4 **b)** 5.6×10^2 **c)** 8.9×10^{-14} **d)** 4.6×10^{-7}

12. a) 0.000 103 2 **b)** 108 000 **c)** 0.000 000 125 **d)** 0.000 000 8

13. C **14.** B **15.**

7			

Exponents Lesson #5:
Rational Exponents - Part One

Investigating the The Meaning of $a^{\frac{1}{n}}$

a) Complete and evaluate the following.

i) $\sqrt{5} \cdot \sqrt{5} = \sqrt{25} = 5$ **ii)** $5^{\frac{1}{2}} \cdot 5^{\frac{1}{2}} = 5^{\boxed{\frac{1}{2}} + \boxed{\frac{1}{2}}} = 5^{\boxed{1}} = 5$

Deduce a meaning for $5^{\frac{1}{2}}$. $\sqrt{5}$

b) Complete and evaluate the following.

i) $\sqrt[3]{2} \cdot \sqrt[3]{2} \cdot \sqrt[3]{2} = \sqrt[3]{8} = 2$ **ii)** $2^{\frac{1}{3}} \cdot 2^{\frac{1}{3}} \cdot 2^{\frac{1}{3}} = 2^{\boxed{\frac{1}{3}} + \boxed{\frac{1}{3}} + \boxed{\frac{1}{3}}} = 2^{\boxed{1}}$ = 2

Deduce a meaning for $2^{\frac{1}{3}}$. $\sqrt[3]{2}$

c) Write the following in radical form and evaluate manually. Verify with a calculator.

i) $25^{\frac{1}{2}} = \sqrt{25} = 5$ **ii)** $64^{\frac{1}{3}} = \sqrt[3]{64} = 4$ **iii)** $81^{\frac{1}{4}} = \sqrt[4]{81} = 3$

d) Write the following in radical form.

i) $x^{\frac{1}{2}} = \sqrt{x}$ **ii)** $b^{\frac{1}{3}} = \sqrt[3]{b}$ **iii)** $p^{\frac{1}{10}} = \sqrt[10]{p}$ **iv)** $a^{\frac{1}{n}} = \sqrt[N]{a}$

Investigating The Meaning of $a^{\frac{m}{n}}$ **Part One**

÷3 both $\frac{6}{2} \rightarrow \frac{3}{1}$

a) Complete and evaluate the following.

i) $\sqrt{5^3} \cdot \sqrt{5^3} = \sqrt{5^6} = \sqrt{5^3} = 125$ **ii)** $5^{\frac{3}{2}} \cdot 5^{\frac{3}{2}} = 5^{\boxed{\frac{3}{2}} + \boxed{\frac{3}{2}}} = 5^{\boxed{3}} = 125$

Deduce a meaning for $5^{\frac{3}{2}}$. $\sqrt{5^3}$

÷3 each $\frac{6}{3} \rightarrow \frac{2}{1}$

b) Complete and evaluate the following.

i) $\sqrt[3]{2^2} \cdot \sqrt[3]{2^2} \cdot \sqrt[3]{2^2} = \sqrt[3]{2^6} = 2^2 = 4$ **ii)** $2^{\frac{2}{3}} \cdot 2^{\frac{2}{3}} \cdot 2^{\frac{2}{3}} = 2^{\boxed{\frac{2}{3}} + \boxed{\frac{2}{3}} + \boxed{\frac{2}{3}}} = 2^{\boxed{2}}$

Deduce a meaning for $2^{\frac{2}{3}}$. $\sqrt[3]{2^2}$

c) Write the following in radical form.

i) $x^{\frac{5}{3}} = \sqrt[3]{x^5}$ **ii)** $b^{\frac{4}{5}} = \sqrt[5]{b^4}$ **iii)** $p^{\frac{5}{2}} = \sqrt{p^5}$ **iv)** $a^{\frac{m}{n}} = \sqrt[n]{a^m}$

Investigating The Meaning of $a^{\frac{m}{n}}$ Part Two

a) Evaluate i) $8^{\frac{2}{3}} = (8^{\frac{1}{3}})^2 = \left(\sqrt[3]{8}\right)^2 =$ ii) $8^{\frac{2}{3}} = (8^2)^{\frac{1}{3}} = \sqrt[3]{(8^2)} =$

$\sqrt[3]{8^2}$

b) Which of the calculations above is the easier method for evaluating $8^{\frac{2}{3}}$?

c) Write the following in radical form and evaluate manually. Verify with a calculator.

i) $64^{\frac{3}{2}} = \sqrt{64^3}$ **ii)** $4^{\frac{5}{2}}$ $\sqrt{4^5}$ **iii)** $81^{\frac{3}{4}}$

$(\sqrt{64})^3$ $(8)^3 = 512$ $(\sqrt{4})^5$ $(2)^5 = 32$ $(\sqrt[4]{81})^3$

$(3)^3 = 27$

Investigating The Meaning of $a^{-\frac{m}{n}}$

a) Use exponent laws to simplify $8^{\frac{2}{3}} \times 8^{-\frac{2}{3}}$. $8^{\frac{2}{3}-\frac{2}{3}} = 8^0 = 1$

b) Use the result in a) to write $8^{-\frac{2}{3}}$ in a form with a positive exponent.

Evaluate $8^{-\frac{2}{3}}$ without using a calculator.

Rational Exponents

$a^{\frac{m}{n}} = \left(\sqrt[n]{a}\right)^m$ or $a^{\frac{m}{n}} = \sqrt[n]{a^m}$, $m \in I$, $n \in N$, $a \neq 0$ when m is 0.

Note that if n is even, then a must be non-negative.

$a^{-\frac{m}{n}} = \dfrac{1}{\left(\sqrt[n]{a}\right)^m}$ or $a^{-\frac{m}{n}} = \dfrac{1}{\sqrt[n]{a^m}}$, $m \in I$, $n \in N$, $a \neq 0$ when m is 0.

Note that if n is even, then a must be positive.

Class Ex. #1

Write the following in radical form and evaluate without using a calculator.
Verify with a calculator.

a) $25^{\frac{3}{2}}$ **b)** $1000^{\frac{4}{3}}$ **c)** $27^{-\frac{2}{3}}$ **d)** $16^{-\frac{3}{4}}$

e) $(-8)^{\frac{2}{3}}$ **f)** $-8^{\frac{2}{3}}$ **g)** $(3^2 + 4^2)^{\frac{1}{2}}$

Class Ex. #2 Write the following in radical form and evaluate without using a calculator. Verify with a calculator.

a) $\left(\dfrac{9}{4}\right)^{\frac{3}{2}}$ $\left(\sqrt{\dfrac{9}{4}}\right)^3$ ★ **b)** $\left(\dfrac{9}{4}\right)^{-\frac{3}{2}}$ $\left(\sqrt{\dfrac{9}{4}}\right)^{-3} \rightarrow \left(\sqrt{\dfrac{4}{9}}\right)^3$

$\left(\dfrac{3}{2}\right)^3 = \dfrac{27}{8}$ $\left(\dfrac{2}{3}\right)^3 = \dfrac{8}{27}$

Complete Assignment Questions #1 - #5

Class Ex. #3 Write an equivalent expression using radicals.

a) $r^{\frac{1}{3}} =$ **b)** $s^{\frac{4}{7}} =$ **c)** $t^{-\frac{1}{6}}$ **d)** $v^{-\frac{3}{2}} =$

$\sqrt[3]{r}$ $\left(\sqrt[7]{5}\right)^4$ $\sqrt[6]{\dfrac{1}{t}}$ $\left(\dfrac{1}{v}\right)^{\frac{3}{2}}$ or $\left(\sqrt{\dfrac{1}{v}}\right)^2$

No even $\sqrt{}$ ★

Class Ex. #4 Consider the following powers.

A $64^{\frac{2}{3}} =$ **B** $(-64)^{\frac{2}{3}} =$ **C** $64^{\frac{3}{2}}$ **D** $(-64)^{\frac{3}{2}}$ Not possible

$2(-) \neq (-)$

Explain why three of the above powers can be calculated but the other has no meaning.

Class Ex. #5 A cube has a volume of $60 \, \text{m}^3$.

a) Write a power which represents the edge length of the cube. m $\sqrt[3]{60m^3}$ $\sqrt[3]{60}\,m$ $60^{\frac{1}{3}}$

b) Write a power which represents the surface area of the cube. m^2 $\sqrt[3]{60}\,m$ $3.1\,m$

c) Use a calculator to calculate the edge length and surface area to the nearest tenth.

Class Ex. #6 Write the number 10 in the following forms:

a) as a power with an exponent of $\dfrac{1}{2}$ **b)** as a power with an exponent of $\dfrac{1}{3}$

Complete Assignment Questions #1 - #13

Assignment

1. Evaluate without the use of a calculator.

 a) $4^{\frac{1}{2}}$ $\sqrt{4} = 2$ b) $100^{\frac{1}{2}}$ $\sqrt{100}$ $= 10$ c) $64^{\frac{1}{3}}$ $\sqrt[3]{64}$ $= 4$ d) $9^{\frac{3}{2}}$ $(\sqrt{9})^3$ $(3)^3 = 27$ e) $49^{\frac{3}{2}}$ $(\sqrt{49})^3$ $(7)^3 = 343$

 f) $16^{\frac{3}{4}}$ $(\sqrt[4]{16})^3$ $(2)^3 = 8$ g) $8^{\frac{2}{3}}$ $(\sqrt[3]{8})^2$ $(2)^2 = 4$ h) $125^{\frac{1}{3}}$ $\sqrt[3]{125} = 25$ i) $(6^2 + 8^2)^{\frac{3}{2}}$ $36 + 64 = 100$ $(\sqrt{(100)})^3 = 1000$ j) $(0.04)^{0.5}$

2. Determine the exact value without using a calculator.

 a) $9^{-\frac{1}{2}}$ b) $4^{-\frac{7}{2}}$ c) $25^{-\frac{3}{2}}$ d) $1000^{-\frac{2}{3}}$ e) $64^{-\frac{5}{6}}$

 $\sqrt{\frac{1}{9}} = \sqrt{\frac{1}{3}}$

 f) $8^{-\frac{4}{3}}$ g) $49^{-\frac{1}{2}}$ h) $32^{-\frac{2}{5}}$ i) $(5^2 - 3^2)^{-\frac{5}{4}}$ j) $(0.09)^{-\frac{3}{2}}$

3. Determine the exact value without using a calculator.

 a) $\left(\frac{1}{25}\right)^{\frac{1}{2}}$ b) $\left(\frac{1}{4}\right)^{-\frac{1}{2}}$ c) $\left(\frac{1}{8}\right)^{\frac{4}{3}}$ d) $\left(\frac{9}{4}\right)^{-\frac{3}{2}}$ e) $\left(\frac{16}{81}\right)^{-\frac{3}{4}}$

4. Determine the exact value without using a calculator.

 a) $(-8)^{\frac{1}{3}}$ b) $(-27)^{\frac{2}{3}}$ c) $-25^{-\frac{1}{2}}$ d) $-(-32)^{-\frac{4}{5}}$ e) $(-0.008)^{\frac{2}{3}}$

5. Use a calculator to evaluate the following to the nearest hundredth.

 a) $4^{\frac{2}{3}}$ b) $7^{\frac{3}{4}}$ c) $(-5)^{\frac{6}{5}}$ d) $6^{-\frac{1}{4}}$ e) $-(-0.8)^{\frac{2}{3}}$

6. Write an equivalent expression using radicals.

a) $a^{\frac{1}{4}} =$ **b)** $b^{\frac{1}{2}} =$ **c)** $c^{\frac{1}{5}} =$ **d)** $d^{-\frac{1}{2}} =$

e) $e^{-\frac{1}{10}} =$ **f)** $f^{\frac{2}{3}} =$ **g)** $g^{\frac{4}{3}} =$ **h)** $h^{\frac{5}{2}} =$

i) $i^{-\frac{3}{2}} =$ **j)** $j^{-\frac{4}{5}} =$ **k)** $k^{-\frac{3}{4}} =$ **l)** $l^{\frac{m}{n}} =$

7. Assuming that x represents a positive integer, state which of the following expressions has no meaning.

a) $(-x)^{\frac{7}{3}}$ **b)** $(-x)^{\frac{3}{2}}$ **c)** $-(-x)^{\frac{1}{9}}$ **d)** $-(-x)^{\frac{5}{6}}$

8. A cube has a volume of 216 cm^3.

a) Write a power which represents the edge length of the cube.

b) Write a power which represents the surface area of the cube.

c) Calculate the exact edge length and surface area of the cube.

9. A cube has a volume of V cm^3.

a) Write a power and a radical which represents the edge length of the cube.

b) Write a power and a radical for the area of one of the faces of the cube.

10. In each case write the given number as a power with the given exponent.

a) 5 as a power with an exponent of $\frac{1}{2}$ **b)** 8 as a power with an exponent of $\frac{1}{3}$

c) -3 as a power with an exponent of $\frac{1}{3}$ **d)** $\frac{1}{4}$ as a power with an exponent of $-\frac{1}{2}$

e) 6 as a power with an exponent of $-\frac{1}{2}$ **f)** 100 as a power with an exponent of $\frac{2}{3}$

Multiple Choice

11. $\left(\frac{9}{16}\right)^{-0.5}$ is equal to

A. $\frac{256}{81}$

B. $\frac{4}{3}$

C. $-\frac{4}{3}$

D. $\frac{81}{256}$

12. $\left(-\frac{1}{4}\right)^{-1.5}$ is equal to

A. -8

B. 8

C. 6

D. has no meaning

Numerical Response

13. Evaluate the following and arrange the answers from greatest to least.

Calculation 1. $-(27)^{-\frac{2}{3}}$

Calculation 2. $\left(\frac{1}{27}\right)^{\frac{1}{3}}$

Calculation 3. $(-27)^{\frac{2}{3}}$

Calculation 4. $\left(-\frac{1}{27}\right)^{-\frac{1}{3}}$

Place the calculation # with the greatest answer in the first box.
Place the calculation # with the second greatest answer in the second box.
Place the calculation # with the third greatest answer in the third box.
Place the calculation # with the smallest answer in the fourth box.

(Record your answer in the numerical response box from left to right)

Answer Key

1.a) 2 **b)** 10 **c)** 4 **d)** 27 **e)** 343 **f)** 8 **g)** 4 **h)** 5 **i)** 1000 **j)** 0.2

2.a) $\frac{1}{3}$ **b)** $\frac{1}{128}$ **c)** $\frac{1}{125}$ **d)** $\frac{1}{100}$ **e)** $\frac{1}{32}$ **f)** $\frac{1}{16}$ **g)** $\frac{1}{7}$ **h)** $\frac{1}{4}$ **i)** $\frac{1}{32}$ **j)** $\frac{1000}{27}$

3.a) $\frac{1}{5}$ **b)** 2 **c)** $\frac{1}{16}$ **d)** $\frac{8}{27}$ **e)** $\frac{27}{8}$

4.a) -2 **b)** 9 **c)** $-\frac{1}{5}$ **d)** $-\frac{1}{16}$ **e)** 0.04 **5.a)** 2.52 **b)** 4.30 **c)** 6.90 **d)** 0.64 **e)** -0.86

6.a) $\sqrt[4]{a}$ **b)** $\sqrt{b}$ **c)** $\sqrt[5]{c}$ **d)** $\frac{1}{\sqrt{d}}$ **e)** $\frac{1}{\sqrt[10]{e}}$ **f)** $\left(\sqrt[3]{f}\right)^2$ **g)** $\left(\sqrt[3]{g}\right)^4$ **h)** $\left(\sqrt{h}\right)^5$

i) $\frac{1}{\left(\sqrt{i}\right)^3}$ **j)** $\frac{1}{\left(\sqrt[5]{j}\right)^4}$ **k)** $\frac{1}{\left(\sqrt[4]{k}\right)^3}$ **l)** $\left(\sqrt[n]{l}\right)^m$ **7. b)** and **d)** have no meaning

8.a) $(216)^{\frac{1}{3}}$ **b)** $6(216)^{\frac{2}{3}}$ **c)** edge length = 6 cm, surface area = 216 cm^2

9.a) edge length = $V^{\frac{1}{3}} = \sqrt[3]{V}$ **b)** area = $V^{\frac{2}{3}} = \left(\sqrt[3]{V}\right)^2$

10.a) $5 = 25^{\frac{1}{2}}$ **b)** $8 = 512^{\frac{1}{3}}$ **c)** $-3 = (-27)^{\frac{1}{3}}$ **d)** $\frac{1}{4} = 16^{-\frac{1}{2}}$ **e)** $6 = \left(\frac{1}{36}\right)^{-\frac{1}{2}}$ **f)** $100 = 1000^{\frac{2}{3}}$

11. B **12.** D **13.**

3	2	1	4

Exponents Lesson #6:
Rational Exponents - Part Two

Add fractions when (×).

Bedmas ... (handwritten margin notes)

Review Complete the following as a review.

Product Law $x^m x^n = $ $x^{(m+n)}$ **Quotient Law** $x^m \div x^n = $ x^{m-n}

Power of a Power $(x^m)^n = $ $x^{m \cdot n}$ **Power of a Product** $(xy)^m = $ $x^m \cdot y^m$

Power of a Quotient $\left(\dfrac{x}{y}\right)^m = \dfrac{x^m}{y^m}$, $y \neq 0$

$$\frac{2}{4} + \frac{3}{4} = \frac{5}{4}$$

Integral Exponent Rule $x^{-m} = \dfrac{1}{x^m}$, where $x \neq 0$

$$x^{\frac{1}{2}} \cdot x^{\frac{3}{4}}$$

Rational Exponents $x^{\frac{m}{n}} = \sqrt[n]{x^m}$ or ()m

$$x^{\frac{5}{4}}$$

Writing Powers as Radicals

Class Ex. #1 Write each power as a radical.

a) $x^{\frac{1}{6}}$ **b)** $-y^{\frac{5}{4}}$ **c)** $(-z)^{\frac{5}{3}}$ **d)** $(-z)^{-\frac{5}{3}}$ **e)** $5t^{\frac{3}{4}}$ **f)** $(5t)^{\frac{3}{4}}$

$\sqrt[6]{x}$ $-\sqrt[4]{y^5}$ $\sqrt[3]{-z^5}$ $\left(\frac{1}{-z}\right)^{\frac{5}{3}} \rightarrow \sqrt[3]{\left(\frac{1}{-z}\right)^5}$ $5\sqrt[4]{t^3}$ $\sqrt[4]{5t^3}$

Class Ex. #2 Simplify the following. Write each expression as a power with positive exponents and then as an entire radical.

a) $x^{\frac{3}{2}} \times x^{\frac{1}{1}}$ **b)** $y^{\frac{1}{3}} \div y^{\frac{5}{3}}$ **c)** $(a^{\frac{1}{2}})^{\frac{2}{3}}$ **d)** $\left(\dfrac{x^2}{y}\right)^{-\frac{1}{2}}$

$\frac{3}{2} + \frac{2}{2} = \frac{5}{2}$ $y^{\frac{1}{3} - \frac{5}{3}} = -\frac{4}{3}$ $a^{\frac{2}{6}}$

$= x^{\frac{5}{2}}$ $\sqrt{x^5}$ $y^{-\frac{4}{3}} \quad \sqrt[3]{\frac{1}{y^4}}$ $\sqrt[6]{a^2}$ $\left(\frac{y}{x^2}\right)^{\frac{1}{2}} = \sqrt{\frac{y}{x^2}} \rightarrow \frac{\sqrt{y}}{x}$

$\int x^{\frac{2}{2}}$ cancel out

Class Ex. #3 Simplify the following. Write each expression as a power with positive exponents and then as an entire radical.

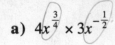

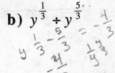

a) $4x^{\frac{3}{4}} \times 3x^{-\frac{1}{2}}$ **b)** $\dfrac{5x^{\frac{3}{5}}}{25x^{-\frac{3}{5}}}$ **c)** $(8a^{\frac{1}{2}})^{\frac{4}{3}}$

$12x^{\frac{1}{4}}$ $\frac{1}{5} \quad x^{\frac{3}{5} + \frac{3}{5} = \frac{6}{5}}$ $8^{\frac{4}{3}} \quad a^{2 \cdot \frac{4}{3}}$ $\frac{4}{6}$

$12\sqrt[4]{x}$ $\frac{1}{5}x^{\frac{6}{5}} \quad \frac{1}{5}\sqrt[5]{x^6}$ $8^{\frac{4}{3}} \quad a^{\frac{4}{6}}$ $\sqrt[3]{8^4 a^2}$

 $\sqrt[3]{8^4} \quad \sqrt[6]{a^2}$

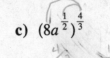

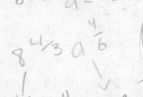

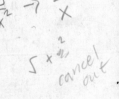

Complete Assignment Questions #1 - #3

Writing Radicals as Powers

We can use the rule $a^{\frac{m}{n}} = \left(\sqrt[n]{a}\right)^m = \sqrt[n]{a^m}$ to write radicals as powers.

Class Ex. #4

Write each radical as a power in the form a^n, $n \in Q$.

a) $\sqrt[3]{a^5}$ **b)** $\sqrt[5]{a^2}$ **c)** $\sqrt{a^9}$ **d)** $\dfrac{1}{\sqrt{a^7}}$

Class Ex. #5

Write as a power and evaluate.

a) $\sqrt{\sqrt{1296}}$ **b)** $\dfrac{1}{\sqrt{169}}$ **c)** $\sqrt[3]{\sqrt{64}}$

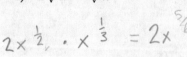

Class Ex. #6

Write each expression in the form ax^n, where $a \in I$, and $n \in Q$.

a) $\sqrt[3]{8x^5}$ **b)** $\sqrt[5]{32x^3}$ **c)** $\sqrt{900x}$

d) $\left(\sqrt[3]{x^5}\right)\left(\sqrt[3]{x}\right)$ **e)** $2\sqrt{x} \times \sqrt[3]{x}$

Class Ex. #7

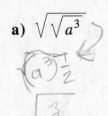

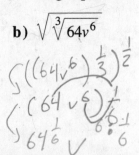

Write an equivalent expression using exponents.

a) $\sqrt{\sqrt{a^3}}$

$\left(a^3\right)^{\frac{1}{2}}$

$\sqrt{a^{\frac{3}{2}}}$

b) $\sqrt{\sqrt[3]{64v^6}}$

$\left(\left(64v^6\right)^{\frac{1}{3}}\right)^{\frac{1}{2}}$

$\left(64v^6\right)^{\frac{1}{6}}$

$64^{\frac{1}{6}} \cdot v^{6 \cdot \frac{1}{6}}$

$2v$

c) $\left(\sqrt[4]{x^5 y^3}\right)^{\frac{3}{2}}$

$2v\left(\sqrt[4]{x^5} \cdot \sqrt[4]{y^3}\right)^{\frac{3}{2}}$

$\left(x^{\frac{5}{4}} \cdot y^{\frac{3}{4}}\right)^{\frac{3}{2}}$

$\left(x^{\frac{5}{4}}\right)^{\frac{3}{2}} \cdot \left(y^{\frac{3}{4}}\right)^{\frac{3}{2}}$

$x^{\frac{15}{8}} \cdot y^{\frac{9}{8}}$

$^{15}\sqrt{x^{?}}$

| **Complete Assignment Questions #4 - #17** |

Assignment

1. Write each power as an entire radical.

a) $a^{\frac{4}{5}}$

$\left(\sqrt[5]{a}\right)^4$

b) $b^{\frac{3}{2}}$

$\left(\sqrt{b}\right)^3$

c) $c^{\frac{1}{4}}$

$\sqrt[4]{c}$

d) $x^{-\frac{2}{5}}$

$\left(\frac{1}{x}\right)^{\frac{2}{5}}$

$\sqrt[5]{x^2}$

e) $y^{-\frac{1}{3}}$

$\left(\frac{1}{y}\right)^{\frac{1}{3}}$ $\sqrt[3]{\frac{1}{y}}$

f) $5h^{\frac{2}{3}}$

g) $(5h)^{\frac{2}{3}}$

h) $-r^{\frac{5}{4}}$

$-\sqrt[4]{r^5}$

i) $(-r)^{\frac{5}{4}}$

$\sqrt[4]{-r^5}$

j) $2x^{-\frac{1}{2}}$

$\left(\frac{1}{2x}\right)^{\frac{1}{2}} \rightarrow \sqrt{\frac{1}{2x}}$

2. Simplify the following. Write each expression as a power with positive exponents and then as an entire radical.

a) $x^{\frac{7}{2}} \times x^{\frac{2}{2}}$

b) $y^{\frac{6}{5}} \div y^{\frac{4}{5}}$

c) $\left(a^{\frac{2}{5}}\right)^{\frac{3}{4}}$

$a^{\frac{6}{20}}$

$\sqrt[20]{a^6}$

d) $\left(e^3f\right)^{\frac{3}{2}}$ $^{\frac{9}{2}}$

$(ef)^{\frac{9}{2}}$

$\sqrt{ef^9}$

e) $x^{\frac{1}{2}} \times x^{-1}$

$\frac{1}{2} + \left(-\frac{2}{2}\right) = -\frac{1}{2}$

$x^{-\frac{1}{2}}$

$\left(\frac{1}{x}\right)^{\frac{1}{2}} \rightarrow \sqrt{\frac{1}{x}}$

f) $y^{\frac{2}{7}} \div y^{\frac{5}{7}} = \frac{3}{7}$

$= y^{\frac{3}{7}}$

g) $\left(\frac{x}{y^4}\right)^{\frac{1}{2}}$

$\sqrt{\frac{x}{y^4}}$

h) $\left(\frac{x^2}{y}\right)^{-\frac{3}{2}}$

$\left(\frac{y}{x^2}\right)^{\frac{3}{2}} \rightarrow \left(\sqrt{\frac{y}{x^2}}\right)^3$

$\rightarrow \left(\frac{\sqrt{y}}{x}\right)^3$

3. Simplify the following. Write each expression as a power with positive exponents and then as an entire radical.

a) $2x^{\frac{3}{8}} \times 5x^{-\frac{1}{8}}$ **b)** $64(a^{\frac{1}{2}})^{\frac{1}{3}}$ **c)** $((64a)^{\frac{1}{3}})^{\frac{1}{2}}$ **d)** $(64a^{\frac{1}{3}})^{\frac{1}{2}}$

e) $\dfrac{y^{\frac{2}{3}}y^{\frac{1}{2}}}{y^{\frac{1}{4}}}$ **f)** $\dfrac{a^3b^{\frac{1}{2}}}{b^3(a^{\frac{3}{2}})^2}$ **g)** $\dfrac{10x^{-\frac{3}{5}}}{5x^{\frac{1}{5}}}$ **h)** $\dfrac{(a^4)^{\frac{1}{3}}}{9} \div \dfrac{a}{81^{3/4}}$

4. Write each radical as a power in the form a^n, $n \in Q$.

a) $\sqrt[5]{a^3}$ **b)** $\sqrt[5]{a^4}$ **c)** $\sqrt{a^5}$ **d)** $\dfrac{1}{\sqrt[4]{a}}$ **e)** $\dfrac{1}{\sqrt[4]{a^5}}$

5. Write as a power and evaluate.

a) $\sqrt{\sqrt[3]{64}}$ **b)** $\dfrac{1}{\sqrt[4]{625}}$ **c)** $\sqrt{\sqrt{2401}}$

6. Write each expression in the form ax^n, where $a \in I$, and $n \in Q$.

a) $\sqrt[3]{27x^7}$ **b)** $\sqrt[4]{81x^3}$ **c)** $\sqrt[3]{-64x}$

d) $\left(\sqrt[4]{x^3}\right)\left(\sqrt{x}\right)$ **e)** $3\sqrt[3]{x} \times 3\sqrt[3]{x}$ **f)** $\left(\dfrac{25\sqrt[3]{x^5}}{5x^{\frac{1}{3}}}\right)^2$

7. Write an equivalent expression using positive exponents.

a) $\sqrt{\sqrt{x^5}}$ **b)** $\sqrt[3]{\sqrt{a^8}}$ **c)** $\sqrt[3]{\sqrt{729y^{12}}}$

d) $\sqrt[3]{\sqrt[4]{x^{\frac{2}{3}}}}$ **e)** $\left(\sqrt[4]{2y-3}\right)^{-3}$ **f)** $\left(\sqrt[4]{x^4y^3}\right)^{\frac{3}{2}}$

g) $-\sqrt[3]{x^2}$ **h)** $\sqrt[3]{(-x)^2}$

Matching Match each item in column 1 with the equivalent item in column 2. Each item in column 2 may be used once, more than once, or not at all.

Column 1	Column 2
8. $\left(\frac{p}{q}\right)^{\frac{4}{3}}$	**A.** $\sqrt[4]{\frac{q^3}{p^3}}$
9. $\left(\frac{p}{q}\right)^{\frac{3}{4}}$	**B.** $\sqrt[4]{\frac{p^3}{q^3}}$
10. $\left(\frac{q}{p}\right)^{-\frac{4}{3}}$	**C.** $-\sqrt[4]{\frac{p^3}{q^3}}$
11. $\left(\frac{p}{q}\right)^{-\frac{3}{4}}$	**D.** $\sqrt[3]{\frac{p^4}{q^4}}$
12. $\left(\frac{q}{p}\right)^{\frac{3}{4}}$	**E.** $\sqrt[3]{\frac{q^4}{p^4}}$
13. $\left(\frac{p}{q}\right)^{-\frac{4}{3}}$	**F.** $-\sqrt[3]{\frac{q^4}{p^4}}$

Multiple Choice **14.** Which of the following is equivalent to $(-x^3)^{-\frac{5}{3}}$?

A. x^5

B. $-x^{\frac{1}{5}}$

C. $\frac{1}{x^5}$

D. $-\frac{1}{x^5}$

15. Which expression is not equivalent to the others?

A. $a^{-\frac{4}{3}}$

B. $\left(\frac{1}{a^4}\right)^3$

C. $\left(\sqrt[3]{a}\right)^{-4}$

D. $\frac{1}{\sqrt[3]{a^4}}$

16. For all positive integers a and b, which of the following is not equivalent to $a^3\sqrt{b}$?

A. $a^3b^{\frac{1}{2}}$

B. $(a^6b)^{\frac{1}{2}}$

C. $\sqrt{a^6b}$

D. All of the expressions are equivalent to $a^3\sqrt{b}$.

Numerical Response

17. The value, to the nearest tenth, of the expression $\left(\sqrt[3]{x^{\frac{4}{5}} - y^{\frac{1}{2}} + \sqrt[3]{z}}\right)^2$ when $x = 32$, $y = 36$, and $z = 125$ is _____ .

(Record your answer in the numerical response box from left to right)

Answer Key

Unless otherwise indicated in the question, radicals can be given in the form $\sqrt[n]{x^m}$ or $\left(\sqrt[n]{x}\right)^m$ and powers can be given in the form x^{-n} or $\dfrac{1}{x^{n}}$. Equivalent versions of some answers are possible.

1. a) $\sqrt[5]{a^4}$ b) $\sqrt{b^3}$ c) $\sqrt[4]{c}$ d) $\dfrac{1}{\sqrt[5]{x^2}}$ e) $\dfrac{1}{\sqrt[3]{y}}$ f) $5\sqrt[3]{h^2}$

g) $\sqrt[3]{(5h)^2}$ h) $-\sqrt[4]{r^5}$ i) $\sqrt[4]{(-r)^5}$ j) $\dfrac{2}{\sqrt{x}}$

2. a) $x^{\frac{9}{2}} = \sqrt{x^9}$ b) $y^{\frac{2}{5}} = \sqrt[5]{y^2}$ c) $a^{\frac{3}{10}} = \sqrt[10]{a^3}$ d) $e^{\frac{9}{2}}f^{\frac{3}{2}} = \sqrt{e^9f^3}$

e) $\dfrac{1}{x^{\frac{1}{2}}} = \dfrac{1}{\sqrt{x}}$ f) $\dfrac{1}{y^{\frac{3}{7}}} = \dfrac{1}{\sqrt[7]{y^3}}$ g) $\dfrac{x^{\frac{1}{2}}}{y^2} = \dfrac{\sqrt{x}}{y^2}$ h) $\dfrac{y^{\frac{3}{2}}}{x^3} = \dfrac{\sqrt{y^3}}{x^3}$

3. a) $10x^{\frac{1}{4}} = 10\sqrt[4]{x}$ b) $64a^{\frac{1}{6}} = 64\sqrt[6]{a}$ c) $2a^{\frac{1}{6}} = 2\sqrt[6]{a}$ d) $8a^{\frac{1}{6}} = 8\sqrt[6]{a}$

e) $y^{\frac{11}{12}} = \sqrt[12]{y^{11}}$ f) $\dfrac{1}{b^{\frac{5}{2}}} = \dfrac{1}{\sqrt{b^5}}$ g) $\dfrac{2}{x^{\frac{4}{5}}} = \dfrac{2}{\sqrt[5]{x^4}}$ h) $3a^{\frac{1}{3}} = 3\sqrt[3]{a}$

4. a) $a^{\frac{3}{5}}$ b) $a^{\frac{4}{5}}$ c) $a^{\frac{5}{2}}$ d) $a^{-\frac{1}{4}}$ e) $a^{-\frac{5}{4}}$

5. a) $64^{\frac{1}{6}} = 2$ b) $625^{-\frac{1}{4}} = \dfrac{1}{5}$ c) $2401^{\frac{1}{4}} = 7$

6. a) $3x^{\frac{7}{3}}$ b) $3x^{\frac{3}{4}}$ c) $-4x^{\frac{1}{3}}$ d) $x^{\frac{5}{4}}$ e) $9x^{\frac{2}{3}}$ f) $25x^{\frac{8}{3}}$

7. a) $x^{\frac{5}{4}}$ b) $a^{\frac{4}{3}}$ c) $3y^2$ d) $x^{\frac{1}{18}}$

e) $\dfrac{1}{(2y-3)^{\frac{3}{4}}}$ f) $x^{\frac{3}{2}}y^{\frac{9}{8}}$ g) $-x^{\frac{2}{3}}$ h) $(-x)^{\frac{2}{3}}$

8. D **9.** B **10.** D **11.** A **12.** A **13.** E

14. D **15.** B **16.** D **17.**

6	.	1	

Exponents Lesson #7:
Practice Test

1. The base and the exponent in the power $(-2)^4$ are respectively

A. 4 and −2 **B.** 4 and 2 **C.** −2 and 4 **D.** 2 and 4

2. The coefficient in $-\frac{2x^5}{3}$ is

A. −2 **B.** $-\frac{2}{3}$ **C.** 5 **D.** 2

3. $-a^0$ is equivalent to

A. 0 **B.** 1 **C.** $-a$ **D.** −1

4. Consider the following two statements about repeated multiplication.

<u>Statement 1</u>. $5pq^3 = 5 \times p \times q \times q \times q$ <u>Statement 2</u>. $6(xy)^2 = 6 \times 6 \times x \times x \times y \times y$

Which one of the following is true?

A. Statement 1 is correct and Statement 2 is incorrect.

B. Statement 2 is correct and Statement 1 is incorrect.

C. Both statements are correct.

D. Both statements are incorrect.

5. Which of the following can be simplified to a^6?

I $a^3 \times a^2$ II $a^4 + a^2$ III $a^{12} \div a^2$ IV $a^8 - a^2$

A. I and III only

B. II and IV only

C. I, II, III, and IV

D. none of I, II, III, and IV

6. $5a^3 \times 2a^4$ can be simplified to

A. $7a^{12}$ **B.** $10a^7$ **C.** $10a^{12}$ **D.** $7a^7$

Use the following information to answer the next question.

$(2^a)^4 = 2^8$	$(3^2)^b = 3^8$
$\dfrac{4^c}{4^2} = 4^3$	$5^d \cdot 5^3 = 5^9$

Numerical Response 1. Write the value of a in the first box.
Write the value of b in the second box.
Write the value of c in the third box.
Write the value of d in the fourth box.
(Record your answer in the numerical response box from left to right)

7. $\dfrac{5a^{16}}{10a^4}$ can be written as

A. $\frac{1}{2}a^{12}$ **B.** $2a^{12}$ **C.** $\frac{1}{2}a^4$ **D.** $2a^4$

Use the following information to answer the next two questions.

> $(-2p^3q)(-3pq^2)(-4q^6)^2$ can be written in the form $a\,p^xq^y$ where a, x, and y are integers.

8. The value of a is

A. 96

B. −96

C. 24

D. −24

Numerical Response 2. The value of $x + y$ is ______ .
(Record your answer in the numerical response box from left to right)

9. x^{-3} is equivalent to

A. $\dfrac{1}{x^3}$ **B.** $\dfrac{1}{x^{-3}}$ **C.** $-3x$ **D.** $\dfrac{1}{x^{\frac{1}{3}}}$

10. $\dfrac{6x^3}{2x^{-4}}$ can be simplified to

A. $3x^{-1}$ **B.** $3x^7$ **C.** $4x^7$ **D.** $4x^{-1}$

11. $5x^{-2}$ is equivalent to

A. $\dfrac{1}{5x^2}$ **B.** $-10x$ **C.** $\dfrac{1}{25x^2}$ **D.** $\dfrac{5}{x^2}$

12. If $(4.6 \times 10^{-3}) \times (3.5 \times 10^7) = 1.61 \times 10^n$, then the value of n is

A. 3
B. 4
C. 5
D. 6

13. A piece of paper is 8.1×10^{-5} m thick. Approximately how many pieces of paper are required to make a stack two metres high?

A. 25 000
B. 40 000
C. 250 000
D. 400 000

14. Expressed in radical form $x^{\frac{3}{5}}$ is equivalent to

A. $\sqrt[3]{x^5}$ **B.** $5\sqrt{x^3}$ **C.** $\sqrt[5]{x^3}$ **D.** $\frac{1}{5}\sqrt{x^3}$

Numerical Response 3. The number 27.1×10^4 can be written in scientific notation in the form $a \times 10^n$. The value of $a + n$ is ____.

(Record your answer in the numerical response box from left to right)

15. If a is positive, which of the following must be negative?

A. $a^{-\frac{4}{5}}$ **B.** $a^{-\frac{5}{4}}$ **C.** $(-a)^{-\frac{4}{5}}$ **D.** $-a^{\frac{5}{4}}$

Numerical Response

4. If $p = 4$ and $q = -8$ the value of $p^{\frac{3}{2}} - q^{-\frac{2}{3}}$ to the nearest hundredth is ____.

(Record your answer in the numerical response box from left to right)

Numerical Response

5. $\left(\sqrt[3]{a^4}\right)\left(\sqrt{a^3}\right)$ can be written in the form $a^{\frac{p}{6}}$. The value of p is _____.

(Record your answer in the numerical response box from left to right)

Written Response - 5 marks

Use the following information to answer the next question.

The average person is 1.65 m tall.
The average human has 1.25×10^5 hairs on his/her head.
The current population of the earth is approximately 6.80×10^9.
The circumference of the Earth is about 4.00×10^7 metres.
The mass of the Earth is about 5.98×10^{24} kg.
The mass of the Sun is about 1.99×10^{30} kg.
The mass of the lightest planet Mercury is about 3.30×10^{23} kg.
The mass of an electron is approximately 9.11×10^{-31} kg.

1.

- Determine, to the nearest million, the number of people laid end to end it would it take to encircle the earth.

- Determine an estimate for the total number of hairs on the heads of all the people on the earth. Answer in scientific notation to the nearest hundredth.

- Approximately how many electrons would have the same mass as the planet Mercury. Answer in scientific notation to the nearest hundredth.

- How many times heavier is the Sun than the combined mass of the Earth and Mercury? Answer in standard decimal form to the nearest one thousand.

Answer Key

1. C **2.** B **3.** D **4.** A **5.** D **6.** B **7.** A **8.** A

9. A **10.** B **11.** D **12.** C **13.** A **14.** C **15.** D

1.

2	4	5	6

2.

1	9		

3.

7	.	7	1

4.

7	.	7	5

5.

1	7		

Written Response #1

- 24 000 000
- 8.50×10^{14}
- 3.62×10^{53}
- 315 000

Measurement Lesson #1:
Review and Preview

This lesson looks at two topics which will occur throughout the unit - rounding and substitution.

thousands	hundreds	tens	ones		tenths	hundredths	thousandths
5	1	8	2	.	4	9	1

Rounding

Often, when we do a calculation, the answer is a non-terminating decimal or contains a large number of digits. In such cases we are often asked to round off the answer to a particular degree of accuracy. Rounding also aids us in determining whether or not an answer is reasonable.

Round to the nearest one, or round to the nearest whole number.

One (or nearest whole number)

65 182.491 rounds to **65 182**

tenths digit is less than 5 — round by leaving the ones digit

One (or nearest whole number)

65 182.741 rounds to **65 183**

tenths digit is 5 or more — round to the next whole number

Round to the nearest ten.

Ten

65 182.491 rounds to **65 180**

ones digit is less than 5 — round by leaving the tens digit

65 186.491 rounds to **65 190**

ones digit is 5 or more — round to the next ten

Round to the nearest hundred.

Hundred

65 132.491 rounds to **65 100**

tens digit is less than 5 — round by leaving the hundreds digit

65 186.491 rounds to **65 200**

tens digit is 5 or more — round to the next hundred

Round to the nearest tenth (1 decimal place).

Tenth (or first decimal place)

65 182.431 rounds to **65 182.4**

hundredths digit is less than 5 — round by leaving the tenths digit

65 182.491 rounds to **65 182.5**

hundredths digit is 5 or more — round to the next tenth

Round to the nearest hundredth (2 decimal places).

Hundredth (or second decimal place)

65 182.491 rounds to **65 182.49**

thousandths digit is less than 5 — round by leaving the hundredths digit

65 186.497 rounds to **65 186.50**

thousandths digit is 5 or more — round to the next hundredth

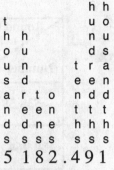

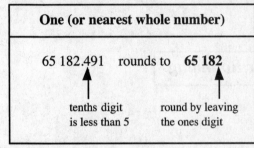

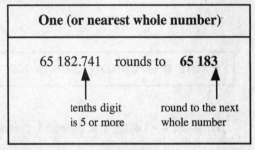

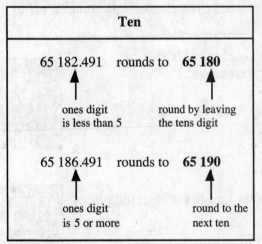

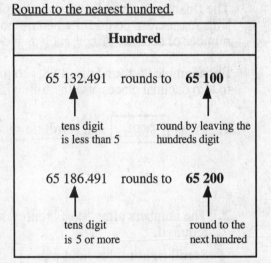

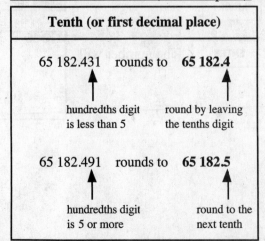

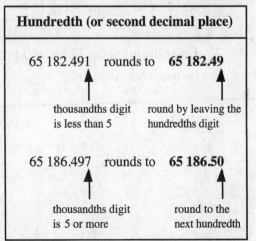

Complete the following table.

Round to the nearest / Number	One	Ten	Hundred	Tenth	Hundredth	First Decimal Place	Second Decimal Place
538.5968							
10 964.893							

Using a Graphing Calculator for Rounding

Method 1 - Using the Mode Feature

The floating decimal feature of a graphing calculator may be used to round off numbers. This feature can be useful when numbers need to be consistently rounded off to the same number of decimal places, such as money.

For example, to round off 3.885 to the nearest hundredth, or to two decimal places, use the following procedure:

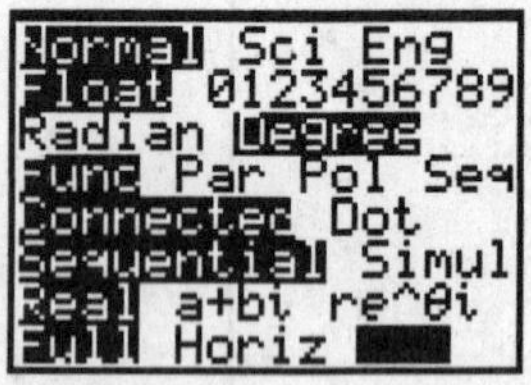

1. Press MODE and scroll down to "**Float**".

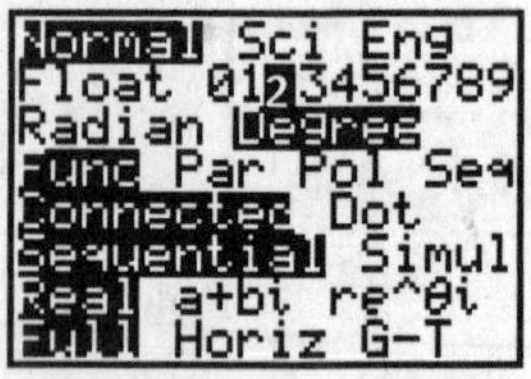

2. The numbers after "**Float**" represent the number of decimal places required.
   Scroll right to "**2**" and press ENTER.
   Then "QUIT" by pressing 2nd MODE.

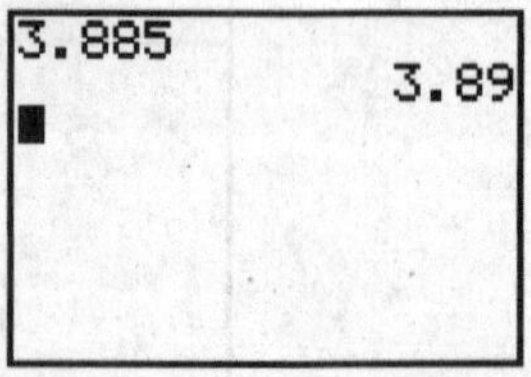

3. Enter the number 3.885 and press ENTER. The number will be rounded off to 3.89.

Method 2 - Rounding Feature

This feature is useful when the number of decimal places used in rounding is changed from question to question.

Example: Calculate 0.95×0.83. Write your answer to two decimal places.

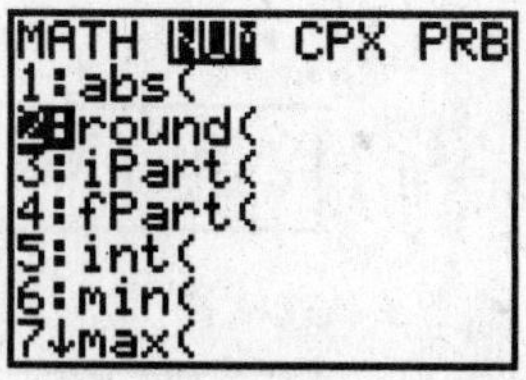

1. • Press [MATH].

• Cursor over to NUM.

 • Select **2:round(**

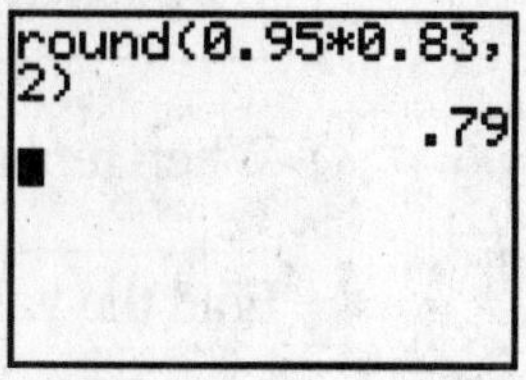

2. • On your home screen you will see **round(** .

• Enter the calculation **or** the number to be rounded.

 • Then enter a comma followed by the required number of decimal places.

Use a graphing calculator to round off where indicated.

a) 10.6217 to three decimal places.

b) 15.382 to the nearest hundredth.

c) $4\,863 \div 219$ to the nearest tenth.

d) 1.95×4.68 to the second decimal place.

Rounding in Scientific Notation

Some numbers are so large, or so small, that they are written in **scientific notation**.

Recall that this is a number written in the form $a \times 10^n$ where $1 \le a < 10$ and n is an integer. For example, the distance between the earth and the sun, which is approximately 150 000 000 km, may be written in scientific notation as illustrated.

Standard Scientific
Notation Notation

$$150\,000\,000 \ = \ 1.5 \times 10^8$$

At least one but power of 10
less then ten

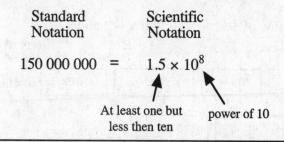

Express each number in scientific notation to the nearest tenth.

a) 75 300 000

b) 0.000 038 92

Class Ex. #4

In each case perform the calculation and give the answer in scientific notation to one decimal place.

a) $(4.35 \times 10^{2})(5.13 \times 10^{-6})$ **b)** $\dfrac{8.64 \times 10^{-2}}{5.18 \times 10^{-10}}$ **c)** $79.308 \times 34.602\,1$

Complete Assignment Questions #1 - #8

Substitution in Algebraic Expressions

Class Ex. #5

When replacing variables with numbers, **always use brackets.**

Find the value of each of the following if $x = 2$, and $y = -3$.

a) $y^2 - 7x - 3$ **b)** $9x^2 - y + y^3$

Substitution Using the Graphing Calculator

A graphing calculator may be used to substitute numbers for the variables in an algebraic expression by accessing the [STO→] key. The calculator automatically uses brackets for the substitution.

The following instructions may be used for a TI-83/84 Plus Graphing Calculator to do Class Ex. #5 b):

"Find the value of $9x^2 - y + y^3$ if $x = 2$ and $y = -3$."

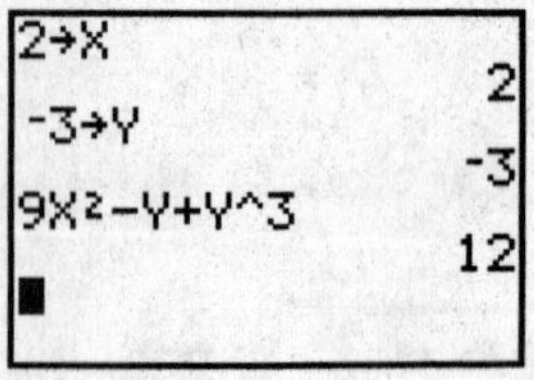

1. Press [2] [STO→] [x,T,θ,n] [ENTER] to enter $x = 2$.

2. Press [(-)] [3] [STO→] [ALPHA] [1] [ENTER] to enter $y = -3$.

3. Enter in the expression $9x^2 - y + y^3$ and press [ENTER].

Use a graphing calculator to find the value of the expression $2a + 4b - a^2 + b^2$ when $a = -2$ and $b = -3$.

Substitution in Formulas

In each of the following
i) substitute the given value, then
ii) calculate the value for the variable indicated (to the nearest tenth where necessary).

a) $v = 12$, calculate t

$60 = vt$

b) $S = 100$, calculate r

$S = 4\pi r$

c) $V = 95$, calculate r

$V = \frac{4}{3}\pi r^3$

In each of the following
i) solve for the variable indicated, then
ii) substitute the given value and answer to the nearest tenth where necessary.

a) If $S = \frac{\pi r}{4}$, solve for r and calculate the value of r when $S = 75$.

b) If $A = \pi r^2$, solve for r and calculate the value of r when $A = 72$.

c) If $V = \frac{1}{3}\pi r^2 h$, solve for h and calculate the value of h when $V = 20$ and $r = 9$.

Complete Assignment Questions #9 - #11

Assignment

1. Complete the table.

Round to the nearest / Number	One	Ten	Hundred	Tenth	Hundredth	First Decimal Place	Second Decimal Place
1 389.5263							
$\frac{73}{7}$			X				
547.77							
$\sqrt{3750}$							

2. Complete the table.

Round to the nearest / Number	Tenth	Ten	Hundredth	Three Decimal Places	Integer	One Decimal Place
75.5825						
$83\frac{2}{3}$						
–252.7839						
$\sqrt{8563}$						
25						

3. Without the aid of a calculator, express each of the following numbers in scientific notation, rounded to the nearest tenth.

a) 2 354 **b)** 678 923 450 **c)** 0.000 078 32

d) 0.089 567 812 423 **e)** 10 **f)** 0.004 31

4. Without the aid of a calculator, express each of the following numbers in scientific notation, rounded to two decimal places.

a) 0.003 87 **b)** 56 912 478 **c)** 123 456 789 101 **d)** 0.200 1

5. Use the scientific notation features of a graphing calculator to perform the following calculations. Express the answers in scientific notation to the nearest hundredth.

Brackets

a) $(9.37 \times 10^5)(4.06 \times 10^4)$
3.80 (3.8)

b) $\dfrac{8.25 \times 10^6}{1.19 \times 10^{-7}}$
6.93

c) 533.07×3.6812
1962.34

d) $(3.39 \times 10^{-8})(1.28 \times 10^5)$
0.01

e) $\dfrac{72\ 345\ 100}{273}$
265000.37

f) $\dfrac{3.99 \times 10^{-2}}{7.80 \times 10^2}$
5.12

6. Express each number below <u>in kilometres</u> using scientific notation to the first decimal place.

a) Venus has an approximate average distance of 108.2 million km from the sun.

b) Uranus has an approximate average distance of 2.875 billion km from the sun.

7. Express each of the following numbers in standard notation to the nearest million km.

a) Jupiter has an approximate average distance of 778 545 000 km from the sun.

b) Earth has an approximate average distance of 1.496×10^8 km from the sun.

8. Calculate the following giving the answer in standard notation to the nearest hundred.

a) $(3.69 \times 10^8)(4.265 \times 10^{-4})$ **b)** $(1.84 \times 10^6) \div (3.2 \times 10^2)$

9. Evaluate the following if $c = 2$ and $b = -3$. Show your substitutions.

a) $c - b$ **b)** $2c - 5b$ **c)** c^4b^2

d) $2c^3 + 20$ **e)** $\frac{1}{2}c^2b^3$ **f)** $\sqrt{2cb^2}$

10. Use the substitution features of a graphing calculator to evaluate the following if $x = 4$ and $y = -5$.

a) $x - y$ **b)** $4x - 5y$ **c)** x^2y^3

d) $6y^3 + 50$ **e)** $\frac{1}{2}x^2y - \frac{x}{y}$ **f)** $\frac{2}{5}\sqrt{25xy^4}$

11. In each of the following, substitute the given value, then calculate the value of the variable indicated (to the nearest tenth where necessary).

a) $h = 15$, calculate b

$75 = bh$

$75 = b(15)$, $\frac{75}{15} = \frac{b(15)}{15}$

$5 = b$

$75 = 5(15)$

b) $C = 175$, calculate r

$C = 2\pi r$,

$(175) = 2\pi r$, $\frac{175}{2} = \frac{2\pi r}{2}$

$\frac{87.5}{\pi} = \frac{\pi r}{\pi}$

$27.9 = r$

c) $A = 60$ and $b = 7$, calculate h

$A = \frac{bh}{2}$

$(60)(2) = \frac{b(7)}{2}(2)$

$\frac{120}{7} = \frac{b(7)}{7}$

$17 = b$

d) $V = 512$, calculate s

$V = s^3$

$(512)^{\frac{1}{3}} = (s^3)^{\frac{1}{3}}$

$\sqrt[3]{512}$

$8 = s$

e) $V = 270$, and $h = 3$, calculate r

$V = \frac{1}{3}\pi r^2h$

$(270) = \frac{1\pi r^2(3)}{3}$

f) $r = 6.5$, calculate A

$A = \pi r^2$

$\pi r^2 = A$

$\pi(6.5)^2 = A$

$132.7 = A$

12. In each of the following

i) solve for the variable indicated, then

ii) substitute the given value and answer to the nearest tenth where necessary.

a) If $A = s^2$, where $s > 0$, solve for s and calculate the value of s when $A = 441$.

b) If $V = lbh$, solve for b and calculate the value of b when $V = 75$, $l = 10$ and $h = 6$.

c) If $S = 2\pi r^2$, where $r > 0$, solve for r and calculate the value of r when $S = 343$.

d) If $V = \frac{1}{3}\pi r^2 h$, solve for h and calculate the value of h when $V = 20$ and $r = 9$.

e) If $V = \frac{4}{3}\pi r^3$, solve for r and calculate the value of r when $V = 512$.

Multiple Choice **13.** Which of the following calculations rounds off to 6.35 to the nearest hundredth?

i) $25.745 \div 4.051$ ii) $\dfrac{2.985 \times 10^{-4}}{4.702 \times 10^{-3}}$ iii) $(2.501 \times 10^{-6})(2.539 \times 10^{6})$

A. i) only
B. ii) only
C. iii) only
D. i), ii) and iii)

Numerical Response **14.** The surface area of a cylinder is given by the formula $S = 2\pi r^2 + 2\pi rh$. If $S = 1435$ and $r = 4.87$ then the value of h, to the nearest tenth, is ______.

(Record your answer in the numerical response box from left to right)

Answer Key

1.

Round to the nearest / Number	One	Ten	Hundred	Tenth	Hundredth	First Decimal Place	Second Decimal Place
1 389.5263	1390	1390	1400	1389.5	1389.53	1389.5	1389.53
$\frac{73}{7}$	10	10	X	10.4	10.43	10.4	10.43
547.77	548	550	500	547.8	547.77	547.8	547.77
$\sqrt{3750}$	61	60	100	61.2	61.24	61.2	61.24

2.

Round to the nearest / Number	Tenth	Ten	Hundredth	Three Decimal Places	Integer	One Decimal Place
75.5825	75.6	80	75.58	75.583	76	75.6
$83\frac{2}{3}$	83.7	80	83.67	83.667	84	83.7
–252.7839	–252.8	–250	–252.78	–252.784	–253	–252.8
$\sqrt{8563}$	92.5	90	92.54	92.536	93	92.5
25	25.0	30	25.00	25.000	25	25.0

3. a) 2.4×10^3 b) 6.8×10^8 c) 7.8×10^{-5}
d) 9.0×10^{-2} e) 1.0×10^1 f) 4.3×10^{-3}

4. a) 3.87×10^{-3} b) 5.69×10^7 c) 1.23×10^{11} d) 2.00×10^{-1}

5. a) 3.80×10^{10} b) 6.93×10^{13} c) 1.96×10^3
d) 4.34×10^{-3} e) 2.65×10^5 f) 5.12×10^{-5}

6. a) 1.1×10^8 km b) 2.9×10^9 km 7. a) 779 million b) 150 million

8. a) 157 400 b) 5 800

9. a) 5 b) 19 c) 144 d) 36 e) –54 f) 6

10. a) 9 b) 41 c) –2000 d) –700 e) –39.2 or $-\frac{196}{5}$ f) 100

11. a) $b = 5$ b) $r = 27.9$ c) $h = 17.1$ d) $s = 8$ e) $r = 9.3$ f) $A = 132.7$

12. a) $s = \sqrt{A} = 21$ b) $b = \frac{V}{lh} = 1.3$ c) $r = \sqrt{\frac{S}{2\pi}} = 7.4$
d) $h = \frac{3V}{\pi r^2} = 0.2$ e) $r = \sqrt[3]{\frac{3V}{4\pi}} = 5.0$

13. C 14.

4	2	.	0

Measurement Lesson #2:
Referents in Measurement

Before measuring tools were created, people often used common objects as an aid, or a point of reference, in measurement.
We use the term **referents** to describe objects used as a point of reference in measurement.
Below are some examples of referents.

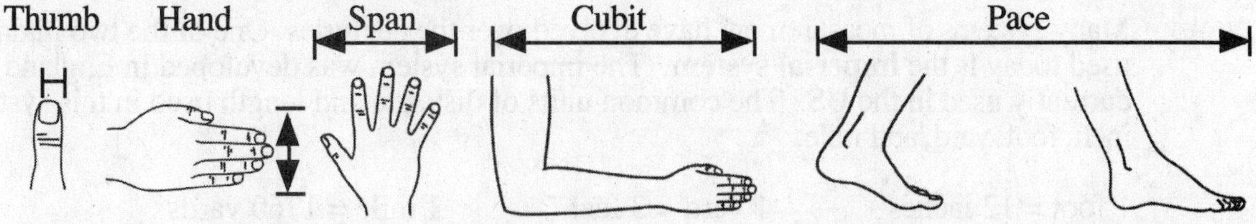

Referents coming from a person's immediate environment are called personal referents.

Many measurements used in Ancient Britain have an interesting history. For instance:

- The "yard" was established after the Norman Conquest of 1066, and it is said that at the time King Henry I declared that the yard should be defined as the distance from the tip of his nose to his outstretched finger.
- The term "furlong", used by the Saxon farmers in England long before 1066, represented the distance a team of oxen could plow without needing rest. Even today, the furlong is used to describe the length of horse races in Britain. 8 furlongs = 1 mile.
- The term "rod"simply meant a pole with a length of about 11 cubits
- The term "league" had many referents in measurement. The two most commonly used personal referents for league were the distance a person or a horse could walk in one hour. Although no longer in common use, a league was about the equivalent of 3 miles.
- A "chain" is the length of a cricket pitch and is equivalent to about four rods. 10 chains = 1 furlong.
- The hand is the width of a clenched fist, and is still used today to quantify the height of a horse. 1 hand = 4 inches.

Which one of the referents mentioned above could be used to estimate the following?

a) The length of a football field. **b)** The length of a compact flash card.

c) The height of a horse.

Describe how you could determine an estimate of the perimeter of the base of a house using one of the above referents.

Imperial System of Measurement

Before measuring tools were invented, people relied on referents to measure. Throughout time the need for more accurate and precise measurements became necessary. Mathematics made it easier to create systems of measurements.

Many systems of measurement have evolved over the centuries. One of the two main systems used today is the **imperial system**. The imperial system was developed in England and is currently used in the US. The common units of distance and length used in this system are inch, foot, yard, and mile.

1 foot = 12 inches   1 yard = 3 feet   1 mile = 1760 yards

If we consider other systems of measurement from around the world, such as the Ancient Greek system, the ancient Roman system, the Biblical system, the Japanese system, the Chinese imperial system, and so on, we can see the need for a single, world-wide measurement system.

SI System of Measurement (Metric System)

Over 300 years ago, as early as 1670, Gabriel Mouton and Jean Picard proposed systems which used base 10 to facilitate the use of the simpler decimal system instead of the more complex systems in use at the time. Even though other proposals were made, it wasn't until 1790 that the National Assembly of France asked the French Academy of Sciences to create a standard measurement that was simple and scientific. As an offshoot of the ideas of Gabriel Mouton, Jean Picard, and others, the unit of length was to be a portion of the earth's circumference and versions of each unit were to be multiplied or divided by units of 10 to relate easily to each other and to nature. This system is known today as the metric system - and has, as standard units, the metre for distance, the gram for mass, and the litre for fluid volume capacity.

The common unit of distance and length used in the SI system is the metre.

1 centimetre = 10 millimetres   1 metre = 100 centimetres   1 kilometre = 1000 metres

Canada began to use the International System of Measurement (abbreviated SI after Système International d' Unités) officially in 1976.
The system is commonly called the **metric system**. By this time most nations in the world were using the metric system.

Although the United States has now adopted the metric system and uses it widely in scientific contexts, the US still uses the imperial system in many aspects of everyday life . Because the imperial system is so predominant in the US, we still need to study both systems.

Using Referents to Measure

Referents are still used everyday in measuring. One of the best ways to learn any measurement system is to relate the measurement to a referent.

Examples of referents used in the imperial system for linear measurement are:

- the width of a thumb across the joint is about 1 inch.
- the length of an adult male foot is about 1 foot.
- one adult pace is about 1 yard.

Examples of referents used in the SI system for linear measurement are:

- the width of the fingernail from an adult little finger ("pinky" finger) is about 1 centimetre.
- the width of five toes of an adult is about 1 decimeter ($\frac{1}{10}$th of a metre).
- the thickness of a dime is about 1 millimetre.
- the average height of a four year old in North America is about 1 metre.
- the height of a standard doorway is almost 2 metres.
- the width of this workbook is about 20 centimetres.
- the diameter of a CD or DVD is 12 centimetres.
- the length of a CFL football field is approximately 100 metres.

In this course we only discuss referents for measurements of length and distance.

Consider the task of estimating the length of standard letter size paper.

a) Identify a referent which could be used to measure the length in SI units.

b) Identify a referent which could be used to measure the length in imperial units.

c) Explain the process of measuring the length in imperial units.

Class Ex. #4

Describe and explain a personal strategy which could be used to determine the measurement of the circumference of a DVD using a referent for metric units.

Class Ex. #5

Shown below is a 1:2 scale image of a bank note (in this case a Canadian five dollar bill).

Used and altered with permission from the Bank of Canada

a) Measure the length of the scaled bill in SI units and imperial units.

b) Use the answer in a) to determine the actual length of a five dollar bill. Verify this measurement on a real bank note.

c) Could the length of an actual five dollar bill (or other Canadian bank notes) be used as a referent in either system of measurement?

Class Ex. #6

Stacey was asked to provide a referent for 1 kilometre. She could not think of anything that was 1 kilometre in length, so she used a referent for a smaller measure to provide a referent for a kilometre. Suggest how she might have done this.

Complete Assignment Questions #1 - #15

Assignment

1. In each of the following:
- State a referent which could be used to determine the imperial system measure.
- Use the referent to determine an approximate measurement.
- Determine the actual measurement using a ruler, metre stick, or tape measure.

a) length of a whiteboard **b)** height of your friend **c)** length of a CD case

2. In a game of curling, the players are unable to determine which of two curling stones (rocks) is closer to the middle. Describe and explain a personal strategy which could be used to determine which rock is closer if

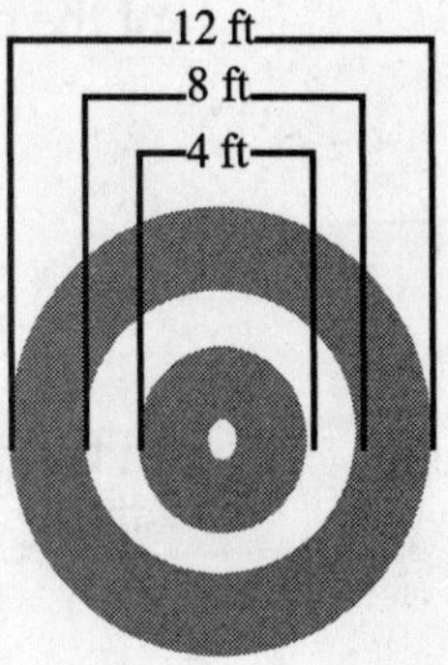

a) the two rocks are in the outer ring.

b) the two rocks are near the inner ring.

Matching **3.** Match each approximate measurement on the left with the referent on the right.

Measurement		**Referent**
i.	1 inch	**A.** width of an adult pinky fingernail
ii.	1 metre	**B.** thickness of a dime
iii.	1 foot	**C.** width of five toes of an adult
iv.	1 millimetre	**D.** diameter of a CD or DVD
v.	100 metres	**E.** width of a thumb across the joint
vi.	20 cm	**F.** length of an adult male foot
vii.	2 metres	**G.** height of a standard doorway
viii.	12 centimetres	**H.** width of a workbook
ix.	0.1 metres	**I.** average height of a four year old child
x.	1 centimetre	**J.** length of an adult pace
xi.	1 yard	**K.** length of a CFL football field

4. Use a personal referent to estimate the length of your calculator. Check the accuracy of your answer by measuring with a ruler.

5. Provide a personal referent for the following linear measurements different from those provided in this lesson.

a) millimetre **b)** centimetre **c)** metre

d) inch **e)** foot **f)** yard

6. Describe and explain a personal strategy which could be used to determine the measurement of the circumference of a soccer ball.

7. In the past, 12 city blocks was a common referent for a mile. What is the assumption in stating that 12 city blocks is about 1 mile?

Multiple Choice

Choose the most sensible unit of measure for each.

8. Length of a soccer field
A. millimetre **B.** mile **C.** metre **D.** foot

9. Distance between two cities
A. millimetre **B.** metre **C.** foot **D.** mile

10. Diagonal measurement of a computer screen
A. mile **B.** metre **C.** inch **D.** millimetre

11. Length of a safety pin
A. millimetre **B.** mile **C.** metre **D.** yard

12. Length of a room
A. centimetre **B.** mile **C.** yard **D.** inch

13. Width of an iPhone
A. millimetre **B.** yard **C.** metre **D.** foot

14. Height of an elephant
A. millimetre **B.** inch **C.** mile **D.** foot

Numerical Response

15. The length of most high school and college basketball courts is approximately 25 metres. The number of basketball courts which would have to be used as a referent to measure one kilometre is _____ .

(Record your answer in the numerical response box from left to right)

Answer Key

1. Answers may vary
- **a)** adult foot or cubit **b)** adult foot or cubit **c)** thumb

2. **a)** Ask one player to measure the distances by using his/her foot (heel to toe). If you still cannot determine which is closer, use a smaller measurement like the width of your hand.
b) Ask one player to measure the distances by using the width of finger(s) or thumb(s)

3. **i)** E **ii)** I **iii)** F **iv)** B **v)** K **vi)** H
vii) G **viii)** D **ix)** C **x)** A **xi)** J

4. Use the width of your pinky fingernail as a personal referent for 1 cm. The length is approximately 19 cm.

5. Answers may vary
- **a)** width of pencil lead **b)** diameter of a pen **c)** distance from the floor to your navel
- **d)** width of the face of a watch **e)** distance from your elbow to your wrist
- **f)** half the distance between the tips of your fingers when your arms are outstretched.

6. Wrap a piece of string around the circumference of the ball, then straighten out the string and measure it using the width of your thumb across the joint as a referent for one inch.

7. The blocks are of equal length.

8. C **9.** D **10.** C **11.** A

12. C **13.** A **14.** D **15.**

4	0		

Measurement Lesson #3:
Measuring Devices

Choosing an Appropriate Measuring Device

Choosing an appropriate measuring device is important when taking a measurement. For example, a ruler may not be helpful to measure the length of a football field or the thickness of a coin. The following measuring devices can be used to determine very large to very small linear distances.

<u>Trundle Wheel</u>

A measuring instrument which consists of a wheel, rod, and handle. It is used to measure long lengths such as a soccer field.

<u>Tape Measure</u>

A measuring instrument which consists of a long strip of metal marked in inches, centimetres or both.

<u>Ruler</u>

A straight edged strip for measuring lengths and drawing straight lines

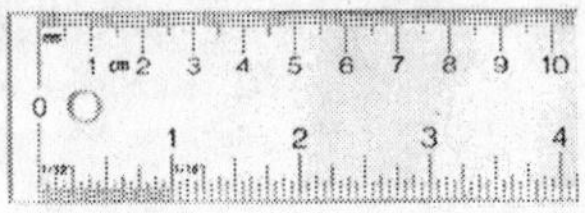

<u>Vernier Caliper</u>

A vernier caliper is a precision measuring tool which can be used to make very fine measurements of outside dimensions, inside dimensions, or the depths of holes.

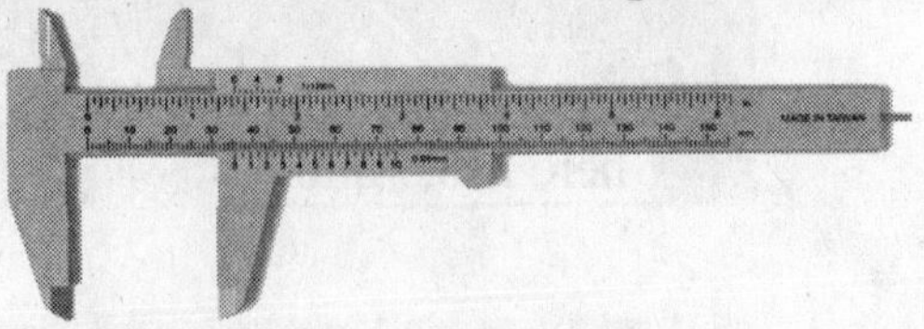

<u>Micrometer</u>

A micrometer is a precision measuring tool used to measure outside dimensions, or the thickness of small objects.

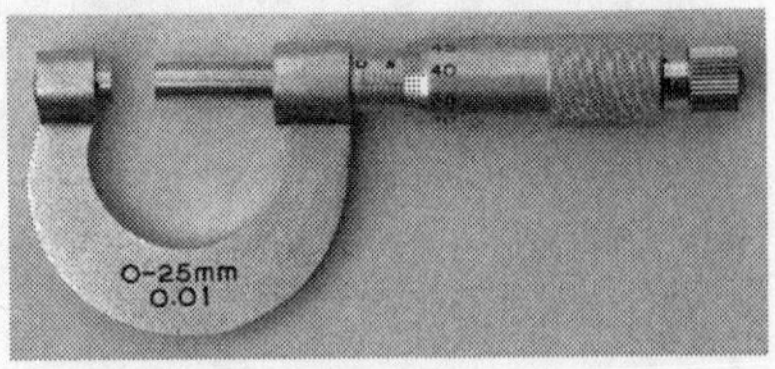

- A micrometer is a more precise measuring instrument than a vernier caliper. In general, a micrometer will measure to the nearest 0.01 mm while a vernier caliper will measure to the nearest 0.1 mm or 0.05 mm.

- Although the next few pages in this lesson will explain how to use a vernier caliper and a micrometer, the following web links have video and applet features which may aid in your understanding of these measuring devices.

  <u>Video and Applet Web Links for Vernier Caliper</u>
  http://phoenix.phys.clemson.edu/labs/cupol/vernier/index.html
  http://members.shaw.ca/ron.blond/Vern.APPLET/

  <u>Applet Web Link for Micrometer</u>
  http://www.upscale.utoronto.ca/PVB/Harrison/Micrometer/Micrometer.html

Using a Micrometer to Measure Objects

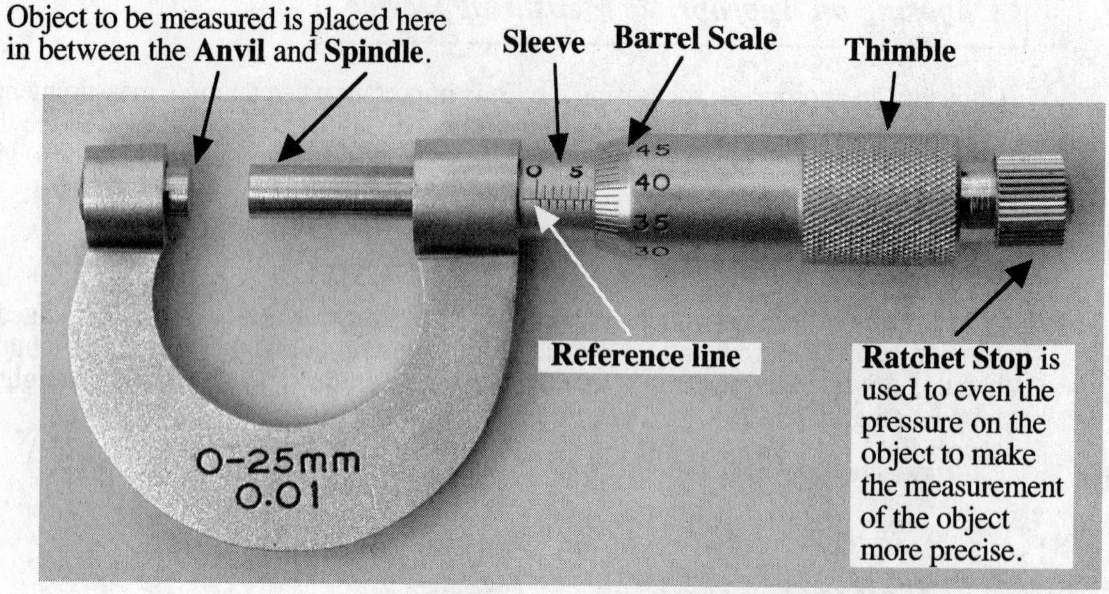
Object to be measured is placed here in between the **Anvil** and **Spindle**.
Sleeve
Barrel Scale
Thimble
0 5
45
40
35
30
Reference line
Ratchet Stop is used to even the pressure on the object to make the measurement of the object more precise.
0-25mm
0.01

1. The course reading will be the value of the last fully visible line on the sleeve. The course value in the illustration is 6.5 mm.

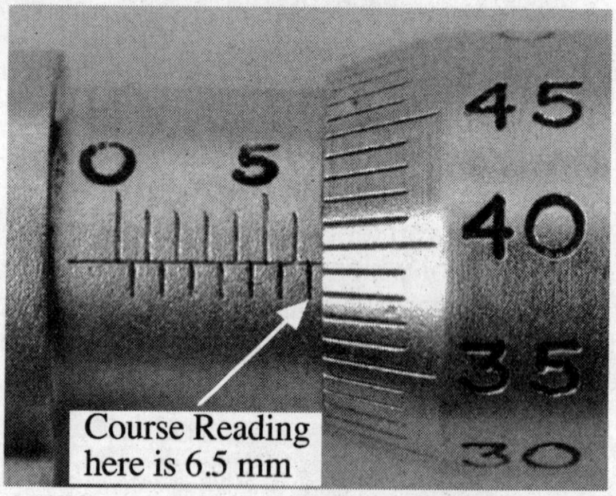
45
0
5
40
35
30
Course Reading here is 6.5 mm

2. Look at the reference line on the sleeve. Match this reference line with the line on the barrel scale. If these two lines do not match exactly, then use the line on the barrel scale closest to the reference line.

The value of the barrel scale reading in this illustration is 0.39 mm .

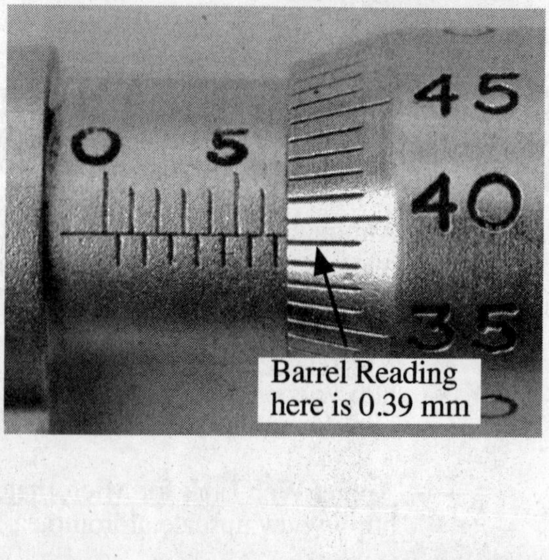
45
0
5
40
35
Barrel Reading here is 0.39 mm

3. Add the course reading to the barrel scale reading to obtain the micrometer reading. In this illustration the measurement of the object will be

$$6.5 \text{ mm} + 0.39 \text{ mm} = 6.89 \text{ mm}$$

Determine the micrometer reading in metric units.

a)

b)

Complete Assignment Question #1

Using a Vernier Caliper (to the nearest 0.01cm) to Measure Objects

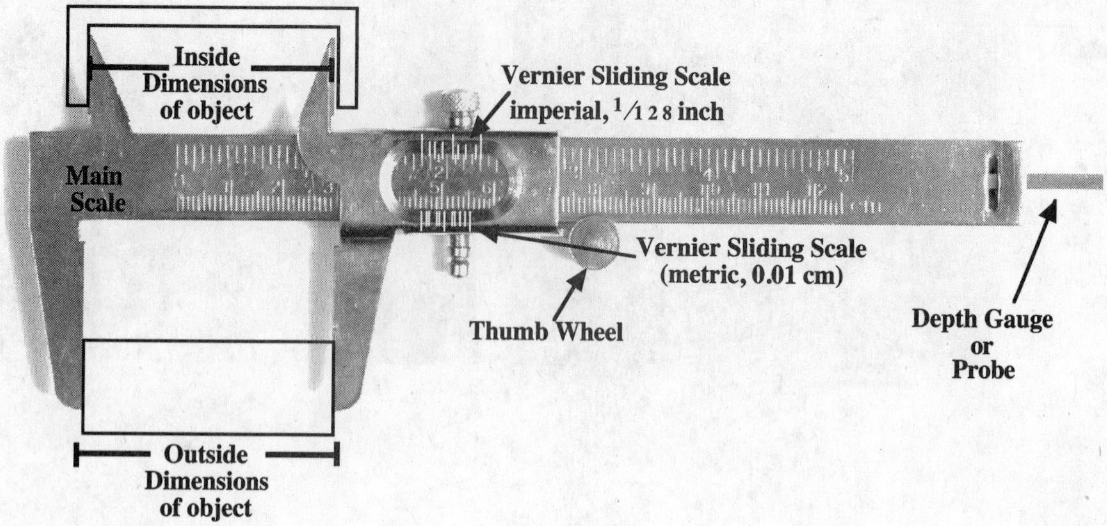

1. Decide which system to use: metric or imperial.

2. Look at the dividing line on the far left of the vernier sliding scale. Then look at the value on the main scale of the first mark **to the left** of this dividing line.
This is the **course reading**.
For this illustration, the course reading in the metric system is 6.1 cm and the course reading in the imperial system is $2\ ^{6}/_{16} = 2^{3}/_{8}$ inch or 2.375 inches.

3. To refine the reading, find the line on the vernier sliding scale that best matches a line on the main scale. This is the **vernier sliding scale reading**. In the metric system this line measures to the nearest 0.01 cm and in the imperial system it measures to the nearest $^{1}/_{128}$ inch.
For this illustration, the vernier sliding scale reading in the metric system is 0.05 cm and the vernier sliding scale reading in the imperial system is $^{5}/_{128}$ inch or 0.0390625 inches.

4. Add the value of the course reading to the value of the vernier sliding scale reading to get the caliper reading, or the measurement of the object.

<u>Metric Reading</u> → 6.1 cm + 0.05 cm = 6.15 cm
or 61 mm + 0.5 mm = 61.5 mm

<u>Imperial Reading</u> → $2^{3}/_{8} + {}^{5}/_{128} = {}^{309}/_{128} = 2\ ^{53}/_{128}$ inch (using fraction function on calculator)
or 2.0625 + 0.015625 = 2.4140625 inches

Note: Usually imperial readings are given in fraction form.

Using a Vernier Caliper (to the nearest 0.05mm) to Measure Objects

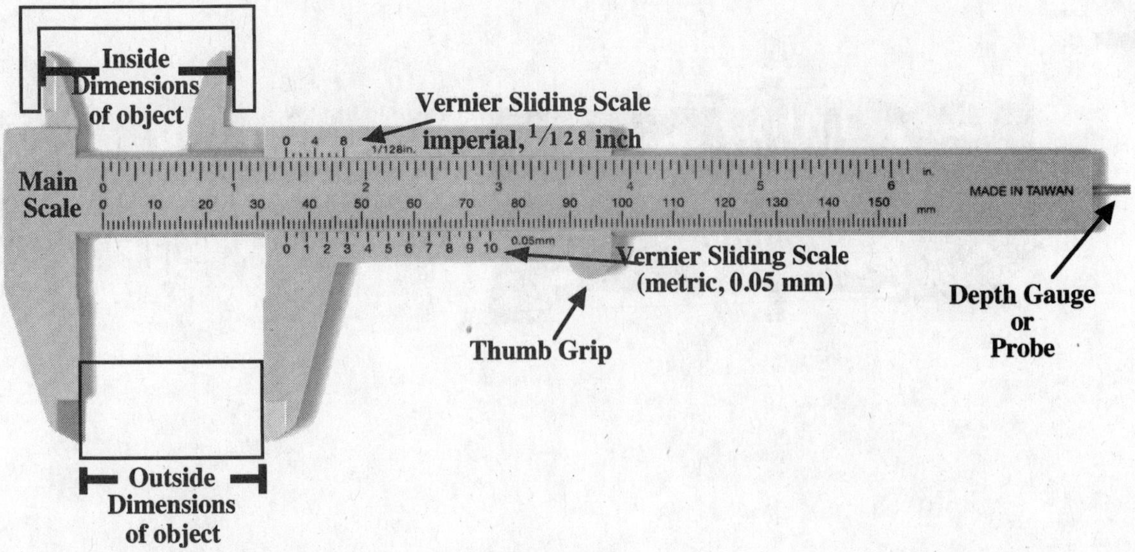

1. Decide which system to use: metric or imperial.

2. Look at the zero on the far left of the vernier sliding scale. Then look at the value on the main scale of the first mark **to the left** of the vernier 0. This is the **course reading**. For this illustration, the course reading in the metric system is 13mm and the course reading in the imperial system is $\frac{8}{16} = \frac{1}{2}$ inch or 0.5 inches.

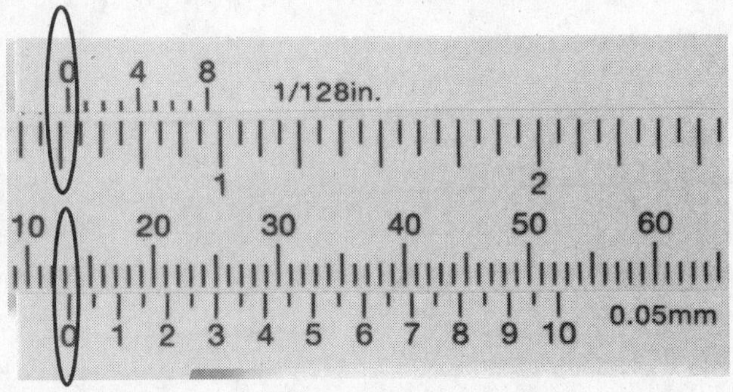

3. To refine the reading, find the line on the vernier sliding scale that best matches a line on the main scale. This is the **vernier sliding scale reading**. In the metric system, this line measures to the nearest 0.05 mm and in the imperial system it measures to the nearest $\frac{1}{128}$ inch. For this illustration, the vernier sliding scale reading in the metric system is 0.35 mm and the vernier sliding scale reading in the imperial system is $\frac{3}{128}$ inch or 0.023 437 5 inch.

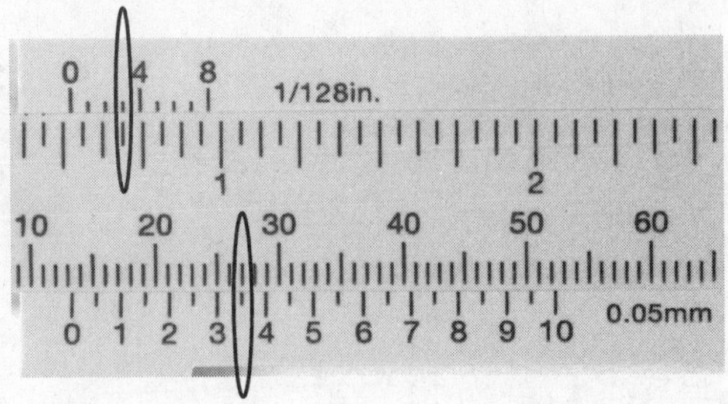

4. Add the value of the course reading to the value of the vernier sliding scale reading to get the caliper reading, or the measurement of the object.

<u>Metric Reading</u> → 13 mm + 0.35 mm = 13.35 mm

<u>Imperial Reading</u> → $\frac{1}{2} + \frac{3}{128} = \frac{67}{128}$ inch
or 0.5 + 0.023 437 5 = 0.523 427 5

Class Ex. #2

Determine the vernier caliper readings in metric and imperial units. Imperial measurements are to be in lowest mixed fraction form.

a)

b)

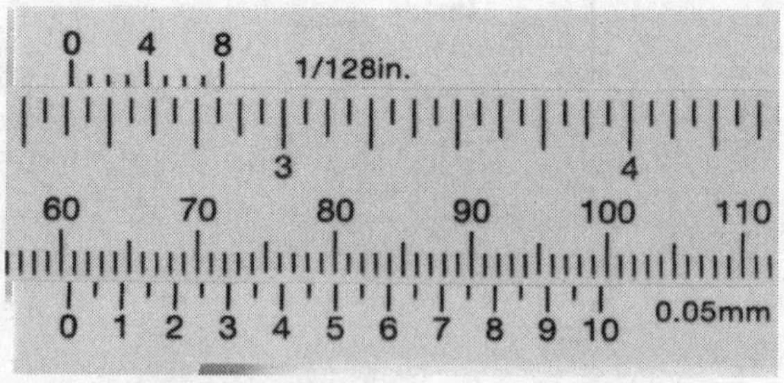

Complete Assignment Questions #2 - #11

Assignment

1. Determine the micrometer readings in metric units.

a)

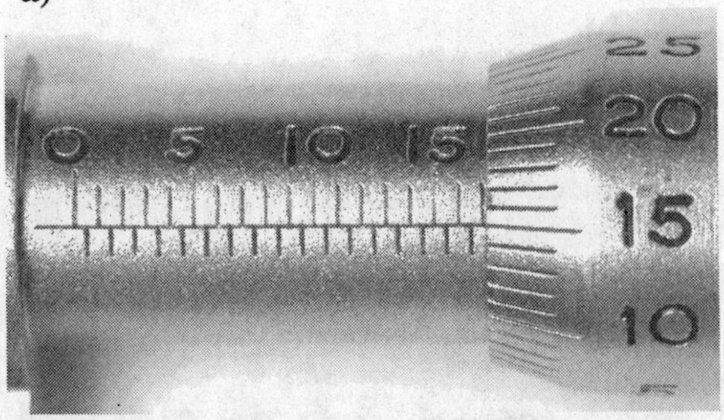

b)

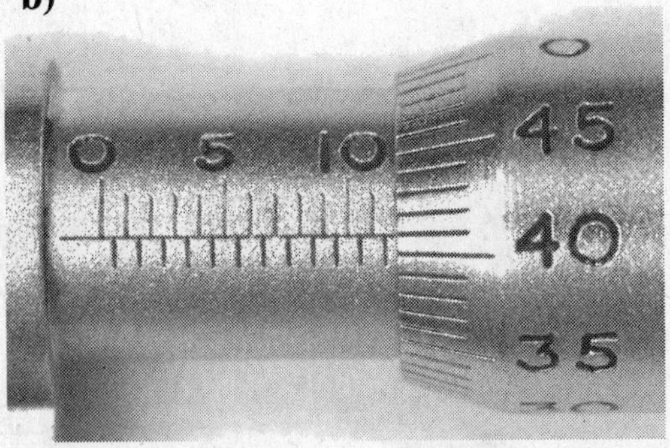

c)

d)

e)

f)

g)

h)

2. Determine the vernier caliper reading in metric and imperial units. Imperial measurements are to be in lowest mixed fraction form.

a)

b)

c)

d)

3. Determine the vernier caliper reading in metric and imperial units. Imperial measurements are to be in lowest mixed fraction form.

a)

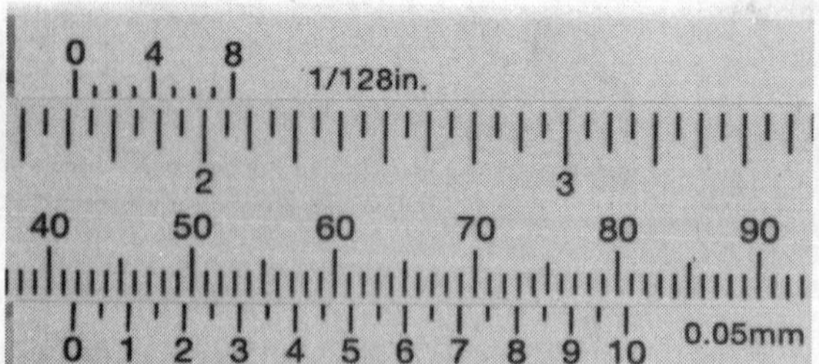

b)

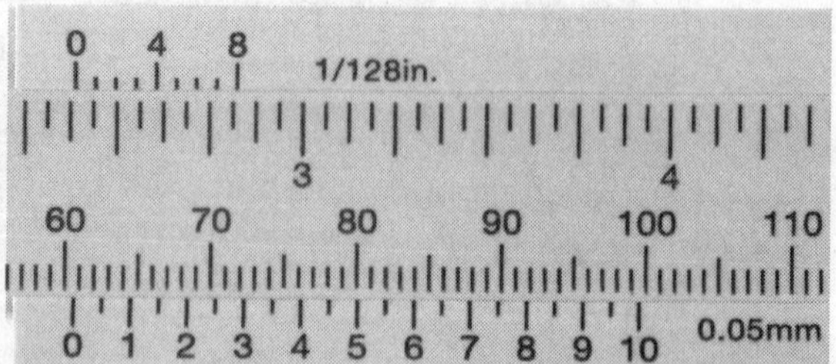

c)

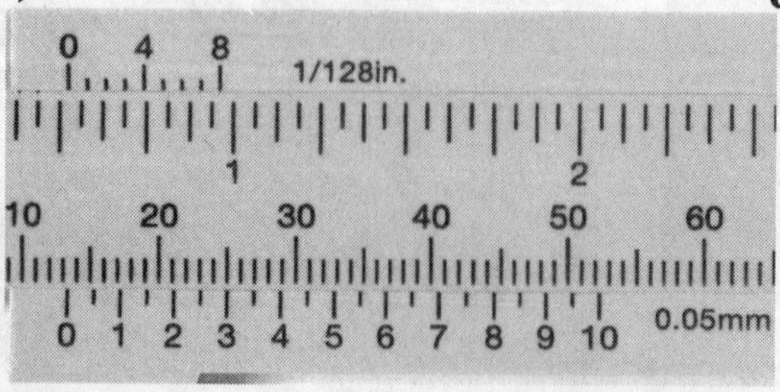

d)

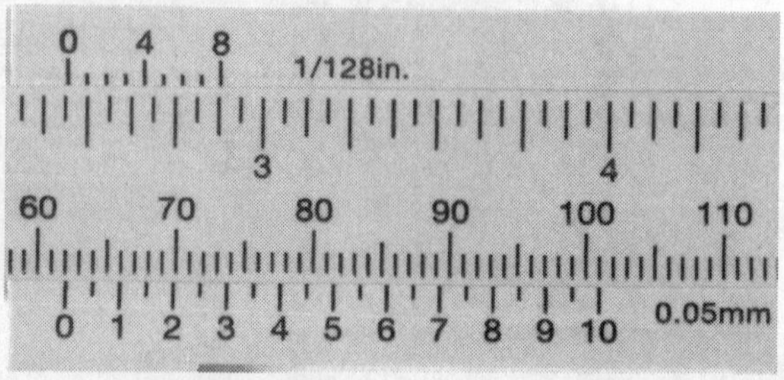

4. Use a micrometer to measure the following objects in metric units.
Note that answers will vary on some objects depending on brand and type.

a) The thickness of a pen

b) The thickness of a pencil

c) The thickness of 20 pages of this workbook

d) The thickness of a loonie

e) The diameter of a quarter

f) The radius of a nickel

5. Use a vernier caliper to measure the following objects in metric and imperial units.

	Metric Units	**Imperial Units**
a) The length of a pen		
b) The length of a pencil		
c) The diameter of a quarter		
d) The radius of a dime		
e) The thickness of a graphing calculator (no cover)		

6. State which of the following measuring devices could be used to measure the following objects. If possible, measure the object in metric and imperial units.

Measuring devices: ruler, tape measure, trundle wheel, micrometer.

a) The length and width of the whiteboard in your classroom

b) The length of this straight line

c) The thickness of an eraser

d) The height of a door

e) The length of a football field from goal post to goal post

Matching Match each object on the left with the best measuring instrument on the right. Each measuring instrument may be used once, more than once, or not at all.

Object		Measuring Instruments	
7.	The thickness of a page	**A.**	Trundle Wheel
8.	The length of a city block	**B.**	Micrometer
9.	The diameter of a hole that a screw will be screwed into	**C.**	Ruler
10.	The perimeter of a wallet sized photo	**D.**	Vernier Caliper

Answer Key

1. **a)** 17.15 mm **b)** 11.91 mm **c)** 6.00 mm **d)** 5.50 mm
e) 12.01 mm **f)** 11.49 mm **g)** 12.85 mm **h)** 1.23 mm

2. Answers may vary slightly.
a) 9.77 cm $3\frac{105}{128}$ in. **b)** 5.05 cm $1\frac{63}{64}$ in. **c)** 6.15 cm $2\frac{53}{128}$ in. **d)** 11.21 cm $4\frac{53}{128}$ in

3. Answers may vary slightly.
a) 41.65 mm $1\frac{41}{64}$ in. **b)** 60.55 mm $2\frac{25}{64}$ in **c)** 13.30 mm $\frac{67}{128}$ in. **d)** 62.05 mm $2\frac{57}{128}$ in

4. Answers may vary depending on the accuracy of the measuring instrument.

5. Answers may vary depending on the accuracy of the measuring instrument.

6. **a)** tape measure **b)** ruler **c)** micrometer **d)** tape measure **e)** trundle wheel

7. B **8.** A **9.** D **10.** C

Measurement Lesson #4:
Conversion Within the SI System

Overview

The next three lessons will involve the conversion of units within and between the SI system and the imperial system of measurements.

- Lesson 4: Conversion Within the SI System of Measurement using three different methods:
  - Method 1: Using the SI Chart (the Metric Unit Chart) as a Number Line
  - Method 2: Proportional Reasoning
  - Method 3: Unit Analysis (or Dimensional Analysis)
- Lesson 5: Conversion Between the SI System and the Imperial System of Measurement.
- Lesson 6: Conversion involving square units and cubic units.

Conversion of Units Within the International System of Units (SI)

The metric unit chart below gives the main units used in the metric system of measurement together with their relationship to 1 metre, 1 gram or 1 litre.

Prefix	giga	mega	kilo	hecto	deca		deci	centi	milli	micro	nano
Symbol	G	M	k	h	da		d	c	m	μ	n
Units	10^9 1 000 000 000	10^6 1 000 000	10^3 1 000	10^2 100	10^1 10	10^0 1	10^{-1} 0.1	10^{-2} 0.01	10^{-3} 0.001	10^{-6} 0.000 001	10^{-9} 0.000 000 001
Symbol	Gm Gg GL	Mm Mg ML	km kg kL	hm hg hL	dam dag daL	*m,* *g,* *L*	dm dg dL	cm cg cL	mm mg mL	μm μg μL	nm ng nL

Complete the following:

1 gigametre (Gm) = 10^9 m

1 megametre (Mm) = 10^6 m

1 kilometre (km) = 10^3 m (1000)

1 centimetre (cm) = 0.01 (10^{-2}) m

1 millimetre (mm) = 0.001 (10^{-3}) m

1 micrometre (μm) = 0.000001 (10^{-6}) m

1 nanometre (nm) = 10^{-9} m

1 litre (L) = 1000 millilitres (mL)

1 gram (g) = 1000 milligrams (mg)

1 kilogram (kg) = 1000 grams (g)

1 millilitre (mL) = ____________ L

1 milligram (mg) = ____________ g

1 gram (g) = ____________ kg

The prefixes hecto and deca are not often used nowadays.

Method 1: Using the Metric Unit Number Line to Convert within SI Units

The biggest advantage that the metric system has over other systems of measurement is that the units are related to each other by factors of ten. From the metric unit chart we can create a metric unit number line for use in conversions. When converting between units, we need to know how many positions on the line we have to move. Each movement of one position represents a power of 10.

For example, to convert from kilometres to centimetres we move 5 positions to the <u>right</u>.
i.e. $1 \text{ km} = 10^5$ or 100 000 cm

To convert from centimetres to kilometres we move 5 positions to the left.
i.e. $1 \text{ cm} = 10^{-5}$ or $\dfrac{1}{100\,000}$ km.

1 Km = 1000 m
100cm = 1m

Larger *smaller* $\curvearrowleft = \div 10$

×10 → G
×10 L
m

G M k h da Unit d c m μ n

Class Ex. #1

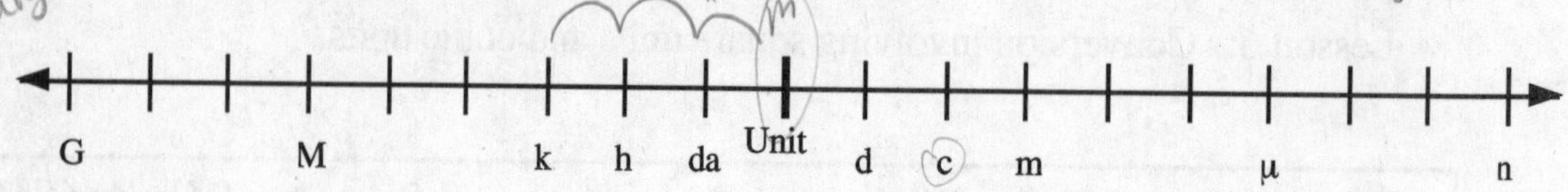

Use the metric unit number line above to complete the following established conversions in the metric system. Write each answer as a power of 10 and then in standard notation.

a) 1 m = __100__ cm b) 1 mm = __0.001__ m c) 1 L = __1000__ mL

10^3 $\times 10^3$

Class Ex. #2

Convert the following measures.

a) 7.5 m to cm b) 72 350 mg to kg c) 325 micrometres to nanometres.

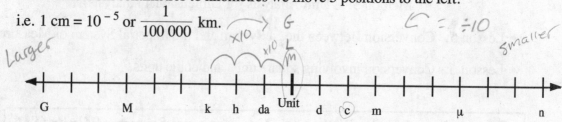

×10 ×10 *÷10^6*

750cm *0.072350*

Class Ex. #3

Convert the following, leaving the answer in scientific notation.

a) 12 km to mm b) 580 μg to grams c) 15 700 cL to ML

Complete Assignment Questions #1 - #3

Method 2: Using Proportional Reasoning to Convert Within SI Units

In mathematics, a proportion is a statement of equality between two ratios.

In order to use proportional reasoning, we need to know one of the following:
i) a commonly known conversion, such as 1 metre is 100 cm, or,
ii) a ratio given in the question.

As in previous math courses, set the ratio in the form $\frac{a}{b} = \frac{c}{d}$.

There are a number of ways of setting out the work for proportional reasoning. Whichever method is used, it is essential that we keep a careful eye on the units involved. The units must be equivalent in each ratio.

Alice, Jim and Rema were asked to convert 300 cm into metres. Part of their work is shown below. Each knew that 1 m = 100 cm.

Alice

$$\frac{1\text{ m}}{100\text{ cm}} = \frac{x}{300\text{ cm}}$$

$$\frac{1\text{ m}}{100\text{ cm}}\frac{\times(3)}{\times(3)} = \frac{x}{300\text{ cm}}$$

x =

300 cm = ______ m

Jim

$$\frac{1\text{ m}}{100\text{ cm}} = \frac{x}{300\text{ cm}}$$

$$(1\text{ m})(300\text{ cm}) = (x)(100\text{ cm})$$

$$\frac{(1\text{ m})(300\ \cancel{\text{cm}})}{100\ \cancel{\text{cm}}} = x$$

$x =$

Rema

$$\frac{100\text{ cm}}{1\text{ m}} = \frac{300\text{ cm}}{x}$$

$$(100\text{ cm})(x) = (300\text{ cm})(1\text{ m})$$

$$x = \frac{(300\text{ cm})(1\text{ m})}{100\text{ cm}}$$

$x =$

- Alice's method is very difficult to use if the multiplier used is not a whole number.
- Both Jim and Rema used cross product (or cross multiplication) to solve the problem. Notice that the cm cancel out leaving the required unit, m.
- When the cross product calculation is performed, the units should cancel out where necessary and the remaining unit left is the required one.
- An alternative approach is to leave the units as headings, and to carry out the cross product as shown below.

m	cm
1	100
x	300

OR

m	1	x
cm	100	300

Notice that in each case x is measured in metres.

$$\frac{1}{x} = \frac{100}{300} \qquad\qquad \frac{1}{100} = \frac{x}{300}$$

Class Ex. #5

A photograph of an African elephant has a scale of 1 cm represents 0.6 m. The elephant's trunk in the photograph measures 3.5 cm. What is the actual length of the elephant's trunk?

$$\frac{3.5cm}{1cm} \cdot \frac{0.6m}{} = \frac{x \cdot 3.5cm}{3.5cm} \qquad x = \frac{3.5cm \cdot 0.6m}{1cm} \qquad x = 2.1m$$

Class Ex. #6

Reba followed a recipe for rice bean soup and used 175 mL of beans and 650 mL of rice. She realized that she had not made enough soup and added 70 mL of beans to the soup. How much rice should she add?

$$\frac{175\,mL\ beans}{650\,ml\ rice} = \frac{70\,mL\ beans}{x\ rice} \qquad \frac{650n, ^{70}}{175} = \frac{x\ rice\ ^{<70}}{70\,ml\ beans}$$

$$\frac{70 \cdot 650}{175\,mL} = x = 260\,ml\ rice$$

> **Complete Assignment Questions #4 - #6**

> **Method 3: Using Unit (or Dimensional) Analysis to Convert within SI Units**

Proportional reasoning is useful when only one conversion of units is required. If several changes of units are required, you need to do proportional reasoning several times, or use a different process like unit analysis.

Unit Analysis, or **Dimensional Analysis**, is another method for converting between different units. Unit analysis is commonly used in high school and higher level science classes and is particularly useful when many units are involved. See Class Ex. #8.

If only one conversion is required, the basic set-up in this approach is

$$\text{required} = (\text{given}) \times (\text{conversion})$$

with units being placed properly in the numerator and denominator. If done correctly, as in proportional reasoning, the unit left over is the unit required in the answer.

Consider the process of converting 75 millimetres to metres.

Like proportional reasoning, a known conversion is used. In this case, 1 m = 1000 mm.

We then multiply as shown:

$$\boxed{\text{required} = (\text{given}) \times (\text{conversion})}$$

$$= \frac{75\ mm}{1} \times \frac{1\ m}{1000\ mm}$$

$$\left(\frac{1m}{1000mm} \right)$$

$$\times 1$$

$$= \frac{75\ \cancel{mm}}{1} \times \frac{1\ m}{1000\ \cancel{mm}}$$

$$= \frac{75\ m}{1000} \qquad \boxed{= 0.075\ m}$$

Class Ex. #7 Convert the following measurements using unit analysis.

a) 12 kilometres =_____ m **b)** 2730 nanometres =_____ m

$12 \ \text{km} \left(\dfrac{1000 \ m}{1 \ km} \right) = 12000m$ $2730 \ \text{nm} \left(\dfrac{1 \ m}{10^9 \ nm} \right) = 2.73 \times 10^{-6} \ m$

$\left(\dfrac{1m}{0.001} \right) \Leftarrow \left(\dfrac{800m}{0.9} \right)$ $* (12 \times 1000)$

Note Unit analysis is particularly useful when multiple conversions would be required.
Unit analysis can do multiple conversions in one calculation (as shown below).

For example, to convert 2.4 km to mm you would first convert from km to m and then
from m to mm.

Complete the unit analysis calculation started below.

$$\dfrac{2.4 \ km}{1} \times \dfrac{1000 \ m}{1 \ km} \times \dfrac{1000 \ mm}{1 \ m} = \qquad 2.4 \times 10^6 \ mm$$

Class Ex. #8 Convert 0.25 Gm to Mm using unit analysis and known conversions involving metres.

Class Ex. #9 Zimmer needed to convert 50 m/s to km/min.

a) What conversions will Zimmer need to know to solve this problem?

b) Complete Zimmer's work below to solve the problem. Show the cancellation in units.

$$\left(\dfrac{50 \ m}{s} \times \dfrac{km}{m} \times \dfrac{s}{min} \right.$$

$\left(\dfrac{1 \ km}{1000 \ m} \right)$

$s \to min \quad \left(\dfrac{60 \ s}{1 \ min} \right)$

$\dfrac{50}{1000} \times 60$

$= 3 \ km/min$

$3000 m/min$

Complete Assignment Questions #7 - #16

Assignment

Some of the solutions may be more conveniently written in scientific notation.

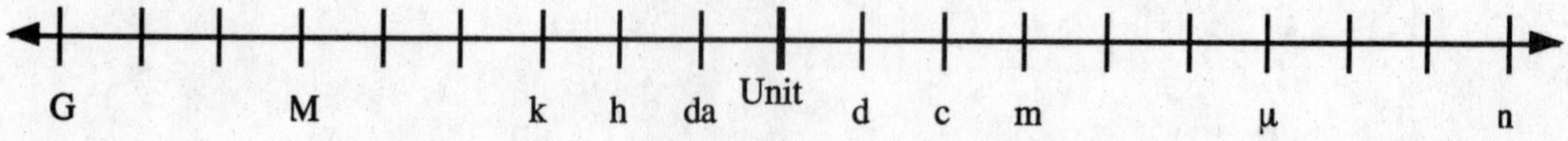

1. Use the metric unit number line above to convert the following to the indicated units.

a) 6780 cm = ______________ m **b)** 0.91 km = ______________ m

c) 14 km = ______________ cm **d)** 87 mm = ______________ cm

e) 65.23 m = ______________ cm **f)** 0.04 mm = ______________ m

g) 0.88 m = ______________ km **h)** 27.39 cm = ______________ mm

i) 0.736 µm = ______________ mm **j)** 29 Gm = ______________ km

k) 5830 nm = ______________ µm **l)** 2.17 Mm = ______________ Gm

2. Convert the following to the indicated measurements.

a) 52 kL = ______________ L **b)** 891 ml = ______________ L

c) 85.2 L = ______________ cL **d)** 27 mg = ______________ cg

e) 0.9875 kg = ______________ g **f)** 4257 g = ______________ kg

g) 89 gigajoules = ______________ megajoules **h)** 67 230 nm = ______________ cm

3. The loudness of a sound was originally measured in Bels, named after Alexander Graham Bell. Currently the most commonly used unit is the decibel (dB). A telephone dial tone is measured at 82 dB. Determine the loudness of a telephone dial tone in Bels.

4. Use **proportional reasoning** to do the following conversions. Show all work.

a) 15 km = ______________ m

b) 28500 cm = ______________ m

c) 0.35 mm = ______________ cm

d) 112 cm = ______________ mm

e) 857.8 m = ______________ cm

f) 0.03 mm = ______________ m

g) 5 200 m = ______________ km

h) 0.014 megawatts = ______________ watts

i) 59 000 μm = ______________ m

j) 6.7GHz = ______________ Hz
(gigahertz)

k) 29 080 nm = ______________ cm

l) 5.15 Mm = ______________ Gm

5. On a map of Alberta, 4 cm represents 62 km. If the actual distance from Calgary to Lethbridge is 217 km, use proportional reasoning to calculate the distance between Calgary and Lethbridge on this map.

6. In preparation for a school trip to Italy, Meghan exchanged C$900 for 1400 euros. Her friend Josh, exchanged C$720. Use proportional reasoning to determine how many euros Josh should receive.

7. Convert the following to the indicated measurements using **unit analysis**. Show all work.

a) 3.7 km = ______________ m **b)** 77 500 cm = ______________ mm

c) 920 mL= ______________ L **d)** 33.1 m = ______________ mm

8. Convert the following to the indicated measurements using **unit analysis**. Show all work.

a) 29 km = ______________cm **b)** 34 200 mm = ______________ km

c) 950 mm = ______________ μm **d)** 162.8 Mm = ______________ Gm

9. Convert the following to the indicated measurements using **unit analysis**. Show all work.

a) 240 m/s = ______________ km/min **b)** 8.4 m/s = ______________ km/h

c) 120 m/h = ______________ mm/min **d)** 2 m/min = ______________ km/h

e) 72 km/h = ______________ m/sec **f)** 35 mm/s = ______________ km/h

Multiple Choice **10.** Which statement is incorrect?

A. 1 kg = 1 000 000 mg
B. 1 μg = 1 000 ng
C. 1 Mg = 1000 Gg
D. 1 cL = 10 000 μL

Matching Match each question number on the left with the equivalent letter on the right.

11. 9000 millimetres	**A.** 9 million kilometres
12. 0.9 cm	**B.** 9 micrometres
13. 9 Gm	**C.** 9×10^5 metres
14. 9000 nm	**D.** 9000 micrometres
15. 0.9 Mm	**E.** 9 metres

Numerical Response **16.** Ciaren buys a string 1.4 m long for a hobby class. The project he is working on requires that the string be cut into 1 cm lengths. The number of 1 cm lengths he will have is ______.

(Record your answer in the numerical response box from left to right)

Answer Key

1. **a)** 67.8 **b)** 910 **c)** 1 400 000 or 1.4×10^6
d) 8.7 **e)** 6523 **f)** 0.000 04 or 4×10^{-5}
g) 0.000 88 or 8.8×10^{-4} **h)** 273.9 **i)** 0.000 736 or 7.36×10^{-4}
j) 29 000 000 or 2.9×10^7 **k)** 5.83 **l)** 0.002 17

2. **a)** 52 000 **b)** 0.891 **c)** 8520 **d)** 2.7
e) 987.5 **f)** 4.257 **g)** 89 000 **h)** 0.006 723

3. 8.2 Bels

4. **a)** 15 000 **b)** 285 **c)** 0.035 **d)** 1120 **e)** 85 780 **f)** 0.000 03
g) 5.2 **h)** 14 000 **i)** 0.059 **j)** 6 700 000 000 **k)** 0.002 908 **l)** 0.005 15

5. 14 cm **6.** 1120 euros

7. **a)** 3700 **b)** 775 000 **c)** 0.92 **d)** 33 100

8. **a)** 2 900 000 **b)** 0. 034 2 **c)** 950 000 **d)** 0.162 8

9. **a)** 14.4 **b)** 30.24 **c)** 2000 **d)** 0.12 **e)** 20 **f)** 0.126

10. C **11.** E **12.** D **13.** A **14.** B **15.** C

16.

1	4	0	

Measurement Lesson #5:

Conversion Within and Between the SI and Imperial Systems

In the last lesson we converted between units in the SI system of measurement using the following methods:

- metric unit number line
- proportional reasoning, and
- unit (or dimensional) analysis

In this lesson we convert measurements within the imperial system and between the SI and imperial systems.

The chart below shows the relationship between the units in the imperial system and some of the relationships between imperial and SI units.

We will complete the chart as we go through the class examples and assignment questions.

Imperial to Imperial	Imperial to SI (Metric)	SI (Metric) to Imperial
1 foot (ft) = 12 inches (in)	1 in = 2.54 cm	1 cm = 0.3937 in
1 yard (yd) = 3 feet (ft)	1 ft = 0.3048 m	1 m = ft
1 mile (mi) = 5280 ft	1 yd = m	1 m = yds
1 mi = 1760 yards (yds)	1 mi = km	1 km = mi

Conversion Within the Imperial System

Class Ex. #1

Convert the following:

a) 6 ft 7 in to inches **b)** 5 yds 2 ft to feet **c)** 1 mi 255 yds to yards

d) 51 in to feet and inches **e)** 73 ft to yards and feet **f)** 4215 yds to miles and yards

---

Class Ex. #2

Convert 0.4 miles to inches by the following methods:

<u>Proportional Reasoning</u> <u>Unit Analysis</u>

Complete Assignment Questions #1 - #3

Conversion Between SI (Metric) and Imperial Systems

Class Ex. #3

Consider the table on the previous page.
A student is using unit analysis to determine how many metres are in one foot, i.e. convert one foot to metres. The required unit is metres per foot.

Part of her work is shown below. Complete her work by: **a)** cancelling out the correct units in step 2, **b)** calculating the answer to two decimal places and **c)** writing the answer in the table.

Step 1

$$\frac{2.54\text{ cm}}{1\text{ in}} \cdot \frac{12\text{ in}}{1\text{ ft}} \cdot \frac{1\text{ m}}{100\text{ cm}} =$$

Step 2

$$\frac{2.54\text{ cm}}{1\text{ in}} \cdot \frac{12\text{ in}}{1\text{ ft}} \cdot \frac{1\text{ m}}{100\text{ cm}} =$$

Complete Assignment Question #4

- The conversion chart on the previous page lists some of the conversions between units. More conversions can be found on the internet at:

  www.convert-me.com or www.convert-me.com/en/

  and www.unit-conversion.info/speed.html (for speed and velocity conversions).

Class Ex. #4

Convert the following

a) 5 ft 10 in = __________ m (to three decimal places).

b) 2.0573 m = ________ft _____ in (to the nearest inch).

Class Ex. #5

Before the digital age, video was often made on different types of film. 16 mm film was often used in industrial or educational film making. 16 mm films are now being transferred to DVDs and other digital forms of storage. If 1 500 feet of film can fit on one DVD, determine how many DVDs will be needed for 2183 metres of film footage.

Complete Assignment Questions #5 - #15

Assignment

1. Convert the following:

a) 3 ft 11 in to inches

Calc $3 \text{ ft} \left(\dfrac{12 \text{ in}}{1 \text{ ft}} \right) = 36 + 11 = 47 \text{ in}$

b) 7 yds 1 ft to feet

c) 2 mi 325 yds to yards

Calc $2 \text{ .} 325 \text{ yd} \left(\dfrac{1760}{1 \text{ mi}} \right) = 3520 + 325 =$

c) 384

d) 75 in to feet and inches

e) 82 ft to yards and feet

$82 \text{ ft} \left(\dfrac{1 \text{ yd}}{3 \text{ ft}} \right) = 27.\overline{3} = 27 \text{ yds and } 1 \text{ ft}$

f) 18 480 feet to miles and feet

g) 4 yds 2 ft 6 in to inches

h) 100 in to yards, feet and inches

3
2

$\dfrac{1}{3} \text{ yd} \left(\dfrac{3 \text{ ft}}{1 \text{ yd}} \right)$
$= 1 \text{ ft}$

2. Use proportional reasoning or unit analysis to convert

a) 2.3 mi to in

$2.3 \text{ mi} \left(\dfrac{5280 \text{ ft}}{1 \text{ mi}} \right) \left(\dfrac{12 \text{ in}}{1 \text{ ft}} \right)$

$2.3(5280)(12) = 145728 \text{ in}$

b) 200 000 in to mi (to the nearest hundredth of a mile)

$2.3 \text{ mi} = 145728 \text{ in}$

3. The Olympic Marathon is run over a distance of 26 miles and 385 yards. Convert this distance to

a) yards

$26 \text{ mi} \left(\dfrac{1760 \text{ yds}}{1 \text{ mi}} \right) = 4576 + 385 = 4961 \text{ yds}$

b) feet

c) inches

4. Determine the missing entries on the chart at the beginning of this lesson (to four decimal places). Use the space below to show your work. Then complete the chart by filling in the missing entries.

a) 1 yd = _____ m

b) 1 mi = _____ km

c) 1 m = _____ ft

d) 1 m = _____ yds

e) 1 km = _____ mile

Use the chart at the beginning of the lesson to complete the rest of the assignment.

5. Convert the following.

a) 17 ft 4 in = ________ m (two decimal places) **b)** 4.25 m = _____ ft_____ in (nearest inch)

Use the following information to answer questions #6 and #7.

The symbols ′ and ″ are often used to represent feet and inches respectively.

For example, 7 feet 3 inches can be written as 7′ 3″.

Conversions

Height: 1 in = 2.54 cm Weight: 1 kilogram (kg) = 2.2 pounds (lbs)

6. Consider the heights and weights of the following famous people.

a) General Tom Thumb (Charles S. Stratton) → 3′3″, 71 lbs
b) Celine Dion → 5′7″, 118 lbs
c) Steve Nash → 6′3″, 195 lbs

Convert each of their heights to the nearest hundredth of a metre, and their weights to the nearest kilogram.

7. Consider the heights and weights of the following famous celebrity/characters.

a) Terri Hatcher → 1.67 m 58.1 kg
b) Chewbacca the Wookiee→ 2.28 m 170 kg
c) Sidney Crosby → 1.80 m 91 kg

Convert each of their heights to feet and inches to the nearest inch, and their weights to the nearest pound.

8. In 1954 Roger Bannister became the first athlete to run a mile in less than four minutes. In current athletics championships the imperial mile has been replaced by the 1500 m, often called the "metric mile". Which distance, 1 mile or 1500 metres, is longer and by how much? Answer in metres and in yards to the nearest whole number.

9. The quarter mile race has been replaced in current times by the 400 metres race. Which distance, a quarter mile or 400 metres, is longer and by how much? Answer in metric units and in imperial units to the nearest whole number.

Use the following information to answer questions #10 - #12.

In Physics, the speed of light is denoted by the letter *c*. Its value is recorded as exactly 299 792 458 m/s in a vacuum where there is no other external matter that can slow it down.

10. *c* is often approximated in kilometres per second. State the speed of light to the nearest one hundred thousand kilometres per second.

Multiple Choice

11. In the imperial measurement system, *c* is usually estimated in miles per second. Determine the speed of light to the nearest one hundred thousand miles per second.

A. 186 000
B. 483 000
C. 186 000 000
D. 483 000 000

12. It takes light 100 000 years to travel across the Milky Way (the galaxy in which our solar system is located). Assuming an average of 365 ¼ days in a year, the approximate distance in miles across the Milky Way is

A. 1.5×10^{13} **B.** 1.5×10^{18} **C.** 5.9×10^{12} **D.** 5.9×10^{17}

13. The number of inches in 3 yards and 7 inches is

A. 43
B. 115
C. 133
D. 307

Numerical Response

14. A Canadian driver crosses the border near Abbotsford. His speedometer reading is 85 km/hr. To the nearest whole number, the speedometer reading in miles per hour (mph) is _____ .

(Record your answer in the numerical response box from left to right)

15. A plane is travelling at 510 mph. To the nearest whole number, the speedometer reading in kilometres per hour is _____ .

(Record your answer in the numerical response box from left to right)

Answer Key

1. **a)** 47 in **b)** 22 ft **c)** 3845 yds **d)** 6 ft 3 in
e) 27 yds 1 ft **f)** 3 mi 2640 ft **g)** 174 in **h)** 2 yds 2 ft 4 in

2. **a)** 145 728 in **b)** 3.16 mi **3.** **a)** 46 145 yds **b)** 138 435 **c)** 1 661 220 in

4. **a)** 0.9144 m **b)** 1.6093 km **c)** 3.2808 ft **d)** 1.0936 yds **e)** 0.6214 km

5. **a)** 5.28 m **b)** 13 ft 11 in

6. **a)** 0.99 m, 32 kg **b)** 1.70 m, 54 kg **c)** 1.91 m, 89 kg

7. **a)** 5′ 6″, 128 lbs **b)** 7′ 6″, 374 lbs **c)** 5′ 11″, 200 lbs

8. One mile is longer by 120 yds or 109 m. **9.** Quarter mile is longer by 3 yds or 2 m.

10. 300 000 km/s **11.** A **12.** D **13.** B

14.

5	3		

15.

8	2	1	

Measurement Lesson #6:

Conversion in the SI and Imperial Systems: Square Units & Cubic Units

Investigation #1 **Conversions between Units of Area in the Metric System**

a) Calculate the area of the square in m^2.

b)
- Convert the sides of the square in a) to cm and mm and write them below.
- Calculate the area in cm^2 and mm^2.

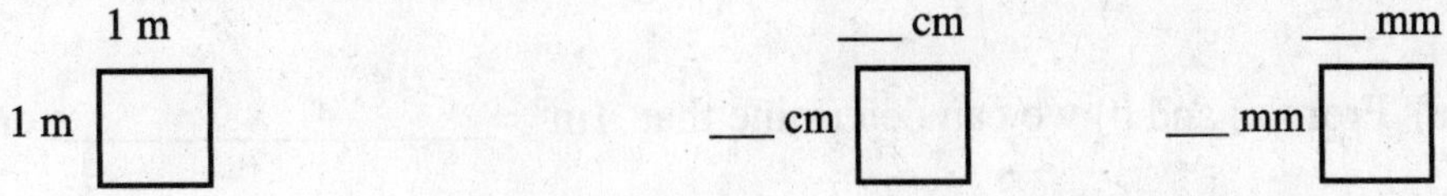

c) From a) and b) we can determine that $1m^2 =$ ________ cm^2 and $1m^2 =$ ________ mm^2.

d) Calculate the area of the rectangle in m^2.

e)
- Convert the sides of the rectangle in d) to cm and mm and write them below.
- Calculate the area in cm^2 and mm^2.

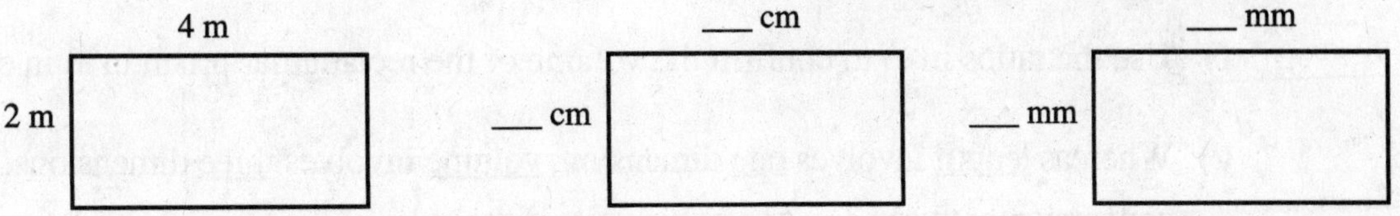

$A =$ ____ m^2 $A =$ ______________ cm^2 $A =$ ______________ mm^2

f) Use the ratios in c) to confirm the area of the rectangle in e) in cm^2 and mm^2.

g) Whereas <u>length</u> involves <u>one</u> dimension, <u>area</u> involves <u>two</u> dimensions. The area conversion between any two square units is the square of the length conversion between the linear units, e.g. to convert from km^2 to m^2 multiply by 1000×1000 or 1000^2.
Converting 2.5 km to m, we multiply by 10^3. On the metric unit number line we move 3 places to the right and hence move the decimal point 3 places to the right in the conversion. 2.5 km = ________ m.
Converting 2.5 km^2 to m^2, we multiply by $(10^3)^2 = 10^6$ and move the decimal point $3 \times$ ___ = ___ places to the right. 2.5 km^2 = ______________ m^2

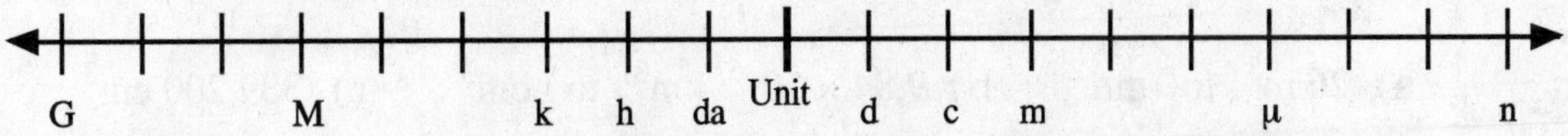

Class Ex. #1

Convert the following. Express the answers in standard and scientific notation.

a) 12 m^2 to mm^2

b) 41 500 cm^2 to km^2

c) 389 275 km^2 to Mm^2

Investigation #2 ***Conversions between Units of Volume in the Metric System***

a) Calculate the volume of the cube in m^3.

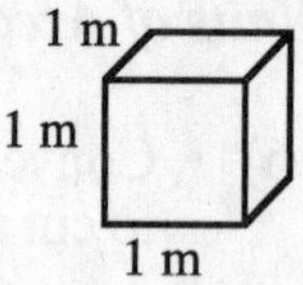

b) • Convert the sides of the cube in a) to cm and write them on the cube.
• Calculate the volume of the cube in cm^3.

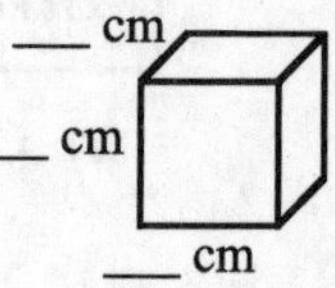

c) From a) and b) we can determine that $1m^3$ = ________________ cm^3.

d) Calculate the volume of the rectangular prism in m^3.

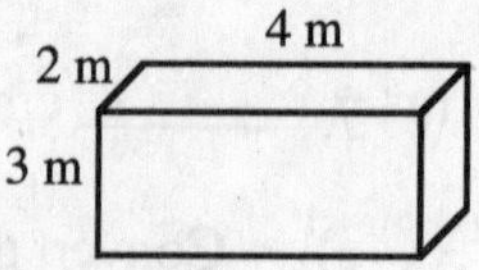

e) • Convert the sides of the rectangular prism in d) to cm.
• Write them on the diagram and calculate the volume in cm^3.

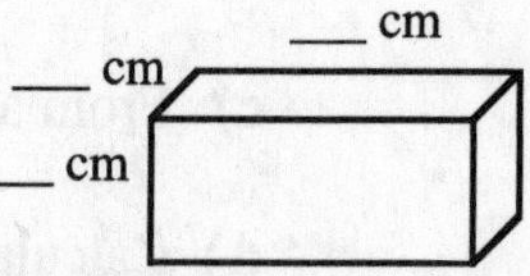

f) Use the ratios in c) to confirm the volume of the rectangular prism in e) in cm^3.

g) Whereas length involves one dimension, volume involves three dimensions. The volume conversion between any two cubic units is the cube of the length conversion between the linear units, e.g. to convert from km^3 to m^3 multiply by $1000 \times 1000 \times 1000$ or 1000^3. Converting 1.6 km to m we multiply by 10^3 and on the metric unit number line we move 3 places to the right and hence move the decimal point 3 places to the right in the conversion. 1.6 km = ________ m.
Converting 1.6 km^3 to m^3 we multiply by $(10^3)^3 = 10^9$ and move the decimal point $3 \times$ ___ = ___ places to the right. 1.6 km^3 = ______________ m^3

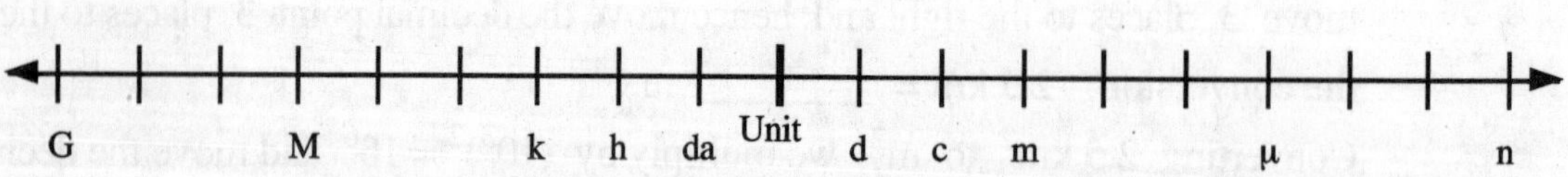

Class Ex. #2

Convert the following. Express the answers in standard and scientific notation.

a) 26 m^3 to mm^3 **b)** 9.84×10^{-6} km^3 to cm^3 **c)** 389 200 cm^3 to μm^3

Complete Assignment Questions #1 - 2

Investigation #3 ***Conversions between Units of Area in the Imperial System***

a) Calculate the area of the square in ft^2.

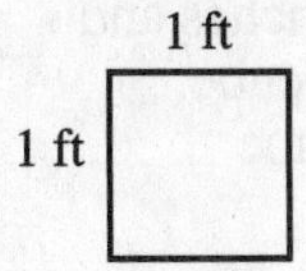

b) • Convert the sides of the square in a) to inches and write them below.
• Calculate the area in in^2.

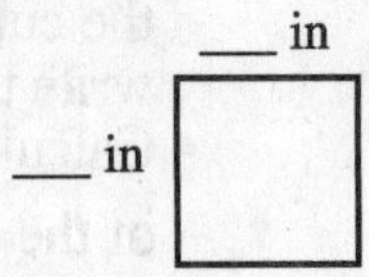

c) From a) and b) we can determine that $1ft^2$ = ________ in^2.

d) Calculate the area of the rectangle in ft^2.

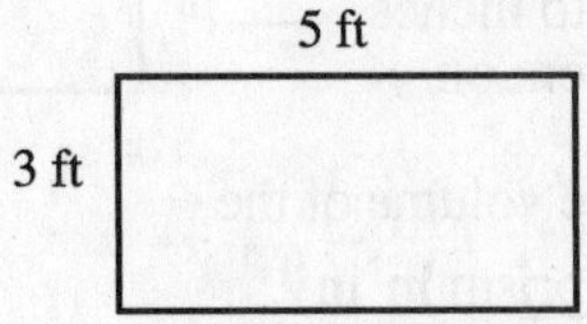

A = ____ ft^2

e) • Convert the sides of the rectangle in d) to inches and write them below.
• Calculate the area in in^2.

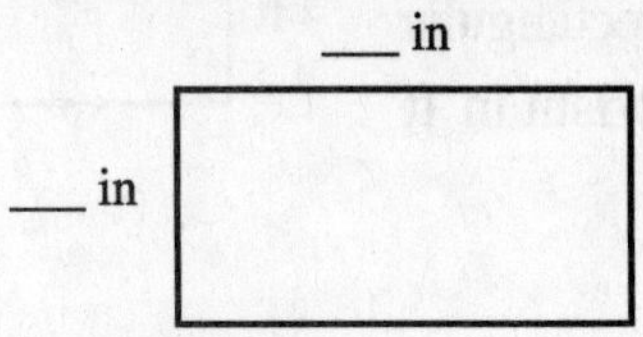

A = ___________ in^2

f) Use the ratios in c) to confirm the area of the rectangle in e) in in^2.

g) From the patterns in a) - f), we can see that to convert between units of area in the imperial system we follow the same process as in the metric system - we multiply/divide by the square of the corresponding linear conversion factor.

For example to convert from square yards to square feet we _________ by ___.

To convert from square inches to square feet we multiply by _____ or divide by _____.

Convert the following measurements.

a) 15 yd^2 to ft^2

b) 10 841 600 yd^2 to $mile^2$

c) 450 in^2 to $mile^2$ (Answer in scientific notation to 3 decimal places.)

Investigation #4

Conversions between Units of Volume in the Imperial System

a) Calculate the volume of the cube in ft^3.

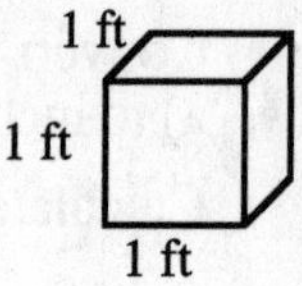

b) • Convert the sides of the cube in a) to inches and write them on the cube.
• Calculate the volume of the cube in in^3.

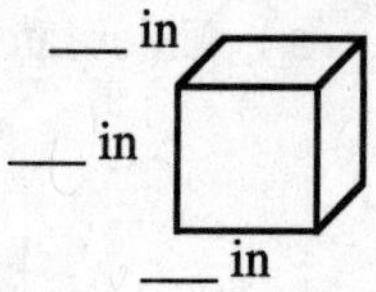

c) From a) and b) we can determine that $1\ ft^3$ = _____ in^3.

d) Calculate the volume of the rectangular prism in ft^3.

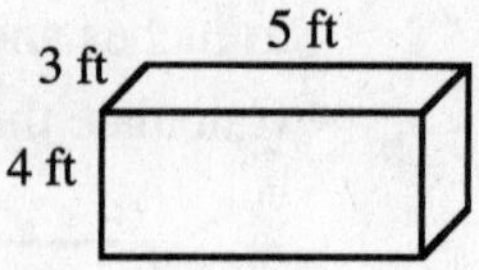

e) • Convert the sides of the rectangular prism in d) to inches. and write them on the diagram.
• Calculate the volume of the rectangular prism in in^3.

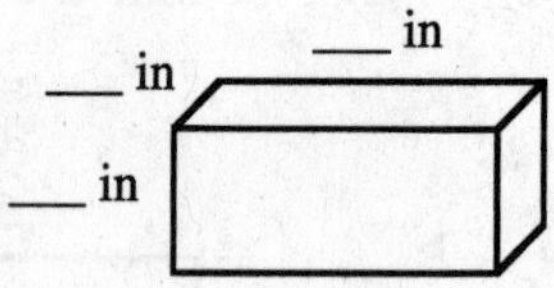

f) Use the ratios in c) to confirm the volume of the rectangular prism in e) in in^3.

g) From the patterns in a) - f), we can see that to convert between units of volume in the imperial system we follow the same process as in the metric system - we multiply/divide by the cube of the corresponding linear conversion factor.

For example, to convert from cubic yards to cubic inches we ____________ by ______.
To convert from cubic yards to cubic miles we divide by __________.

Convert the following measurements.

a) 233 280 in^3 = _______________ yd^3 **b)** 40.5 ft^3 = _______________ yd^3

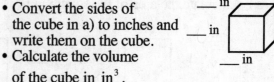

Convert 5 cubic miles into cubic inches. Answer in scientific notation to two decimal places.

Complete Assignment Questions #3 - #5

Class Ex. #6

A box in the shape of a rectangular prism measures 0.8 m by 0.6 m by 0.6 m. A second box measures 2.5 ft by 2 ft by 2 ft. Using the conversion 2.54 cm = 1 in,

a) determine, to the nearest cm^3, which box has the greater volume and by how much.

b) determine, to the nearest in^2, which box has the greater surface area and by how much.

Complete Assignment Questions #6 - #9

Assignment

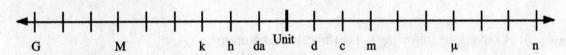

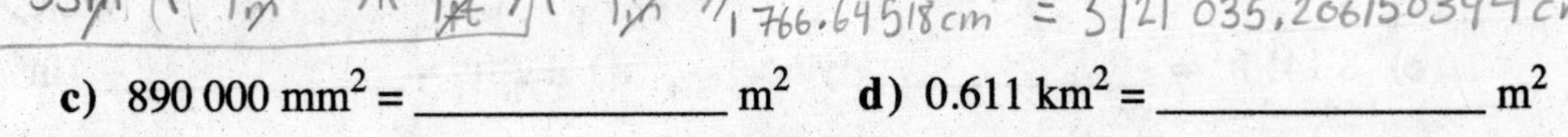

1. Convert the following to the indicated measurements.

57.9608ft **a)** $53 \text{ m}^2 =$ ______________ cm^2 **b)** $1326 \text{ mm}^2 =$ ______________ cm^2

5.5296in $53m^2\left(\left(\frac{1.0936ft}{1m}\right)\left(\frac{12in}{1ft}\right)\left(\frac{2.54cm}{1in}\right)\right)^2 = 1766.64518cm^2 = 3121035.206150394cm$

c) $890\,000 \text{ mm}^2 =$ ______________ m^2 **d)** $0.611 \text{ km}^2 =$ ______________ m^2

e) $78 \text{ cm}^3 =$ ______________ mm^3 **f)** $0.003\,58 \text{ cm}^2 =$ ______________ mm^2

$78cm^3 = \left(\frac{10mm}{1cm}\right)^3 = 780^3 = 474552000$

g) $92\,400 \text{ m}^3 =$ ______________ km^3 **h)** $0.07 \text{ m}^3 =$ ______________ mm^3

i) $415 \text{ cm}^3 =$ ______________ m^3 **j)** $415 \text{ m}^3 =$ ______________ cm^3

2. Convert the following to the indicated measurements. Answer in scientific notation.

a) $2.1\ m^2$ = ______________ km^2 **b)** $0.289\ km^2$ = ______________ cm^2

c) $7\ 450\ mm^2$ = ______________ m^2 **d)** $0.37\ km^3$ = ______________ m^3

e) $50\ 000\ Mm^2$ = ______________ Gm^2 **f)** $920\ mm^2$ = ______________ nm^2

g) $0.289\ km^2$ = ______________ Gm^2 **h)** $2.14 \times 10^4\ mm^2$ = ______________ μm^2

i) $560\ 000\ \mu m^3$ = ______________ mm^3 **j)** $780\ cm^3$ = ______________ dm^3

3. Convert the following to the indicated measurements.

a) $720\ in^2$ = ______________ ft^2 **b)** $0.5\ mi^2$ = ______________ yds^2

c) $8\ 145\ ft^2$ = ______________ yds^2 **d)** $4.2\ ft^2$ = ______________ in^2

e) $7\ mi^2$ = ______________ ft^2 **f)** $123\ 904\ yds^2$ = ______________ mi^2

g) $3.5\ yds^2$ = ______________ in^2 **h)** $1\ 944\ in^2$ = ______________ yds^2

4. Convert the following to the indicated measurements.

a) 7.1 ft^3 to in^3 **b)** 5.4 ft^3 to yds^3 **c)** 0.05 $miles^3$ to yds^3

d) 24 yds^3 to ft^3 **e)** 1123.2 in^3 to ft^3 **f)** 2 yds^3 to in^3

5. Convert the following to the indicated measurements. Answer in scientific notation to 2 decimal places.

a) 24.5 ft^2 to mi^2 **b)** 440 yds^3 to mi^3 **c)** 60 yds^2 to in^2

d) 24.5 ft^3 to yds^3 **e)** 78.9 in^3 to ft^3 **f)** 0.4 mi^2 to in^2

Use the Conversion Factor 2.54 cm = 1 in for the remainder of this assignment.

6. A rectangular mat measures 90 cm by 60 cm. Calculate, to the nearest whole number, the area of the mat in each of the following:

a) square centimetres **b)** square inches **c)** square feet

7. A storage container in the shape of a rectangular prism measures 4.8 m by 3 m by 2.5 m. A second storage container measures 15 ft by 12 ft by 7 ft.

a) Determine, to the nearest ft^3, which container has the greater volume, and by how much.

b) Determine, to the nearest cm^2, which container has the greater surface area, and by how much.

Use the following information to answer the next two questions.

A 2.5 km stretch of road is to be paved. The road is 14 m wide and is to be filled to a depth of 8 cm.

8. Determine, to the nearest cubic metre, the volume of material used in paving this road.

9. The material to be used to pave the road costs \$3.50 per ft^3. Using 1 in = 2.54 cm, determine the cost of paving material for this road to the nearest hundred dollars.

Answer Key

1. a) 530 000 **b)** 13.26 **c)** 0.89 **d)** 611 000 **e)** 78 000
f) 0.358 **g)** 0.000 092 4 **h)** 70 000 000 **i)** 0.000 415 **j)** 415 000 000

2. a) 2.1×10^{-6} **b)** 2.89×10^{9} **c)** 7.45×10^{-3} **d)** 3.7×10^{8} **e)** 5×10^{-2}
f) 9.2×10^{8} **g)** 2.89×10^{-13} **h)** 2.14×10^{10} **i)** 5.6×10^{-4} **j)** 7.8×10^{-1}

3. a) 5 **b)** 1 548 800 **c)** 905 **d)** 604.8
e) 195 148 800 **f)** 0.04 **g)** 4536 **h)** 1.5

4. a) 12 268.8 **b)** 0.2 **c)** 272 588 800 **d)** 648 **e)** 0.65 **f)** 93 312

5. a) 8.79×10^{-7} **b)** 8.07×10^{-8} **c)** 7.78×10^{4}
d) 9.07×10^{-1} **e)** 4.57×10^{-2} **f)** 1.61×10^{9}

6. a) 5400 cm^2 **b)** 837 in^2 **c)** 6 ft^2

7. a) Container 1 = 1271.3 ft^3, Container 2 = 1260 ft^3. Container 1 is greater by 11 ft^3.
b) Container 1 = 678 000 cm^2, Container 2 = 685 624 cm^2, Container 2 is greater by 7624 cm^2

8. 2800 m^3 **9.** \$346 100

Measurement Lesson #7:
Surface Area and Volume of Prisms and Cylinders

Right Prism

In geometry, a **prism** is a three-dimensional object which has two bases or ends that have the same size and shape and are parallel to one another, and each of whose sides is a parallelogram.

In this course, we study **right prisms**, a specific category of prisms. A **right prism** is a prism whose sides are rectangles.

The following diagrams illustrate types of right prisms which are studied in this lesson.

The bases or ends of the prisms below are at the top and bottom of each diagram.

Right Triangular Prism

A right triangular prism has two triangular ends and three rectangular sides.

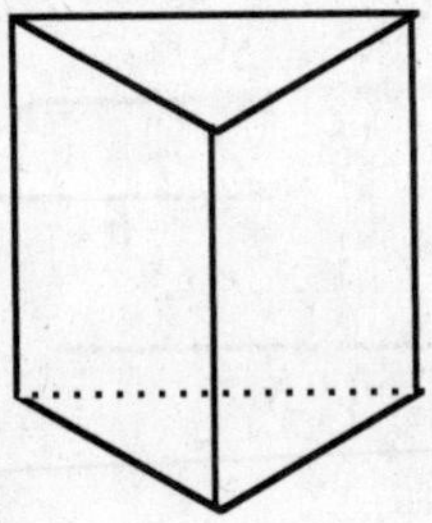

Right Rectangular Prism

A right rectangular prism has two rectangular ends and four rectangular sides.

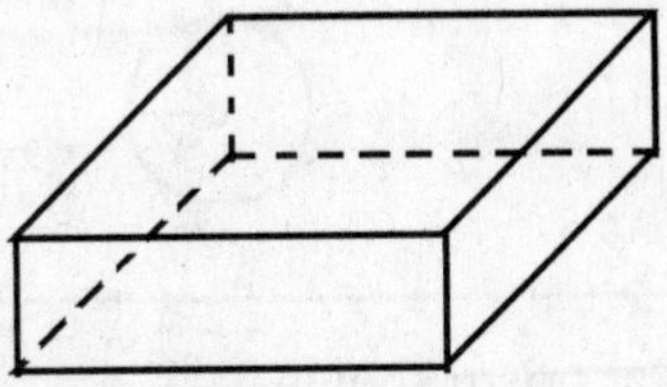

Cube

A cube is a right prism with two square ends and four square sides resulting in six square faces.

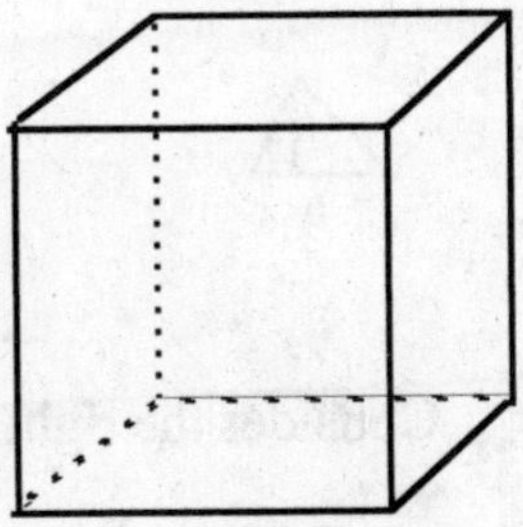

Recall the following Formulas from earlier math courses.

<u>Volume of Prism</u>

Volume = the area of the base of prism × height.

$V_{Prism} = A_{Base} \times h$

<u>Surface Area of Prism</u>

Add the areas of all the surfaces (faces) of the prism.

Formulas

The base of the right prism could be any one of a variety of shapes. Recall the following formulas from earlier math courses which may be useful in this lesson.

Perimeter (one dimensional)

- General → Calculate the distance around the figure.

- For a **circle**: $C = \pi d$ or $C = 2\pi r$

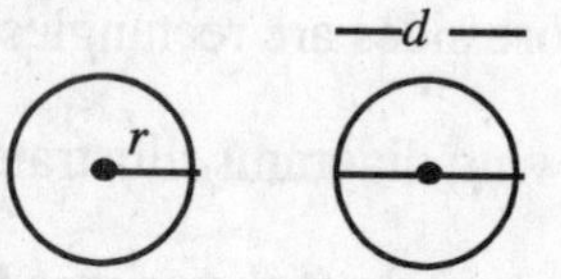

Area (two dimensional)

- $A_{Rectangle} = bh$

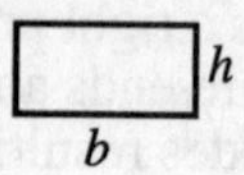

- $A_{Square} = s^2$

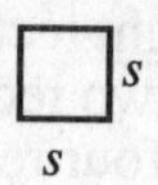

- $A_{Parallelogram} = bh$

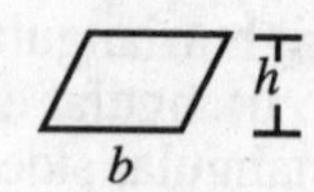

- $A_{Triangle} = \frac{1}{2}bh$ or $\frac{bh}{2}$

- $A_{Circle} = \pi r^2$

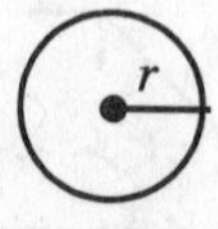

- $A_{Trapezoid} = \frac{1}{2}h(a + b)$

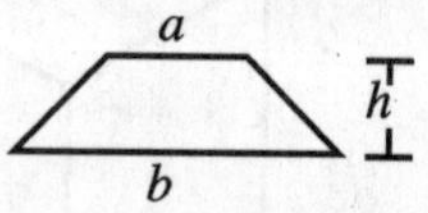

Consider the right triangular prism shown.

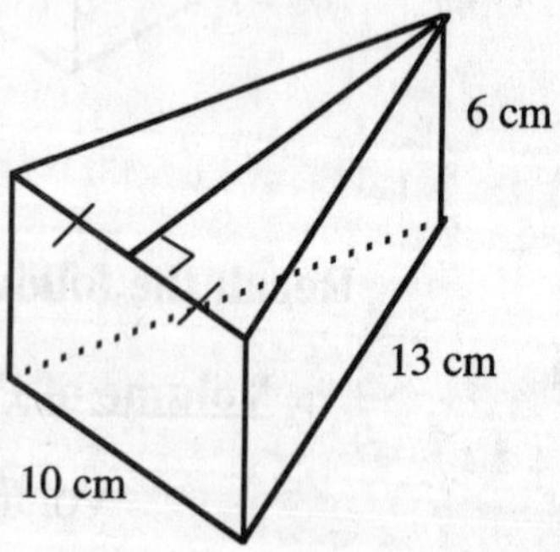

a) Determine the area of the base of the prism.

b) Determine the volume of the prism.

c) Determine the surface area of the prism.

- The table below shows the common units used in the metric system and in the imperial system for volumes of solids and liquids.

Volume	**Solid**	**Liquid**
Metric	cm^3, m^3, km^3, etc.	litres (L), millilitres (mL), etc.
Imperial	in^3, ft^3, yds^3, etc.	gallons, pints, etc.

Conversions: $1\ cm^3 = 1$ mL

1000 mL = 1 L

1 US gallon = 3.7854 L

1 imperial gallon (UK) = 4.5461 L

1 gallon = 8 pints

- ml can also be used as an abbreviation for millilitre.

Receptacle Inc. is a manufacturing company that makes containers of various sizes from materials such as corrugated cardboard, metal, glass, plexiglass, or plastic. Two companies ask Receptacle Inc. to produce containers of the same size in the shape of right rectangular prisms.

Cubical Ltd. needs a plastic container 15 cm long, 10 cm deep, and 8 cm high in which to pack their 1 cm sponge cubes that they sell to elementary school educators.
Waterworld Aquariums Inc. needs small glass aquariums with the same dimensions in which to keep their Samurai Fighting Fish.

a) Calculate the volume of the container for Cubical Ltd. Is the cm^3 unit an appropriate unit to represent the volume of their container?

b) The small glass aquariums for Waterworld Aquariums Inc. will be filled with water. The volume, or capacity, of the aquariums is given in litres or US gallons. Determine the capacity of a glass aquarium in both litres and US gallons to two decimal places.

Complete Assignment Questions #1 - #3

Surface Area and Volume of a Right Cylinder

A right cylinder is similar to a right prism in that it also has bases or ends which are parallel, congruent, and aligned directly above each other.
The volume and surface area of a right cylinder have been studied in previous math courses. The net of the cylinder shown below can be used to develop the formula for the surface area of a right cylinder with radius r and height h.

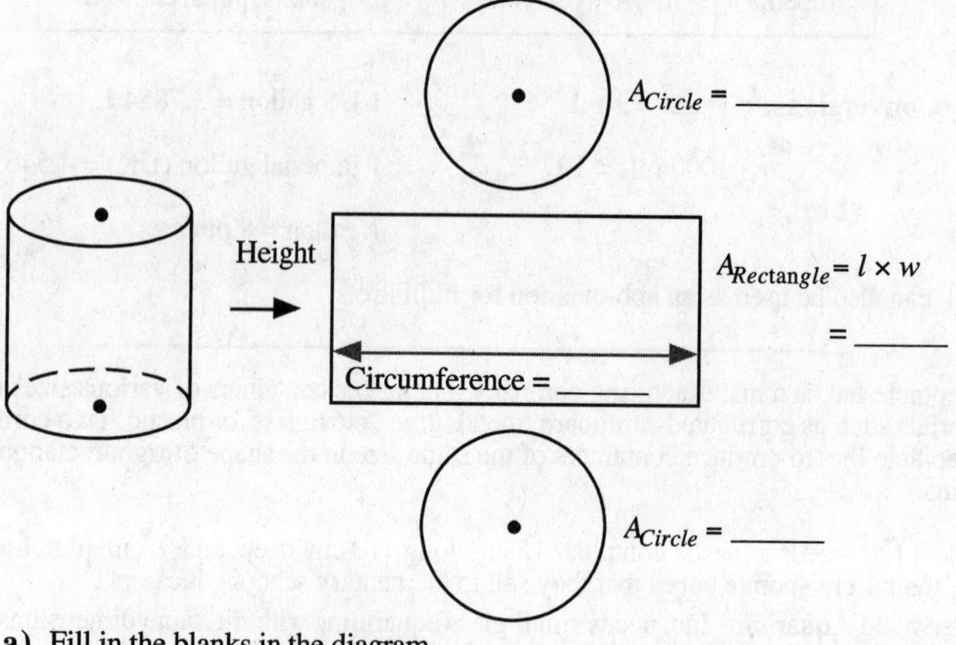

a) Fill in the blanks in the diagram.

b) Use the diagram to demonstrate that the formula for the surface area of a cylinder is $SA_{Cylinder} = 2\pi r^2 + 2\pi rh$.

c) Use the general formula for the volume of a right prism to develop the specific formula for the volume of a cylinder with radius r and height h.

Formulas for Surface Area and Volume of a Cylinder

<u>**Surface Area**</u> (three dimensional)

$$SA_{Cylinder} = 2 \times \text{area of a circle} + \text{area of a rectangle}$$

or $$SA_{Cylinder} = 2\pi r^2 + 2\pi rh \text{ or } 2\pi r(r + h)$$

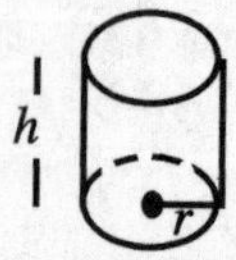

<u>**Volume**</u>

$$V_{Cylinder} = A_{Base} \times h \Rightarrow V_{Cylinder} = \pi r^2 h$$

Class Ex. #3

Calculate the volume and surface area of a cylindrical can whose height is 15.4 cm and whose base diameter is 10.2 cm. Write your answer correct to one decimal place.

Solving for a Measurement Given the Volume

Class Ex. #4

a) A commercial garbage bin in the shape of a cube has a volume of 60.24 m^3. Determine the dimensions of the garbage bin to the nearest cm.

b) The box for a Toblerone chocolate bar is in the shape of a triangular prism. The triangular faces have a base of 3.7 cm and a height of 3.2 cm.

If the space in the empty box has a volume of 123.7 cm^3, determine the length of the box to the nearest tenth of a cm.

Class Ex. #5

A poster company has decided that all of its posters will be shipped in cylindrical containers with a height of 17 inches and a circumference of 2 inches. The curved surface area of the container will be wrapped with a paper label containing the company logo.

Calculate, to the nearest square inch, the curved surface area wrapping of the container.

Complete Assignment Questions #4 - #15

Assignment

1. Convert the following volumes to the indicated unit. Answer to the nearest thousandth where necessary.

a) 1 049 cm^3 to litres **b)** 4.7 litres to cm^3 **c)** 686.5 m^3 to litres

d) 20 000 litres to m^3 **e)** 75 US gallons to litres **f)** 901 litres to UK gallons

$2\ m^3$

$75\ gal\left(\frac{3.785\ L}{1\ gal}\right) = 283.875L$

2. Calculate the surface area and volume of each right prism. Round off to the nearest tenth where necessary.

	Surface Area	Volume

a)

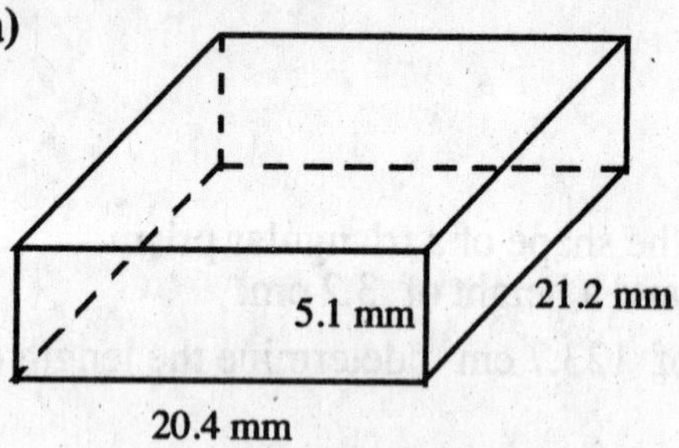

b)

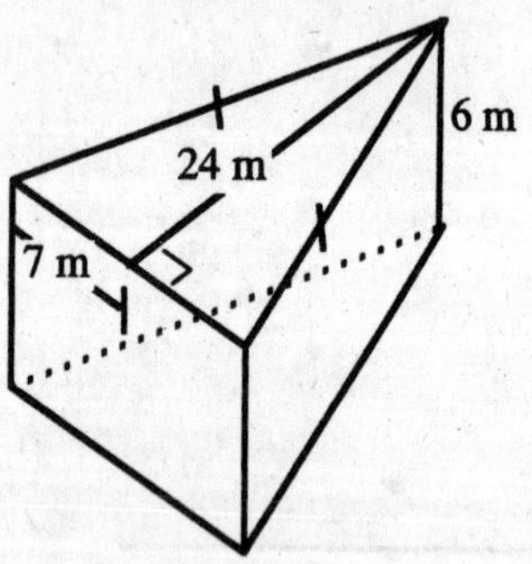

c)

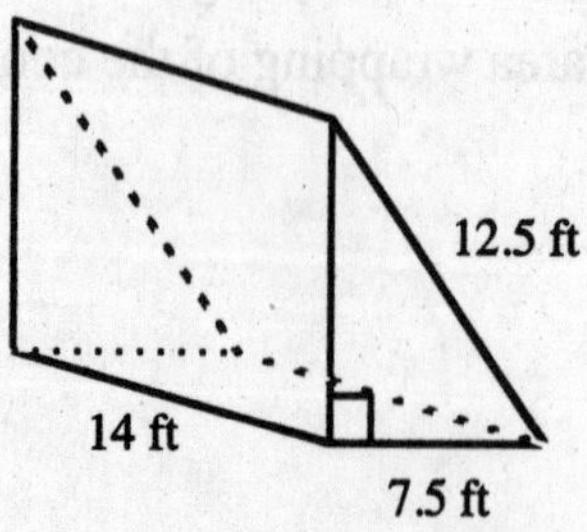

3. A cross section of the water in a swimming pool is shown.

a) Calculate the area of the cross section.

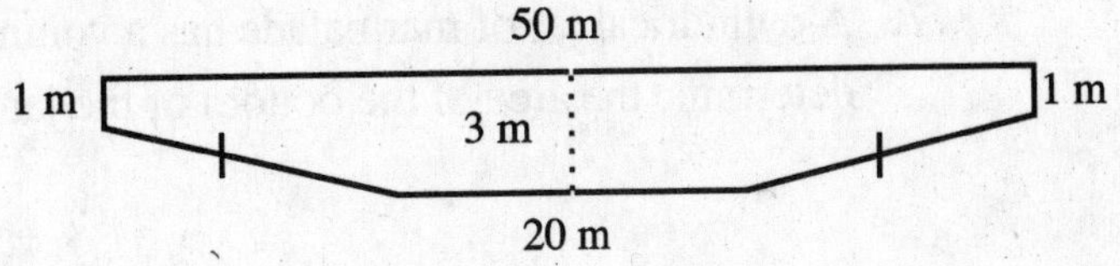

b) Determine the number of litres of water in the pool if the pool is 25 metres wide.

4. Calculate the volume and surface area of the cylinder shown. Answer in appropriate units to the nearest tenth.

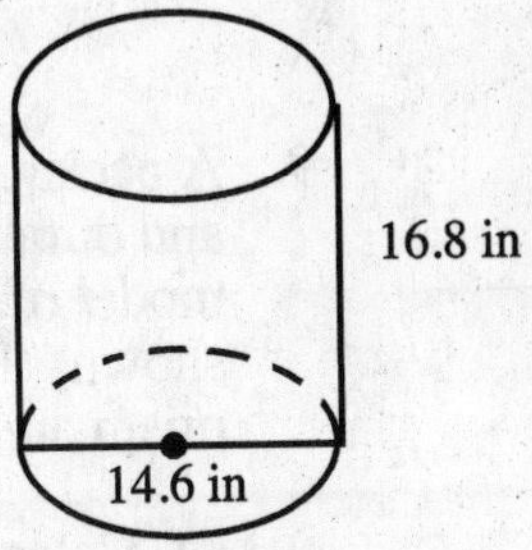

5. Some types of liquid chemical waste are stored in metal drums (barrels) which have a diameter of 56 cm and a height of 84 cm.

a) Determine the volume of the drum to the nearest tenth of a litre.

b) Determine the volume of the drum in US gallons (to the nearest tenth).

c) The exterior of the drum, except the base, is to be painted blue. Calculate how many litres of paint will be needed to paint 400 drums if one litre of paint covers 8.8 m^2. Answer to the nearest tenth of a litre.

6. A cube has a volume of 0.512 litres. Determine the length of each side of the cube in cm.

7. A cylindrical jar of marmalade has a volume of 528 cm^3. If the height of the jar is 5.3 cm, determine the area of the bottom of the jar to the nearest tenth of a cm^2.

8. A cylindrical pop can has a volume of 355 mL. Determine, to the nearest 0.1 cm, the diameter of the can if the height is 12.0 cm.

9. A packaging company is advertising the strength and durability of their boxes. A sketch of the model of the logo used by the box company is shown. The outer dimensions of the rectangular prism are marked in the diagram.

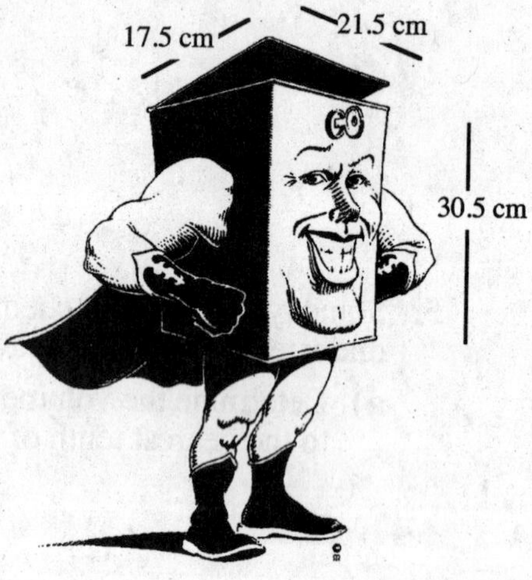

a) Calculate the volume of the interior of the box, to the nearest 0.1 cm^3, if the thickness of the box is 1.5 cm.

b) All the outside surfaces of the box (except the front) and the inside of the lid are to be painted black. If the diameter of each shoulder coming out of the box is 7 cm, and the radius of each thigh coming out of the box is 3 cm, determine, to the nearest cm^2, the surface area of the box to be painted.

10. A pup tent in the shape of a triangular prism has a triangular entrance with an area of $16\ \text{ft}^2$. If the space in the tent has a volume of $8.15\ \text{m}^3$, determine the length of the tent to the nearest foot.

Multiple Choice **11.** Yin cuts out the lid from a cylindrical can containing fruit cocktail. To correctly calculate the surface area of the can without the top lid, she could use the formula:

A. $2\pi r^2 + 2\pi rh$ **B.** $\pi r^2 + 2\pi rh$ **C.** $\pi r^2 + \pi rh$ **D.** $2\pi r(r + h)$

Use the following information to answer the next three questions.

The Isuzu NQR truck shown is used to transport gravel to construction sites.

The box is a rectangular prism 11 ft long, 7 ft wide and 4 ft high. The box does not have a top. The gravel is covered with a tarp when filled.

Multiple Choice **12.** The volume of gravel that the truck can transport is

A. $0.03\ \text{m}^3$

B. $8.7\ \text{m}^3$

C. $20.5\ \text{m}^3$

D. $308.0\ \text{m}^3$

Numerical Response **13.** Before the box is attached to the truck, all the inside and outside faces of the box are to be coated with a primer.

The amount of primer, to the nearest $0.1\ \text{m}^2$, required to coat the box is _____ .

(Record your answer in the numerical response box from left to right)

14. Isuzu designers are working on a new truck which will be able to haul 10 m^3 of gravel. The designers have decided that only the height of the box will change. The new height of the box can be written in the form a feet and b inches, to the nearest inch. The value of $a + b$ is _____ .

(Record your answer in the numerical response box from left to right)

15. While on vacation in England, Bob went to a local store and bought a pint of milk. To the nearest ml, the number of ml in a pint is _____ .

(Record your answer in the numerical response box from left to right)

Answer Key

1. a) 1.049 L **b)** 4700 cm^3 **c)** 686 500 L **d)** 20 m^3 **e)** 283.905 L **f)** 198.192 UK gal

2. a) 1289.3 mm^2, 2205.6 mm^3 **b)** 720 m^2, 1008 m^3 **c)** 495 ft^2, 525 ft^3

3. a) 120 m^2 **b)** 3 000 000 L **4.** 2812.6 in^3, 1105.4 in^2

5. a) 206.9 L **b)** 54.7 US gal **c)** 78.4 L

6. 8 cm **7.** 99.6 cm^2 **8.** 6.1 cm

9. a) $7\ 376.9\text{ cm}^3$ **b)** 2718 cm^2 **10.** 18 ft **11.** B **12.** B

13.

4	1	.	1

14.

1	1		

15.

5	6	8	

Measurement Lesson #8:
Surface Area and Volume of Pyramids and Cones

Right Pyramid

A right pyramid is a pyramid whose sides are triangles and which has its apex (the vertex at the tip of the pyramid) aligned directly over the centre of the base. The base is a regular polygon.

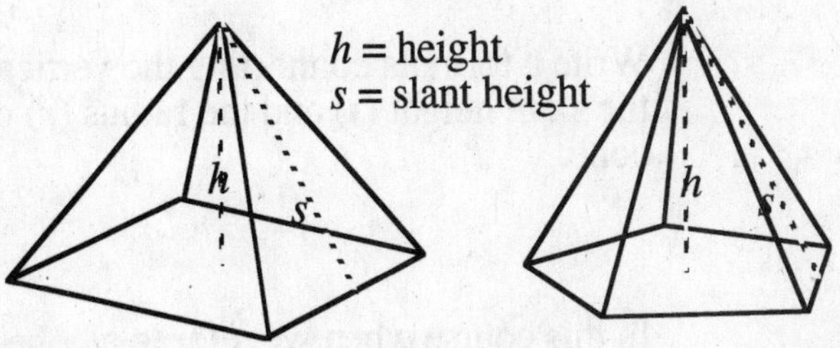

Volume of a Right Pyramid

Ruby designed a right prism and right pyramid out of cardboard for her grade eight volume assignment. The right pyramid had an identical base and the same height as the prism.

Max, her little brother, took the right prism and right pyramid from her room and played with them in a sandbox. He filled the pyramid with sand and emptied the sand into the prism. He continued to do this until the prism was full of sand. He repeated the whole process and discovered that each time he could fill the prism with three pyramids of sand.

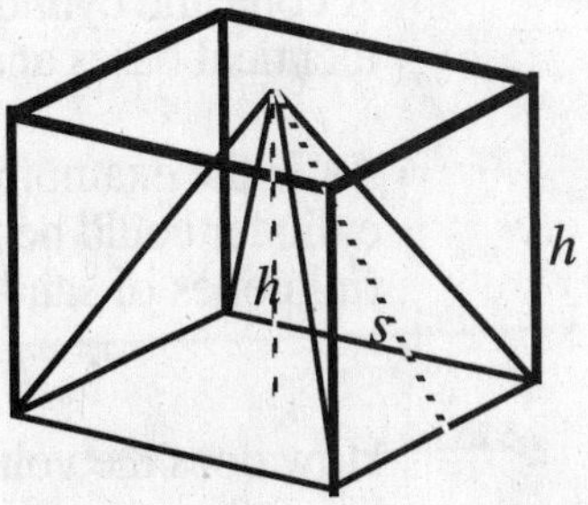

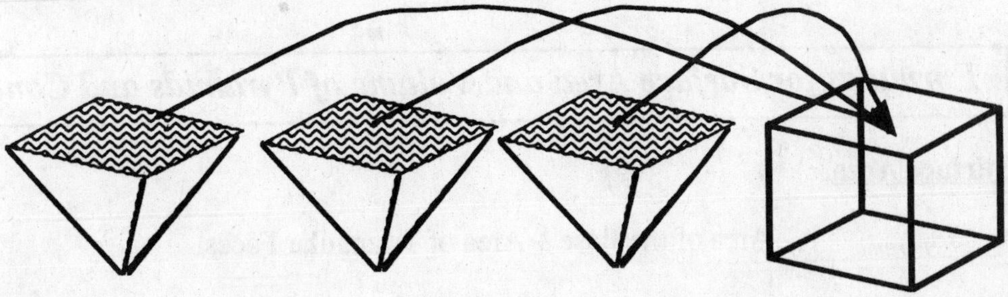

How does the volume of a pyramid compare to the volume of a prism with identical base and height?

In this course when we refer to a pyramid we will be referring to a right pyramid.

Right Circular Cone

A right circular cone has a circular base and has its vertex directly above the centre of its base.

Write a formula connecting the vertical height (h), the slant height (s) and the radius (r) of a right circular cone.

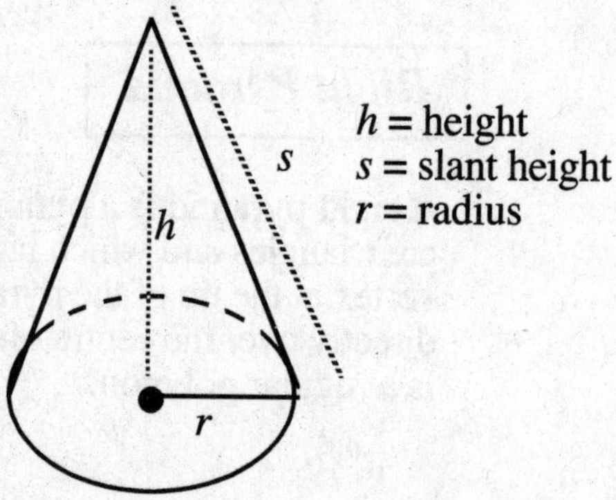

In this course when we refer to a cone we will be referring to a right circular cone.

Volume of a Right Circular Cone

A cone and cylinder were constructed with identical bases and the same height.

As in the example on the previous page the cylinder could be filled exactly with three full cones of sand.

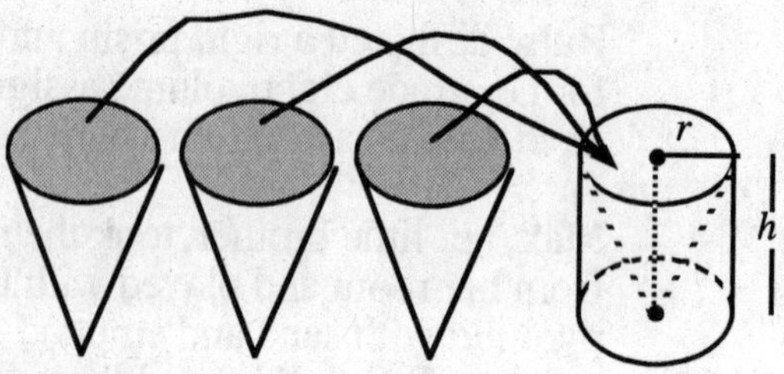

How does the volume of a cone compare to the volume of a cylinder with identical base and height?

Formulas for Surface Area and Volume of Pyramids and Cones

Surface Area

$SA_{Pyramid}$ = Area of the Base + Area of Triangular Faces.

SA_{Cone} = Area of the Base + Area of Curved Surface.

$= \pi r^2 + \pi rs$

Note that the proof of the formula for the curved surface area of a cone involves calculus which is beyond the scope of this course.

Volume

$V_{Pyramid} = \frac{1}{3}$ Volume of prism $= \frac{1}{3}Ah$

$V_{Cone} = \frac{1}{3}$ Volume of cylinder $= \frac{1}{3}\pi r^2 h$

The Great Pyramid of Giza is considered to be one of the Seven Wonders of the Ancient World. It is approximately 147 metres tall, and has a square base with sides measuring approximately 440 metres.

a) Make a sketch of the pyramid and calculate the volume to the nearest cubic metre.

b) Make a sketch of the net of the pyramid and calculate the surface area to the nearest square metre. Explain why the base is not included in the calculation of the surface area.

A cone shaped container has a height of 15 cm and a base diameter of 16 cm. Determine the volume and surface area of the container to one decimal place.

Complete Assignment Questions #1 - #8

A right pyramid has a height of 20 cm and a hexagonal base with sides measuring 10 cm .

a) Make a sketch of the hexagonal base, and determine its area as an exact value and to the nearest cm^2.

b) The pyramid is filled with water. Determine the volume of water to the nearest ml.

Class Ex. #4

Use the following information to answer Class Ex. #4.

Problem 1: Two cones have radii of equal length. The first cone has a height of 5 cm and a volume of 10 cm^3. State the volume of the second cone if its height is 20 cm.

Problem 2: Two cones have the same height. The first cone has a radius of 5 cm and a volume of 10 cm^3. State the volume of the second cone if its radius is 20 cm.

a) Explain how Problem 1 can be solved using mental math. State the answer.

b) Explain how Problem 2 can be solved using mental math. State the answer.

Complete Assignment Questions #9 - #16

Assignment

1. a) A cylinder has a volume of 27 ft^3. State the volume of a cone that just fits inside the cylinder.

b) A cone has a volume of 6 m^3. State the volume of a cylinder that just holds the pyramid.

c) A rectangular prism has a volume of 300 in^3. State the volume of a rectangular pyramid that just fits inside the prism.

d) An octagonal right pyramid has a volume of 39 mm^3. State the volume of an octagonal right prism that just holds the pyramid.

2. In each of the following make a sketch of the figure and calculate the volume to the nearest whole number.

a) a cone with base radius 8 mm and height 10 mm

b) a square based pyramid with side 18 cm and height 12 cm

c) a cone with base diameter 12 ft and slant height 10 ft

d) a cone with slant height 51 in and vertical height 45 in

e) a triangular based pyramid with base area 35 m^2 and height 8.4 m

3. Calculate the surface area of the figures in #1 a) -c) above. Answer to the nearest whole number.

a)

b)

c)

4. Consider the rectangular based pyramid shown.

a) Draw the net of the pyramid marking all the given measurements on the net.

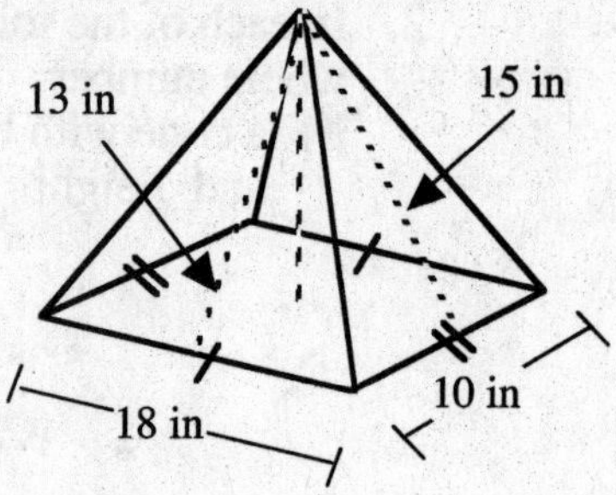

b) Determine the surface area of the pyramid.

c) Calculate the height of the pyramid and hence the volume of the pyramid.

5. Determine the volume and surface areas of each cone. Answer to one decimal place.

a)

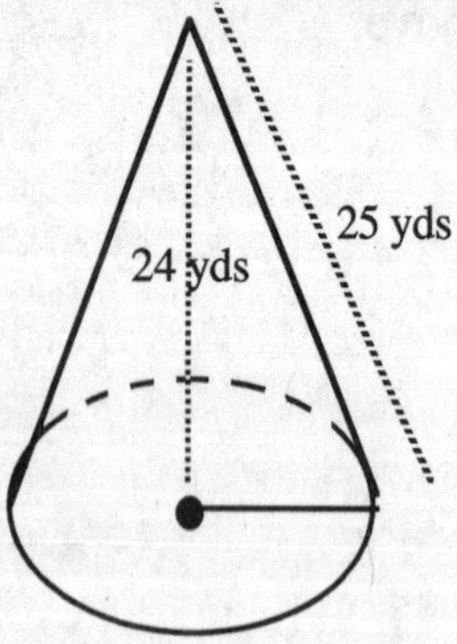

b)

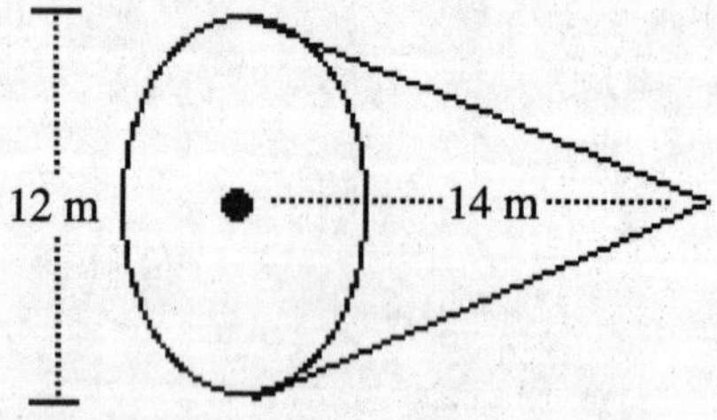

6. Cups Incorporated is a firm which makes conical paper cups for water dispensers. One of the paper cups it makes has a diameter of 6 cm, a height of 7 cm and no base.

a) Determine the slant height of a paper cup to the nearest 0.1 cm.

b) To the nearest whole number, how many ml of water will a paper cup hold?

c) Determine how much paper is required, to the nearest square cm, to make a cup.

7. Jane constructs a cube with interior edges of 9 cm.

a) Determine the volume of the largest possible pyramid which will just fit inside the cube.

b) Determine, to the nearest cubic centimetre, the volume of the largest possible cylinder which will just fit inside the cube.

c) Determine, to the nearest cubic centimetre, the volume of the largest possible cone which will just fit inside the cube.

8. The largest pyramid by volume ever built is the Great Pyramid of Chohula in Mexico. It has a base 450 m by 450 m and a height of 66 m. Determine the volume of the pyramid in cubic metres.

9. One of the Great Pyramids in Egypt has a volume of 2 570 000 m^3 and a height of 147 m. The pyramid has a square base. Determine the length of each side of the base to the nearest metre.

10. Determine the exact volume and surface area of a right pyramid with a height of $\sqrt{3}$ feet and a hexagonal base with six sides of 2 feet.

11. In 1989 a glass pyramid expansion was built at the entrance to the Louvre Museum in Paris. The largest pyramid has a height of 70 ft and a square base with sides of 115 ft. The pyramid consists of 603 rhombus shaped and 70 triangular shaped glass segments. The base of the pyramid is not glass.

The Muttart Conservatory in Edmonton consists of four square based pyramids. One of these pyramids has a side length of 19.5 m and a height of 18.0 m.

a) To the nearest hundred square feet, how many square feet of glass is in the pyramid at the Louvre?

b) How many times as great as the volume of the pyramid in Edmonton is the volume of the pyramid at the Louvre. Answer to the nearest tenth.

12. Gravel is dropped from a conveyer belt on to the ground. It forms a pile of gravel in the shape of a cone. The diameter of the gravel pile is 23.0 ft and the height is 9.2 ft. What is the volume of the gravel pile to the nearest 0.01 m^3?

Multiple Choice

13. A square based pyramid has each side length doubled but the height remains the same. The volume of the original pyramid is what fraction of the volume of the new pyramid?

A. $\frac{1}{2}$ **B.** $\frac{1}{3}$ **C.** $\frac{1}{4}$ **D.** $\frac{1}{12}$

14. A cone has its radius doubled and its height halved. Which statement is correct?

A. The volume of the new cone is the same as the volume of the original cone.
B. The volume of the new cone is twice the volume of the original cone.
C. The volume of the new cone is four times the volume of the original cone.
D. None of the above statements is correct.

Numerical Response

15. An engineer at a grain elevator is constructing a cone shaped storage unit which has a base radius of 10 m and is to hold 3800 m^3 of grain. The height of the storage unit, to the nearest tenth of a metre, is _____.

(Record your answer in the numerical response box from left to right)

16. A rectangular based pyramid has a base length of 5 ft and a height of 12 ft. It has a volume of 160 ft^3. The base width of the pyramid, to the nearest centimetre, is _____ .

(Record your answer in the numerical response box from left to right)

Answer Key

1. **a)** 9 ft^3 **b)** 18 m^3 **c)** 100 in^3 **d)** 117 mm^3

2. **a)** 670 mm^3 **b)** 1296 cm^3 **c)** 302 ft^3 **d)** 27 143 in^3 **e)** 98 m^3

3. **a)** 523 mm^2 **b)** 864 cm^2 **c)** 302 ft^2

4. **b)** 564 in^2 **c)** height = 12 in volume = 720 in^3

5. **a)** volume = 1231.5 yd^3 surface area = 703.7 yd^2 **b)** volume = 527.8 m^3 surface area = 400.2 m^2

6. **a)** 7.6 cm **b)** 66 ml **c)** 72 cm^2

7. **a)** 243 cm^3 **b)** 573 cm^3 **c)** 191 cm^3

8. 4 455 000 m^3 **9.** 229 m **10.** volume = 6 ft^3 surface area = $6\sqrt{6} + 6\sqrt{3}$ ft^2

11. **a)** 20 800 ft^2 **b)** 3.8 times **12.** 36.08 m^3 **13.** C **14.** B

15.

3	6	.	3

16.

2	4	4	

Measurement Lesson #9:
Surface Area and Volume of Spheres

Volume of a Sphere

Gary, a high school student, used the method of displacement to determine the volume of a sphere. He used a cylinder and a sphere (ball) with the same height and diameter. First Gary completely filled a cylinder with 375 ml of water and placed it on an overflow container. Then he pushed a ball into the cylinder and allowed the water to overflow. Finally he measured the volume of water in the overflow container and the volume of water left in the cylinder. He determined after three trials that the volume of the water in the overflow container was 250 ml and the volume of water in the cylinder was 125 ml.

Gary concluded the following:

- The volume of water in the overflow container is the same as the volume of the ball.
- The volume of the water in the overflow container is $\frac{2}{3}$ of the volume of the cylinder.
- The volume of the ball (sphere) is $\frac{2}{3}$ of the volume of the cylinder.
- The volume of water left in the cylinder was $\frac{1}{3}$ of the original volume.

a) Verify Gary's results by conducting your own trials.

- Gary then tried to determine a formula for the volume of a sphere in terms of its radius *r*.

b) First he considered a sphere and a cylinder both with a radius of 5 cm.

i) Mark the radius of the sphere and cylinder on the diagram and explain why the height of the cylinder is 10 cm.

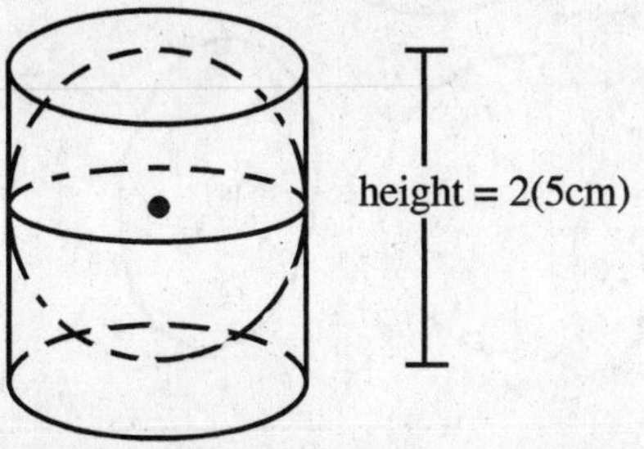

ii) Gary determined the volume of a sphere to the nearest tenth using the formula for the volume of a cylinder. Complete his work.

$V_{sphere} = \frac{2}{3} V_{cylinder}$

$= \frac{2}{3}\pi r^2 h$

and $h = 2(5) = 10$

$= \frac{2}{3}\pi(\quad)^2(10)$

$= \frac{4}{3}\pi(\quad)^3 =$

c) Secondly, he considered a sphere and a cylinder both with a radius of r.

i) Mark the radius of the sphere and cylinder on the diagram and explain why the height of the cylinder is $2r$.

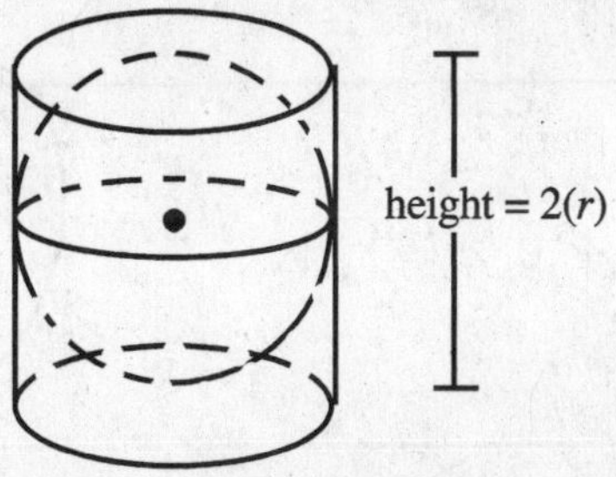

ii) Using the formula for the volume of a cylinder, complete Gary's work to find the volume of a sphere.

$V_{sphere} = \frac{2}{3} V_{cylinder}$

$= \frac{2}{3}\pi r^2 h$

and $h = 2(r)$

$= \frac{2}{3}\pi(\quad)^2(2r)$

$=$

Formulas for Surface Area and Volume of a Sphere

The following formulas are for the surface area and volume of the sphere.

- $SA_{Sphere} = 4\pi r^2$ • $V_{Sphere} = \frac{4}{3}\pi r^3$

Note that the proof of the formula for the surface area of a sphere involves calculus which is beyond the scope of this course.

Surface Area and Volume of a Hemisphere

- Whereas the term **semi-circle** is used to describe half of a circle, the term **hemisphere** is used to describe half of a sphere.
- When considering the surface area of a hemisphere, you may need to include the **circular base plus half the sphere**.

The illustrations below show a sphere cut in half.

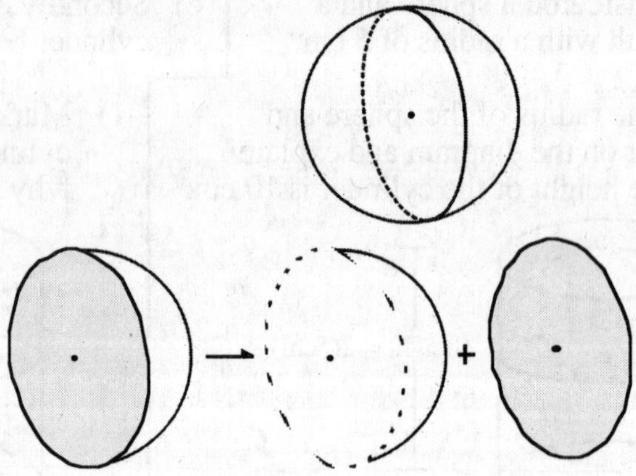

Complete the following:

a) The volume of a hemisphere is ________

b) The surface area of a hemisphere = curved surface area + area of circular base

= ____________ + ___________ = $3\pi r^2$

c) The surface area of a hemisphere = ________ if the base is **not** included.

Note that the surface area of a hemisphere will include the base unless it is specifically excluded in the question or by the context of the question.

Class Ex. #2

The shape of the planet Pluto is approximately that of a sphere with a diameter of about 2302 km.

a) Calculate the surface area of Pluto. Express the answer in scientific notation to the nearest tenth.

b) Calculate the volume of Pluto. Express the answer in scientific notation to the nearest tenth.

Class Ex. #3

Candy used a rope to wrap the outer edge of a beach ball exactly once. She then measured the distance the rope wrapped around the ball by stretching it out straight and using a ruler to measure its length. She determined the length to be 108 cm.

Determine the volume of the beach ball to the nearest 0.1 cm^3.

Class Ex. #4

Dana and Don are constructing dome tents in the shape of hemispheres. Dana's tent has a diameter of 4π and will have a base made of the same material as the dome. Don's tent also has a diameter of 4π but he has chosen not to construct a base for the tent.

a) Calculate, in terms of π, how much material Dana needs to make her tent.

b) Calculate, in terms of π, how much material Don needs to make his tent.

Class Ex. #5

The volume of a basketball is 433.5 inches^3.
Determine the radius of the basketball to the nearest cm.

Complete Assignment Questions #1 - #16

Assignment

1. Calculate the following to the nearest tenth:

a) the surface area of a soccer ball with a diameter of 21 cm

b) the volume of a spherical ornament with a radius of 12 in

c) the volume and surface area of the earth, in scientific notation, if the shape of the earth is spherical and the diameter of the earth is about 12 756 km

d) the volume and surface area of a hemisphere of radius 4.2 ft

2. The diagram is a sketch of a roll-on deodorant. It consists of a cylindrical container into which a ball is placed as shown. Liquid deodorant completely fills the space below the ball.

Calculate, to the nearest ml, the volume of liquid deodorant in the container.

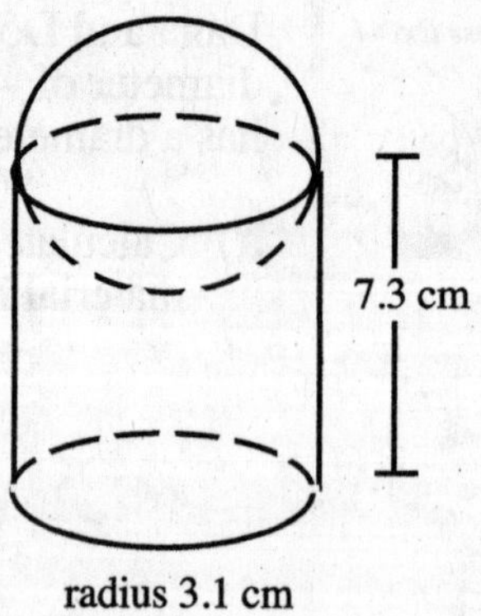

3. a) Solve the equation $V = \frac{4}{3}\pi r^3$ for r.

Write the answer as a radical and as a power.

b) The volume of a beach ball is 50 965 cm^3.

Calculate the radius to the nearest tenth of a cm.

4. A model of a mercury thermometer consists of a spherical base and a cylindrical portion with a hemispherical top.

Use the dimensions shown in the diagram to answer the following questions to the nearest hundredth.
The diagram is not drawn to scale.

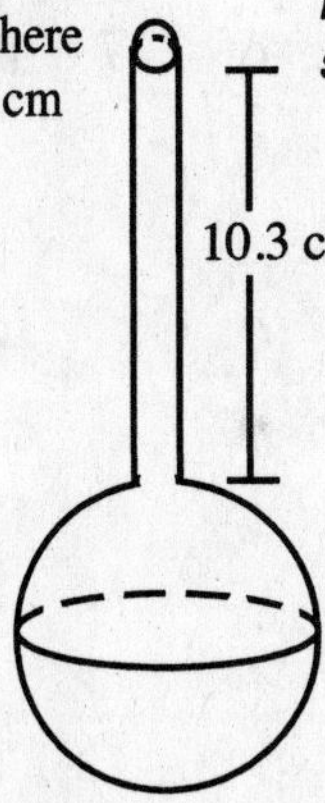

a) Determine the volume of the space inside the thermometer.

b) The thermometer is made of glass. Determine the surface area of glass required to make the thermometer. Assume that the missing glass in the sphere is equal in surface area to the base of the cylinder.

5. Ben designs a pencil case in the shape of a hemisphere and plans to make 500 pencil cases. The cost of the fabric is four cents per hundred square centimetres and the zippers cost five cents each. Each pencil case has one zipper and the insertion of the zipper does not affect the amount of fabric needed for each pencil case.
The diameter of the case is 20 cm.

a) Calculate the surface area of each case to one decimal place.

b) How much will it cost to make 500 pencil cases?

6. The planet Jupiter can be considered as a sphere with an approximate volume of 1.53×10^{15} km^3. Use the information to determine the surface area of Jupiter. Answer in scientific notation to the nearest hundredth.

7. Determine the volume of a size 7 basketball which has a surface area of 277.6 in^2. Write your answer to the nearest tenth.

8. Carlos is to receive an award for being the top goal scorer in a local soccer league. The award is a silver miniature soccer ball. The silver ball is packaged in a cubic container which is just large enough to contain the ball. The volume of the container is 1728 cm^3.

a) Calculate the surface area of the miniature silver ball, to the nearest cm^2.

b) Once the ball is placed inside the cube, bubble wrap is added to the container to prevent damage in transit. The bubble wrap occupies 80% of the remaining space inside the cube. Determine the volume of bubble wrap used to the nearest cm^3.

Multiple Choice

9. Chocolate Rules Ice Cream Company makes a spherical scoop of ice cream with a volume of 65 ml. What diameter of cone would best fit the scoop of ice cream?

A. 2.5 cm
B. 4 cm
C. 5 cm
D. 6 cm

10. The surface area of a sphere is 255 m^2. Its diameter to the nearest tenth of a metre is

A. 28.3
B. 14.2
C. 9.0
D. 4.5

11. A sphere has a radius of 15 mm. The volume of the sphere, in mm^3, is

A. 225π
B. 900π
C. 4500π
D. 14137π

Numerical Response **12.** A cylindrical jar has diameter 7 cm and contains water to the depth of 5 cm. A sphere of diameter 3 cm is dropped into the jar and sinks to the bottom. The water depth, to the nearest tenth of a centimetre, is now _____.
(Record your answer in the numerical response box from left to right)

Use the following information to answer question #13.

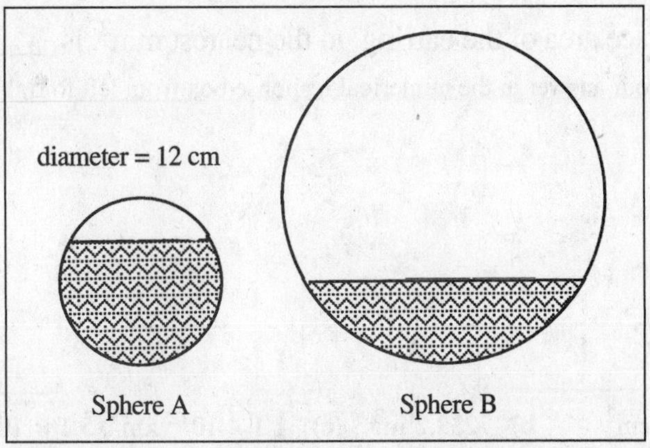

13. Sphere A is 80% full of water and Sphere B is 20% full of water. If both spheres contain an equal volume of water, the diameter of Sphere B, to the nearest tenth of a centimetre, is _____.
(Record your answer in the numerical response box from left to right)

14. A boiler is in the shape of a cylinder with hemispherical ends. Its total length is 14 m and its diameter is 6 m. Its cubic content, to the nearest m^3, is _____ .

(Record your answer in the numerical response box from left to right)

Use the following information to answer questions #15 and #16.

> A solid gold earring has the shape of a hemisphere topped by a cone.
> The diameter of the hemisphere and the height of the cone are each 6.2 mm.
> The mass of 1 cubic centimetre of gold is 19.3 grams.

15. The mass of the earring, to the nearest tenth of a gram, is _____ .
(Record your answer in the numerical response box from left to right)

16. The surface area of the earring, to the nearest mm^2, is _____ .
(Record your answer in the numerical response box from left to right)

Answer Key

1. a) 1385.4 cm^2 **b)** 7238.2 in^3 **c)** $1.1 \times 10^{12} \text{ km}^3$, $5.1 \times 10^8 \text{ km}^2$ **d)** 155.2 ft^3, 166.3 ft^2

2. 158 mL **3. a)** $r = \sqrt[3]{\dfrac{3V}{4\pi}} = \left(\dfrac{3V}{4\pi}\right)^{\frac{1}{3}}$ **b)** 23.0 cm

4. a) 0.76 cm^3 **b)** 10.16 cm^2

5. a) 942.5 cm^2 **b)** \$213.50 **6.** $6.42 \times 10^{10} \text{ km}^2$ **7.** 434.9 in^3

8. a) 452 cm^2 **b)** 659 cm^3 **9.** C

10. C **11.** C

12.

5	.	4	

13.

1	9	.	0

14.

3	3	9	

15.

2	.	4	

16.

1	2	8	

Measurement Lesson #10:
Practice Test

1. Which is the most suitable imperial unit of measurement for measuring the diameter of a golf ball?

A. mile **B.** yard **C.** foot **D.** inch

2. A long panoramic photograph measures 83 cm in width and 1.39 m in length. The difference between these measurements, in mm, is

A. 5.6 **B.** 56

C. 560 **D.** 5600

3. The number of kilometres in 0.028 centimetres is

A. 0.000 000 28 **B.** 280

C. 0.000 028 **D.** 28

4. Consider the following four statements.

Statement 1: 1 m = 0.001 km
Statement 2: 1 mm = 0.001 m
Statement 3: 1 μm = 0.001 mm
Statement 4: 1 nm = 0.001 μm

How many of these statements are false?

A. zero **B.** one **C.** three **D.** four

5. The height of horses is often measured in hands. Using the width of an adult hand as a referent for four inches, the height of a horse measuring $16\frac{1}{2}$ hands is

A. $4\frac{1}{2}$ feet **B.** 5 feet

C. $5\frac{1}{2}$ feet **D.** $6\frac{1}{2}$ feet

6. Which of the following measuring instruments would be easiest to use to measure the width of a gopher hole?

A. micrometer **B.** vernier caliper **C.** ruler **D.** trundle wheel

7. The province of Alberta is 1 216 km from north to south. Using the approximate conversion 5 miles = 8 kilometres, this distance in miles is

A. 242 **B.** 760

C. 788 **D.** 1946

8. The micrometer shown has a measuring range of 0 - 25 mm and is accurate to 0.01 mm. The measurement scale on the sleeve has increments of 0.5 mm and the measuring scale on the barrel has increments of 0.01 mm. The reading is

A. 3.49 mm
B. 2.49 mm
C. 1.99 mm
D. 1.59 mm

Numerical Response 1. Sahil and Nameeta are ordering new tiles for their kitchen floor. The floor is rectangular, six yards long by four and a half yards wide. The tiles they choose are $13\frac{1}{2}$ inches by $13\frac{1}{2}$ inches. The number of tiles they need is _____.

(Record your answer in the numerical response box from left to right)

9. The scale on a map is 1 : 2 000 000. If the distance between two cities is 600 km, the distance between them on the map is

A. 1.2 cm
B. 3 cm
C. 12 cm
D. 30 cm

Numerical Response 2. Quincy owns a large fish tank with dimensions 78.2 cm by 42.5 cm by 25.2 cm. To prevent ick, a fish illness, she buys preventative medicine for the tank. The directions on the bottle are to add 3 drops per 10 litres of water. The number of drops she should put in the tank is ______.

(Record your answer in the numerical response box from left to right)

Numerical Response **3.** Luis and Roberto are arranging a game of beach soccer. They need to make a goal line 8 yards long. Luis knows that his bare foot is 11 inches long, which he uses as a referent to make the goal line. He places his left foot in the sand and then places his right foot heel to toe with his left foot. He then lifts his left foot and places it heel to toe in front of his right foot. He continues this process until he has a goal line as close to 8 yards long as he can get. The number of times he must place his feet is _____.

(Record your answer in the numerical response box from left to right)

Use the following information to answer the next two questions.

> Pierre received a tool set as a birthday present. The tool set contained two sets of wrenches. The metric set included wrenches of 8 mm, 9 mm, 10 mm, 12 mm, 14 mm and 15 mm. The imperial set included wrenches measuring $\frac{1}{4}$ in, $\frac{5}{16}$ in, $\frac{3}{8}$ in, $\frac{7}{16}$ in, $\frac{1}{2}$ in and $\frac{9}{16}$ in.

10. Pierre wants to tighten a nut on a robotic toy he bought for his daughter. The 9 mm wrench is too small and the 10 mm wrench is too large. What wrench from the imperial set should he try?

A. $\frac{5}{16}$ in
B. $\frac{3}{8}$ in
C. $\frac{7}{16}$ in
D. $\frac{1}{2}$ in

11. Pierre bought a self assembly desk and had to use a wrench to tighten nuts. He tried the $\frac{1}{2}$ inch wrench which was too small and the $\frac{9}{16}$ inch wrench which was too large. Which metric wrench should he try?

A. 10 mm
B. 12 mm
C. 14 mm
D. 15 mm

Numerical Response **4.** On August 16, 2009, Usain Bolt won the gold medal at the World Athletics Championships in Berlin running 100 metres in 9.58 seconds. His average speed during the race, to the nearest 0.1 km/h, was ____.

(Record your answer in the numerical response box from left to right)

12. A glass ornament in the shape of a cone is placed onto a horizontal table. The cone has a radius of 7 cm and a vertical height of 24 cm. The surface area of glass, in cm^2, in terms of π, is

A. 49π
B. 175π
C. 217π
D. 224π

Use the following information to answer the next question.

A cylindrical can of soup has a base diameter of 7.4 cm and a height of 10.9 cm.

The paper label completely covers the curved surface of the metal can.

Numerical Response **5.** The surface area of the label, to the nearest cm^2, is ____ .

(Record your answer in the numerical response box from left to right)

13. A sphere has a diameter of 23 inches. The surface area of the sphere, to the nearest square inch, is

A. 1 662
B. 6 371
C. 6 647
D. none of the above

14. A sculpture is in the shape of a triangular pyramid.
The base is an equilateral triangle with sides of 10 m and the height is 12 m.
The volume of the pyramid in m^3 is

A. $300\sqrt{3}$
B. $100\sqrt{3}$
C. 600
D. 200

15. The volume of a hemispherical dome is 2260.5 m^3.
The radius of the dome, to the nearest centimetre, is

A. 1897
B. 1026
C. 814
D. 10

Written Response - 5 marks

1.

- The Fraser Valley Chemical Company in Vancouver stores a particular chemical in a conical (cone shaped) container whose diameter is four times the height. If the height is 6.3 m determine the volume of chemical in the container. Answer in m^3 correct to one decimal place.

- Tanker trucks are to be used to transfer the contents of one conical container to the South Seattle Chemical Company in Washington State. The tanks are cylinders with a radius of 2 m and a length of 10 m. How many trucks are needed?

- In Seattle, the contents of the trucks are transferred to another conical container with a circular base whose diameter is 14 m. Determine the height of this conical container. Answer in metres correct to one decimal place.

- Two companies have submitted a bid for carrying out the transportation.

  Lower Mainland Transportation will charge C$120 per truck plus C$5.20 per m^3 of chemical.

  Tacoma Trucking will charge US$100 per truck plus US$0.14 per ft^3 of chemical.

  Using the conversions C$ 1 = US$0.90 and 2.54 cm = 1 inch, determine which trucking company would be the cheaper to use for the transfer of the chemical. (Use the previously rounded answer in the first bullet in your calculation).

Answer Key

1. D	**2.** C	**3.** A	**4.** A	**5.** C
6. B	**7.** B	**8.** C	**9.** D	**10.** B
11. C	**12.** D	**13.** A	**14.** B	**15.** B

Numerical Response

1. 1 9 2

2. 2 5

3. 2 6

4. 3 7 . 6

5. 2 5 3

Written response

- diameter = 25.2 m. radius = 12.6 m. volume = $\frac{1}{3}(\pi)(12.6)^2(6.3) = 1047.4\text{ m}^3$.
- volume of truck = $\pi(2)^2(10) = 125.7\text{ m}^3$. # trucks = $\dfrac{1047.4}{125.7} = 8.33\ldots = 9$ trucks.
- $\frac{1}{3}(\pi)(7)^2(h) = 1047.4 \quad h = \dfrac{(3)(1047.4)}{(\pi)(7)^2} = 20.4\text{ m}$
- Lower Mainland Transportation : Cost = $(120 \times 9) + (1047.4 \times 5.20)$ = C$6526.48

  Tacoma Trucking : $1047.4\text{ m}^3 \times \dfrac{(100)\text{ cm}^3}{(1)^3\text{ m}^3} \times \dfrac{(1)^3\text{ in}^3}{(2.54)^3\text{ cm}^3} \times \dfrac{(1)^3\text{ ft}^3}{(12)^3\text{ in}^3} = 36988.6\text{ ft}^3$

  Cost = $(100 \times 9) + (36988.6 \times 0.14)$ = US$6078.40 = $\dfrac{6078.40}{0.90}$ = C$6753.78

  It is cheaper to use Lower Mainland Transportation.

Trigonometry Lesson #1:
Trigonometric Ratios

Overview of Unit

Trigonometry (from the Greek trigonon = three angles and metro = measure) is a branch of mathematics dealing with angles, triangles and trigonometric functions such as sine, cosine and tangent. In this unit we study the relationships between sides and angles in right triangles.

Investigation #1

The diagram shows a series of similar right triangles, $\triangle OA_1B_1$, $\triangle OA_2B_2$, etc.
Complete the work below using a ruler to measure the indicated sides to 1 decimal place. Calculate each ratio to 1 decimal place.

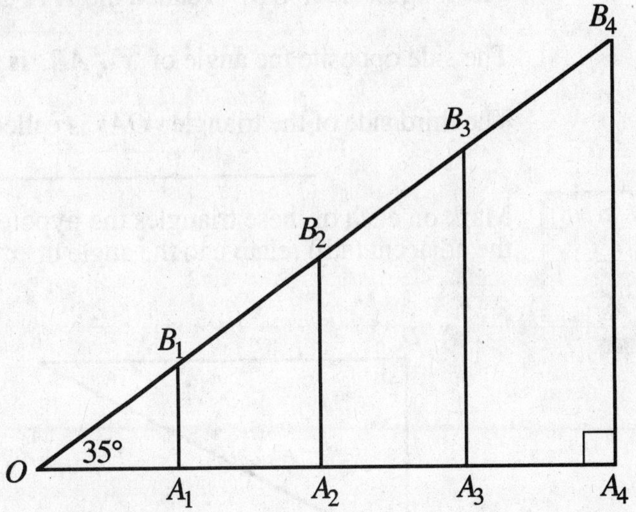

$\dfrac{A_1B_1}{OA_1} = \dfrac{1.4}{2} = 0.7$

$\dfrac{A_2B_2}{OA_2} = \dfrac{\quad}{4} =$

$\dfrac{A_3B_3}{OA_3} = \qquad =$

$\dfrac{A_4B_4}{OA_4} = \qquad =$

We can conclude that the ratio ______ is somehow connected to the angle of 35°.

Investigation #2

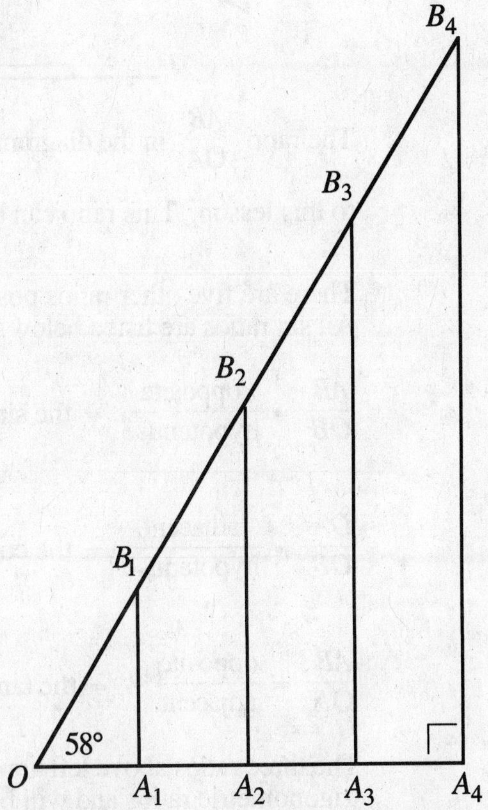

$\dfrac{A_1B_1}{OA_1} = \dfrac{2.4}{1.5} = 1.6$

$\dfrac{A_2B_2}{OA_2} = \dfrac{\quad}{3} =$

$\dfrac{A_3B_3}{OA_3} =$

$\dfrac{A_4B_4}{OA_4} =$

We can conclude that the ratio ______ is somehow connected to the angle of 58°.
We will investigate these ratios further in the rest of the lesson.

Ratios of Sides in a Right Triangle

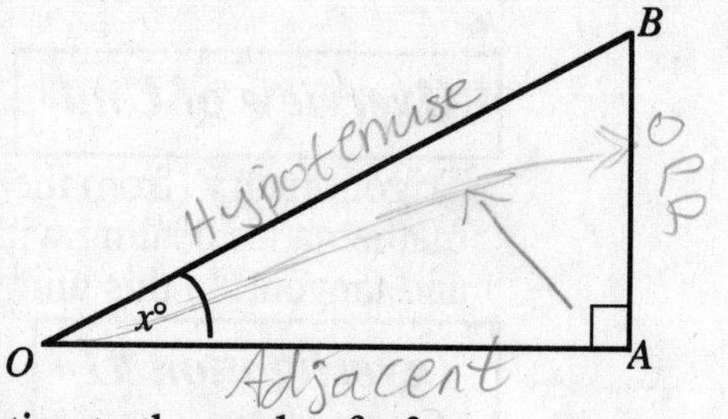

Consider the right triangle *AOB* shown.

Let angle $AOB = x°$.

Each of the sides of the triangle is given a special name relative to the angle of $x°$.

The longest side, *OB*, is called the HYPOTENUSE (hyp).

The side opposite the angle of $x°$, *AB*, is called the OPPOSITE (opp).

The third side of the triangle, *OA*, is called the ADJACENT (adj).

Class Ex. #1

Mark on each of these triangles the hypotenuse (hyp), the opposite (opp) and the adjacent (adj) relative to the angle of $x°$.

a)

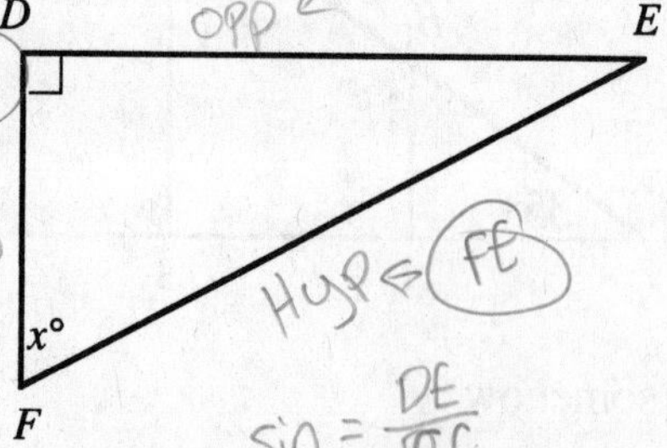

b)

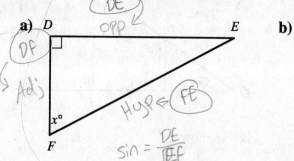

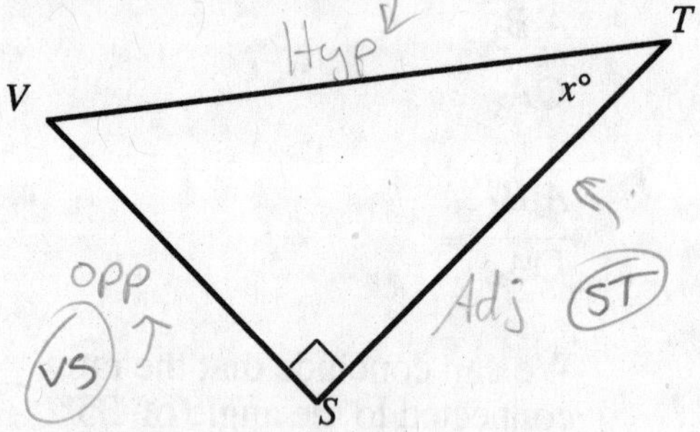

The ratio $\frac{AB}{OA}$ in the diagram at the top of this page is the same ratio we used in the warm up to this lesson. This ratio can be written as $\frac{\text{opposite}}{\text{adjacent}}$ and is known as the tangent ratio.

There are five other ratios possible using two of the sides of triangle *AOB*. All six ratios are listed below.

$\frac{AB}{OB} = \frac{\text{opposite}}{\text{hypotenuse}}$ = the sine ratio

$\frac{OA}{OB} = \frac{\text{adjacent}}{\text{hypotenuse}}$ = the cosine ratio

$\frac{AB}{OA} = \frac{\text{opposite}}{\text{adjacent}}$ = the tangent ratio

The three ratios above left are the primary trigonometric ratios and will be studied in this course.

$\frac{OB}{AB} = \frac{\text{hypotenuse}}{\text{opposite}}$ = the cosecant ratio

$\frac{OB}{OA} = \frac{\text{hypotenuse}}{\text{adjacent}}$ = the secant ratio

$\frac{OA}{AB} = \frac{\text{adjacent}}{\text{opposite}}$ = the cotangent ratio

The three ratios above right are the reciprocal trigonometric ratios and will be studied in higher level math courses.

$\sin = \dfrac{\text{opp}}{\text{Hyp}}$ $\cos = \dfrac{\text{adj}}{\text{hyp}}$ $\tan = \dfrac{\text{opp}}{\text{adj}}$ $S\dfrac{O}{H}$ $C\dfrac{A}{H}$ $T\dfrac{O}{A}$

SOH CAH TOA

The rules for determining the sine ratio, cosine ratio and tangent ratio for an angle in a right triangle can be memorized by using the acronym SOH CAH TOA.

Class Ex. #2

Using the diagrams in Class Example #1, complete the work below to list the sine ratio, the cosine ratio, and the tangent ratio for the angle of $x°$.

a) sine ratio $= \dfrac{\text{opposite}}{\text{hypotenuse}} =$ **b)** sine ratio =

cosine ratio $= \dfrac{\text{adjacent}}{\text{hypotenuse}} =$ cosine ratio =

tangent ratio $= \dfrac{\text{opposite}}{\text{adjacent}} =$ tangent ratio =

Class Ex. #3

For the angle of $a°$ in the diagram, complete the work below to express the three primary trigonometric ratios as rational numbers and in decimal form to the nearest thousandth.

sine ratio $= \dfrac{\text{opp}}{\text{hyp}} = \dfrac{20}{29} =$

cosine ratio $= \dfrac{21}{29} =$

tangent ratio $= \dfrac{20}{21}$

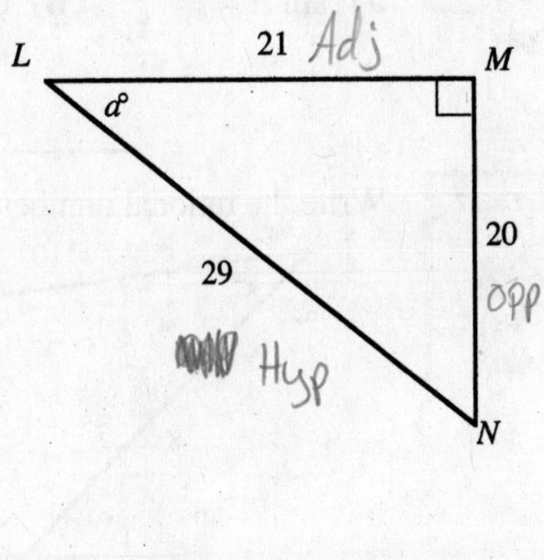

Complete Assignment Questions #1 - #3

Using sin, cos, tan

Consider right triangle PQR shown.

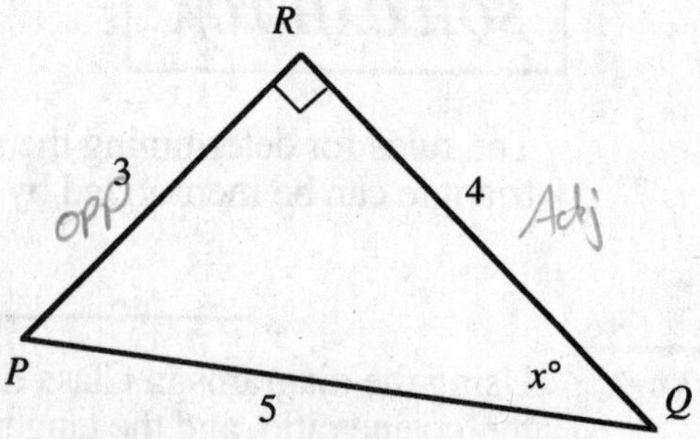

The sine ratio for the angle of $x°$ is $\frac{PR}{PQ} = \frac{3}{5}$.

In short we write $\sin x° = \frac{3}{5}$. RATIOS

Similarly $\cos x° = \frac{4}{5}$ and $\tan x° = \frac{3}{4}$

Sometimes the trigonometric ratios for an angle are given in terms of the letter at which the angle is located. For example, in $\triangle PQR$ above we could write $\sin Q = \frac{3}{5}$.

Complete the following, writing the ratio in simplest rational form.

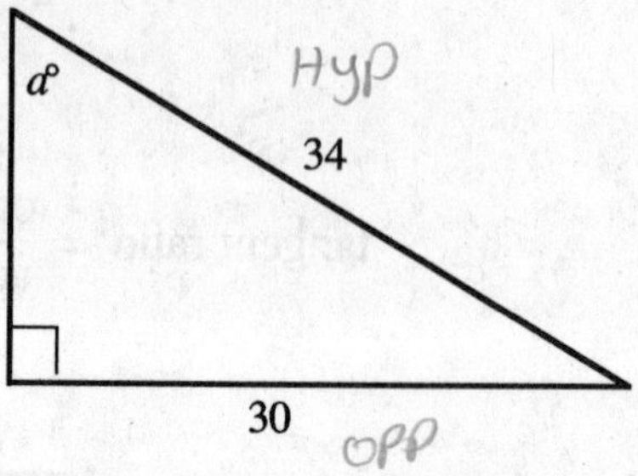

a) $\sin a° = \frac{30}{34} \rightarrow \frac{15}{17}$ **b)** $\cos a° = \frac{16}{34} \rightarrow \frac{8}{17}$

c) $\tan a° = \frac{30}{16} \rightarrow \frac{15}{8}$

Complete the following.

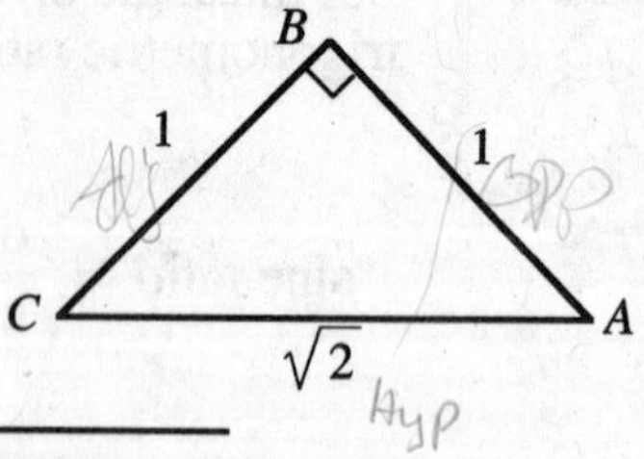

a) $\sin A = \frac{1}{\sqrt{2}}$ **b)** $\cos A = \frac{1}{\sqrt{2}}$ **c)** $\tan A = \frac{1}{1}$

Write the rational number, in simplest form, which represents the trigonometric ratio.

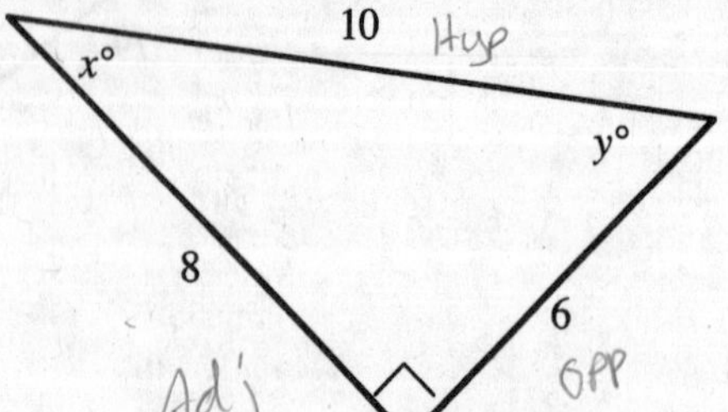

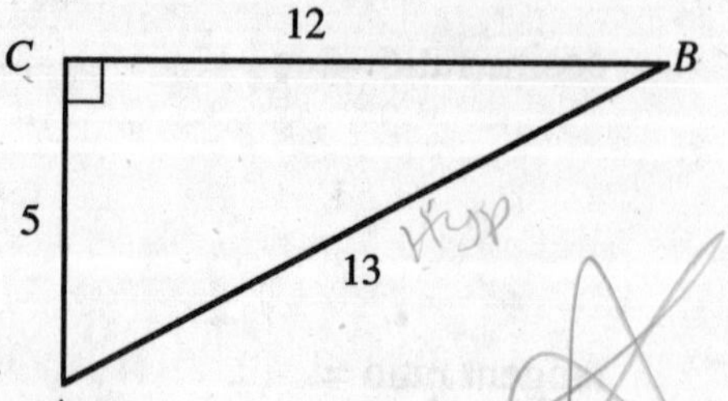

i) $\sin x° =$ **ii)** $\tan y° =$ **iii)** $\cos A =$ **iv)** $\tan B =$

v) $\sin y° =$ **vi)** $\cos x° =$ **vii)** $\cos B =$ **viii)** $\sin A =$

Complete Assignment Questions #4 - #11

SOH CAH TOA

SOH CAH TOA A →ONLY

Assignment

1. Consider the eight triangles below. For each triangle, complete the tables for the angle $x°$.

Triangle	Opposite Side	Adjacent Side	Hypotenuse
a)	FD	DE	EF
b)	PQ	RQ	PR
c)			
d)			
e)			
f)			
g)			
h)			

Triangle	sine ratio	cosine ratio	tangent ratio
a)		$\dfrac{DE}{EF}$	
b)			
c)			
d)			
e)			
f)			
g)			
h)			

SOH CAH TOA

a)

D ▫ ——— F
 $x°$
E

b)

P
 $x°$
R ▫ ——— Q

c)

L ▫ ——— N
 $x°$
M

d)

A $x°$ ——— C ▫
 B

e)

 R
 $x°$
S ——— O ▫

f)

X
 Y $x°$
 Z ▫

g)

W
 $x°$
 ▫ H
Y

h)

 G ▫
E
 $x°$
 F

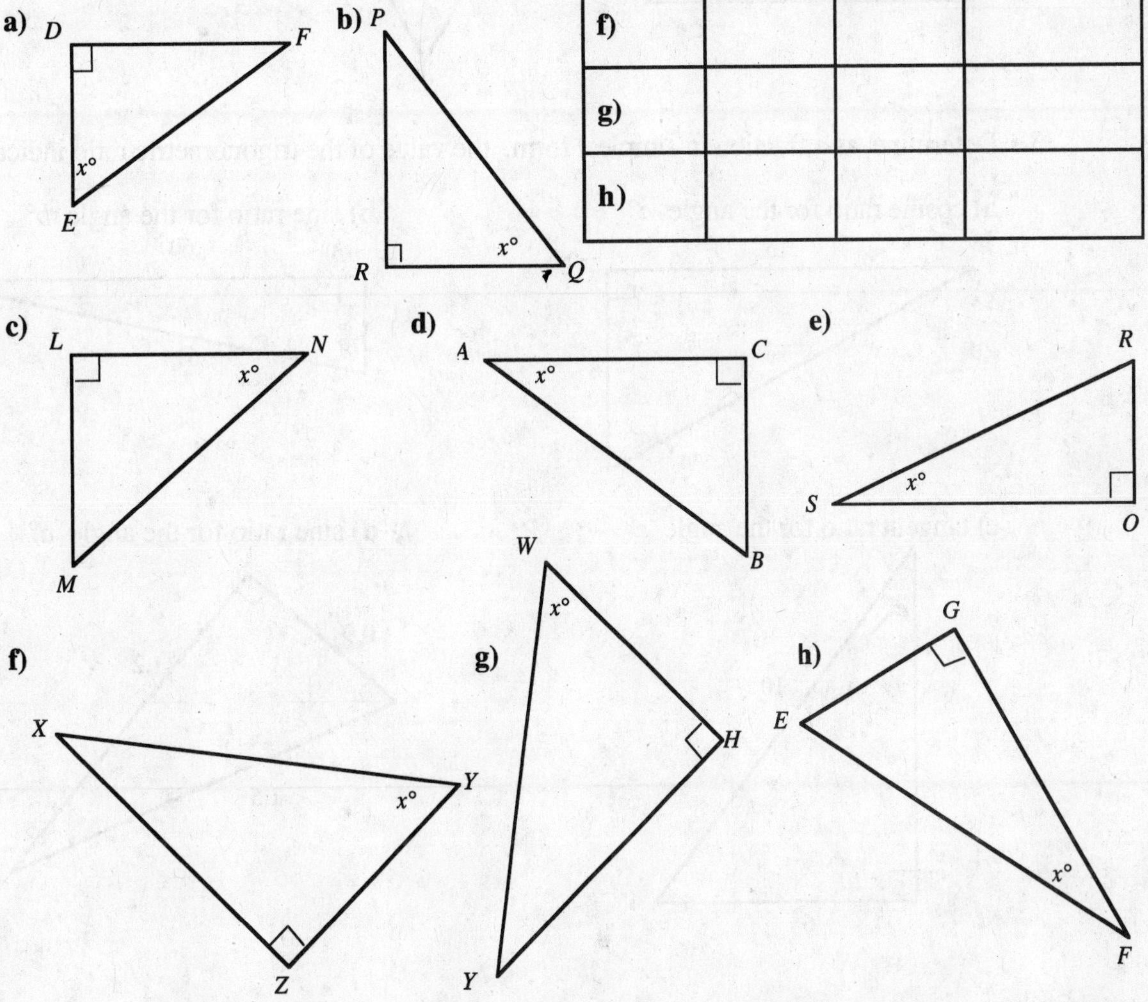

2. On each triangle mark the (hyp), (opp) and (adj) for the angle $a°$ and determine the trigonometric ratios associated with the angle of $a°$.

Complete the table.

Triangle	sine ratio	cosine ratio	tangent ratio
a)	$\frac{4}{5}$		
b)			
c)			

a)

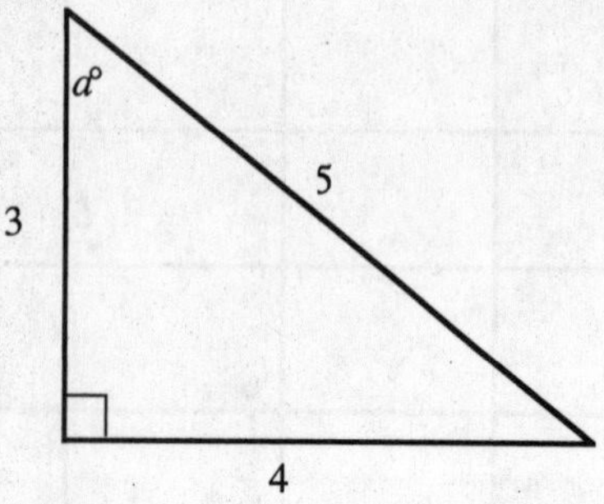

b)

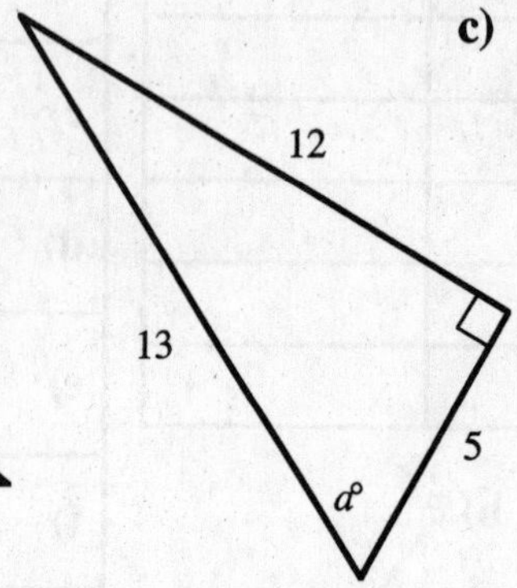

c)

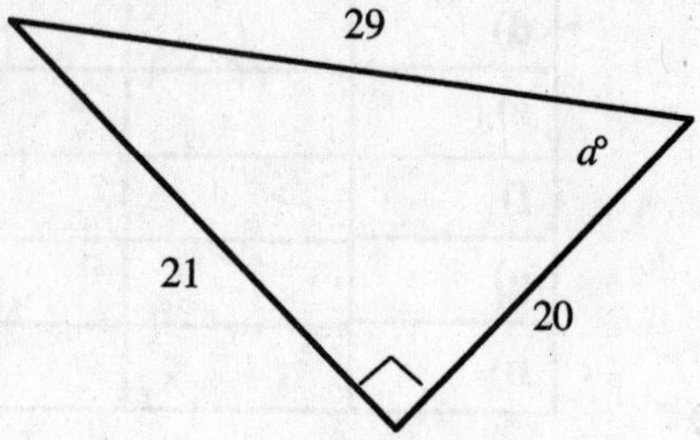

3. Determine, as a fraction in simplest form, the value of the trigonometric ratio indicated.

a) cosine ratio for the angle $a°$

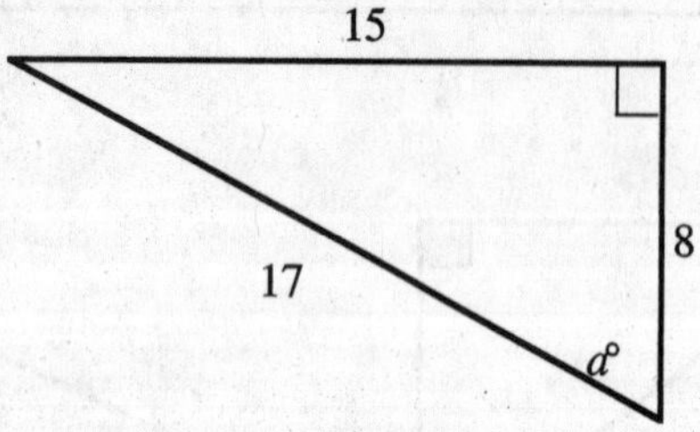

b) sine ratio for the angle $b°$

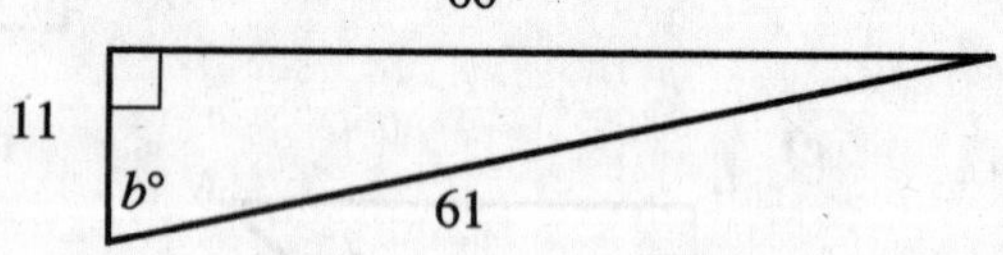

c) tangent ratio for the angle $c°$

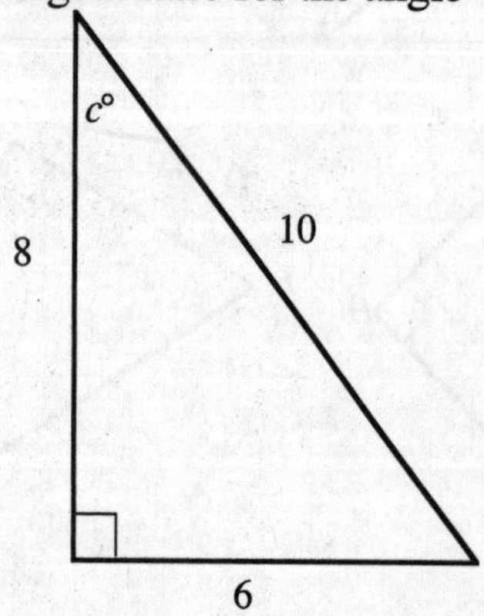

d) sine ratio for the angle $d°$

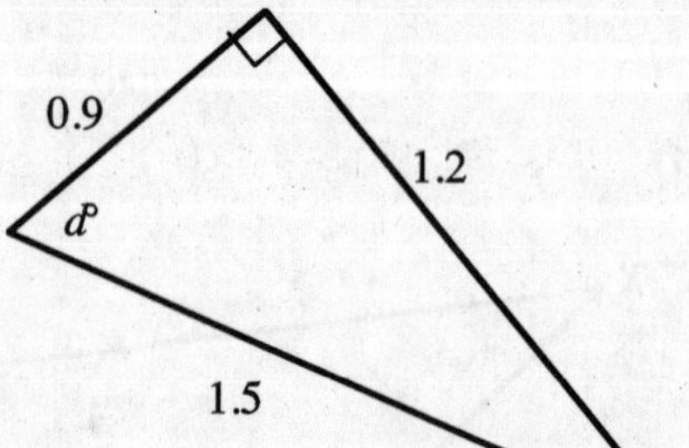

4. On the triangle, mark the (hyp), (opp) and (adj) for the angle $x°$ and determine the values of $\sin x°$, $\cos x°$, and $\tan x°$.

Write each answer as a decimal to the nearest hundredth.

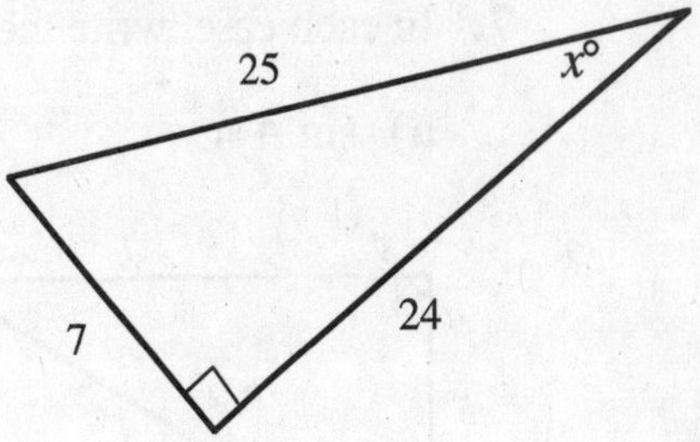

5. In the triangle, determine the exact values of $\sin B$, $\cos B$, and $\tan B$.

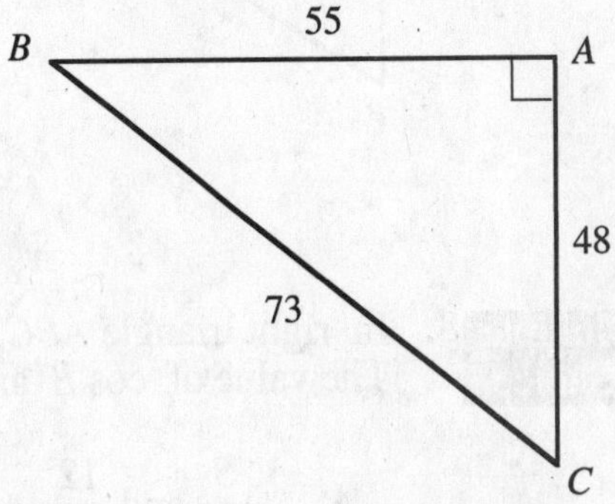

6. In each triangle, determine the values of $\sin x°$, $\cos x°$, and $\tan x°$ in simplest rational form.

Triangle	sin $x°$	cos $x°$	tan $x°$
a)			
b)			
c)			
d)			
e)			
f)			

a)

b)

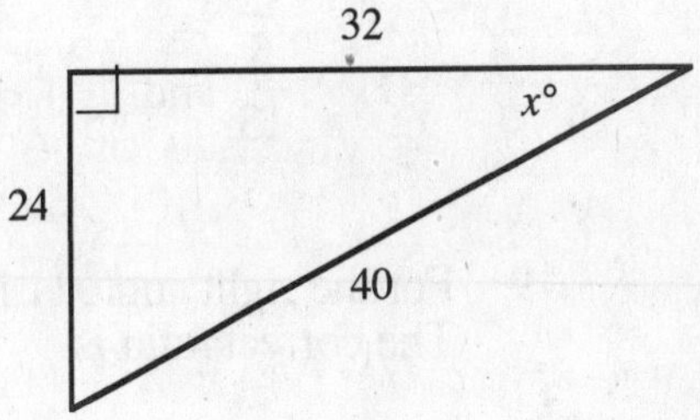

c)

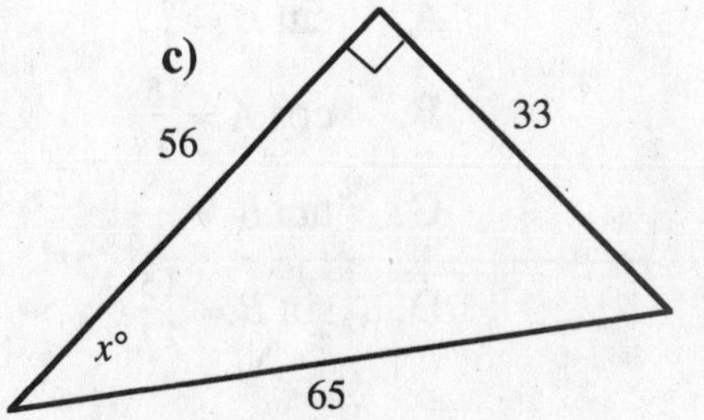

d)

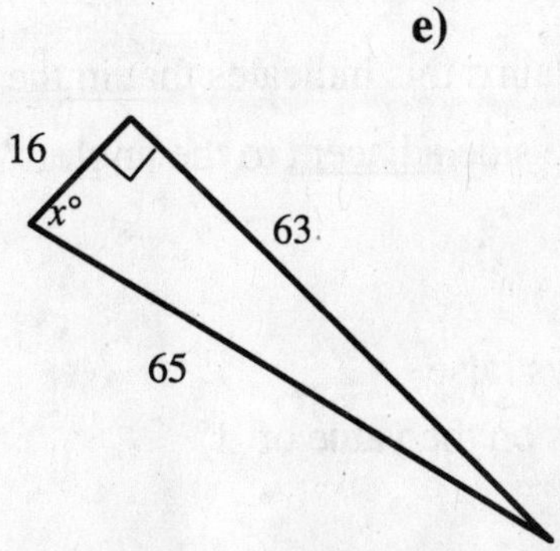

e)

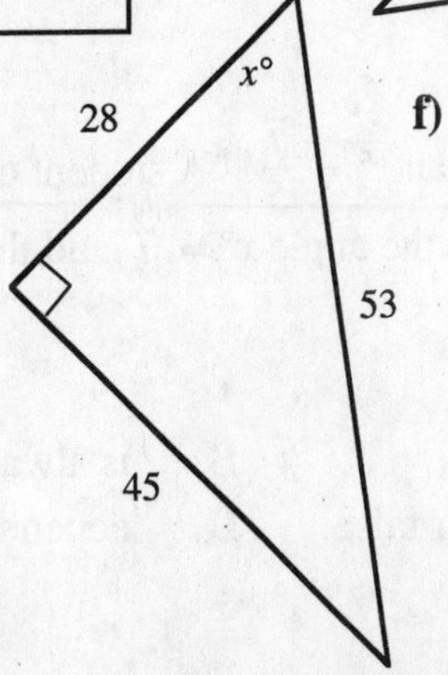

f)

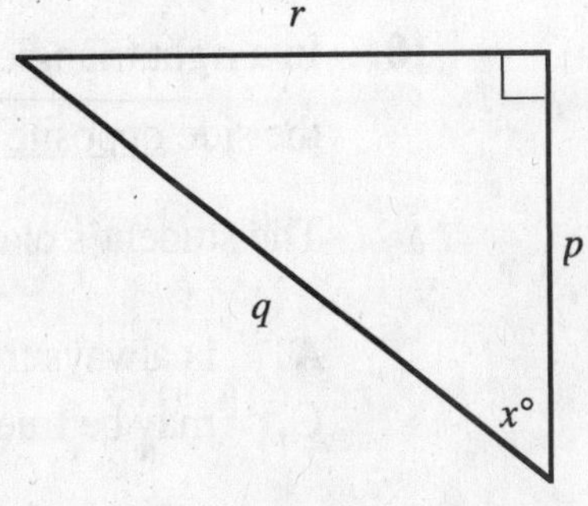

7. In each case, write the rational number which represents the trigonometric ratio.

a) $\sin A =$ **b)** $\cos B =$ **c)** $\tan X =$

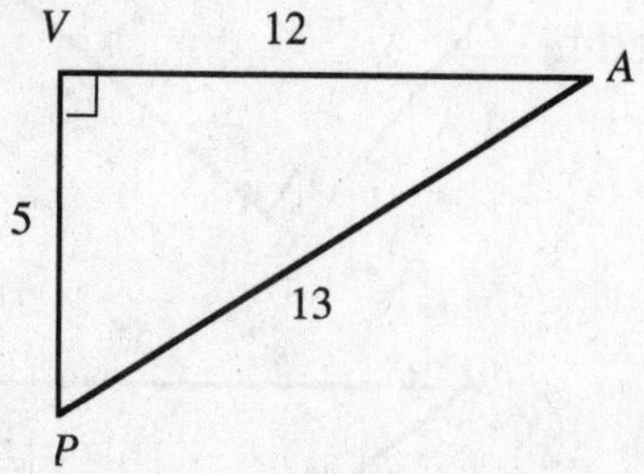

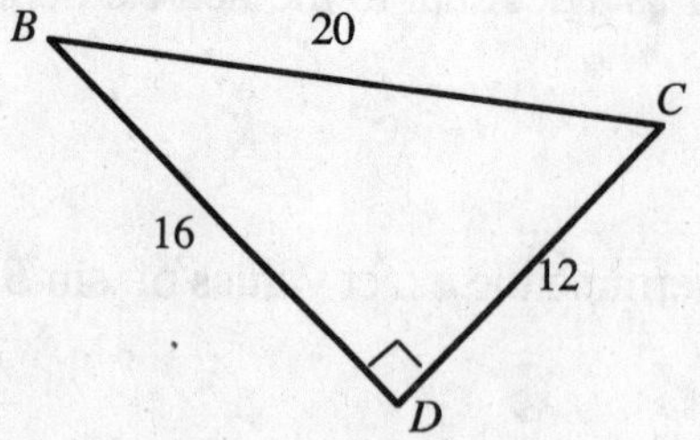

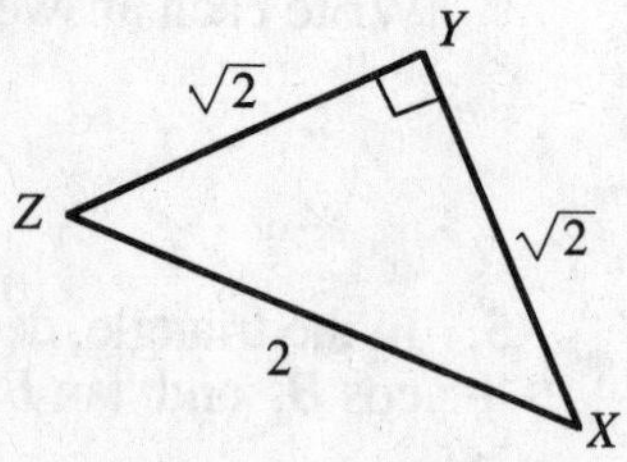

Multiple Choice **8.** In right triangle ABC, $AB = 52$ units, $AC = 48$ units and $BC = 20$ units. The value of $\cos B$ and $\sin B$ are respectively

A. $\frac{5}{13}$ and $\frac{12}{13}$

B. $\frac{12}{13}$ and $\frac{5}{13}$

C. $\frac{5}{12}$ and $\frac{12}{5}$

D. $\frac{5}{13}$ and $\frac{12}{5}$

9 For the right angled triangle ABC, only one of the following ratios is correct. The correct ratio is

A. $\sin A = \frac{8}{15}$

B. $\cos A = \frac{8}{17}$

C. $\tan B = \frac{8}{15}$

D. $\sin B = \frac{15}{17}$

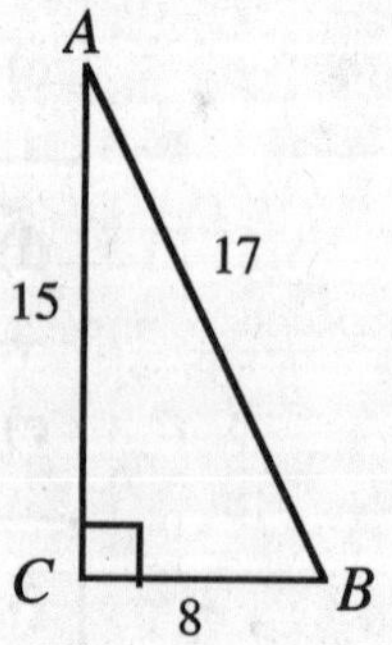

10. In a right triangle $\tan x° = \frac{7}{5}$. A student claims this indicates that in the right triangle the side <u>opposite</u> to the angle $x° = 7$ and the side <u>adjacent</u> to the angle $x° = 5$.

The student's claim

A. is always true **B.** is always false
C. may be true or false. **D.** depends on the value of $x°$

Numerical Response **11.** In the diagram, to the nearest tenth, the value of $\dfrac{\sin t°}{\cos t°}$ is ______.

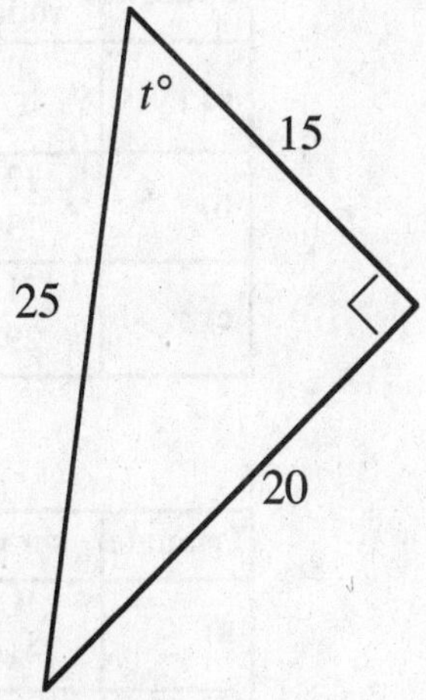

(Record your answer in the numerical response box from left to right)

Answer Key

1.

Triangle	Opposite Side	Adjacent Side	Hypotenuse
a)	*DF*	*DE*	*EF*
b)	*PR*	*QR*	*PQ*
c)	*LM*	*LN*	*MN*
d)	*BC*	*AC*	*AB*
e)	*OR*	*OS*	*RS*
f)	*XZ*	*YZ*	*XY*
g)	*HY*	*HW*	*WY*
h)	*EG*	*FG*	*EF*

Triangle	sine ratio	cosine ratio	tangent ratio
a)	$\frac{DF}{EF}$	$\frac{DE}{EF}$	$\frac{DF}{DE}$
b)	$\frac{PR}{PQ}$	$\frac{QR}{PQ}$	$\frac{PR}{QR}$
c)	$\frac{LM}{MN}$	$\frac{LN}{MN}$	$\frac{LM}{LN}$
d)	$\frac{BC}{AB}$	$\frac{AC}{AB}$	$\frac{BC}{AC}$
e)	$\frac{OR}{RS}$	$\frac{OS}{RS}$	$\frac{OR}{OS}$
f)	$\frac{XZ}{XY}$	$\frac{YZ}{XY}$	$\frac{XZ}{YZ}$
g)	$\frac{HY}{WY}$	$\frac{HW}{WY}$	$\frac{HY}{HW}$
h)	$\frac{EG}{EF}$	$\frac{FG}{EF}$	$\frac{EG}{FG}$

2.

Triangle	sine ratio	cosine ratio	tangent ratio
a)	$\frac{4}{5}$	$\frac{3}{5}$	$\frac{4}{3}$
b)	$\frac{12}{13}$	$\frac{5}{13}$	$\frac{12}{5}$
c)	$\frac{21}{29}$	$\frac{20}{29}$	$\frac{21}{20}$

3. **a)** $\frac{8}{17}$ **b)** $\frac{60}{61}$ **c)** $\frac{3}{4}$ **d)** $\frac{4}{5}$

4. $\sin x° = 0.28$ $\cos x° = 0.96$ $\tan x° = 0.29$

5. $\sin B = \frac{48}{73}$ $\cos B = \frac{55}{73}$ $\tan B = \frac{48}{55}$

6.

Triangle	$\sin x°$	$\cos x°$	$\tan x°$
a)	$\frac{9}{41}$	$\frac{40}{41}$	$\frac{9}{40}$
b)	$\frac{3}{5}$	$\frac{4}{5}$	$\frac{3}{4}$
c)	$\frac{33}{65}$	$\frac{56}{65}$	$\frac{33}{56}$
d)	$\frac{63}{65}$	$\frac{16}{65}$	$\frac{63}{16}$
e)	$\frac{45}{53}$	$\frac{28}{53}$	$\frac{45}{28}$
f)	$\frac{r}{q}$	$\frac{p}{q}$	$\frac{r}{p}$

7. **a)** $\frac{5}{13}$ **b)** $\frac{4}{5}$ **c)** 1

8. A **9.** D **10.** C

11.

1	.	3	

Trigonometry Lesson #2:
Trigonometric Ratios on a Calculator and Patterns in Trigonometric Ratios

Review

Recall the following from the previous lesson.

SOH CAH TOA

sine ratio = $\frac{\text{opposite}}{\text{hypotenuse}}$

cosine ratio = $\frac{\text{adjacent}}{\text{hypotenuse}}$

tangent ratio = $\frac{\text{opposite}}{\text{adjacent}}$

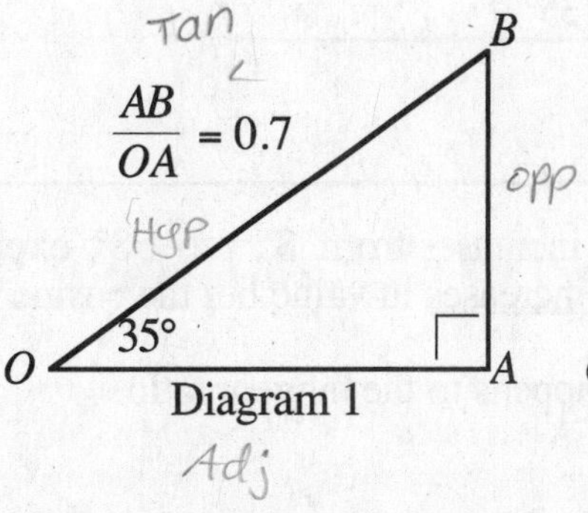

Diagram 1

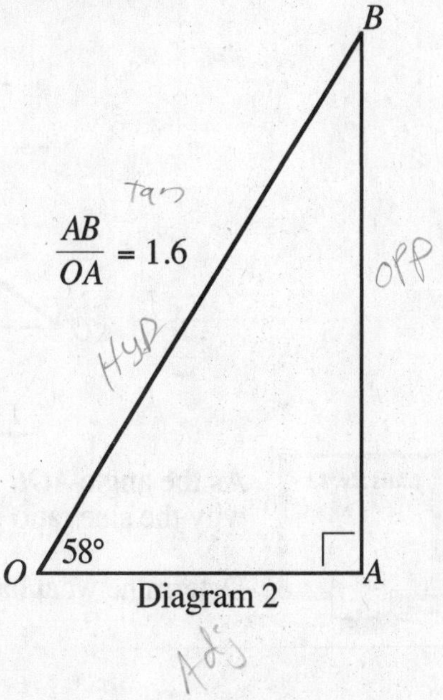

Diagram 2

Using a Calculator to Determine Trigonometric Ratios

In the investigations in the previous lesson, we discovered that the ratio 0.7 is the approximate tangent ratio for an angle of 35° and that the ratio 1.6 is the approximate tangent ratio for an angle of 58°.

We can write the ratios in the form tan 35° = 0.7 and tan 58° = 1.6 (to 1 decimal place).

More accurate approximations can be found using a calculator.

To four decimal places, tan 35° = .7002 and tan 58° = 1.6003 .

a) Use a calculator to determine the value of each trigonometric ratio to four decimal places.

i) sin 35° = .5736 **ii)** cos 35° = .8192

iii) sin 58° = .8480 **iv)** cos 58° = .5299

b) With respect to the diagrams at the top of the page, which ratio of sides is represented by each of the ratios in **a)**?

35° = #1
58° = #2

The diagrams below show triangles similar to the ones on the previous page in which the two hypotenuses are equal to 1 unit.

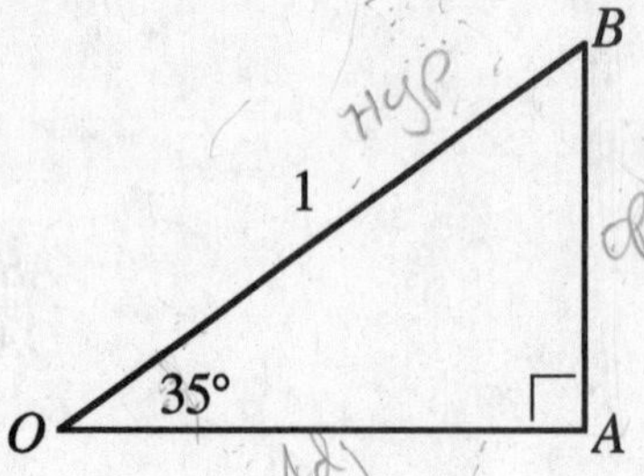

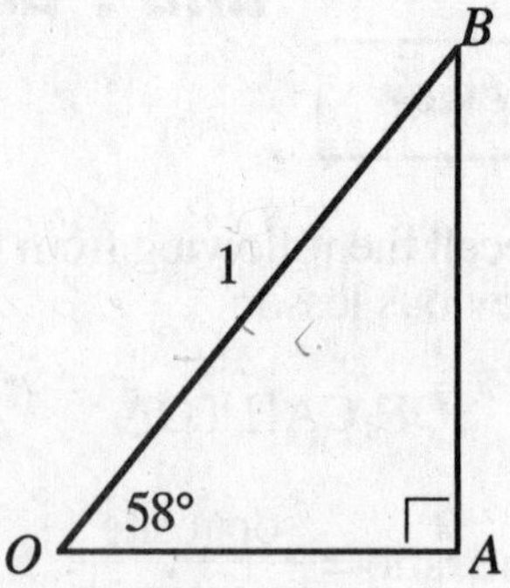

Class Ex. #2

As the angle *AOB* increases from 35° to 58° explain, using SOHCAHTOA, why the sine ratio <u>increases</u> in value but the cosine ratio <u>decreases</u> in value.

Determine what happens to the tangent ratio.

Class Ex. #3

<u>Without</u> using a calculator, state which of the following ratios has the greater value.

a) sin 14°, sin 20° **b)** cos 7°, cos 62°

c) tan 15°, tan 75° **d)** sin 80°, cos 80°, tan 80°

The trigonometric ratios for all angles between 0° and 90° can be approximated using a calculator.

Class Ex. #4

Use a calculator to determine the value of each trigonometric ratio to four decimal places.

a) sin 81° = **b)** tan 14° = **c)** cos 44° =

Determining the Angle Given a Trigonometric Ratio

We have discovered that $\tan 35° = 0.7$ and $\tan 58° = 1.6$, but is there an angle for which the tangent ratio is 1.2?

Use a "guess and check" technique to discover the measure of this angle to 1 decimal place.

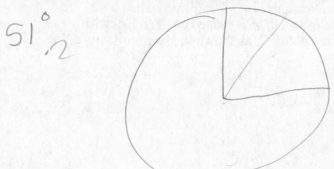

This method is time consuming and the calculator provides us with a quicker method by using the inverse trigonometric function.

If $\tan x° = 1.2$, the measure of the angle $x°$ can be determined by using the inverse tangent function $\tan^{-1}$.

If $\tan x° = 1.2$, then $\tan^{-1}(1.2) = x$.

On a calculator, access the inverse tangent function by pressing | 2nd | tan |.

2nd	tan	1	.	2	)	ENTER

determines the value of x.

In each case, determine the measure of the acute angle to the nearest degree.

a) $\sin a° = 0.3584$ $a° =$ °   **b)** $\cos b° = 0.5389$ $b° =$ °

c) $\tan P = 3.2106$ $\angle P =$ °   **d)** $\sin C = \frac{1}{2}$ $\angle C =$ °

Complete Assignment Questions #1 - #4

Trigonometric Ratios for Angles of 0° and 90°

Although it is not possible to form a triangle when $\angle AOB = 0°$ or when $\angle AOB = 90°$, the trigonometric ratios for angles of $0°$ and $90°$ can be determined using the idea of rotation angles.

A rotation angle of $a°$ is formed when a line of length r is rotated counterclockwise about a point O as shown in Diagram 1.

Diagram 1

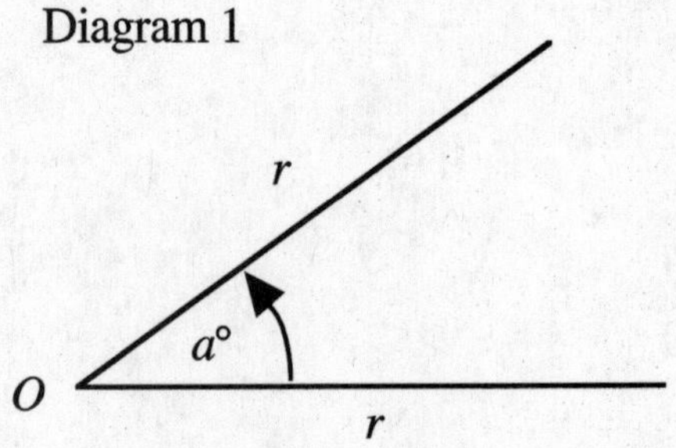

Triangle *AOB* is formed as shown in Diagram 2.

Diagram 2

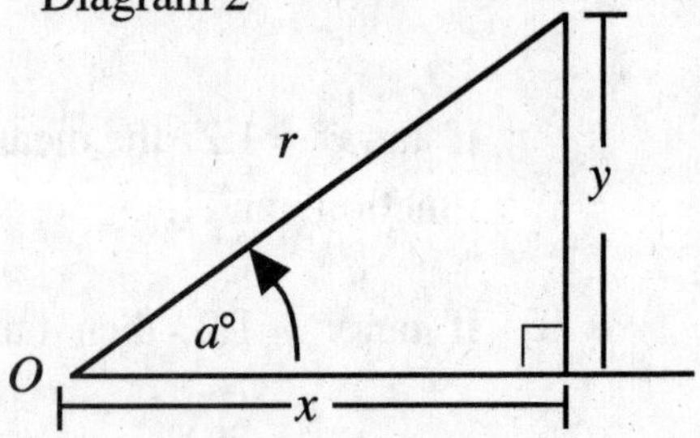

$\sin a° = \dfrac{y}{r}$.

Similarly $\cos a° =$

and $\tan a° =$

If the rotation angle $a°$ is made smaller and smaller, then the opposite side of the triangle, y, decreases in value and the adjacent side, x, increases in value.

If $a = 0$, then the opposite side $y = 0$ and the adjacent side $x = r$.

So $\sin 0° = \dfrac{y}{r} =$ $\qquad$ $\cos 0° = \dfrac{x}{r} =$ $\qquad$ $\tan 0° = \dfrac{y}{x} =$

If the rotation angle $a°$ is made larger and larger, then the opposite side of the triangle, y, increases in value and the adjacent side, x decreases in value.

If $a = 90$, then the adjacent side $x = 0$ and the opposite side $y = r$.

So $\sin 90° = \dfrac{y}{r} =$ $\qquad$ $\cos 90° = \dfrac{x}{r} =$ $\qquad$ $\tan 90° = \dfrac{y}{x} =$

Patterns in Trigonometric Ratios

Class Ex. #6 Complete the following table, rounding if necessary to 2 decimal places.

Angle $x°$	0°	10°	20°	30°	40°	50°	60°	70°	80°	90°
$\sin x°$										

Complete the following statement:

As the angle $x°$ increases from 0° to 90°, $\sin x°$ increases from _____ to _____.

Class Ex. #7 Draw a right triangle *LMN* in which $\angle L = 90°$ and $\angle N = x°$.

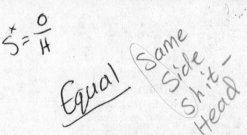

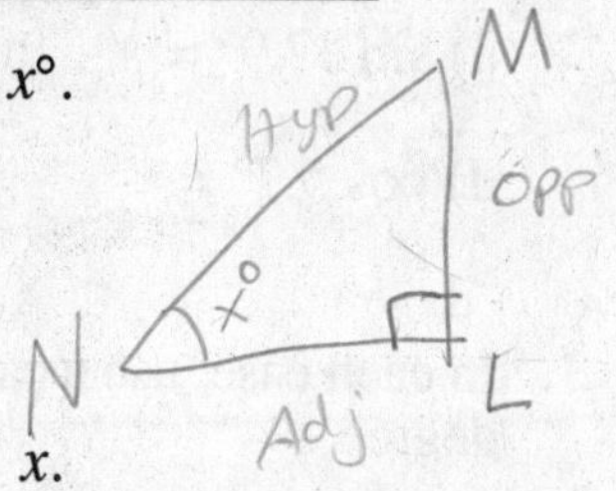

a) Write an expression for the measure of $\angle M$ in terms of x.

$$90 - x$$

b) Explain, using ratios, why $\sin x° = \cos(90 - x)°$.

$S = \dfrac{O}{H}$ $S = \dfrac{O}{H}$

Equal Same Side Shit Head

SOH CAH TOA $\dfrac{90}{x}$

c) Complete the following, using an angle between 0° and 90°.

i) $\sin 20° = \cos \underline{70°}$

ii) $\sin 8° = \cos \underline{82°}$

Complete Assignment Questions #5 - #14

Never - round until FINAL ANSWER

Assignment

1. Use a calculator to determine the value of each trigonometric ratio to four decimal places where necessary.

a) $\sin 68° =$ **b)** $\tan 30° =$ **c)** $\cos 19° =$

d) $\cos 22° =$ **e)** $\tan 85° =$ **f)** $\sin 7° =$

g) $\tan 60° =$ **h)** $\sin 18° =$ **i)** $\cos 72° =$

j) $\cos 45° =$ **k)** $\sin 45° =$ **l)** $\tan 45° =$

2. Use a calculator to determine the value of each trigonometric ratio to four decimal places.

a) $\sin 37.9° =$ **b)** $\tan 4.8° =$ **c)** $\cos 83.2° =$

d) $\cos 5.7° =$ **e)** $\tan 63.6° =$ **f)** $\sin 17.4° =$

3. In each case, use a calculator to determine the measure of the acute angle to the nearest degree.

a) $\sin a° = 0.7612$ $a° =$ ° **b)** $\cos b° = 0.5398$ $b° =$ °

c) $\tan P = 1.2173$ $\angle P =$ ° **d)** $\sin C = \frac{1}{3}$ $\angle C =$ °

e) $\tan t° = \sqrt{3}$ $t° =$ ° **f)** $\cos x° = \frac{\sqrt{2}}{2}$ $x° =$ °

g) $\sin A = \frac{\sqrt{2}}{2}$ $\angle A =$ ° **h)** $\tan X = \frac{1}{\sqrt{3}}$ $\angle X =$ °

4. In each case, use a calculator to determine the indicated acute angle to the nearest tenth of a degree.

a) $\sin A = 0.6789$ **b)** $\cos X = 0.1234$ **c)** $\tan P = 0.55$

d) $\sin a° = 0.09$ **e)** $\cos e° = \frac{7}{24}$ **f)** $\tan y° = \frac{4}{3}$

g) $\cos K = 0.3$ **h)** $\tan M = 50$ **i)** $\sin R = \frac{5}{6}$

5. Explain, using diagrams, why the sine ratio for an angle of 20° is smaller than the sine ratio for an angle of 40°.

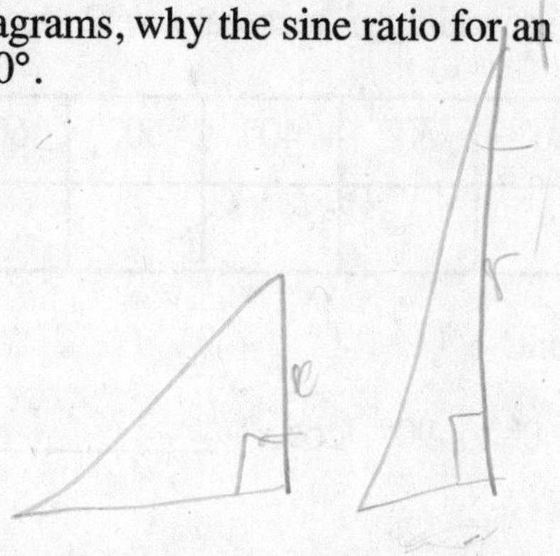

6. Explain, using diagrams, why the cosine ratio for an angle of 30° is greater than the cosine ratio for an angle of 70°.

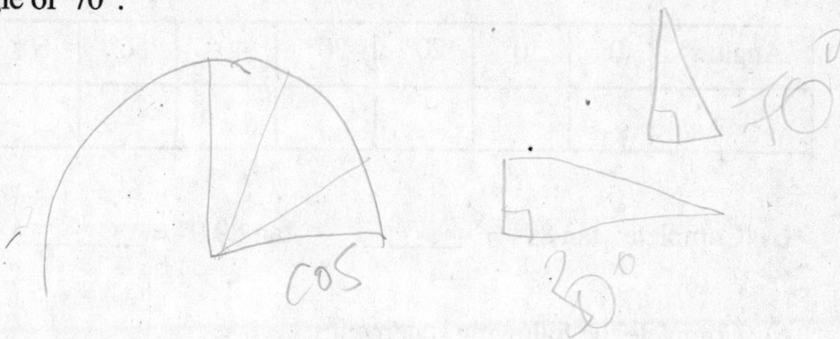

7. Explain, using diagrams, why the tangent ratio for an angle of 15° is smaller than the tangent ratio for an angle of 50°.

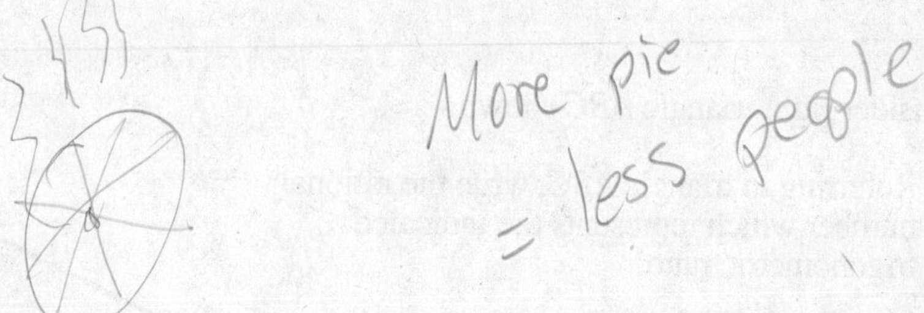

8. <u>Without</u> using a calculator, state which of the following ratios has the greater value.

a) sin 58° , sin 32° **b)** cos 67°, cos 35°

c) tan 56° , tan 86° **d)** sin 29° , cos 29°

e) sin 74° , cos 74° **f)** sin 60° , cos 60°, tan 60°

9. Complete the following table, rounding if necessary to 2 decimal places

Angle $x°$	0°	10°	20°	30°	40°	50°	60°	70°	80°	90°
cos $x°$										

Complete the following statement:

As the angle $x°$ increases from 0° to 90°, cos $x°$ ____________ from _____ to _____.

10. a) Complete the following table, rounding if necessary to 2 decimal places

Angle $x°$	0°	10°	20°	30°	40°	50°	60°	70°	80°	90°
tan $x°$										

b) Complete: tan 89° = ________ tan 89.9° = ________ tan 89.99° = ________

c) Complete the following statement:

As the angle $x°$ increases from 0° to 90°, tan $x°$ ___increases___ from ___0___ to ___infinity___.

11. Consider right triangle *ABC* shown.

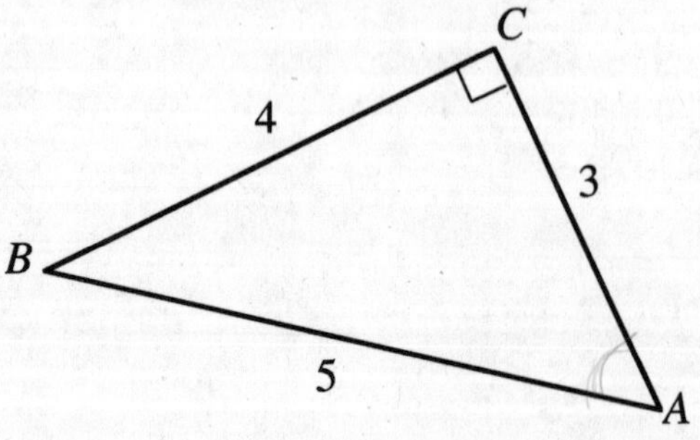

a) Referring to triangle *ABC*, write the rational number which represents the indicated trigonometric ratio.

sin *A* = $\frac{4}{5}$ = .8 sin *B* =

cos *A* = cos *B*=

tan *A* = tan *B* =

b) Which pairs of trigonometric ratios have the same value?

c) How do the values of tan *A* and tan *B* relate to each other?

12. a) Draw a right triangle PQR in which $\angle P = 90°$ and $\angle Q = x°$.

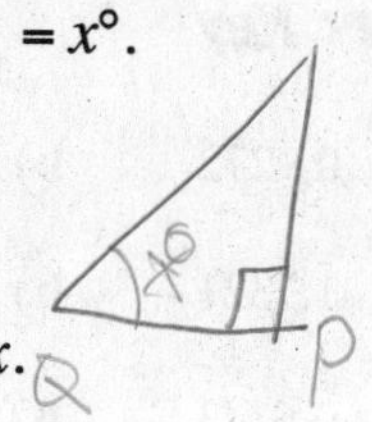

b) Write an expression for the measure of $\angle R$ in terms of x.

c) Explain why $\cos x° = \sin(90 - x)°$

d) Complete the following using an angle less than $90°$.

i) $\cos 76° = \sin$ ______ ii) $\cos 13° = \sin$ ______

Multiple Choice **13.** Triangle LMN is right angled at L with $\tan M = a$.
Three statements are made about the trigonometric ratios in triangle LMN.

Statement 1. $\cos M = \sin N$

Statement 2. $\cos N = \sin M$

Statement 3. $\tan N = \dfrac{1}{a}$

How many of these statements are true?

A. 0 **B.** 1

C. 2 **D.** 3

Numerical Response **14.** To the nearest tenth, the value of $\dfrac{\cos 30° + \sin 30°}{\tan 30°}$ is ______.

(Record your answer in the numerical response box from left to right)

Answer Key

1. **a)** 0.9272 **b)** 0.5774 **c)** 0.9455 **d)** 0.9272 **e)** 11.4301 **f)** 0.1219

g) 1.7321 **h)** 0.3090 **i)** 0.3090 **j)** 0.7071 **k)** 0.7071 **l)** 1

2. **a)** 0.6143 **b)** 0.0840 **c)** 0.1184 **d)** 0.9951 **e)** 2.0145 **f)** 0.2990

3. **a)** 50° **b)** 57° **c)** 51° **d)** 19° **e)** 60° **f)** 45° **g)** 45° **h)** 30°

4. **a)** 42.8° **b)** 82.9° **c)** 28.8° **d)** 5.2° **e)** 73.0° **f)** 53.1° **g)** 72.5° **h)** 88.9° **i)** 56.4°

5. If we keep the hypotenuse the same length, the opposite side is smaller for an angle of 20° than for an angle of 40°. Since the sine ratio is $\frac{\text{opp}}{\text{hyp}}$, the sine ratio for an angle of 20° is smaller than for an angle of 40°.

6. If we keep the hypotenuse the same length, the adjacent side is greater for an angle of 30° than for an angle of 70°. Since the cosine ratio is $\frac{\text{adj}}{\text{hyp}}$, the cosine ratio for an angle of 30° is greater than for an angle of 70°.

7. If we keep the hypotenuse the same length, the opposite side is smaller for an angle of 15° than for an angle of 50°, and the adjacent side is greater for an angle of 15° than for an angle of 50°. Since the tangent ratio is $\frac{\text{opp}}{\text{adj}}$, the tangent ratio for an angle of 15° is smaller than for an angle of 50°.

8. **a)** sin 58° **b)** cos 35° **c)** tan 86° **d)** cos 29° **e)** sin 74° **f)** tan 60°

9.

Angle $x°$	0°	10°	20°	30°	40°	50°	60°	70°	80°	90°
cos $x°$	1	0.98	0.94	0.87	0.77	0.64	0.5	0.34	0.17	0

As the angle $x°$ increases from 0° to 90°, cos $x°$ decreases from 1 to 0.

10 a)

Angle $x°$	0°	10°	20°	30°	40°	50°	60°	70°	80°	90°
tan $x°$	0	0.18	0.36	0.58	0.84	1.19	1.73	2.75	5.67	not defined

b) tan 89° = 57.29 tan 89.9° = 572.96 tan 89.99° = 5729.58

c) As the angle $x°$ increases from 0° to 90°, tan $x°$ increases from 0 to infinity.

11.a) $\sin A = \frac{4}{5}$, $\sin B = \frac{3}{5}$, $\cos A = \frac{3}{5}$, $\cos B = \frac{4}{5}$, $\tan A = \frac{4}{3}$, $\tan B = \frac{3}{4}$.

b) $\sin A = \cos B$, $\cos A = \sin B$ **c)** they are reciprocals

12.b) $(90 - x)°$ **c)** $\cos x° = \frac{PQ}{QR}$ $\sin(90 - x)° = \frac{PQ}{QR}$ so $\cos x° = \sin(90 - x)°$

d) **i)** cos 76° = sin 14° **ii)** cos 13° = sin 77°

13. D **14.**

2	.	4	

Trigonometry Lesson #3:
Calculating The Length of a Side in a Right Triangle

Review - The Pythagorean Theorem

The Pythagorean Theorem can be applied in a right triangle to determine the length of the third side of a triangle in which the lengths of the other two sides are given.

In the triangle shown

$$c^2 = a^2 + b^2 \qquad a^2 = c^2 - b^2$$

$$b^2 = c^2 - a^2$$

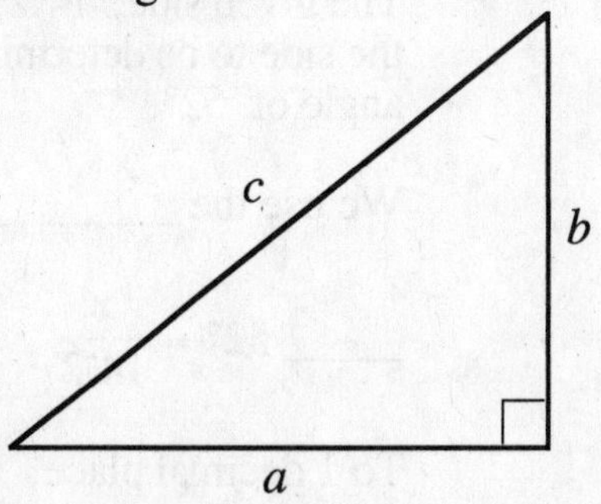

Calculate the length of the third side of each triangle, to the nearest tenth if necessary.

a)

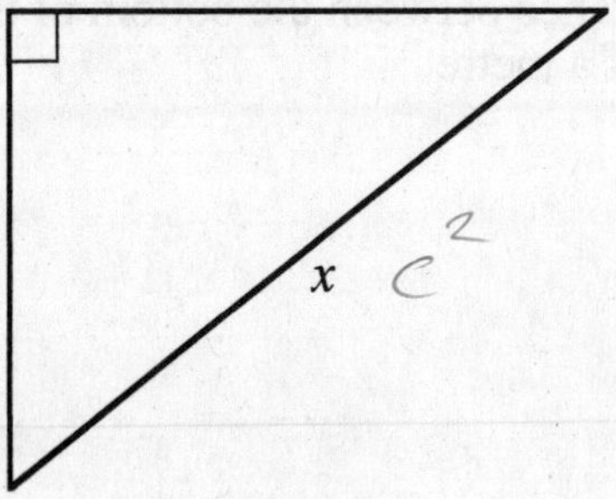

b)

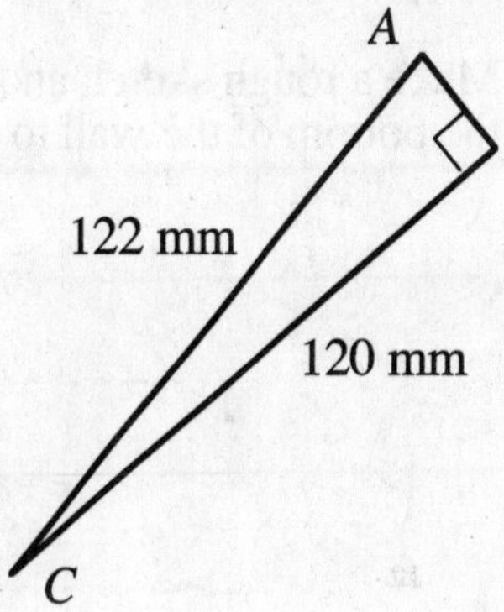

(2.5 · 2.5) + (3.7 + 3.7)

$x^2 = \sqrt{19.94}$

$= 4.47$

Using the Trigonometric Ratios to Calculate the Length of a Side

At the beginning of this lesson we reviewed the procedure for calculating the third side of a right triangle in which the other two sides were given.

It is also possible to determine the length of a side in a right triangle if the length of one side and the measure of one of the acute angles is given.

The procedure is demonstrated on the next page.

In right triangle *ABC* we are given the length of one side and the measure of an acute angle.

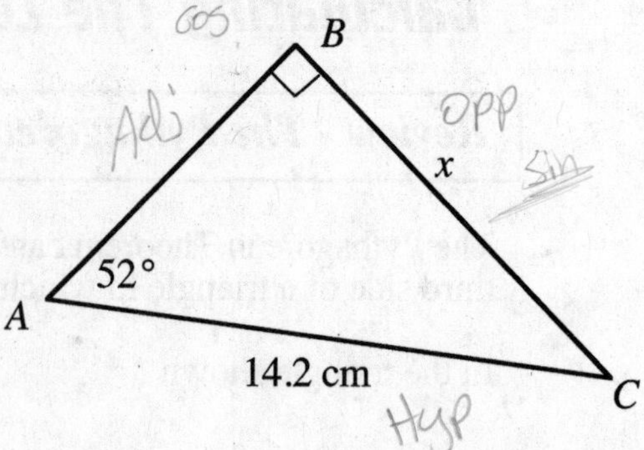

The procedure for determining the length of the side marked *x* is started below.

The given side, 14.2 cm, is the hypotenuse and the side to be determined, *x*, is opposite the given angle of 52°.

We use the ___*Sine*___ ratio.

$$\underline{Sin}\ 52° = \frac{x}{14.2}$$ Cross multiply to get $14.2 \ \underline{\quad\quad} \ 52° = x$

To 1 decimal place, *x* = __11.2__ cm.

Class Ex. #2 A ladder 4.5 m long just reaches the top of a wall. The angle between the ladder and the ground is 65°.

Make a rough sketch and determine the distance between the bottom of the ladder and the bottom of the wall to the nearest tenth of a metre.

$$(4.5)\cos(65°) = \frac{Adj}{4.5m}\ (4.5)$$

Adj side = 1.9m

Class Ex. #3 Determine the height of the wall in Class Ex. #2

a) using trigonometric ratios **b)** using the Pythagorean Theorem

$$(4.5)\cdot\sin(65°) = \frac{0}{4.5}\ (4.5)$$

= 4.1

Complete Assignment Questions #1 - #4

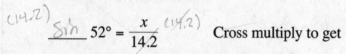

In all of the previous work, the side which had to be determined was in the <u>numerator</u> of the trigonometric ratio. Complete the work below to determine the length of a side which appears in the <u>denominator</u> of the trigonometric ratio.

In the diagram, $\underline{\text{cos}}\ 64° = \dfrac{7.9}{a}$

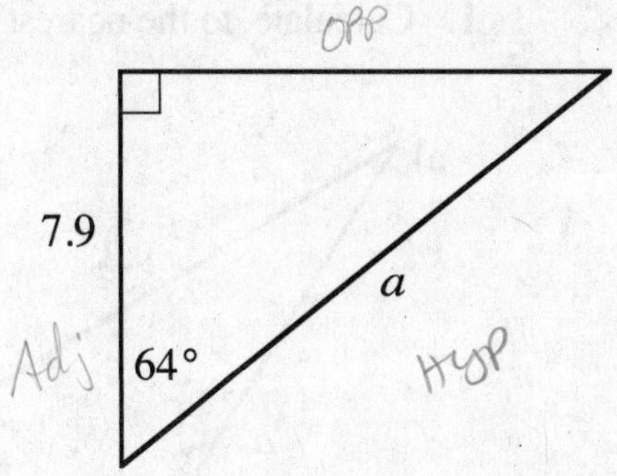

cross multiply to get

$a\ \underline{\text{cos}}\ 64° = 7.9$

divide both sides by _____64° to get

$a = \dfrac{7.9}{\_\_\_\_\_\ 64°}$

$= \_\_\_\_\_\_\_\_\_\_$ (to the nearest tenth)

Determine, to one decimal place, the length of the hypotenuse of triangle PQR in which angle $PQR = 90°$, angle $PRQ = 28°$, and $PQ = 15.6$ mm.

Use trigonometric ratios to determine the lengths of AB and AC in the given triangle. Answer correct to the nearest metre.

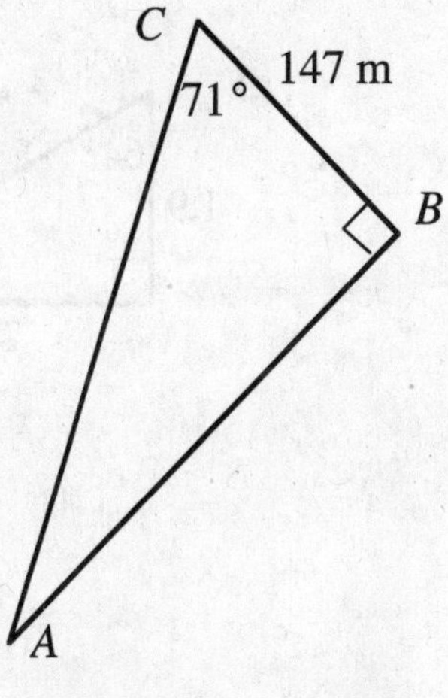

Complete Assignment Questions #5 - #12

Assignment

1. Calculate, to the nearest tenth, the length of the indicated side in each triangle.

a)

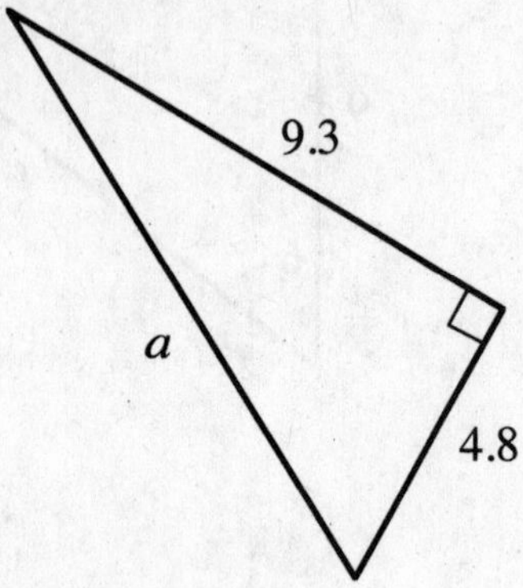

b)

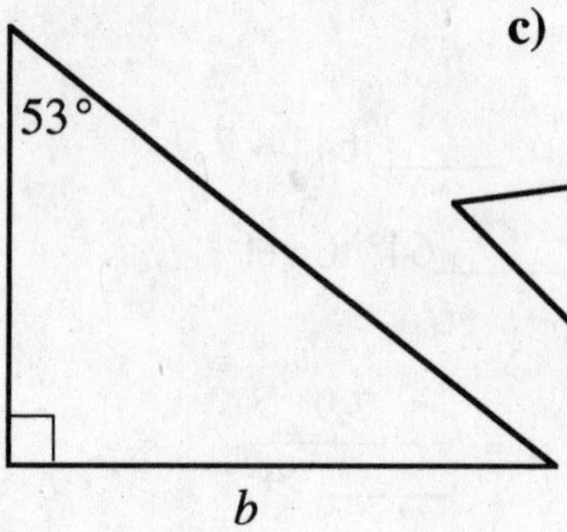

c)

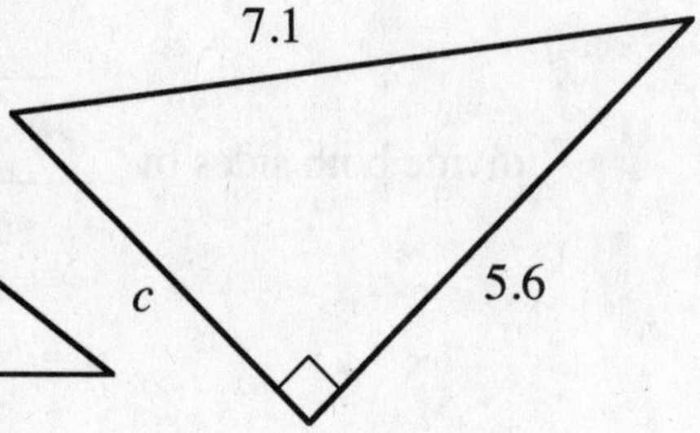

d)

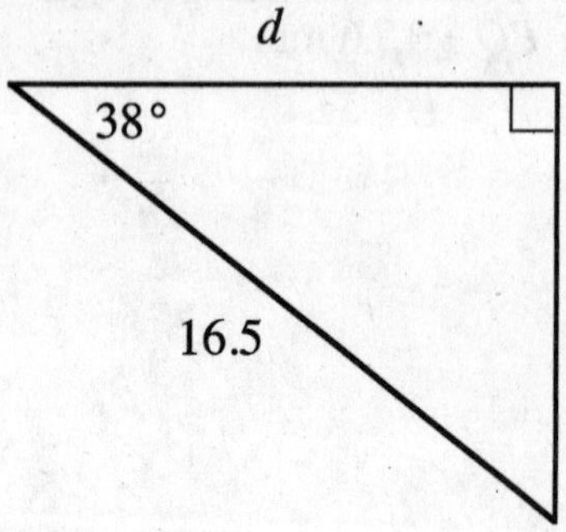

e)

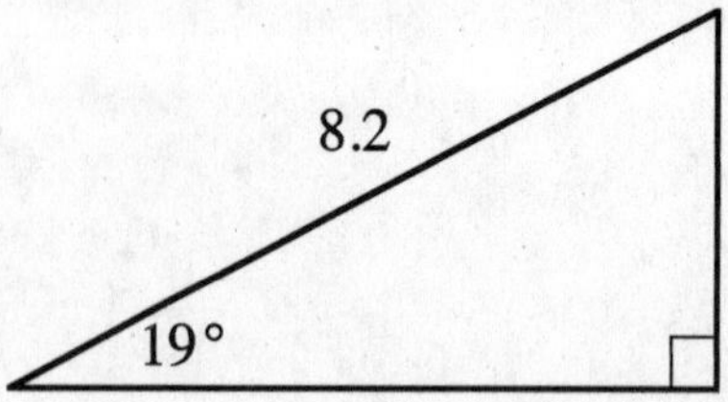

f)

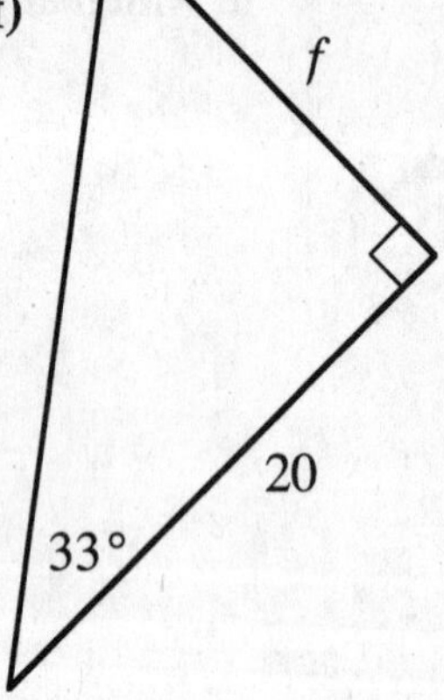

g)

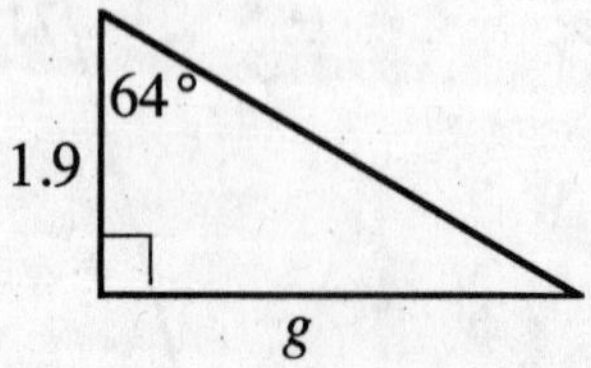

h)

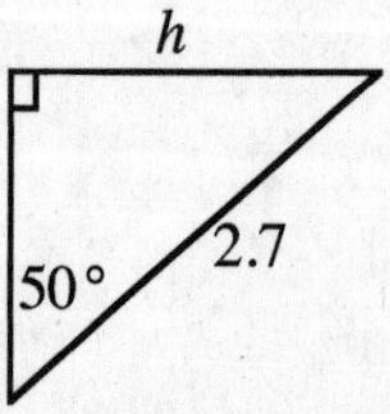

i)

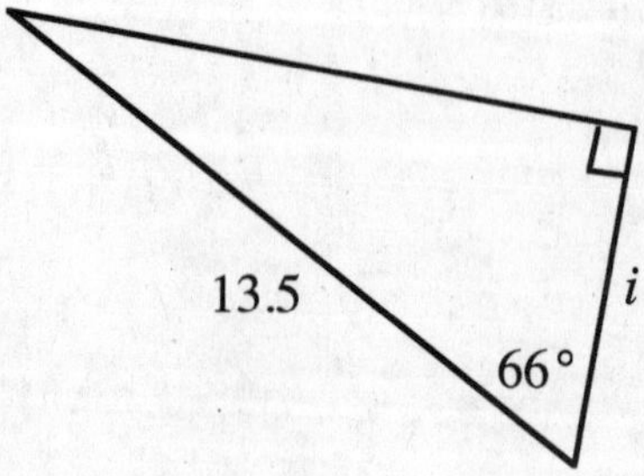

2. The kite string is 65 metres long and makes an angle of 32° with the ground. Calculate, to the nearest metre, the vertical height, h, of the middle of the kite above the ground.

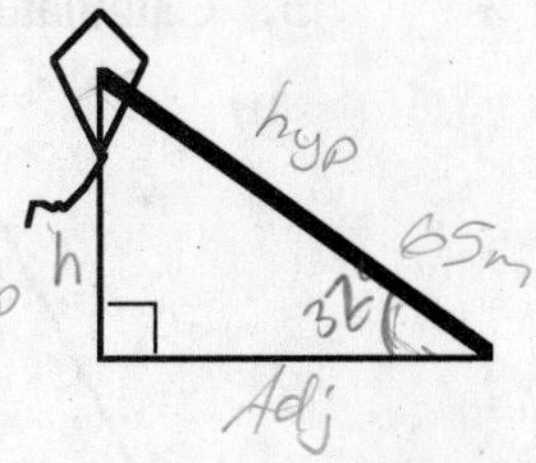

MARKING

3. Use the measurements in the diagram to determine the height of the flagpole to the nearest tenth of a metre.

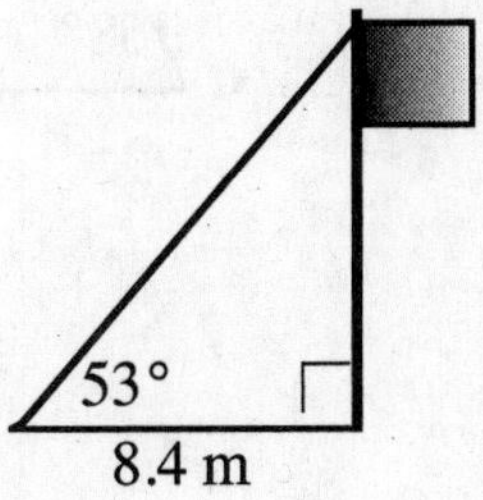

4. A ladder 5.3 m long is inclined at an angle of 72° to the ground.

a) How far up the wall, to the nearest tenth of a metre, does the ladder reach?

b) Use trigonometry to determine, to the nearest tenth of a metre, the distance between the bottom of the ladder and the bottom of the wall.

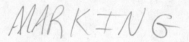

MARKING

c) Use the answer to a) and the Pythagorean Theorem to determine, to the nearest tenth of a metre, the distance between the bottom of the ladder and the bottom of the wall.

d) Explain why the answers to b) and c) are different.

5. Calculate, to the nearest tenth, the length of the indicated side in each triangle.

a)

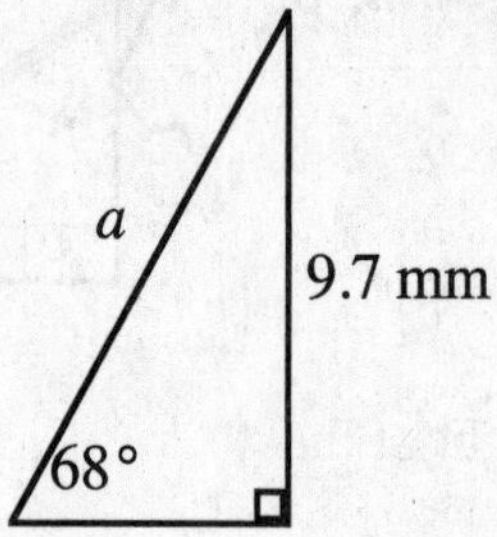

b)

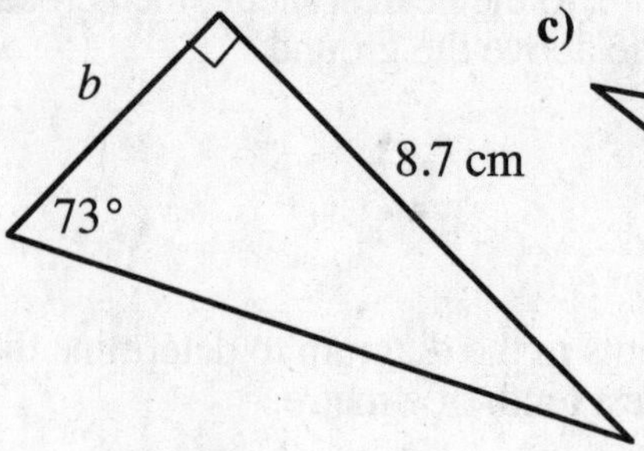

c)

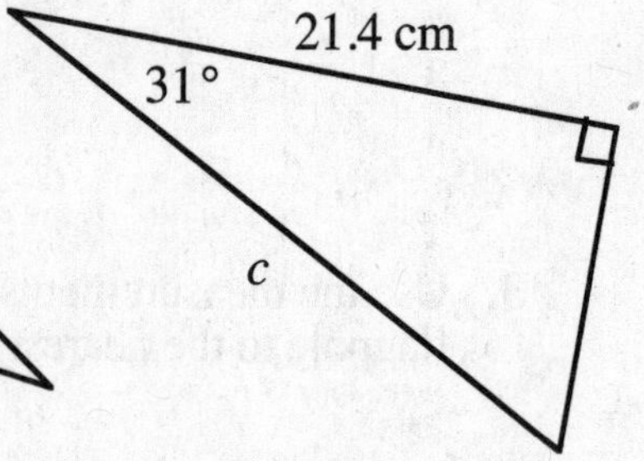

d)

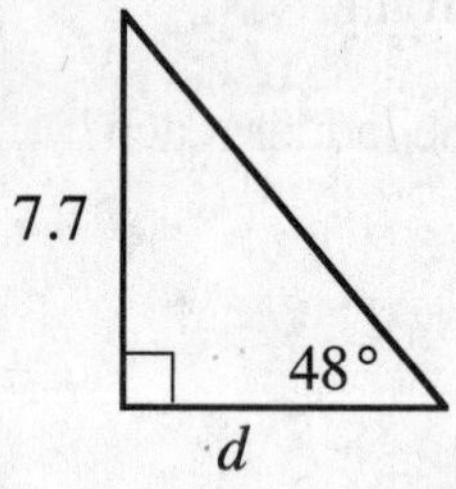

e)

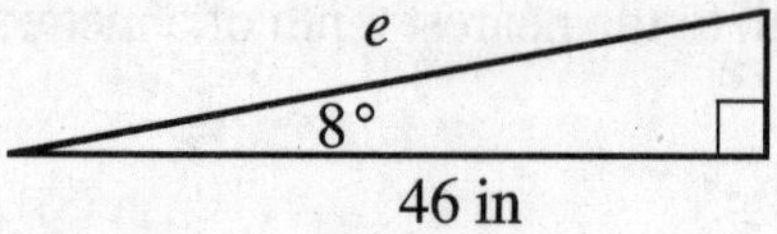

f)

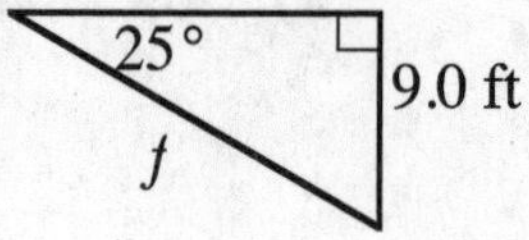

6. Calculate, to the nearest tenth of a cm, the length of the indicated side in each triangle.

a)

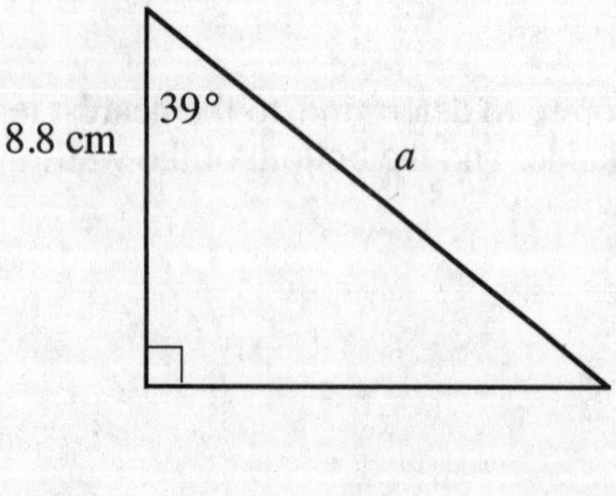

b)

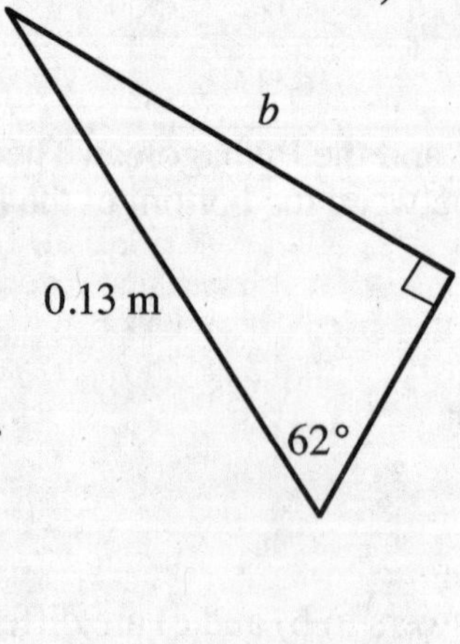

c)

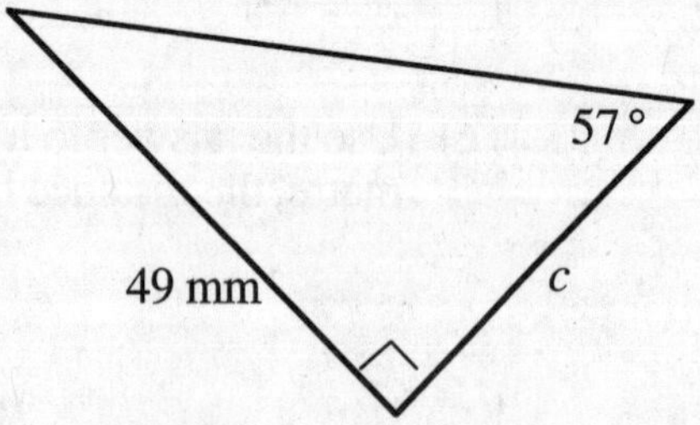

7. Explain why trigonometric ratios could not be used to calculate the side marked x in each of the following triangles.

a)

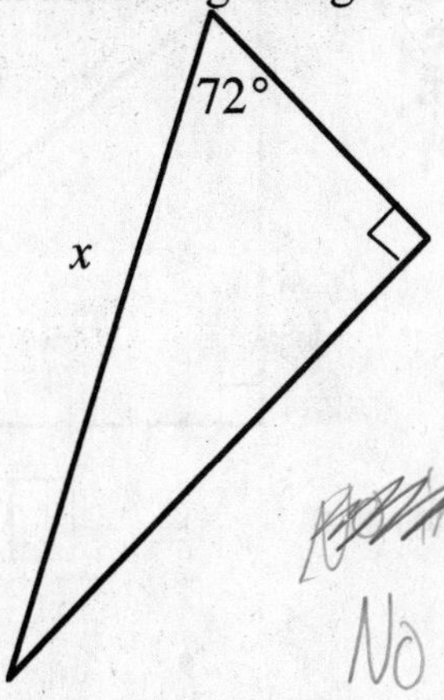

b)

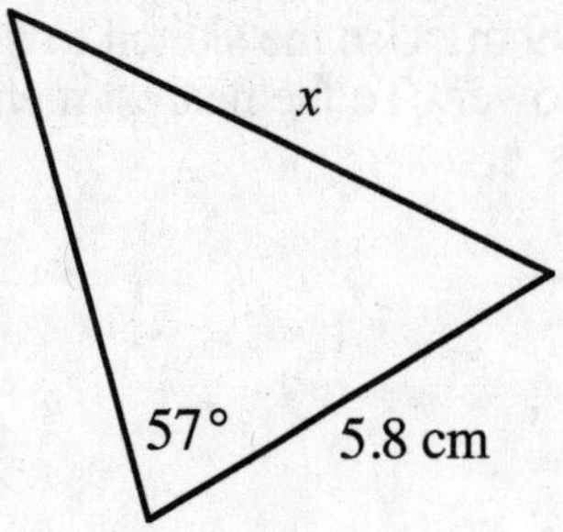

c)

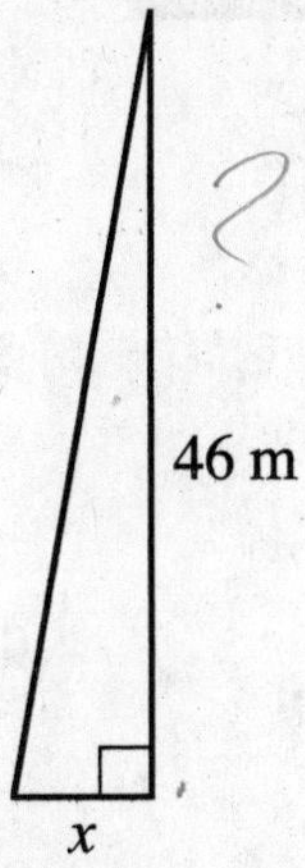

8. Determine, to the nearest tenth, the length of the hypotenuse of the following triangles.

a) Triangle PQR in which angle $QPR = 90°$, angle $PRQ = 47°$ and $PQ = 34.1$ mm.

b) $\triangle ABC$ in which $\angle ABC = 90°$, $\angle BCA = 29°$ and $BC = 8.4$ cm.

9. Calculate, to the nearest tenth, the lengths of LN and MN.

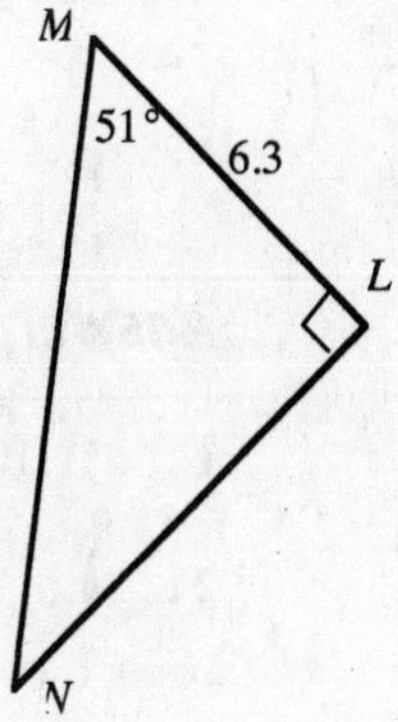

Multiple Choice **10.** Triangle DEF is right angled at F. Angle $DEF = 36°$ and $DF = 15$ cm. The length of DE, in cm, is given by

A. $15 \sin 36°$

B. $\dfrac{15}{\cos 36°}$

C. $15 \cos 54°$

D. $\dfrac{15}{\cos 54°}$

Numerical Response **11.** On a particular day, the Eiffel Tower in Paris casts a shadow of 599 m. Use the sketch to determine the height of the tower. To the nearest metre, the height of the tower is

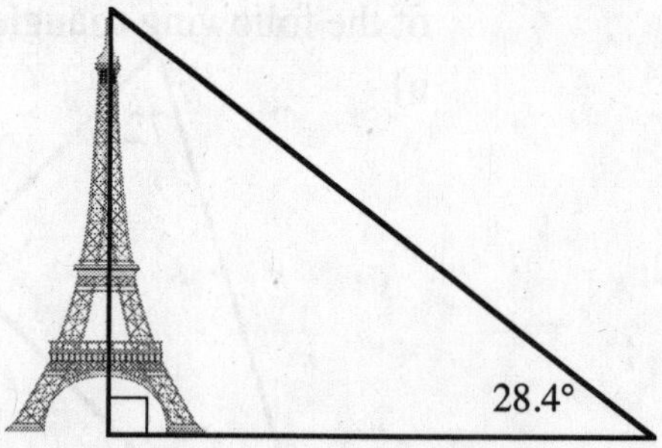

(Record your answer in the numerical response box from left to right)

12. In right triangle *ABC*, angle *ABC* = 90° angle *BAC* = 70° and *AC* = 29 units.

To the nearest whole number, the perimeter of the triangle is ____.

(Record your answer in the numerical response box from left to right)

Answer Key

1. a) 10.5 **b)** 12.7 **c)** 4.4 **d)** 13.0 **e)** 2.7 **f)** 13.0 **g)** 3.9 **h)** 2.1 **i)** 5.5

2. 34 m **3.** 11.1 m **4. a)** 5.0 m **b)** 1.6 m **c)** 1.8 m
d) Using a rounded length leads to a less accurate answer.

5. a) 10.5 mm **b)** 2.7 cm **c)** 25.0 cm **d)** 6.9 **e)** 46.5 in **f)** 21.3 ft

6. a) 11.3 cm **b)** 11.5 cm **c)** 3.2 cm

7. a) There is no side length given. **b)** The triangle is not right angled.
c) We need the measure of one of the acute angles.

8. a) 46.6 mm **b)** 9.6 cm **9.** *LN* = 7.8, *MN* = 10.0 **10.** D

11.

3	2	4	

12.

6	6		

Trigonometry Lesson #4:
Calculating the Measure of an Angle in a Right Triangle

Review

In lesson #2 we learned how to determine the measure of an angle, given a trigonometric ratio for the angle. For review, complete the following example.

Determine, to the nearest degree, the acute angle for which

a) $\sin x° = 0.45$ **b)** $\cos y° = 0.1624$ **c)** $\tan z° = 5.2$

$x° =$ $y° =$ $z° =$

Calculating the Measure of an Angle

In order to use the trigonometric ratios to determine the measure of an angle in a right triangle, we need to know the lengths of two of the sides of the triangle.

Complete the following work for the diagram shown.

Relative to the angle $a°$, 16 is the length of the ADJACENT side and 34 is the length of the ___Hyp___.

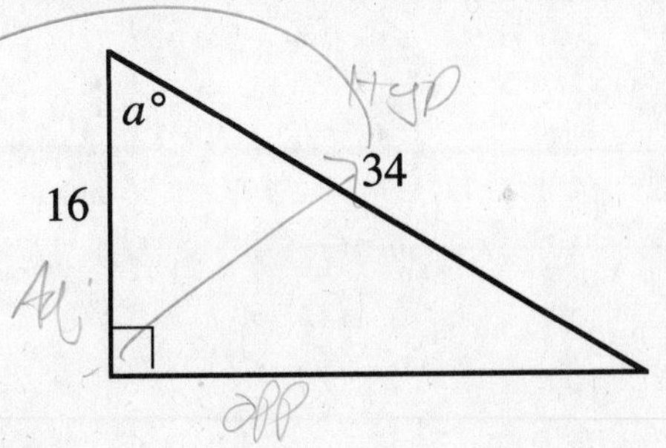

The trigonometric ratio which involves the ADJACENT and the ______ is the ___cos___ ratio.

__cos__ $a° = \frac{16}{34}$ so $a° =$

In each case, calculate the measure of the indicated angle to the nearest degree.

a)

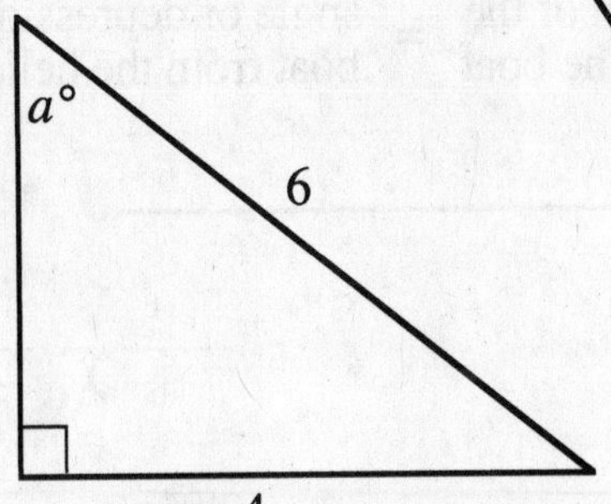

b)

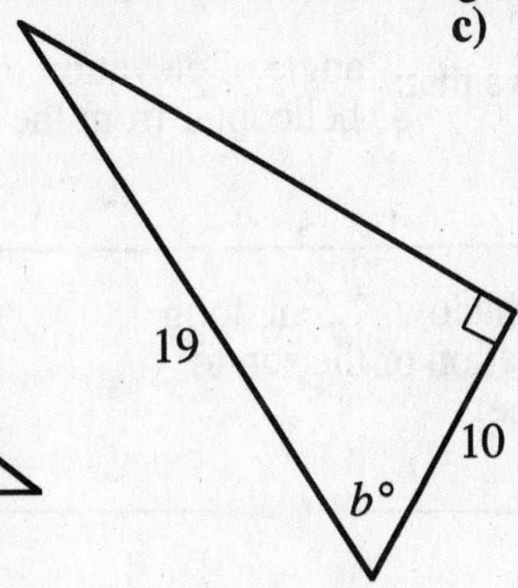

c)

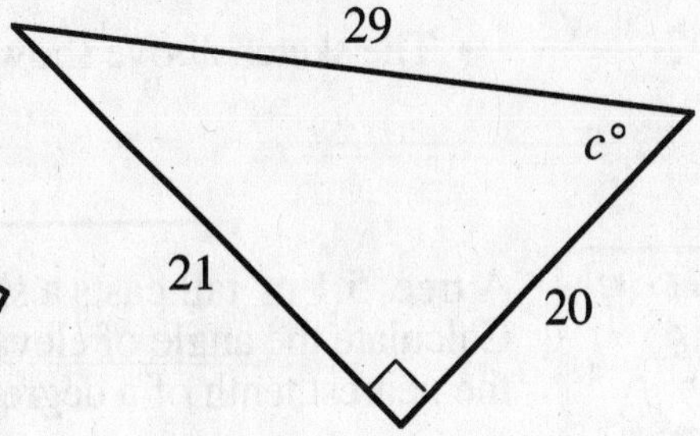

Complete Assignment Questions #1 - #5

Angle of Elevation, Angle of Depression

- The angle of elevation is measured **upwards** from the **horizontal**. The sketch at the right illustrates the angle of elevation of the helicopter from the boat.

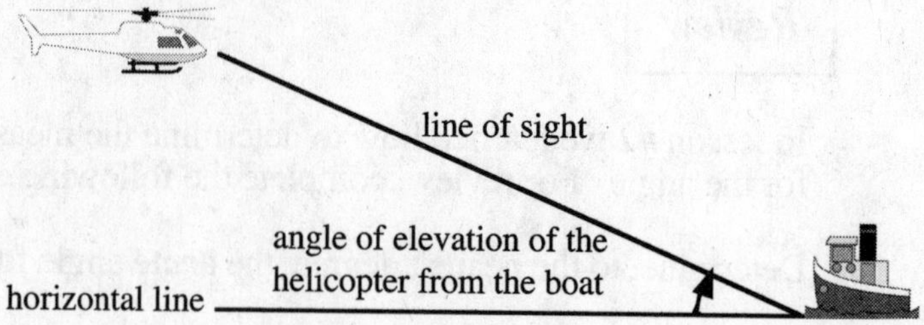

- The angle of depression is measured **downwards** from the **horizontal**. The sketch at the right illustrates the angle of depression of the boat from the helicopter.

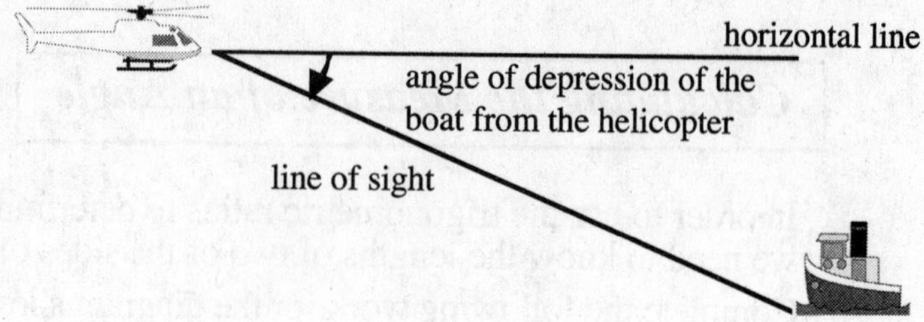

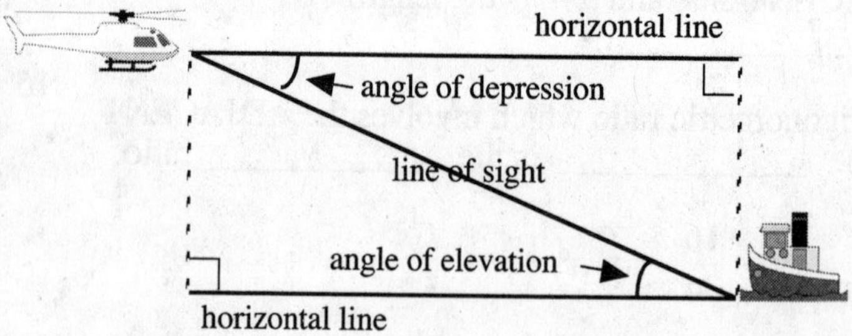

- Note that angles of elevation and angles of depression are determined from the horizontal and NOT from the vertical.

- The sketch above shows that: angle of elevation of the helicopter from the boat = angle of depression of the boat from the helicopter

A tree 5.1 m tall casts a shadow 7.5 m long. Calculate the angle of elevation of the sun to the nearest tenth of a degree.

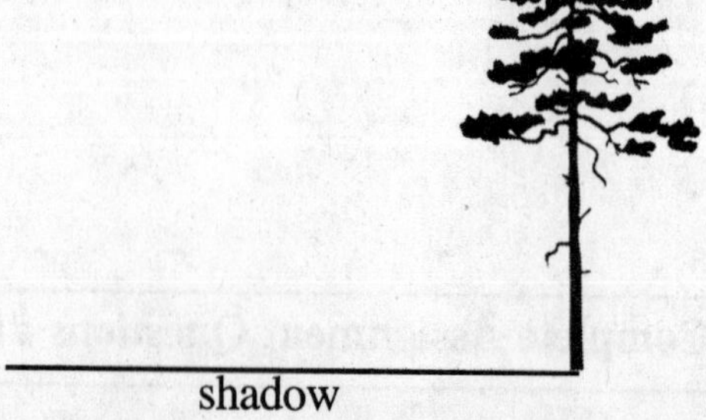

Class Ex. #3

A boat is 130 m from the base of a cliff. The cliff is 80 m high.

a) Draw a diagram to represent this scenario and mark the angle of depression of the boat from the top of the cliff.

b) Determine, to the nearest degree, the angle of depression of the boat from the top of the cliff.

Isosceles Triangles

Class Ex. #4

Consider isosceles triangle *KLM* in which $KL = 20$ cm, $LM = 20$ cm, and $KM = 30$ cm.

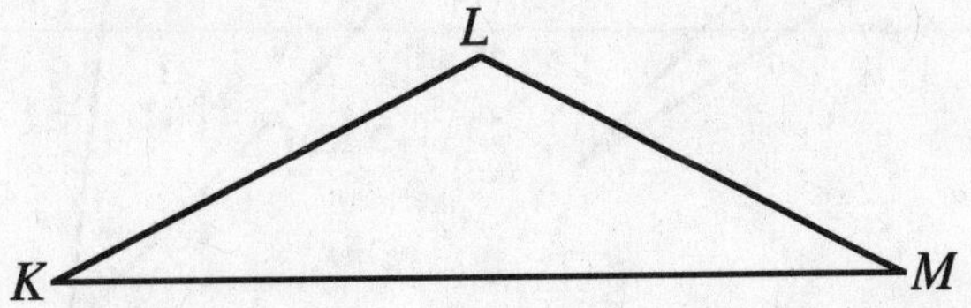

a) Why can we not use SOHCAHTOA in triangle *KLM* to determine the measure of angle *KLM*?

b) Determine, to the nearest degree, the measure of angle *KLM* by splitting triangle *KLM* into two congruent triangles.

Complete Assignment Questions #6 - #14

Assignment

1. In each case, calculate the measure of the indicated angle to the nearest degree.

a)

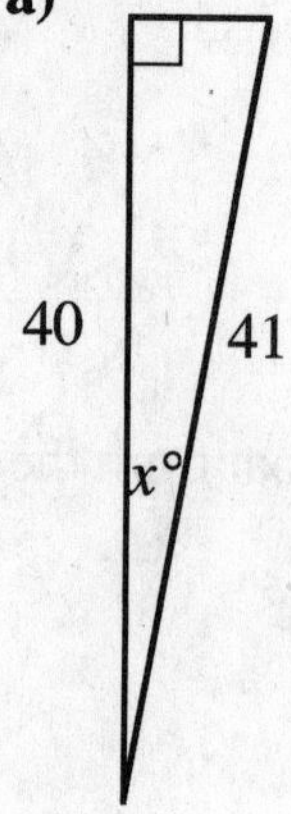

b)

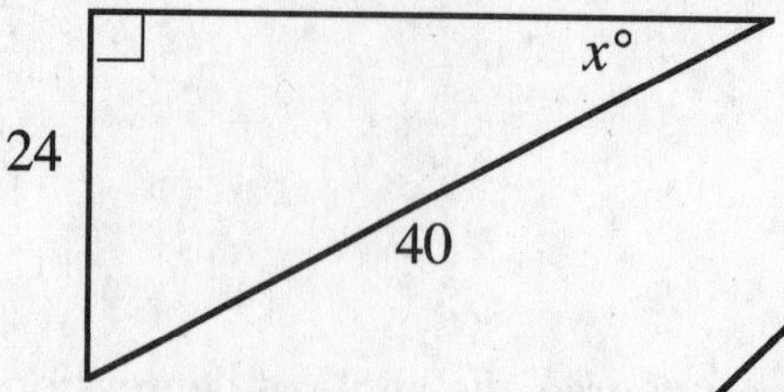

c)

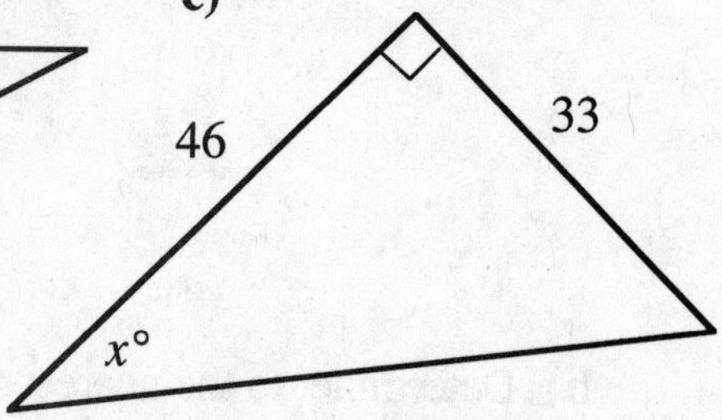

2. In each case, calculate the measure of the indicated angle to the nearest tenth.

a)

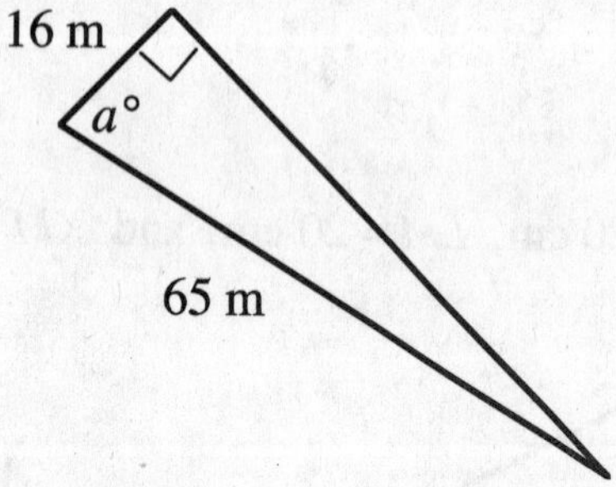

b)

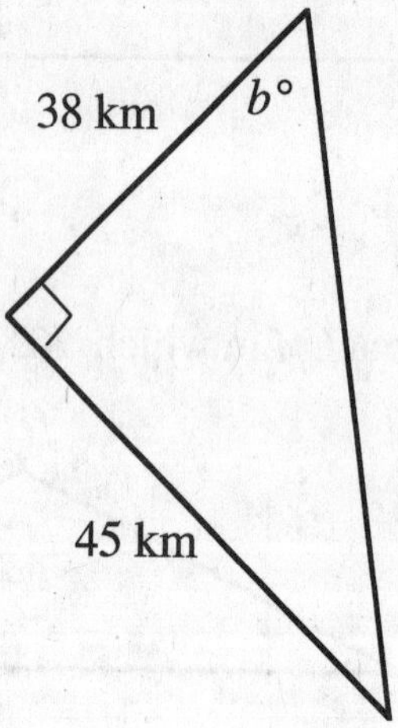

c)

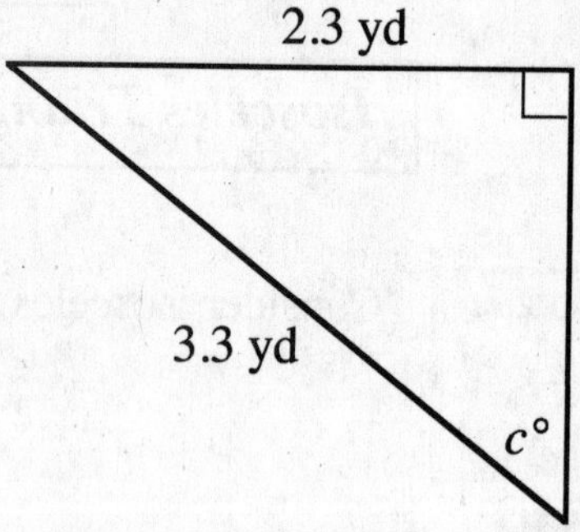

3. In each case, calculate the measure of the indicated angle to the nearest degree.

a)

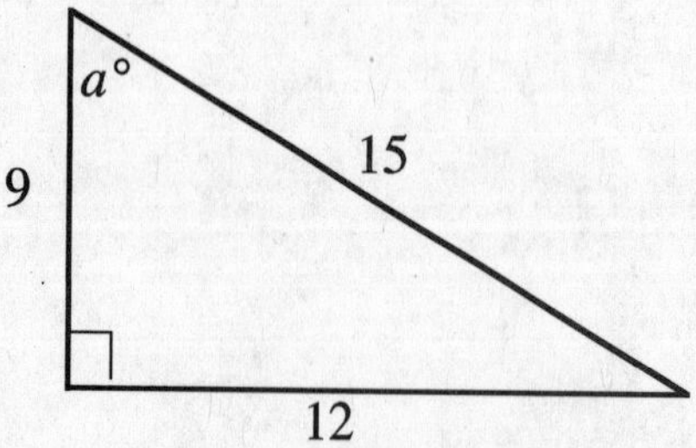

b)

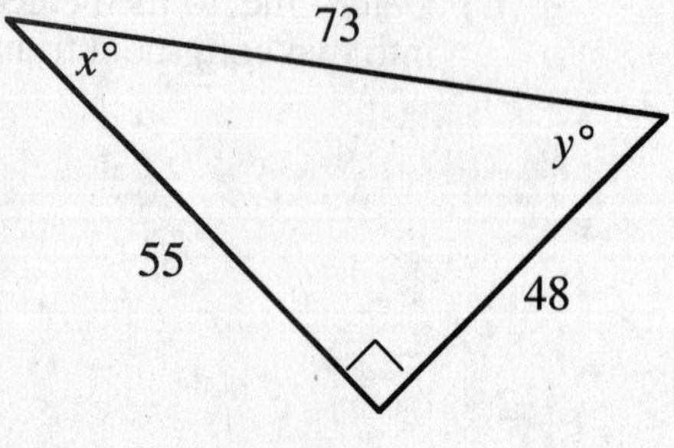

4. Consider the diagram consisting of two right triangles with a common side *AD*.

a) Use the Pythagorean Theorem to calculate the length of *AD*.

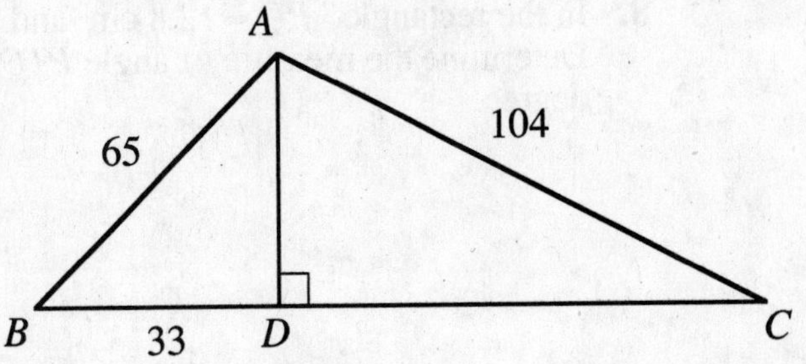

b) Determine, to the nearest degree, the measure of angle *BCA*.

5. Determine the measure of angle *LKN* to the nearest degree.

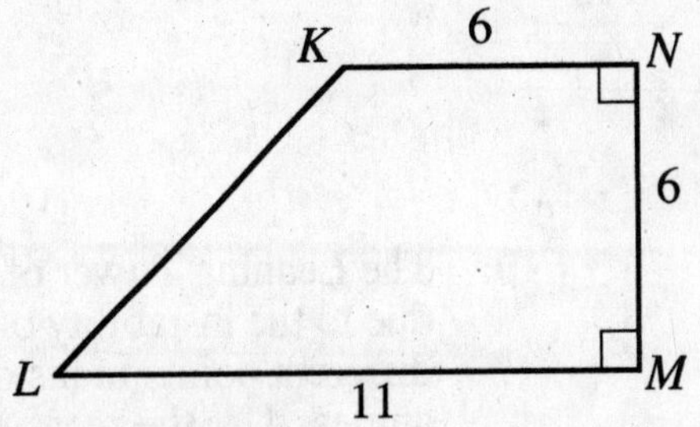

6. A pylon 23.7 m high casts a shadow 46.8 m long.
Determine the angle of elevation of the sun to the nearest tenth of a degree.

7. In each case calculate the size of $\angle BAC$ to the nearest degree.

a)

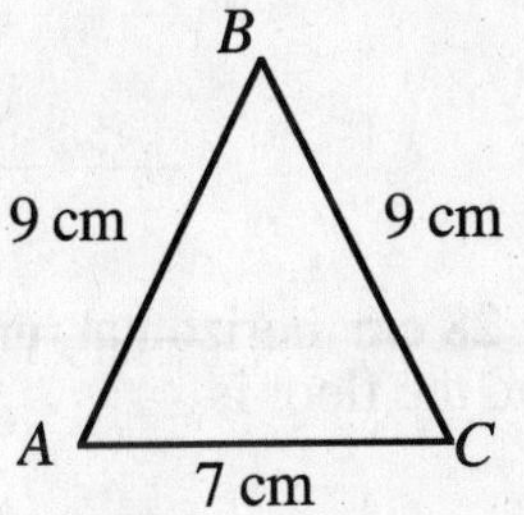

b)

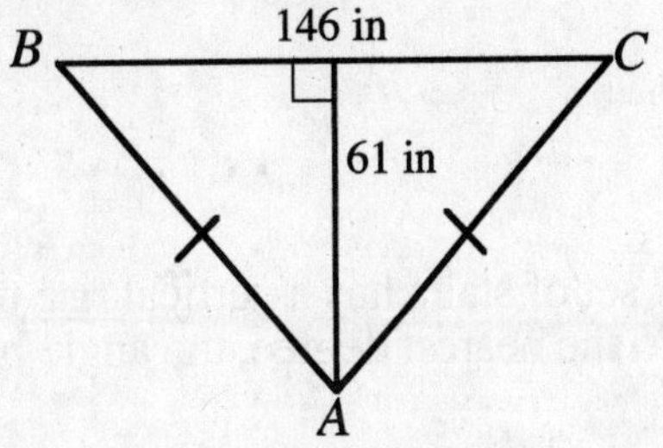

8. In the rectangle, $PQ = 12.8$ cm and $QR = 7.4$ cm. Determine the measure of angle PTQ to the nearest degree.

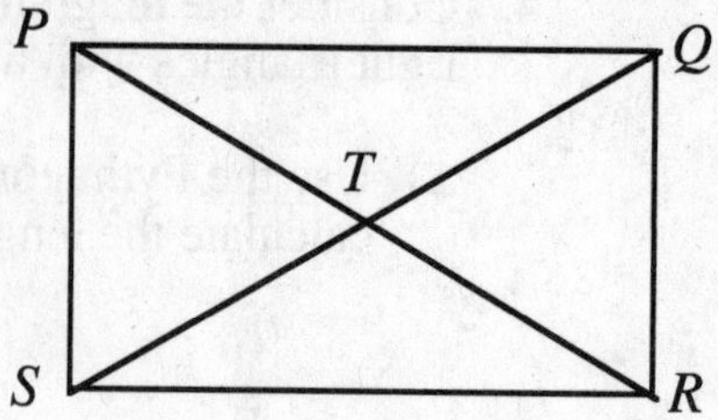

9. The term "% grade" is sometimes used to describe the slope of a road. For example, a road with a 7% grade has a vertical rise of 7 m for every horizontal distance of 100 m. Calculate, to the nearest degree, the angle a road with a 7% grade makes with the horizontal.

10. The Leaning Tower of Pisa is a building in Italy which leans due to the instability of the ground underneath it. At different points in history the tower has leaned at different angles. Use the measurements in the sketch to determine the angle of lean from the vertical to the nearest hundredth of a degree.

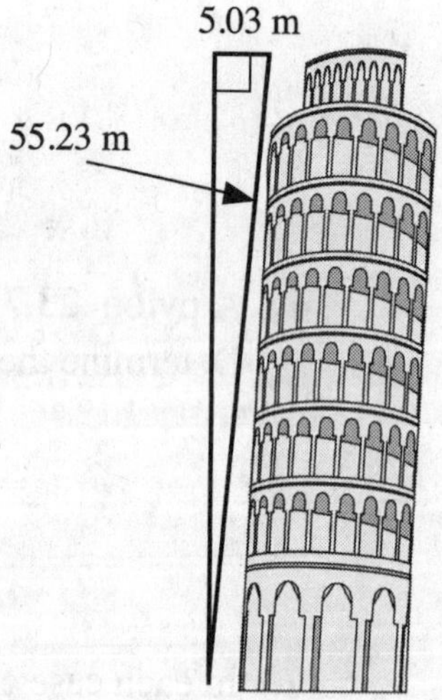

Multiple Choice **11.** A set of stairs has a vertical rise of 15 cm for every 28 cm horizontal run. To the nearest degree, the angle between the stairs and the floor is

A. 28°
B. 32°
C. 62°
D. 64°

Numerical Response **12.** A tourist at the top of a lighthouse spots a boat in the water below. The angle of depression of the boat from the tourist is 35°. At the same moment in time, the angle of elevation of the tourist from the boat, to the nearest degree, is _____.

(Record your answer in the numerical response box from left to right)

Numerical Response **13.** A corner flag in a World Cup soccer match is 5 feet high. At game time, the flag casts a shadow which is 3.2 feet long. To the nearest 0.1 degree, the angle of elevation of the sun is _____.

(Record your answer in the numerical response box from left to right)

Numerical Response **14.** A submarine goes into a dive at a certain angle of depression and travels 275 m while making its dive. When the submarine stops its dive it has dropped a vertical distance of 150 m. To the nearest tenth of a degree, the angle of depression of the dive is _____.

(Record your answer in the numerical response box from left to right)

Answer Key

1. a) 13° **b)** 37° **c)** 36° **2. a)** 75.7° **b)** 49.8° **c)** 44.2°

3. a) 53° **b)** $x = 41°, y = 49°$ **4. a)** 56 **b)** 33° **5.** 130° **6.** 26.9°

7. a) 67° **b)** 100° **8.** 120° **9.** 4° **10.** 5.23° **11.** A

12.

3	5		

13.

5	7	.	4

14.

3	3	.	1

Trigonometry Lesson #5:
Determining Angles and Sides in Right Triangles

Overview

In lesson #3 we learned how to calculate the length of a side in a right triangle using the Pythagorean Theorem and using trigonometry.

In lesson #4 we learned how to calculate the measure of an angle in a right triangle using trigonometry.

In this lesson we combine both procedures in solving right triangles.

Class Ex. #1

In each case, calculate the measure of x to the nearest whole number.

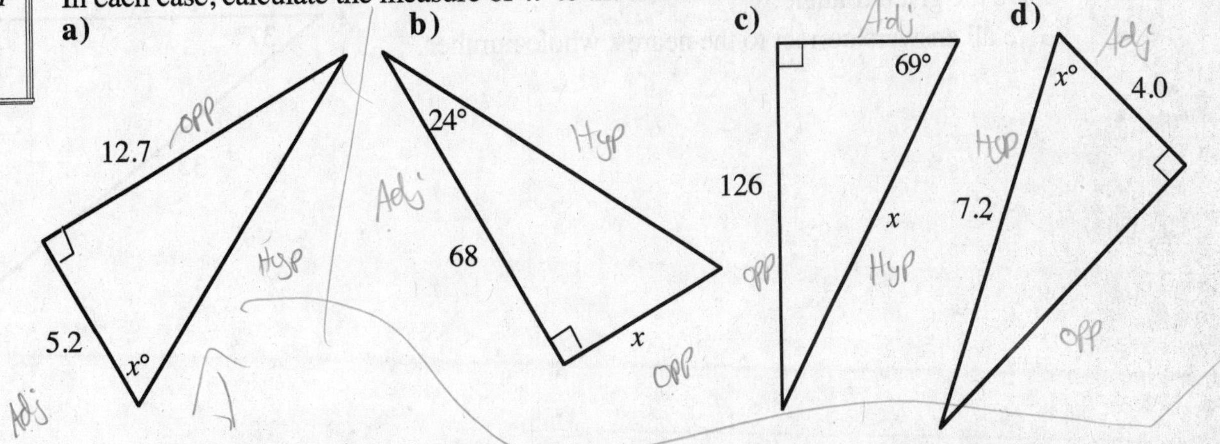

SOH CAH TOA $T = \frac{O}{A} \Rightarrow \frac{12.7}{5.2}$ $\tan^{-1}$ 68°

Class Ex. #2

A telephone pole is 11 m high, and is supported by a wire 13 m long fixed to the top of the pole and to the ground.

a) Calculate, to the nearest degree, the angle between the wire and the ground.

b) Calculate the distance, to the nearest 0.1 m, between the point where the wire is fixed to the ground and the foot of the pole using

i) the Pythagorean Theorem   **ii)** trigonometry.

Complete Assignment Questions #1 - #6

Solving Right Triangles

Solving a right triangle means that we have to determine the length of each side and the measure of each angle. In addition to the right angle, we need to know the length of one side and one other piece of information.

Depending on the information given, we can use the Pythagorean Theorem and/or trigonometry to solve the triangle.

Class Ex. #3

Solve the given triangle.
Give all answers correct to the nearest whole number.

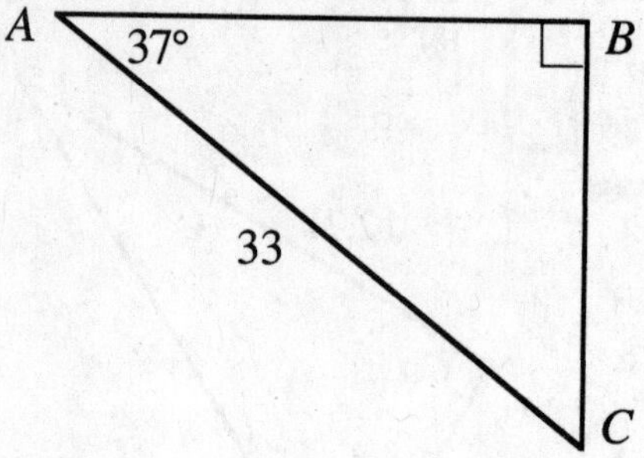

Class Ex. #4

Solve triangle *DEF*. Give all sides correct to the nearest tenth and all angles correct to the nearest whole number.

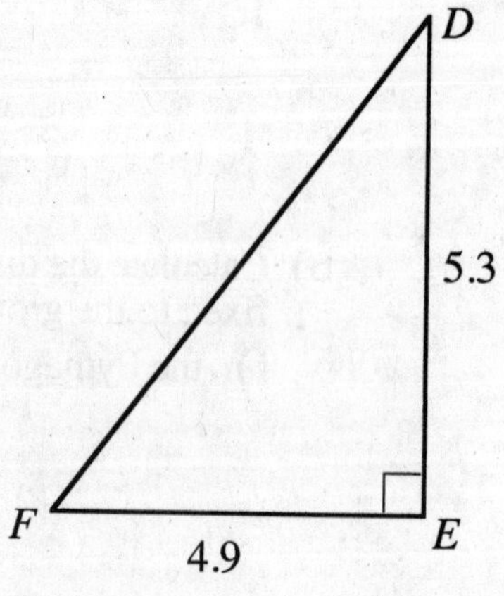

Complete Assignment Questions #7 - #17

Assignment

1. In each case calculate the indicated measure. Give angles to the nearest degree and sides to the nearest tenth.

a)

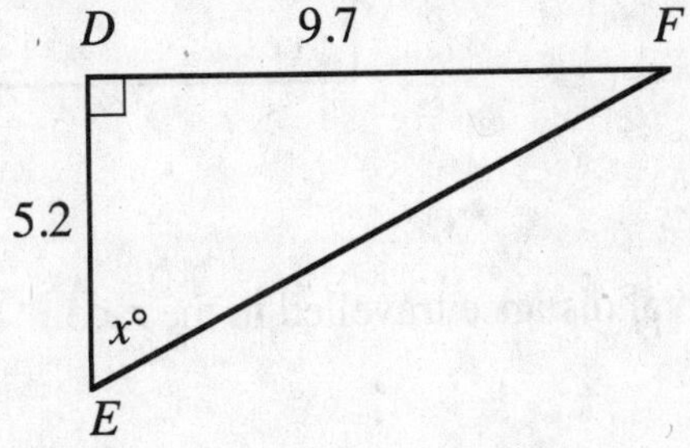

b)

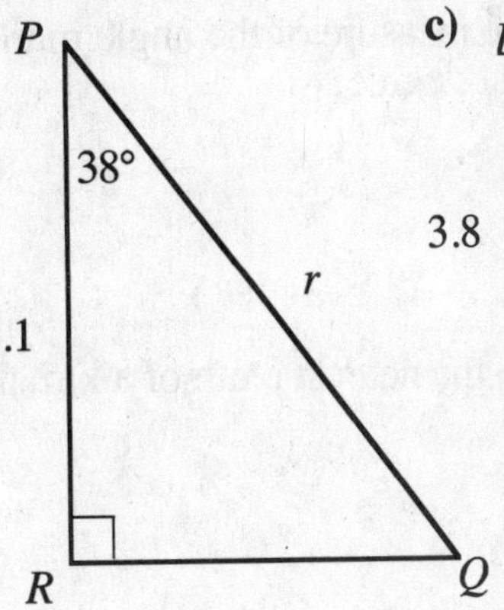

c)

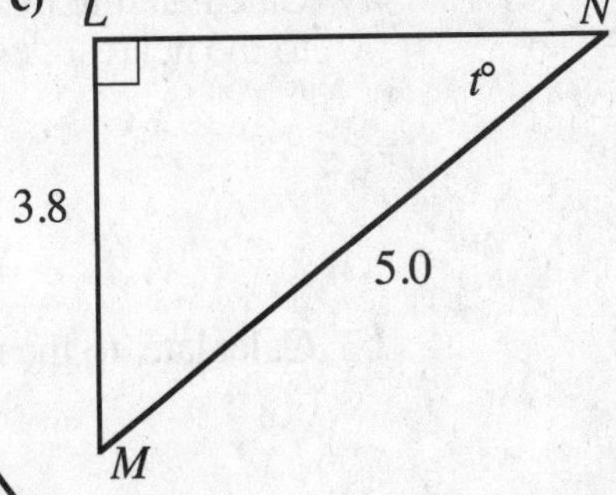

d)

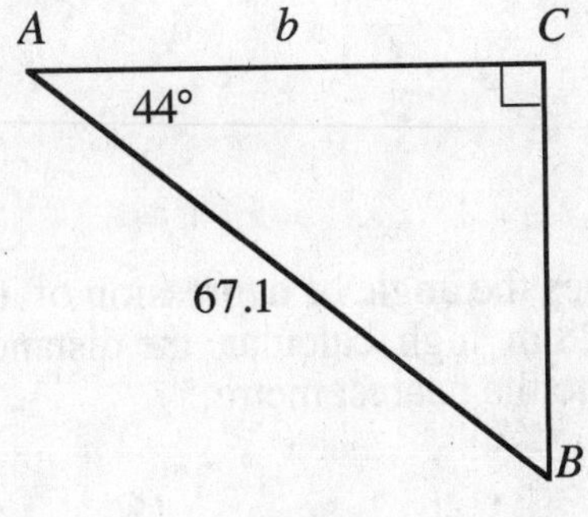

e)

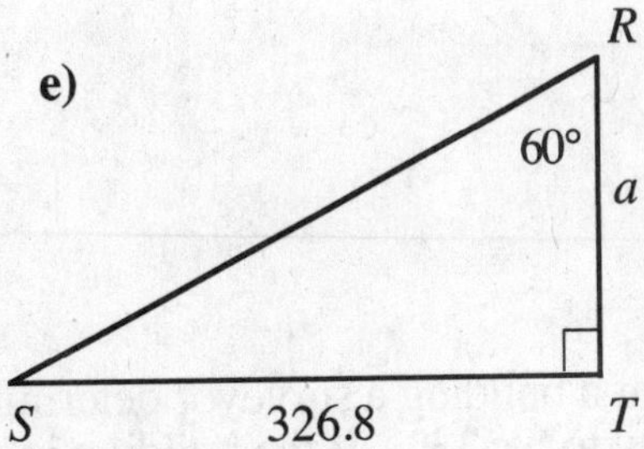

f)

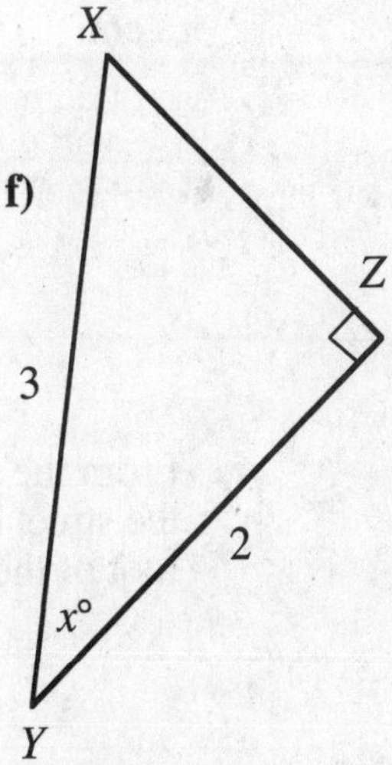

2. A mine shaft which slopes at an angle of 19° to the horizontal is driven into a hillside for 400 m. How much lower, to the nearest metre, is the end of the shaft than the beginning?

3. In a yacht race over a triangular course the instructions are: "Sail due west to a buoy 6 km away, then due north to a buoy 5 km away, and then return directly to the starting point".

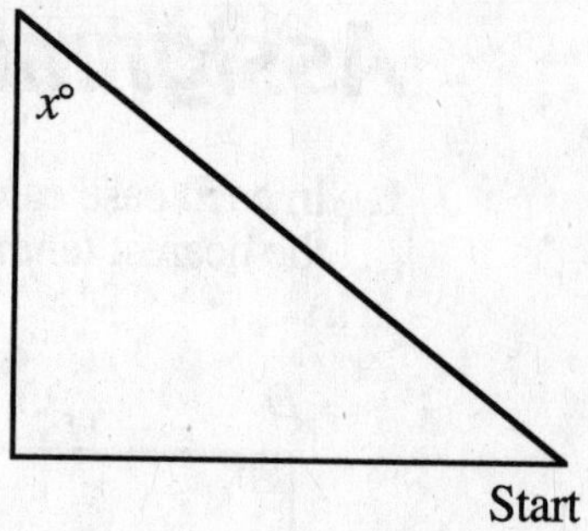

a) Calculate the measure of the angle marked x, to the nearest degree.

b) Calculate, to the nearest tenth of a km, the total distance travelled in the race.

4. The diagonal of a rectangle is 35 cm long and makes an angle of 58° with the shorter side of the rectangle. Determine the length and width of the rectangle to the nearest tenth of a cm.

5. From the top of a building a surveyor determines the angle of depression of a parked car on the street below to be 33°. If the building is 28 m high, calculate the distance from the foot of the building to the parked car. Answer to the nearest metre.

6. A pendulum 65 cm long swings through an angle of 40°. Calculate the distance, to the nearest 0.1 cm, between the two extreme positions of the pendulum bob.

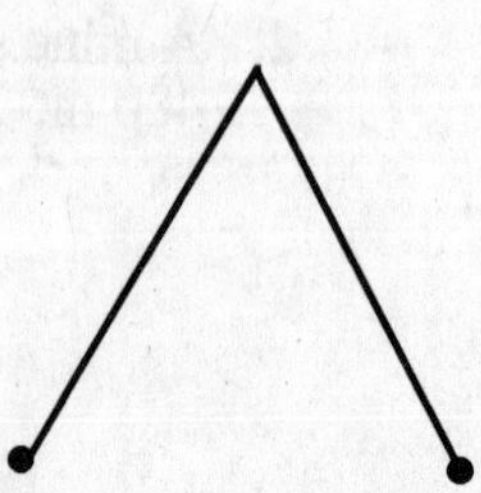

7. Solve triangle *ABC* giving each measure correct to the nearest whole number.

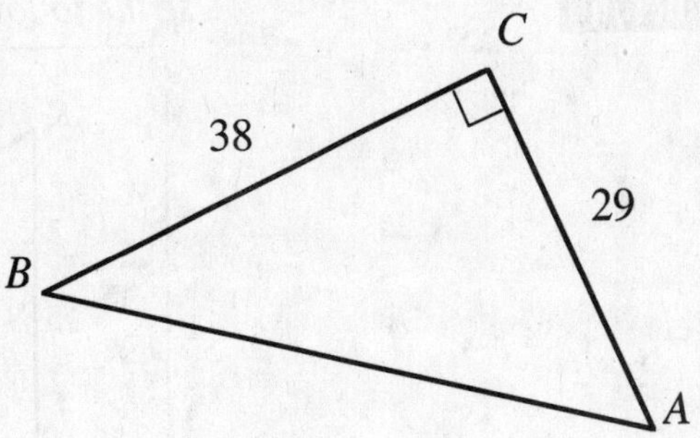

8. Solve triangle *RST*. Give all sides correct to the nearest tenth and all angles correct to the nearest whole number.

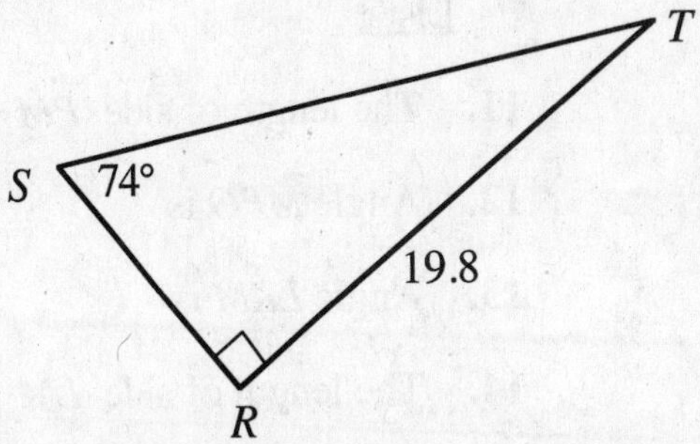

9. Solve triangle *DEF* in which angle *DEF* = 90°, angle *EDF* = 50° and *DF* = 173 mm. Give all answers to the nearest whole number.

10. Why is it not possible to solve $\triangle PQR$ in which $\angle PQR = 90°$, $\angle PRQ = 67°$ and $\angle QPR = 23°$?

Matching

Use the following information for the matching question

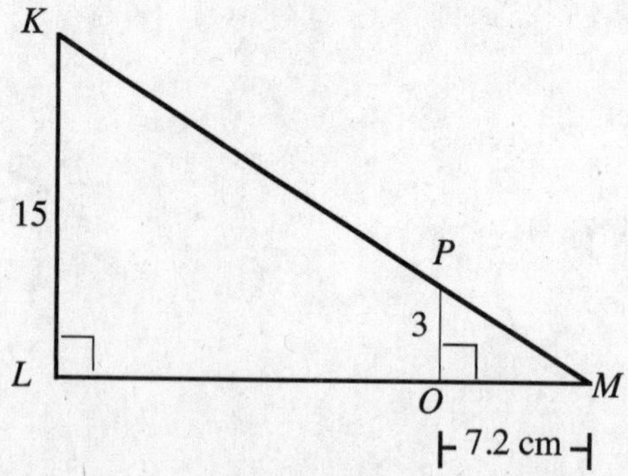

Match each item in List 1 on the left with the equivalent item in List 2 on the right. Each item in List 2 may be used once, more than once, or not at all.

List 1

11. The length of side PM is

12. Angle MPO is

13. Angle LKM is

14. The length of side LM is

15. The length of side LO is

16. Angle PMO is

17. The length of side KP is

List 2

A. 67.4° **B.** 31.2 **C.** 36.0 **D.** 22.6° **E.** 7.8

F. 15.8 **G.** 29.3 **H.** 28.8 **I.** 39.0

Answer Key

1.a) 62° **b)** 67.4 **c)** 49° **d)** 48.3 **e)** 188.7 **f)** 48° **2.** 130 m

3.a) 50° **b)** 18.8 km **4.** length = 29.7 cm, width = 18.5 cm **5.** 43 m **6.** 44.5 cm

7. angle ABC = 37°, angle BAC = 53°, angle ACB = 90°, AB = 48, AC = 29, BC = 38

8. angle RST = 74°, angle SRT = 90°, angle RTS = 16°, RT = 19.8, RS = 5.7, ST = 20.6.

9. angle DEF = 90°, angle EDF = 50°, angle DFE = 40°, DF = 173 mm, DE = 111 mm, EF = 133 mm

10. No side length is given. **11.** E **12.** A **13.** A **14.** C **15.** H **16.** D **17.** B

Trigonometry Lesson #6:
Problem Solving Using Trigonometric Ratios

Overview

In this lesson we use our knowledge of trigonometry to solve problems including situations in which more than one calculation is required to determine the solution to a problem.

The illustrations in this lesson are not to scale and are for sketch purposes only.

Karmen is a surveyor who is using a transit to determine the height of a tree. The transit is placed 52 m from the base of the tree and the angle to the top of the tree is measured to be 12°.

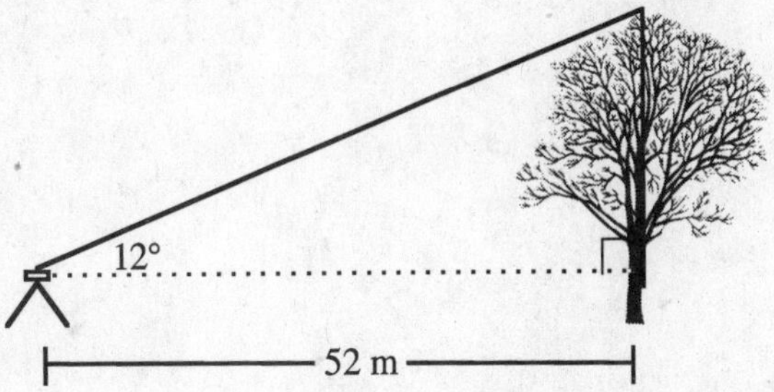

a) If the transit stands 1.8 m high, calculate the height of the tree to the nearest tenth of a metre.

b) Determine the angle the base of the transit makes with the top of the tree. Answer to the nearest degree.

A circle with centre C and radius 20 mm is tangent to the arms of angle POQ.

If angle $POQ = 50°$ determine the length of OC to the nearest mm.

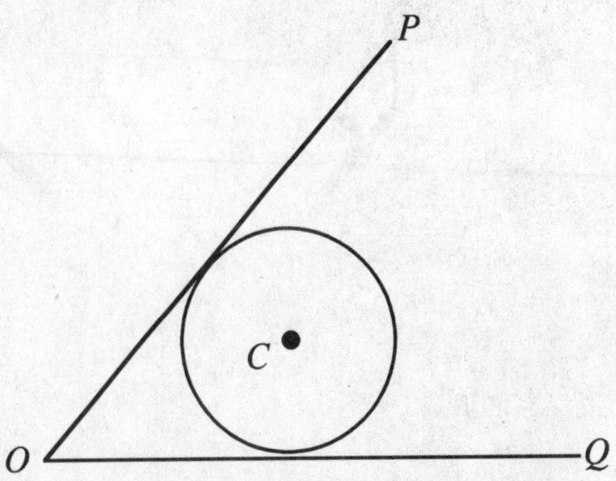

In many problems the angle of elevation or depression is determined from the person's eye level and not from the ground.

In the diagram the man on the ground is standing 12 feet from the wall.
The angle of elevation from his eye level to the eye level of his wife in the building is 62°.

If the man's eye level is 6.0 feet above the ground and his wife's eye level is 5.2 feet from the top of the building, determine the height of the building to the nearest tenth of a foot.

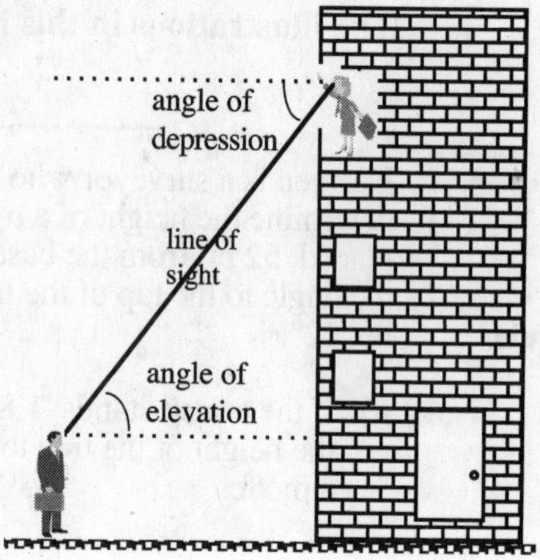

Bearings

A bearing is an angle measured clockwise from the North direction.

The boat is on a bearing of 40° (often written using three figures as 040°)

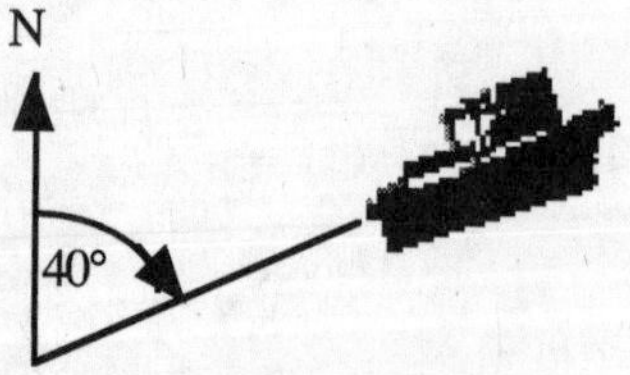

Here are three other bearings.

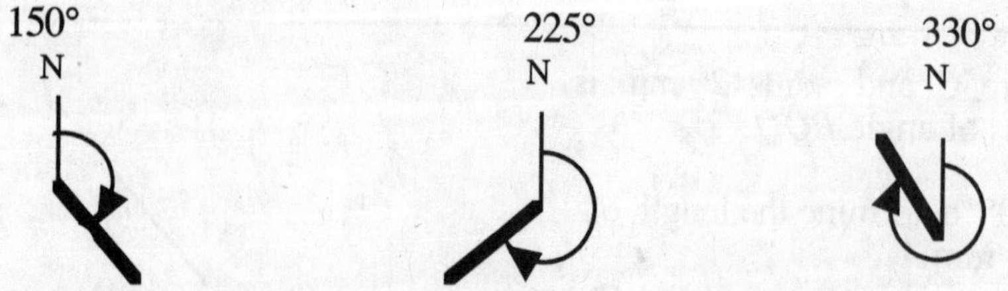

Class Ex. #4

A ship travels 6 km from a port, P, on a bearing of 120° to position Q as shown.

a) The ship changes direction at Q and travels north until it reaches position R which is due east of P.
How far east of P is the ship at position R? Answer to the nearest 0.1 km.

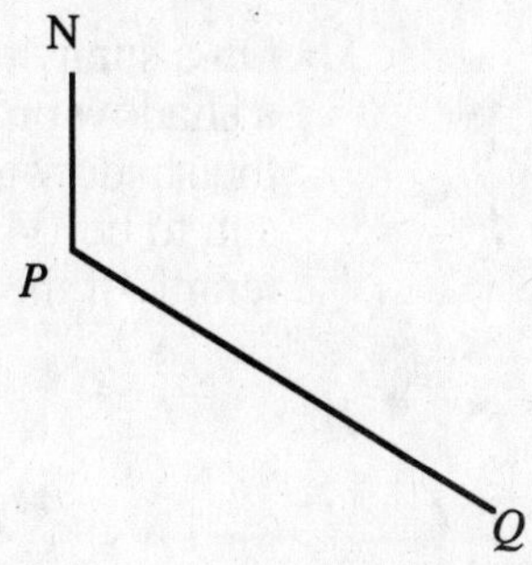

b) The ship continues travelling north for a further 12 km to position S.
Determine the bearing of S from P.

c) If the ship maintains an average speed of 9 km/h throughout the journey, determine, to the nearest tenth of an hour, the time taken for the journey.

Complete Assignment Questions #1 - #9

Assignment

1. On a sunny day, the Eiffel Tower, 1063 ft high, casts a shadow on the ground. A tourist stands at the end of the shadow and measures the angle of elevation of the sun to be 34.1°. Determine, to the nearest foot, the length of the shadow.

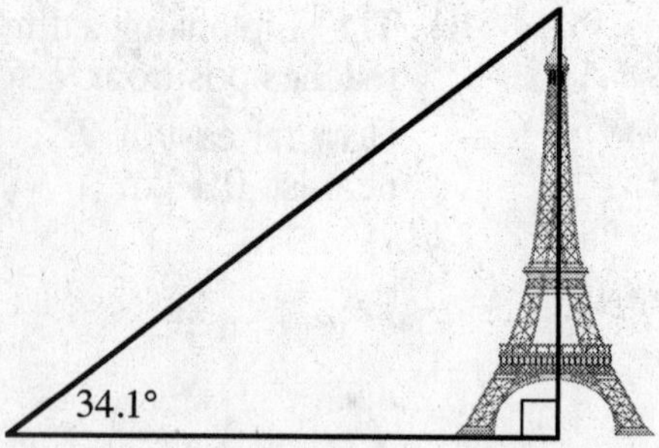

2. In the diagram, AB is a diameter of a circle. $\angle CAB = 38°$ and $CB = 7.1$ cm.

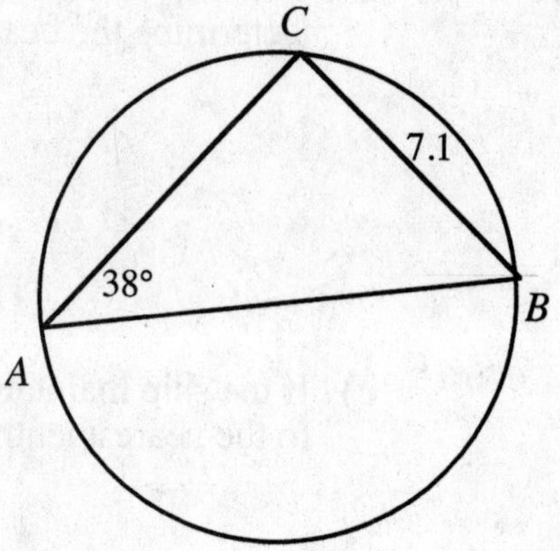

a) Explain why $\angle ACB = 90°$.

b) Determine the radius of the circle to the nearest tenth of a cm.

3. A boat is 300 m away from the foot of a cliff. The angle of elevation from the boat to the top of the cliff is 16°.

a) Show this information on a diagram and determine the height of the cliff to the nearest metre.

b) If the boat then sails 75 m closer to the cliff, determine, to the nearest degree, the new angle of elevation of the cliff top from the boat.

4. A totem pole is being placed in a 2 metre deep hole in the ground. Two ropes attached to the top of the totem pole are used to pull the totem pole upright. The ropes are anchored into the ground on opposite sides of the pole until the hole is filled.
Each rope is 19 m long and is anchored into the ground 12 m horizontally from the centre of the totem pole.

a) Complete the sketch to illustrate this situation.

b) Calculate, to the nearest tenth of a degree, the angle of elevation of the top of the totem pole from the point where the rope is anchored into the ground.

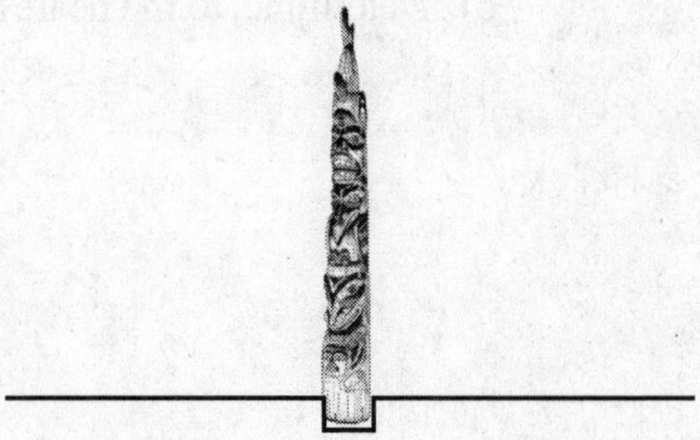

c) Determine, to the nearest 0.1 m, the length of the totem pole before it was placed in the ground.

5. Judy is 60 m south of a main east-west highway. She looks to her right and sees a motor bike rider approaching at a steady speed along the highway. The diagram shows their positions relative to each other.

Twenty seconds later the motor bike rider is directly in front of Judy.
Calculate the speed of the motor bike, to the nearest km/h.

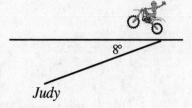

6. A ship sails from a port A on a bearing of 030° for 22 miles to a marker B at which it alters course and sails on a bearing of 075° for 27 miles to its destination C. AN and BM represent north lines.

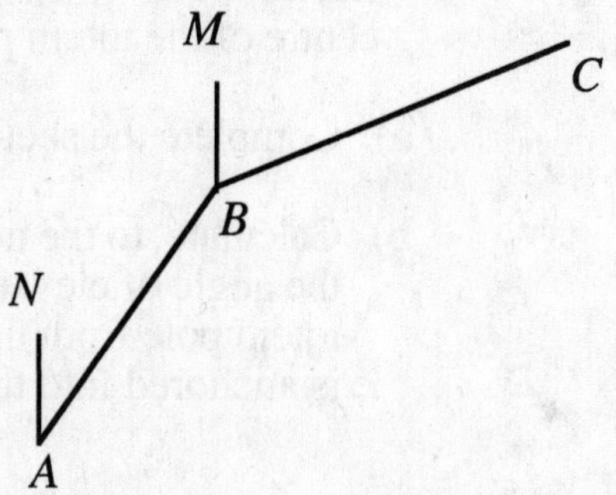

a) On the diagram mark the sizes of $\angle BAN$ and $\angle CBM$.

b) Determine, to the nearest 0.1 mile, how far C is east of A.

c) Determine, to the nearest 0.1 mile, how far C is north of A.

d) Determine, to the nearest 0.1 mile, the direct distance from A to C.

e) Determine the three figure bearing of C from A.

Use the following information to answer questions #7 and #8.

A plane starts from a point P and flies 240 km on a bearing of 120° to Q.
At Q the plane makes a 90° turn and flies 100 km on a bearing of 210° to R.
At R the plane again changes direction and flies back to P.

Multiple Choice

7. The direct distance, in km, from R to P is

A. 140
B. 218
C. 260
D. 340

8. The three figure bearing the pilot uses to fly from R to P is

A. 023°
B. 037°
C. 323°
D. 337°

Numerical Response

9. A set of stairs has a vertical rise of 16 cm for every 27 cm horizontal run. The angle, to the nearest tenth of a degree, between the stairs and the floor is ______.

(Record your answer in the numerical response box from left to right)

Answer Key

1. 1570 ft

2. a) The angle in a semicircle is a right angle. **b)** 5.8 cm

3. a) 86 m **b)** 21°

4. a) see diagram below **b)** 50.8° **c)** 16.7 m

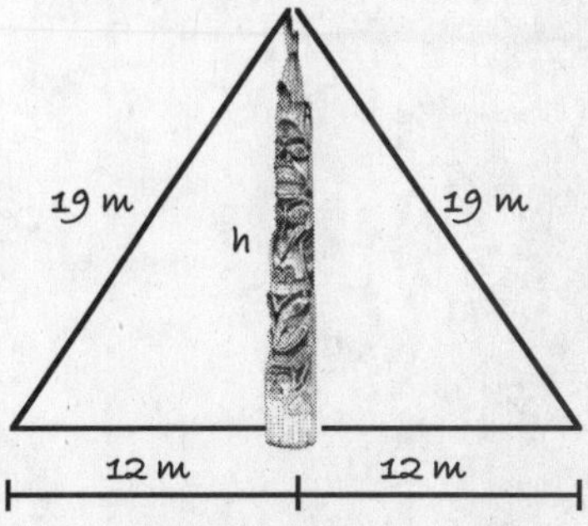

5. 77km/h

6. a) Angle BAN = 30°, angle CBM = 75°. **b)** 37.1 miles
c) 26.0 miles **d)** 45.3 miles **e)** 055°

7. C **8.** C **9.**

3	0	.	7

Trigonometry Lesson #7:
More Problem Solving Using Trigonometric Ratios

Overview

In this lesson we deal with problems involving two right triangles. In many cases we can determine the value of a quantity from one right triangle and then use that value in a second right triangle to determine the solution to a problem. When this situation arises, do not round intermediate answers. Only the final solution should be rounded. **The illustrations in this lesson are not to scale and are for sketch purposes only.**

Problems in Two Dimensions

In the diagram $QS = 32$ mm, angle $PQS = 50°$ and angle $RPS = 61°$.
Use this information to determine the length of QR to the nearest mm.

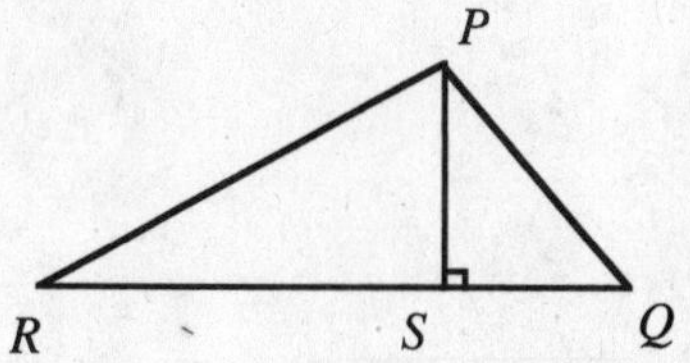

Calculate the measure of $\angle BEC$ to the nearest degree.

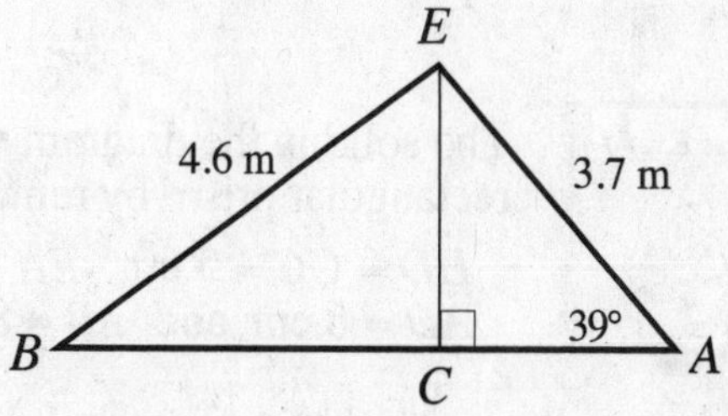

Class Ex. #3

In January 2003, the tallest building in Rockyville was the Metro Building. Recently, a developer was commissioned by the Gammapro Oil Company to build a taller building next to the Metro Building. From the top of the Metro Building, the angle of elevation of the top of the Gammapro Building is $24°$ and the angle of depression to the foot of the Gammapro Building is $56°$. If the buildings are 45 m apart, determine the height of each building to the nearest metre.

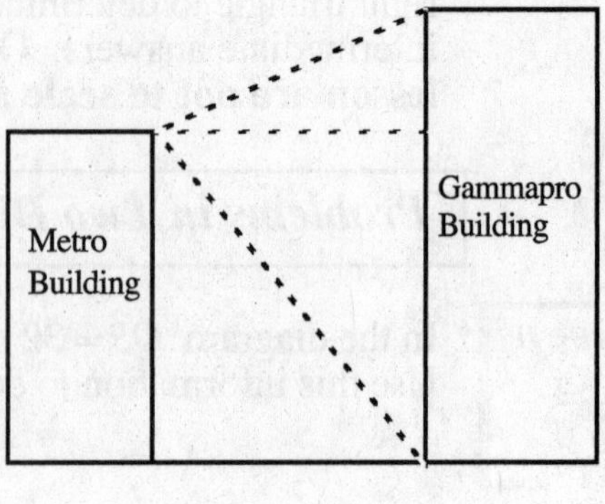

Complete Assignment Questions #1 - #6

Problems in Three Dimensions

As an aid to understanding a problem in three dimensions, we sketch a two dimensional representation of the triangle we are working with.

Class Ex. #4

The solid in the diagram was formed from a rectangular prism by removing a wedge.
$HD = GC = 5$ cm. $EA = FB = 2$ cm.
$AD = 6$ cm and $AB = 8$ cm.

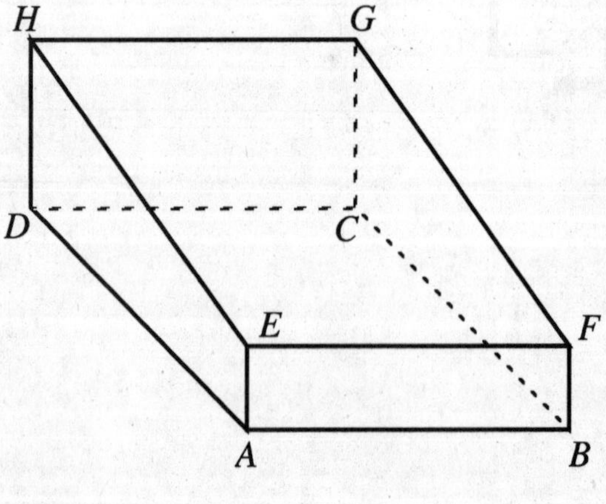

a) Name four rectangles in the diagram.

b) Calculate the measure of $\angle HEA$ to the nearest degree.

c) Calculate the measure of angle *HFE* to the nearest degree.

d) Calculate the measure of angle *HBD* to the nearest degree.

Complete Assignment Questions #7 - #10

Assignment

1. Determine the length of *PQ*, to the nearest 0.1 cm.

a)

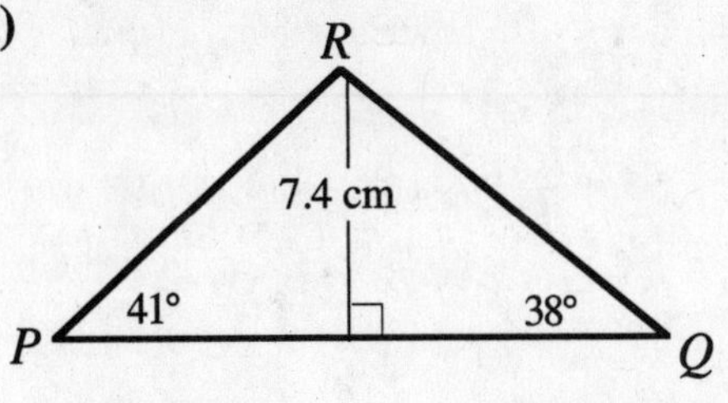

b)

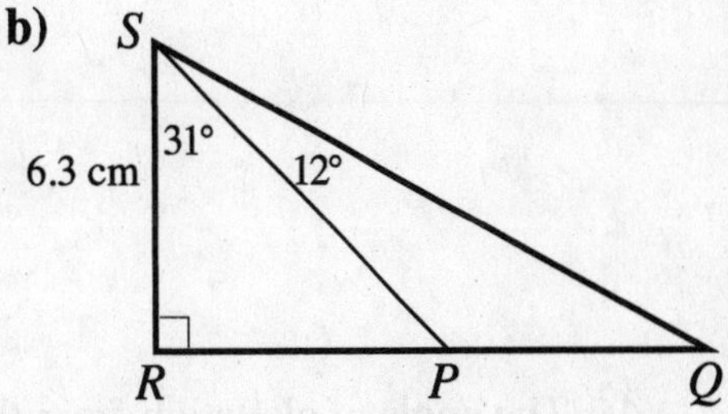

c)

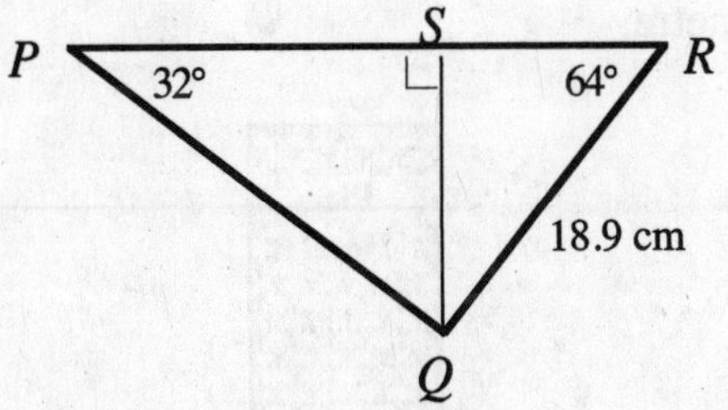

d)

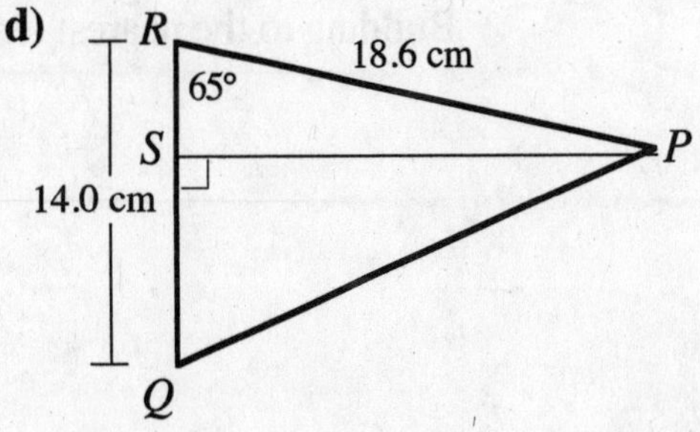

2. Determine the measure of angle *ABC*, to the nearest degree.

a)

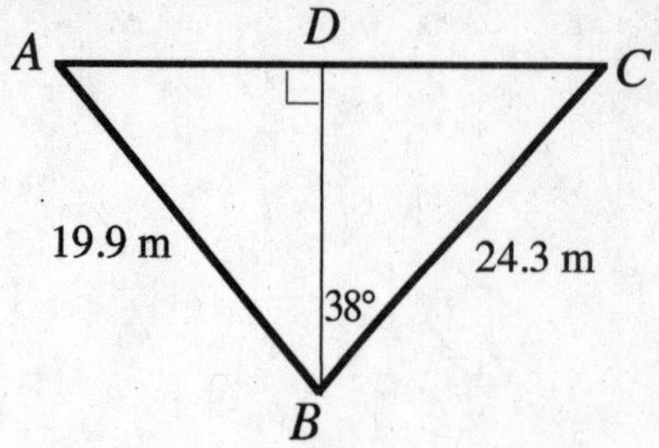

b)

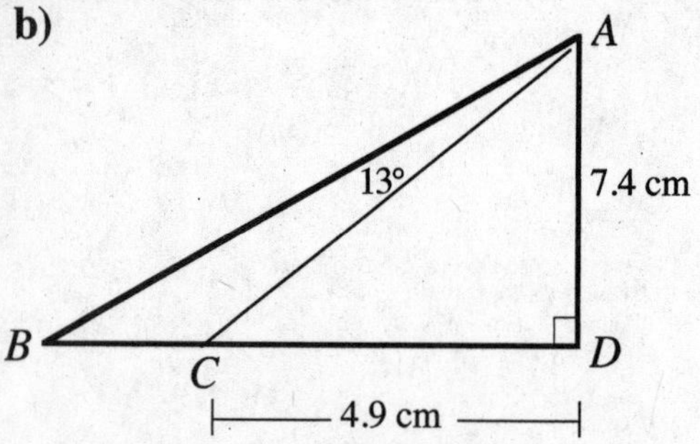

3. Two trees in a park are 14.80 metres apart. An observer, whose eyeline is 1.80 m above the ground, is standing halfway between the trees. The angles of elevation of the tops of the trees from the observer's eyeline are 17° and 23°.

a) Show this information on the diagram.

b) Determine the height of each tree to the nearest 0.01 m.

4. The angle of elevation from the top of the Pie Hotel to the top of the Sigma Office Building is 17°. The angle of depression from the top of the Pie Hotel to the foot of the Sigma Office Building is 60°. The height of the Pie Hotel is 150 m.

a) Complete the sketch to illustrate this situation.

b) Determine the height of the Sigma Office Building to the nearest tenth of a metre.

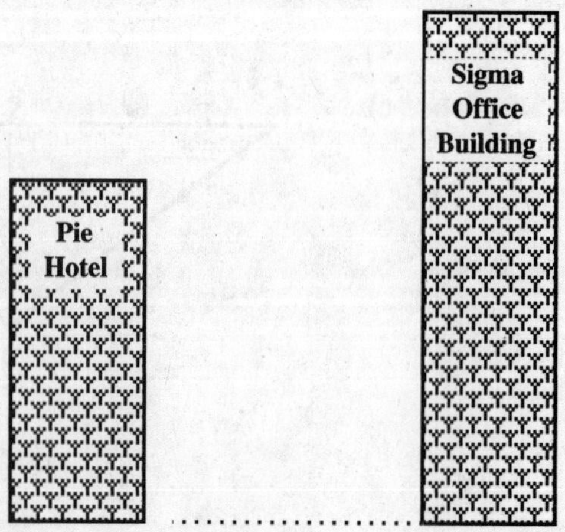

5. From the top of a cliff 110 m high, an observer sees two boats, one directly behind the other, heading for shore. The angle of depression from the observer to the boat farther from the observer is 48° and the angle of depression to the nearer boat is 57°. Calculate the distance between the boats, to the nearest metre.

6. The diagram shows two marathon runners, *A* and *B*, heading towards the finish line of a race. From an apartment window 80 metres above the ground and 20 metres behind the finish line, Tony measures the angle of depression of the runners to be 28° and 24° respectively.

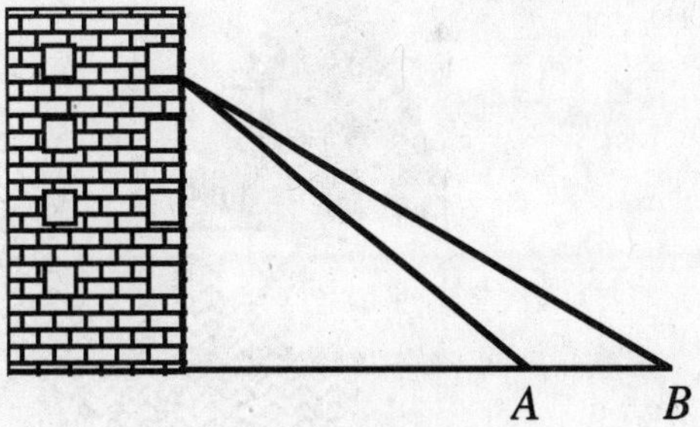

a) Calculate the distance between the runners to the nearest metre.

b) *A* is travelling at a constant speed of 4.5 m/s, while *B* is travelling at a constant speed of 5.1 m/s. Which runner will finish the race first?

7. In the diagram, *ABCD* represents a rectangular sandbox for kindergarten children to play in. A teacher stands at the corner of the area to supervise the children. At a certain time of day, the tip of the shadow cast by the teacher on the play area is exactly at *M*, the midpoint of *CD*. If the teacher is 1.8 m tall, calculate the measure of angle *EMA*, to the nearest degree.

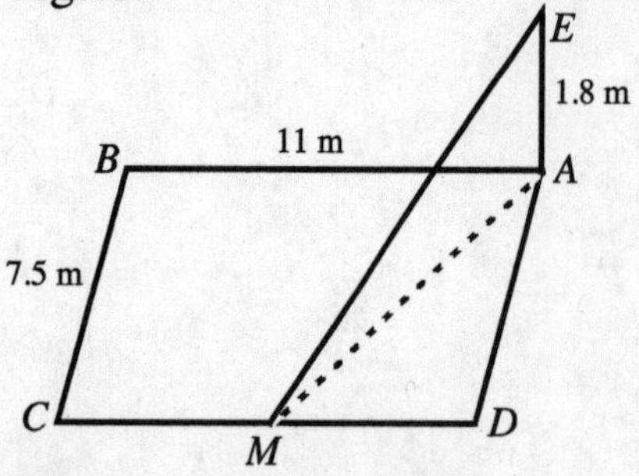

8. In order to find the height of a tree on the opposite bank of a river, Jenny makes the measurements shown on the diagram. Calculate the height of the tree to the nearest metre.

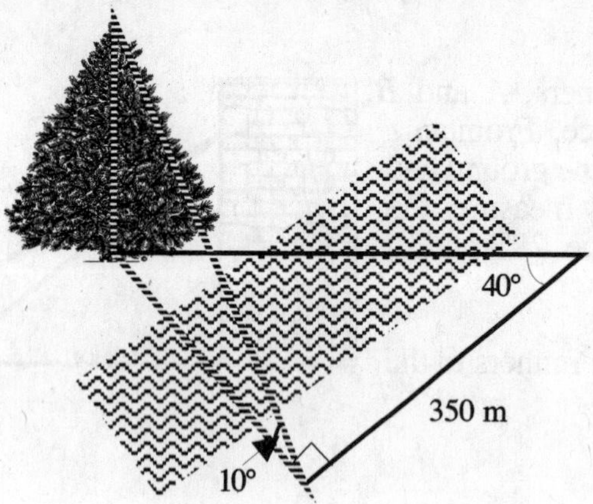

9. A rectangular prism has dimensions 15 m, 20 m, and 25 m as shown. The angle between diagonal *VP* and the plane *TUVW* is defined to be angle *PVT*. The tangent of this angle is

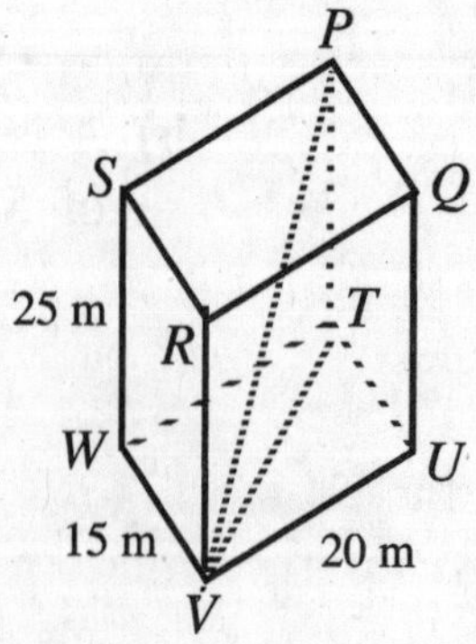

A. $\frac{3}{4}$

B. 1

C. $\frac{5}{4}$

D. $\frac{5}{3}$

Numerical Response **10.** In the diagram, $AB = 28$ m, $DE = 21$ m, $BD = 71$ m, and angle $BAC = 55°$. To the nearest degree, the measure of angle CED is _______.

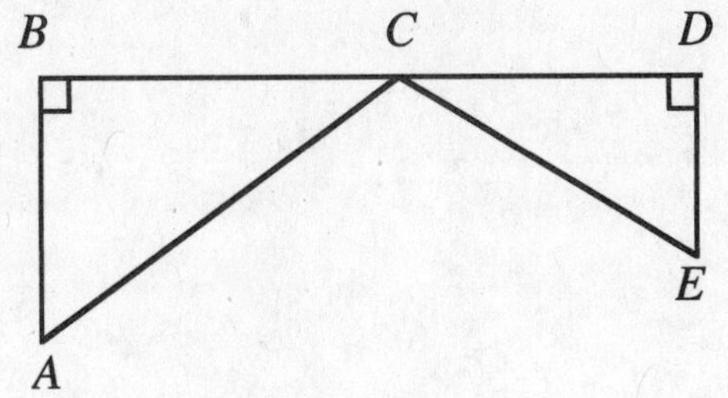

(Record your answer in the numerical response box from left to right)

Answer Key

1. a) 18.0 cm **b)** 2.1 cm **c)** 32.1 cm **d)** 17.9 cm

2. a) 54° **b)** 43°

3. a) See the diagram below. **b)** 4.06 m and 4.94 m

4. a) See below. **b)** 176.5 m

3a

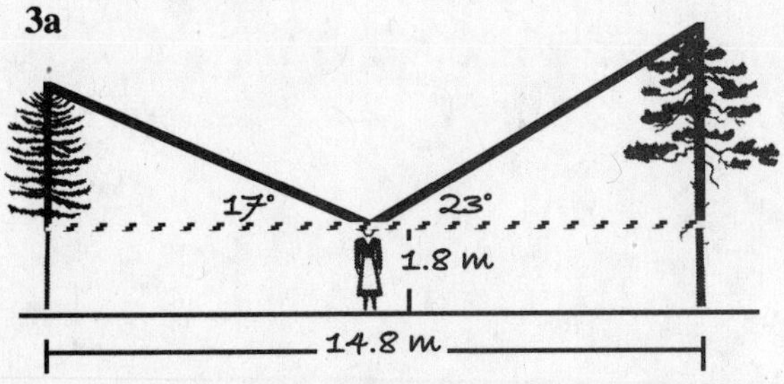

4a

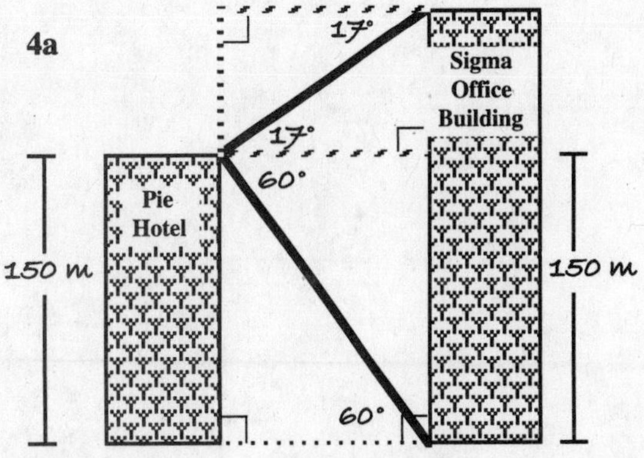

5. 28 m **6. a)** 29 m **b)** *A* takes 29 sec, *B* takes 31 sec, so *A* finishes first.

7. 11° **8.** 52 m **9.** B **10.**

5	6		

Trigonometry Lesson #8:
Practice Test

Use the following information to answer the first three questions.

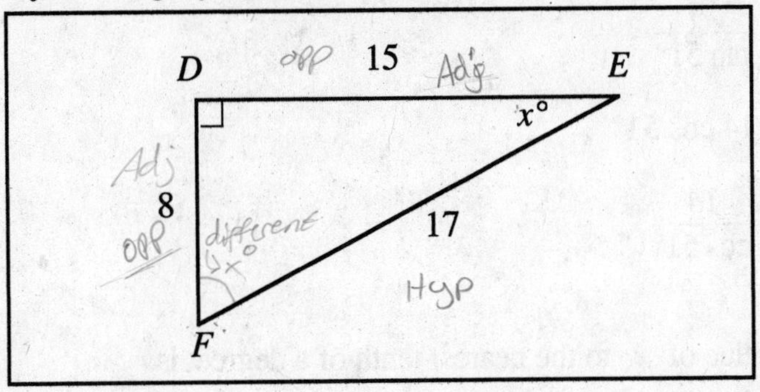

1. The value of $\cos F$ is

A. $\frac{8}{15}$

B. $\frac{8}{17}$

C. $\frac{17}{8}$

D. 62

2. The value of x is

A. $\frac{15}{17}$

B. $\frac{8}{17}$

C. 28

D. 62

3. Which statement is false?

A. $\cos E = \sin F$

B. $\sin E = \cos F$

C. $\tan E = \tan F$

D. $\tan F = \frac{\sin F}{\cos F}$

4. The value of a is

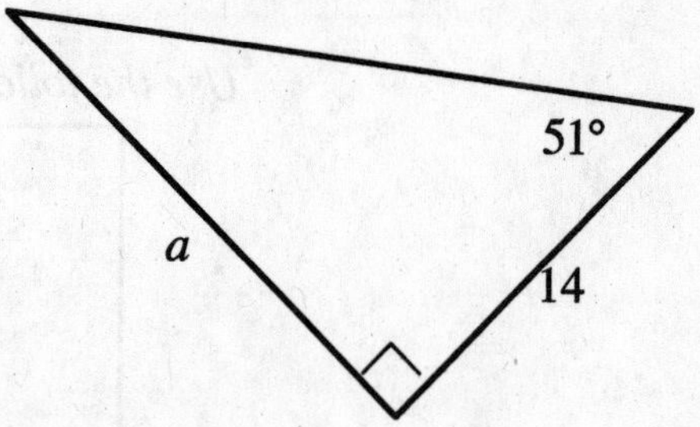

A. 14 tan 51°

B. $\dfrac{14}{\tan 51°}$

C. 14 cos 51°

D. $\dfrac{14}{\cos 51°}$

5. The value of x, to the nearest tenth of a degree, is

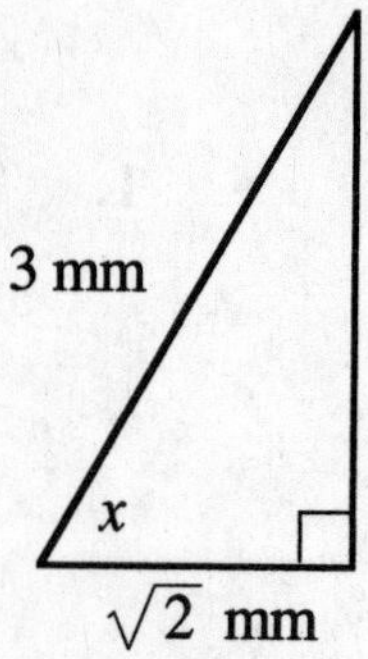

A. 35.0°

B. 61.9°

C. 72.3°

D. 29.3°

6. A guy wire to a pole makes an angle of 71.4° with the level ground and is 13.8 feet from the pole at ground level. How far above the ground is the guy wire attached to the pole?

A. 4.6 feet

B. 13.1 feet

C. 14.6 feet

D. 41.0 feet

SOH CAH TOA (13.8) sin (71.4) = x/13.8 calc =

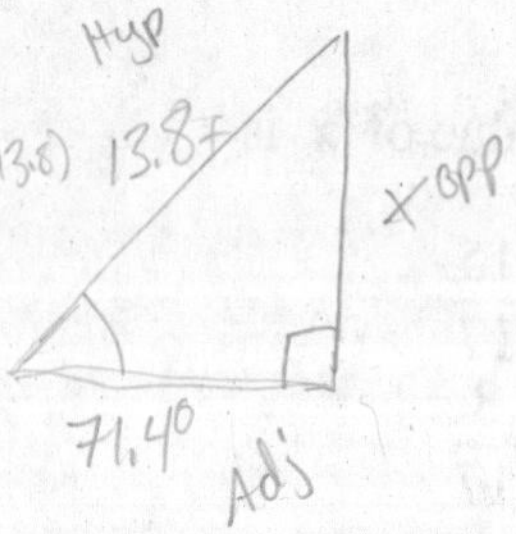

7. The value of length AC, to the nearest tenth, is

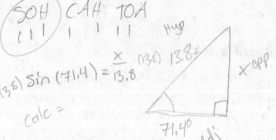

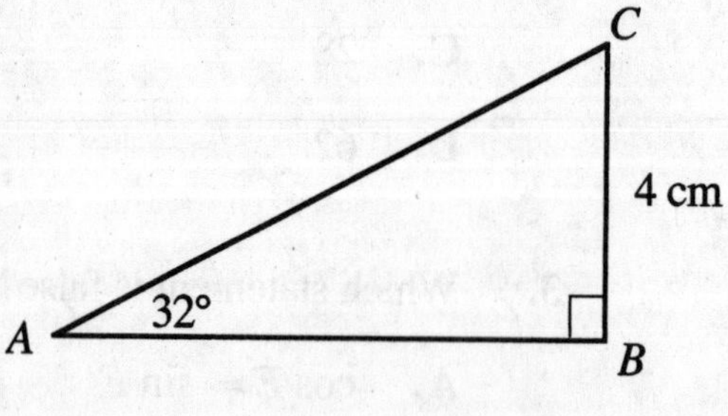

A. 0.1

B. 2.1

C. 7.2

D. 7.5

8. A man, six feet tall, casts a shadow of 10.6 feet. The angle of elevation of the sun is

A. 30°

B. 34°

C. 56°

D. 60°

Use the following information to answer the next three questions.

The diagram shows how a horse breeder has used fencing to divide a parcel of land into two triangular paddocks for his horses. Each of the line segments represents fencing.

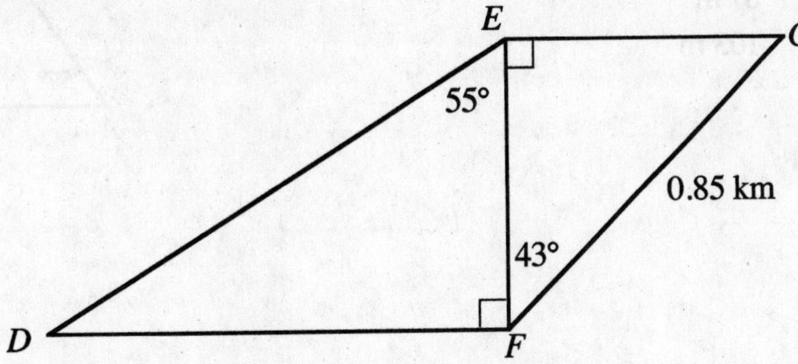

9. The length of the fencing represented by *DF* is

A. 0.89 km

B. 0.79 km

C. 0.62 km

D. 0.58 km

10. The value of cos *G* is

A. 0.68

B. 0.72

C. 0.80

D. impossible to determine from the given information.

Numerical Response **1.** The total area of the two triangular paddocks, to the nearest 0.1 km^2, is ______.

(Record your answer in the numerical response box from left to right)

11. The length of AC, to the nearest metre, is

A. 54 m
B. 70 m
C. 87 m
D. 103 m

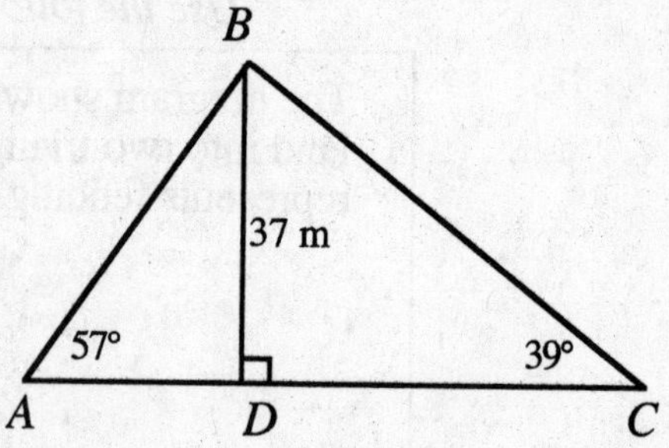

Numerical Response **2.** Determine the area of the following triangle to the nearest square centimetre.

(Record your answer in the numerical response box from left to right)

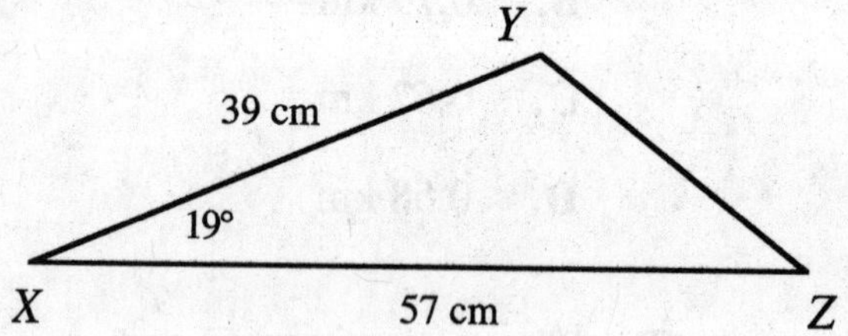

12. $\triangle ABC$ is isosceles with $AB = CB$. The area of the triangle is 30 cm^2 and $AC = 12$ cm. The measure of $\angle ABC$, to the nearest degree, is

A. 100°
B. 50°
C. 45°
D. 23°

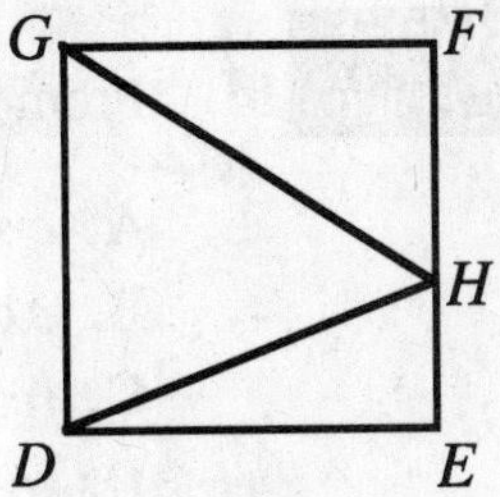

Numerical Response **3.** In the diagram, *DEFG* is a square of side 12 cm and $GH = 15$ cm. To the nearest degree, the difference between the measures of $\angle HGF$ and $\angle HDE$ is _____ .

(Record your answer in the numerical response box from left to right)

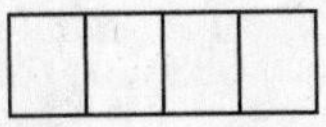

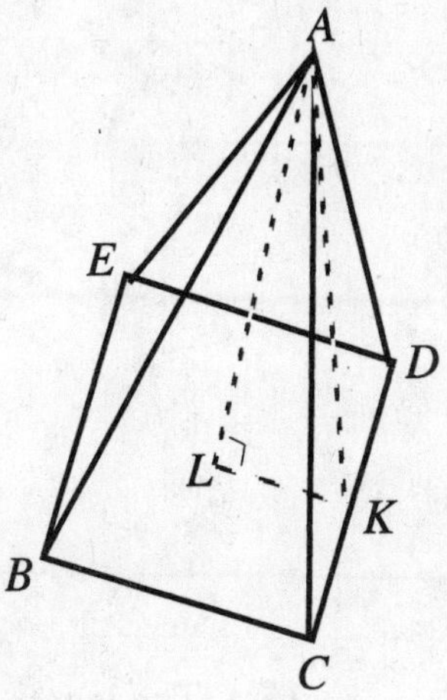

Numerical Response **4.** *ABCDE* is a square based pyramid with vertical height 14 cm. *K* is the midpoint of *CD* and angle $AKL = 70°$. To the nearest degree, the measure of angle *ACK* is _____.

(Record your answer in the numerical response box from left to right)

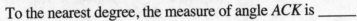

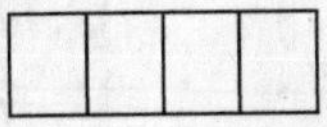

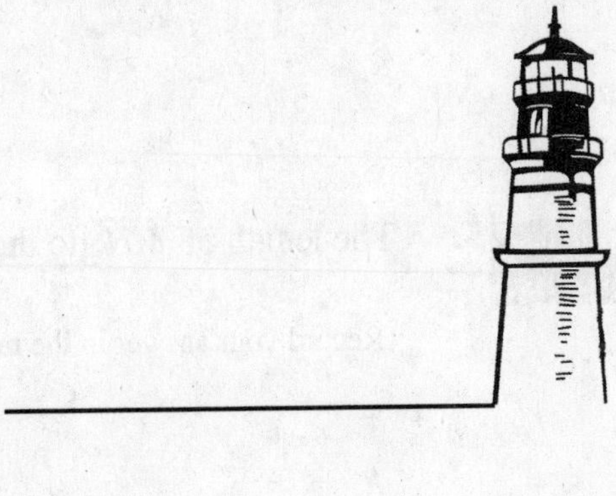

13. From a lighthouse window 30.0 m above sea level, the angles of depression of two buoys which are in a direct line from the lighthouse are 15° and 26° respectively. To the nearest tenth of a metre, the distance between the buoys is _______.

A. 173.5
B. 165.5
C. 50.5
D. 24.4

Multiple Choice

14. From the diagram, the length of CD is

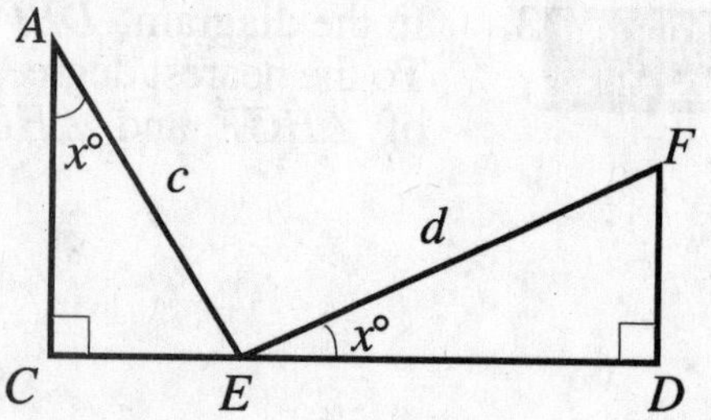

A. $c \sin x° + d \cos x°$
B. $c \cos x° + d \sin x°$
C. $(c + d) \cos x°$
D. $(c + d) \sin x°$

Use the following diagram to answer the next two questions.

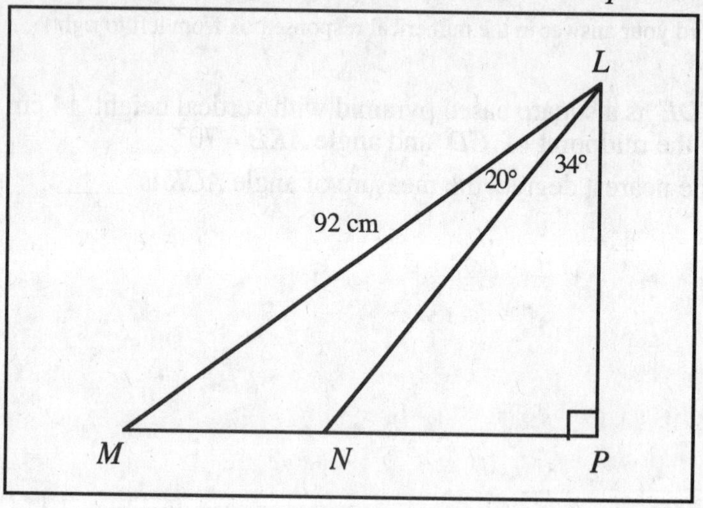

15. The length of LP, to the nearest centimetre, is

A. 51 cm
B. 54 cm
C. 74 cm
D. 76 cm

Numerical Response

5. The length of MN, to the nearest centimetre, is

(Record your answer in the numerical response box from left to right)

Written Response - 5 marks

1. In the diagram $PQ = 16$ m, $QR = 12$ m, and $PT = TR$.

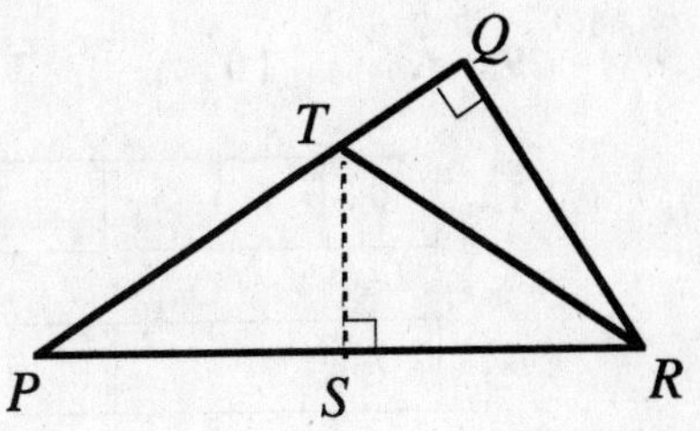

- Make a sketch of triangle PQR only and determine the exact length of PR.

- Explain why you cannot use only triangle QRT to determine the measure of $\angle QRT$.

- Calculate the measure of $\angle QPR$ and use it to determine the measure of $\angle QRT$ to the nearest degree.

- Calculate the length of PT to the nearest tenth of a metre.

Answer Key

1. B **2.** C **3.** C **4.** A **5.** B **6.** D **7.** D **8.** A

9. A **10.** A **11.** B **12.** A **13.** C **14.** A **15.** B

1.

0	.	5	

2.

3	6	2	

3.

2	3		

4.

7	1		

5.

3	8		

Written Response

1. • 20 m
- In triangle QRT, only two pieces of information are given, $\angle TQR$ and side QR. This is not enough information to calculate $\angle QRT$.
- $\angle QPR = 37°$, $\angle QRT = 16°$.
- 12.5 metres.

Polynomial Operations Lesson #1:
Review & Preview

Overview of Unit

In this unit we study algebraic expressions called polynomials. We review the classification of polynomials, addition and subtraction of polynomials, and multiplication by a monomial. We introduce the product of two binomials (concretely, pictorially, and symbolically) and extend this to the multiplication of polynomials. We also solve problems involving polynomial expressions.

Equation (=)

Expression ∅

Review

In algebra, a letter that represents one or more numbers is called a **variable.**

Expressions like $2a - b + 4$ or $\dfrac{5}{x} + 3$ are called **algebraic expressions**.

Certain algebraic expressions are called polynomials as explained below.

A **monomial** is a number or a variable or the product of numbers and variables. (Note that the exponent of any variable must be a positive integer in the numerator of the monomial.)

eg. 6, x, $6x$, $-\dfrac{1}{2}xy$, $0.25x^3$, abc, $2p^4q^2$ etc. are all monomials.

The number that multiplies the variable is called the **numerical coefficient**.

A **polynomial** is a monomial or a sum or difference of monomials.
- 6, x, $6 + x$, $2y + 7z$, $x^2 - 5x - 9$ etc. are all examples of polynomials.
- Explain why $\dfrac{5}{x} + 3$ is <u>not</u> a polynomial.

A polynomial consists of one or more **terms** (which are separated by $+$ or $-$ signs).

A polynomial with 1 term is a **monomial** (eg. $4x$).
A polynomial with 2 terms is a **binomial** (eg. $x + 4$).
A polynomial with 3 terms is a **trinomial** (eg. $x^2 + x + 4$).
A polynomial with 4 or more terms is simply called a polynomial.

Class Ex. #1

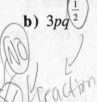

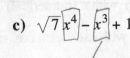

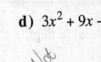

Consider the following algebraic expressions. In each case:
- State whether the expression represents a polynomial or not.
- If the expression does not represent a polynomial, explain why.
- If the expression does represent a polynomial, state whether the polynomial is a monomial, a binomial, or a trinomial.

a) $\dfrac{1}{4}xy - 10$ b) $3pq^{\frac{1}{2}}$ c) $\sqrt{7}x^4 - x^3 + 1$ d) $3x^2 + 9x - 4x^{0.2}$ e) $\dfrac{7}{a}$

NO fraction exp. *whole # exp.* *Not poly: exp. = whole #* *No whole #*

Class Ex. #2

Complete the following table.

Polynomial Expression	# Variables	# Terms	Name of Polynomial
$4x + 3yz$	3	2	binomial
$2a - 4b + 7c$	6	3	
$x^2 + 3x + 4$		2	
$\sqrt{2}\,x$	2	1	
$2x^3 + 3x^2y + 3y^2 - 8$		4	

Classifying Polynomials by Degree

Polynomials can also be classified according to degree.

The **degree of a monomial** is the sum of the exponents of its variable(s).

eg. $2x^5$ has degree 5 $\qquad -\frac{2}{3}ab^3c^2$ has degree 6

The **degree of a polynomial** is the degree of the term with highest degree.

eg. $3x^2y^2 - 2x^4 + xy^4 - 2$ has degree 5 whole poly. = 5

If a polynomial has a term of degree zero (i.e. there is no variable present), this term is called a **constant term**. In the polynomial $3x^2y^2 - 2x^4 + xy^4 - 2$, the constant term is -2.

No variable

Class Ex. #3

Give an example of

a) a binomial of degree 1 in one variable.

b) a trinomial in two variables with a constant term.

c) a monomial of degree 6 with a (numerical) coefficient of 9.

d) a binomial of degree 8 with each term containing two variables.

Polynomials in a Single Variable

Polynomials in a single variable are usually arranged in **ascending** or **descending** order of the powers of the variable.

The **leading coefficient** of a polynomial in a single variable is the coefficient of the term with highest power of the variable.

Consider the polynomial expression $2x - 4x^3 - 7 + \frac{6x^2}{5}$.

a) Write the polynomial in descending powers of x.

b) Write the polynomial in ascending powers of x.

c) State the leading coefficient and the constant term.

d) State the numerical coefficient of the term in x^2.

Complete Assignment Questions #1 - #9

Representing Polynomials Using Algebra Tiles

The following legend will be used for algebra tiles in this workbook.

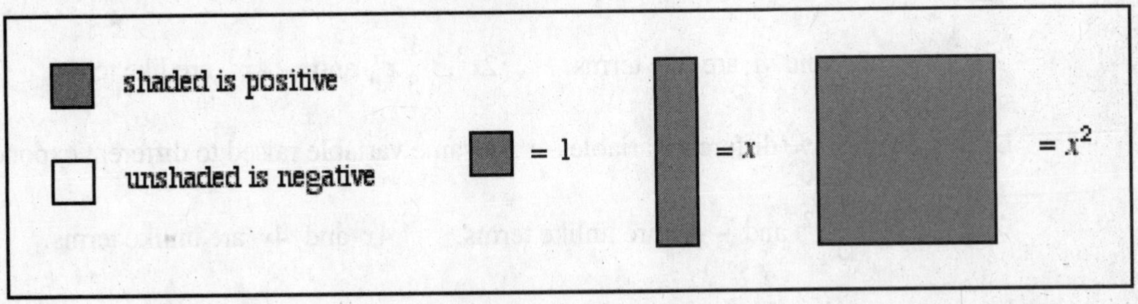

State the polynomial expression which describes each diagram.

a)

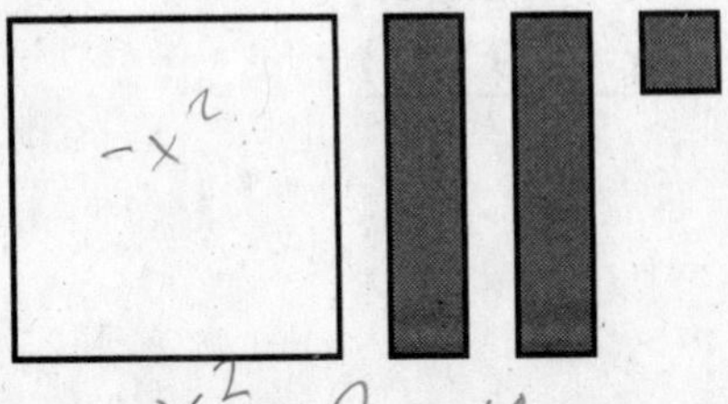

b)

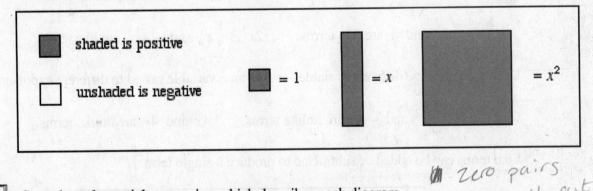

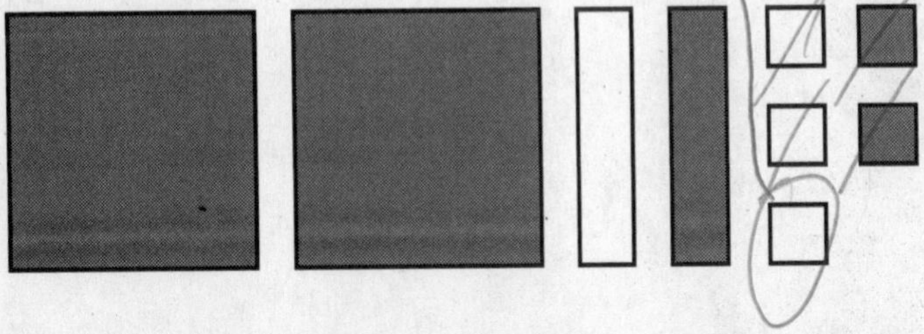

Addition and Subtraction Using Algebra Tiles

Use algebra tiles to determine the result of the addition $(2x^2 + 1) + (x^2 - 2x - 3)$.

$3x^2 - 2x - 2$

Subtracting a polynomial is equivalent to adding the inverse polynomial,

eg. $(4x + 3) - (2x - 5)$ is equivalent to $(4x + 3) + (-2x + 5)$

$4x+3+(2x-5)$? sub.

Use algebra tiles to determine the result of the subtraction $(-x^2 + 3x - 2) - (2x^2 - x - 1)$.

Addition and Subtraction of Polynomial Expressions

Like terms are terms with the same variable raised to the same exponent.

eg. $3a$, $7a$ and a are like terms. $2x^3$, $\frac{1}{5}x^3$ and $-4x^3$ are like terms.

Unlike terms have different variables or the same variable raised to different exponents.

eg. $2x^3$, $\frac{1}{5}x^2$ and $-4x$ are unlike terms. $4x$ and $4y$ are unlike terms.

Like terms can be added or subtracted to produce a single term.

Simplify the following polynomials by collecting like terms.

a) $(3a - 4b + c) + (3b - 5c - 3a)$

b)
$$\begin{array}{r} (4x^2 - 9x + 6) \\ -\ \underline{(2x^2 - 3x - 1)} \end{array}$$

Class Ex. #9

Simplify

a) $4x - 2x^2 + 3 - 6x^2 + 5 - x$ **b)** $a^2b - ab^2 + 4a^3b - 7ab^2 + 5a^2b$

$-4x^2 + 12x^4 + 15$ *$5(a^2b)^2 + 7ab^4 + 4a^3b$*

Complete Assignment Questions #10 - #20

Assignment

1. Identify as a monomial, a binomial, or a trinomial.

a) $x + 1$ **b)** $3x^3$ **c)** $2x^2 + 2x + 2$

2. State the degree of each monomial.

a) 5a **b)** $3x^3y$ **c)** 10 **d)** $-2a^2b^2$ **e)** $3xy^2z^3$

3. State whether or not the following are polynomial expressions.
If they are not polynomial expressions, explain why not.

a) $\frac{1}{2}x^2 - 3x$ **b)** $8m^{-2}$ **c)** $\sqrt{6}$

d) $\frac{7}{x^3}$ **e)** $\frac{8x^2}{3}$ **f)** $x^4 + 3x^{1.5}$

not a whole # exp.

4. Complete the following table.

Polynomial Expression	# Variables	# Terms	Name of Polynomial	Degree
$2y^3 + y^4 - y + 13$	*5*	*2*		
$9ab - 4x + 11c$	*6*	*3*		
25				
$\frac{3}{5}x^3yz^5 + 3x^2yz^4$				

5. Complete the following table for the single variable polynomials.

Polynomial Expression	Leading Coefficient	Constant Term	Degree
$y^4 - y + 13$			6
$0.2t^3 - 0.3t^2 + 0.4t - 0.5$			7
$\sqrt{5} - x^6$			7
$\pi x^2 - 7 - 3x$			6
$-\frac{1}{10}c^2$			3

6. Give an example of

a) a trinomial of degree 2 in one variable.

b) a binomial in four variables with a constant term of 6.

c) a monomial of degree 3 in two variables with a negative numerical coefficient.

d) a monomial with a degree of 0.

7. Arrange the following in descending powers of the variable.

a) $6w^2 - 9w + 5 + 2w^3$

b) $\frac{1}{4}a^2 - \frac{2}{3}a^3 - 1 - a$

c) $z - 3 - 4z^6 + z^3$

8. Arrange the following in ascending powers of the variable.

a) $6w^2 - 9w + 5 - 2w^3$

b) $3x^2 - 4x^5 - 2x^4 - 4x^3 + 9x - 7$

c) $8x^3 - 8x + 8$

9. State which of the following are true and which are false.

a) -54 is a polynomial.

b) The degree of the polynomial $3x^3y^3$ is 9.

c) The numerical coefficient of $\frac{6x}{5}$ is 6.

d) A polynomial may have 1000 terms.

e) $\frac{2}{a^3} - 1$ is a binomial.

f) The degree of the polynomial 0 is 0.

g) The polynomial $x^3 + 2x^2 + 3x + 4$ is written in ascending powers of x.

h) The polynomials $3x^2 - 9x + 1$ and $1 - 9x + 3x^2$ are equivalent.

10. State the polynomial expression which describes each diagram.

a)

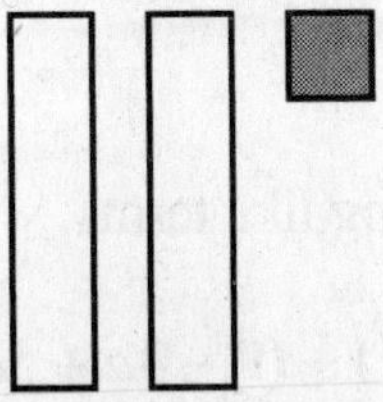

b)

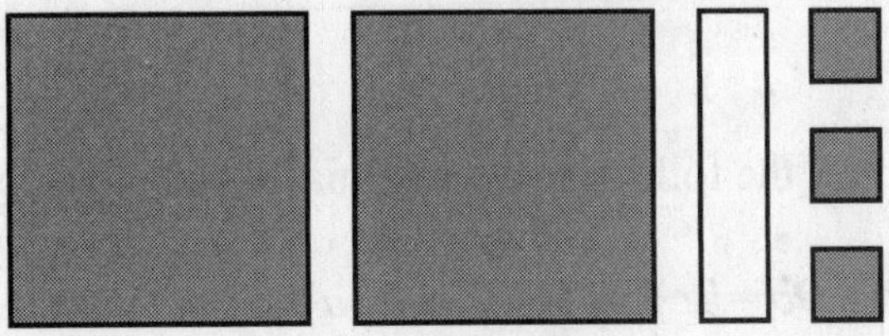

c)

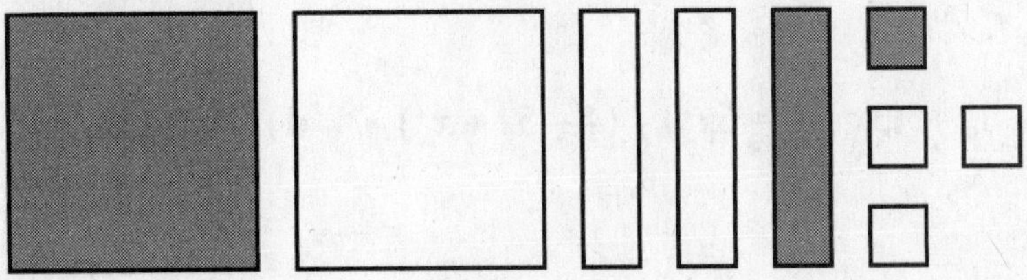

11. Use algebra tiles to determine the result of the addition of :

a) $(x^2 - x - 3) + (x^2 - 2x - 3)$

b) $(3x + 1) + (2x^2 - 3x - 2)$

12. Use algebra tiles to determine the result of the subtraction of:

a) $(x^2 - 3) - (2x^2 + 4x + 1)$ **b)** $(2 - x - x^2) - (1 - 2x + x^2)$

13. Simplify

a) $6p - 7q - 3q - 2p$ **b)** $5x - 3x^2 + 2x - 8x^2$ **c)** $\frac{1}{2}x - 3 + \frac{3}{2}x + 18$

d) $4a^3 + 7a - 2a^2 - 6a - 4a^3 - a^2$ **e)** $3 - 2x + 7y + 4y - 2x + 8z - 9$

14. Simplify the following polynomial expressions by collecting like terms.

a) $(5a - 9b - 2c) + (c - 7b - 3a)$ **b)** $(3 - a - 2a^2) + (9 - 4a + 5a^2)$

c) $(2x^2 + 5x - 1) + (3x - 6 - 6x^2) + (4 - 5x + x^2)$ **d)** $(4a - 6b) - (5a - 2b)$

e) $\begin{array}{r} (5x^2 - 8x + 3) \\ -\ \underline{(3x^2 - 3x - 1)} \end{array}$ **f)** $\begin{array}{r} (7x^2 + 2x - 1) \\ -\ \underline{(-5x^2 - 3x - 1)} \end{array}$ **g)** $\begin{array}{r} (-4x^2 + 2x - 6) \\ \underline{-(3x + 6 - 2x^2)} \end{array}$

15. a) Subtract $3x^2 - 2x + 7$ from $6x^2 - 5x - 2$.

b) Subtract the sum of $2x^3 - 7x^2 - 6x + 1$ and $8 - 3x + 5x^2 - 4x^3$ from $2x^3 - 7x + 9$.

16. A triangle has a perimeter of $(6m + n)$ cm. One side measures $(2m - 3n)$ cm and another side measures $(3n + 2m)$ cm.

a) Write and simplify an expression for the length of the third side of the triangle.

b) Determine the measure of each side when $m = 4$ and $n = -1$.

Multiple Choice

17. Which of the following is a polynomial expression of degree 4?

A. $4x^4 - 4x^7$

B. $5x^4 - 3x^3 + 2x^{-2} + x - 1$

C. $\dfrac{4x^4 - 3x}{x}$

D. $9 + 3x - \frac{1}{3}x^2 - x^3 + \frac{2}{5}x^4$

18. Which of the following polynomial expressions, when simplified, is equal to $5x$?

A. $(3x^2 - 3x) - (2x + 3x^2)$

B. $5x - (2x^2 - 2x) + (2x^2 + 2x)$

C. $8 + (4 - 2x) - (12 - 7x)$

D. $(2x^2 - 2x + 6) - (2x^2 - 2x) + (9x - 6)$

19. The perimeter of the isosceles triangle shown can be represented by

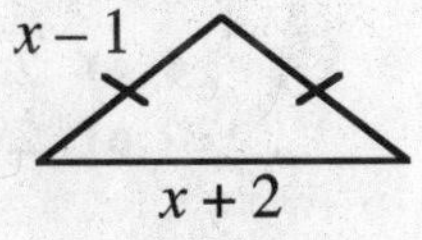

A. a monomial

B. a binomial

C. a trinomial

D. none of the above

Numerical Response

20. If the polynomial $4 - 7x + 2x^2 - 5x^3$ has degree a, leading coefficient b, and constant term c, then the value of $3a - 2b - c$ is ______.

(Record your answer in the numerical response box from left to right)

Answer Key

1. a) binomial b) monomial c) trinomial **2.** a) 1 b) 4 c) 0 d) 4 e) 6

3. a) yes b) no, negative exponent c) yes

d) no, $\frac{7}{x^3} = 7x^{-3}$, which is a negative exponent. e) yes

f) no, the exponent 1.5 is not a positive integer.

4.

Polynomial expression	*# variables*	*# terms*	*name of polynomial*	*degree*
$2y^3 + y^4 - y + 13$	1	4	polynomial	4
$9ab - 4x + 11c$	4	3	trinomial	2
25	0	1	monomial	0
$\frac{3}{5}x^3yz^5 + 3x^2yz^4$	3	2	binomial	9

5.

Polynomial expression	*leading coefficient*	*constant term*	*degree*
$y^4 - y + 13$	1	13	4
$0.2t^3 - 0.3t^2 + 0.4t - 0.5$	0.2	-0.5	3
$\sqrt{5} - x^6$	-1	$\sqrt{5}$	6
$\pi x^2 - 7 - 3x$	π	-7	2
$-\frac{1}{10}c^2$	$-\frac{1}{10}$	0	2

6. answers may vary a) $x^2 - x + 30$ b) $abcd + 6$ c) $-2xy^2$ d) 10

7. a) $2w^3 + 6w^2 - 9w + 5$ b) $-\frac{2}{3}a^3 + \frac{1}{4}a^2 - a - 1$ c) $-4z^6 + z^3 + z - 3$

8. a) $5 - 9w + 6w^2 - 2w^3$ b) $-7 + 9x + 3x^2 - 4x^3 - 2x^4 - 4x^5$ c) $8 - 8x + 8x^3$

9. a) true b) false c) false d) true e) false f) true g) false h) true

10. a) $-2x + 1$ b) $2x^2 - x + 3$ c) $-x - 2$ **11.** a) $2x^2 - 3x - 6$ b) $2x^2 - 1$

12. a) $-x^2 - 4x - 4$ b) $1 + x - 2x^2$

13. a) $4p - 10q$ b) $-11x^2 + 7x$ c) $2x + 15$ d) $-3a^2 + a$ e) $-4x + 11y + 8z - 6$

14. a) $2a - 16b - c$ b) $3a^2 - 5a + 12$ c) $-3x^2 + 3x - 3$ d) $-a - 4b$
e) $2x^2 - 5x + 4$ f) $12x^2 + 5x$ g) $-2x^2 - x - 12$

15. a) $3x^2 - 3x - 9$ b) $4x^3 + 2x^2 + 2x$

16. a) $(2m + n)$ cm b) 11 cm, 5cm, and 7 cm

17. D **18.** C **19.** A **20.**

1	5		

Polynomial Operations Lesson #2:
Multiplying a Polynomial by a Monomial

Using Algebra Tiles

In previous math courses, we learned how to multiply
i) two monomials, and **ii)** a monomial and a binomial or trinomial.

We can use algebra tiles to illustrate the process of multiplying a monomial by a polynomial.

Shaded tiles represent positive quantities and unshaded tiles represent negative quantities.

Class Ex. #1

Complete the diagram to determine the product.

a) $2(x + 1) =$

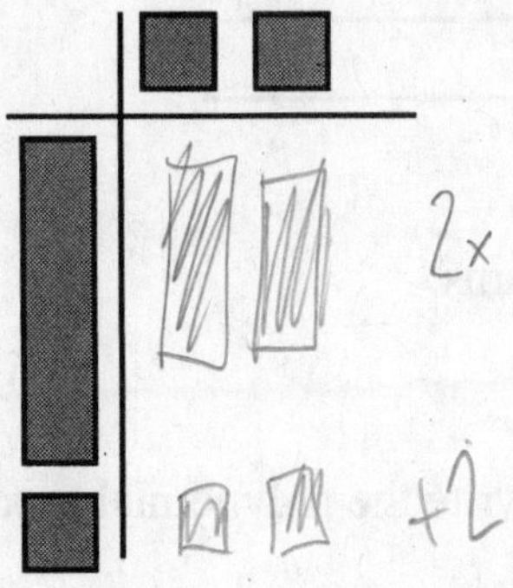

b) $x(x + 3) =$

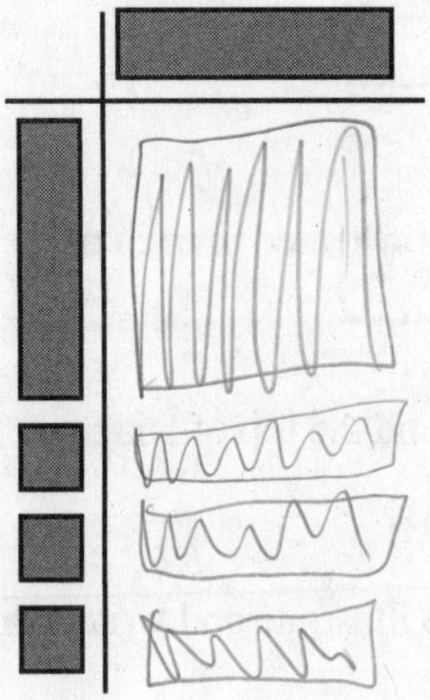

c) $-3(x - 1) =$

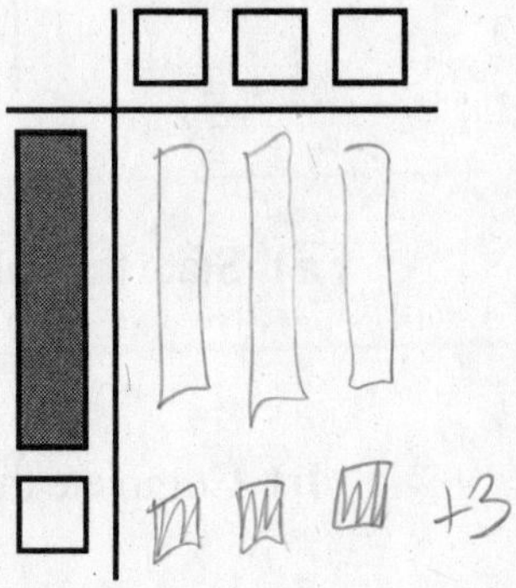

d) $2x(x - 2) =$

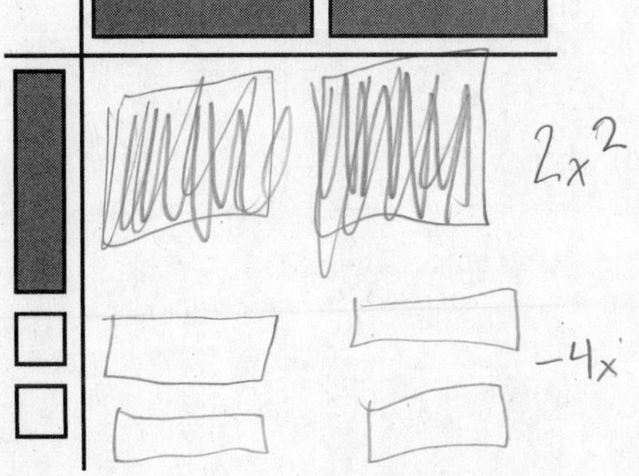

e) $(x - 1)(2x) =$

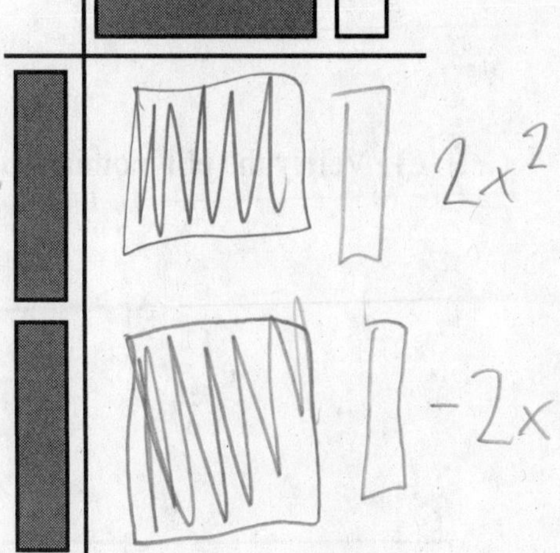

Class Ex. #2

Each diagram below illustrates the result of the product of a monomial and a binomial.

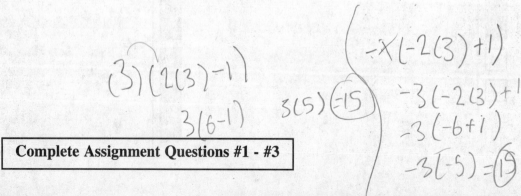

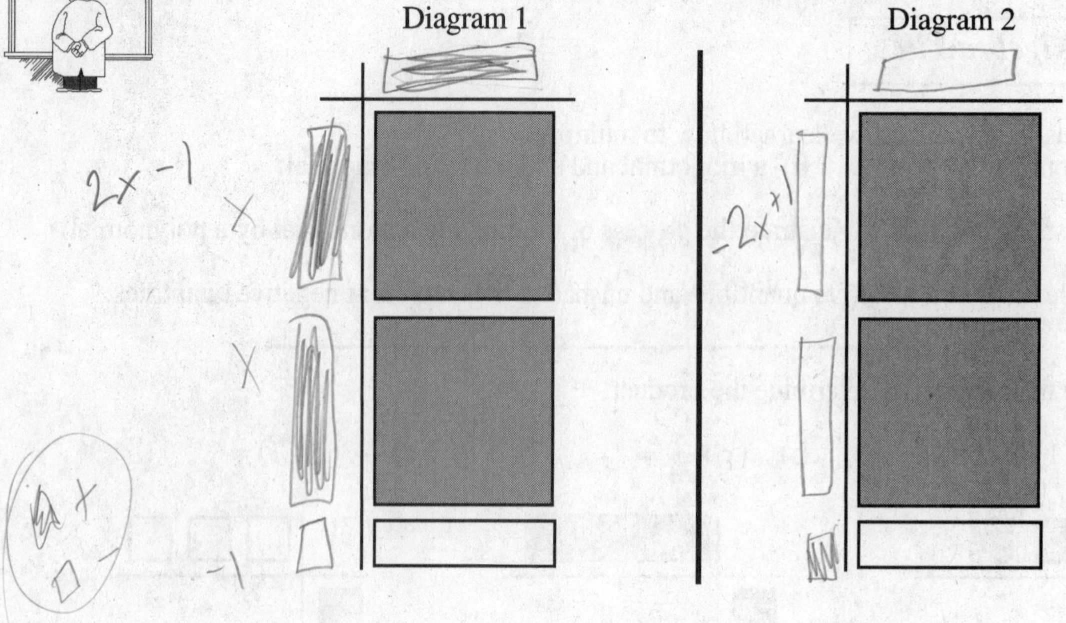

a) State the polynomial represented in each of the diagrams.

$2x^2 - x$

b) Complete the left side and the top of Diagram 1 and write the polynomial product.

c) Complete Diagram 2 to illustrate and write a different polynomial product than in b).

d) Write each product as a sum or difference of terms.

$2x^2 - x$ $\quad x(2x-1)$ or $-x(-2x-1)$

e) Verify the polynomial products in d) when $x = 3$.

$(3)(2(3)-1)$
$3(6-1)$
$3(5) = 15$

$-x(-2(3)+1)$
$-3(-2(3)+1)$
$-3(-6+1)$
$-3(-5) = 15$

Complete Assignment Questions #1 - #3

The Distributive Property

In Class Example #1 we have shown that:

$2(x+1) =$ ________ , $x(x+3) =$ ________ , $2x(x-2) =$ ________ ,

$-3(x-1)$ ________ , and $(x-1)(2x) =$ ________ .

These are examples of the **distributive property** $a(b+c) = ab + ac$ which can be extended to any number of terms.

The property can also be written $(b+c)(a) = ba + ca$ or $ab + ac$.

Class Ex. #3

Use the distributive property to determine the following products.

a) $4(3x+1)$ **b)** $-5(2x^2+x-6)$ **c)** $(x^3-2)x^2$ **d)** $-3x(7x-2y+z)$

In the example above we have written a <u>product of polynomials</u> as a <u>sum or difference of terms</u>.

In this process we **expanded** the polynomial expressions by using the distributive property, $a(b+c) = ab + ac$ and the exponent rule $x^a \times x^b = x^{a+b}$.

Class Ex. #4

Expand and simplify.

a) $6 - 4(8x+1)$ **b)** $4(2x-3) - 2(x-6)$ **c)** $5x(3x^2-7x+1) - (4x+3x^2)$

Class Ex. #5

Determine a simplified expression for the area of the given shape by

i) adding the areas of two rectangles. **ii)** subtracting the areas of two rectangles.

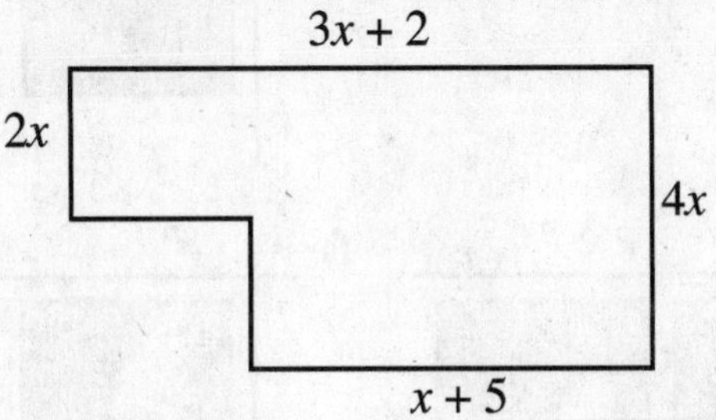

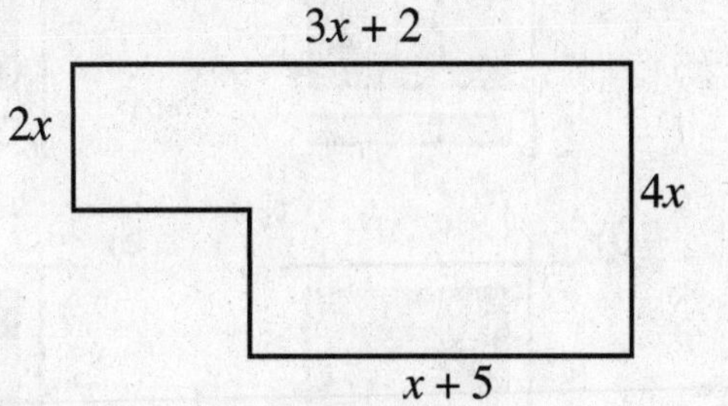

Complete Assignment Questions #4 - #11

Assignment

1. In each case, complete the diagram, state the polynomial product in x, and express the product as a sum or difference of terms.

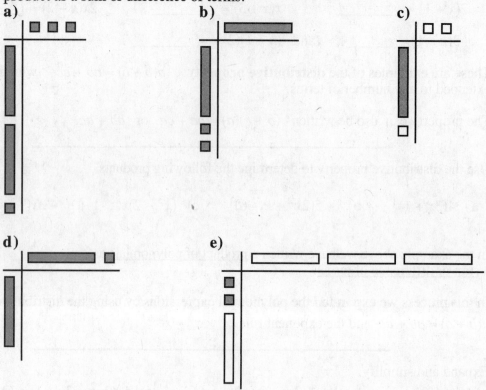

a)

b)

c)

d)

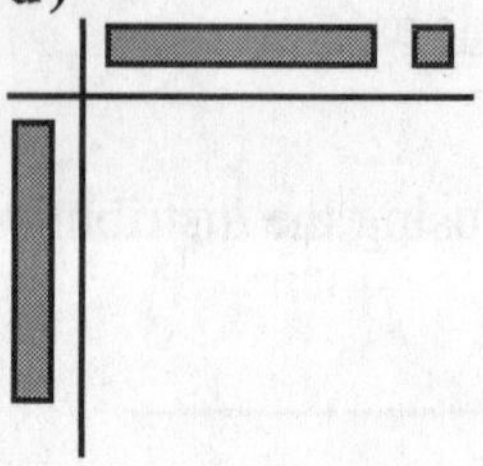

e)

2. In each case, state the polynomial product in x which is indicated by the algebra tile diagram. Express the product as a sum or difference of terms.

a)

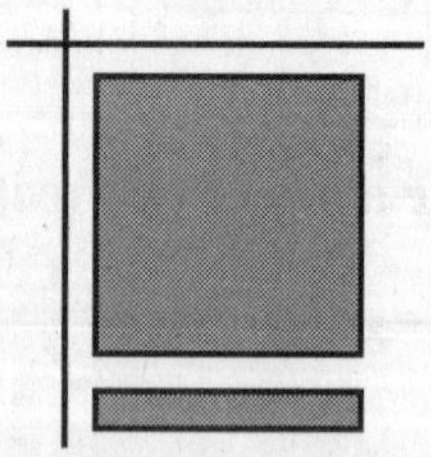

b)

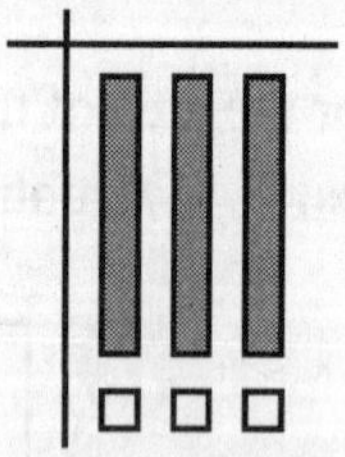

c)

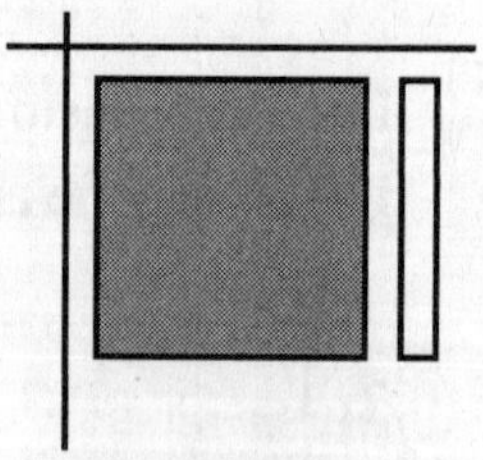

d)

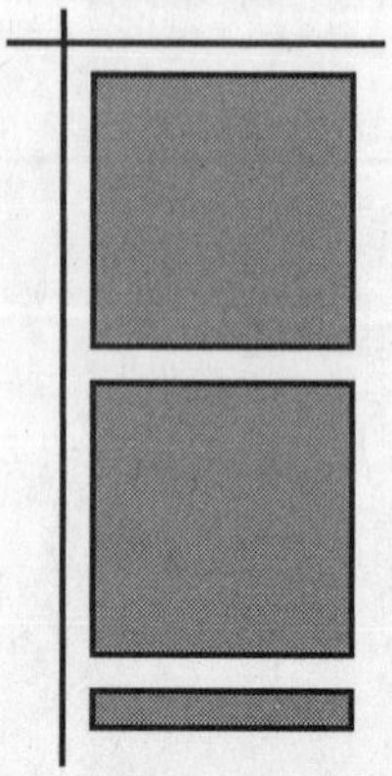

e)

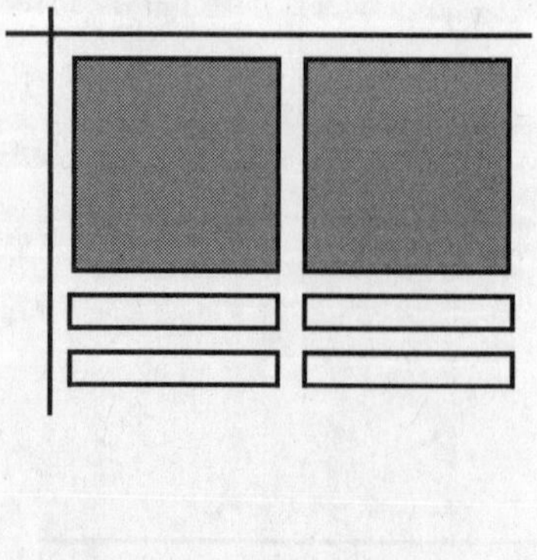

f)

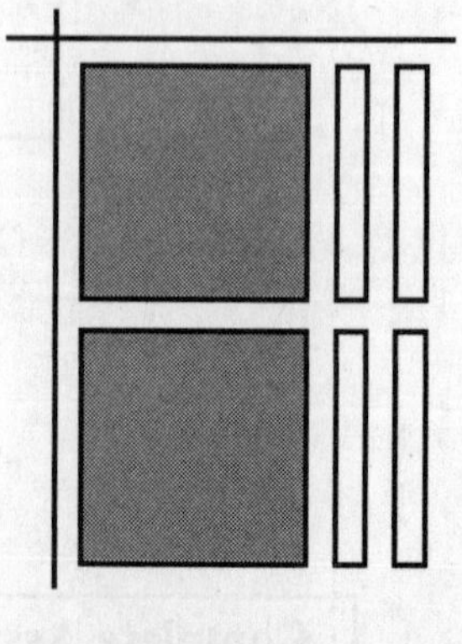

3. For each of the following:

i) Draw an algebra tile diagram to model the product.
ii) Express the product as a sum or difference of terms.
iii) Verify the polynomial product when $x = 4$.

a) $2x(2x - 1)$ **b)** $-3x(2 - x)$

4. Expand.

a) $6(7x - 3)$ **b)** $-4(4x + 9)$ **c)** $4x(2y + 8z)$ **d)** $-x(x - 5y)$

e) $3(x - 2y + 3z)$ **f)** $-2a(b - c + 5d)$ **g)** $(x + 3)3x$

h) $2x(x - 5y + 4z)$ **i)** $x(x - 2x^2 + 3x^3)$ **j)** $(2x^2 + x - 6)(-4x)$

5. Expand and simplify.

a) $3(x + 5) - 7$ **b)** $8 - 2(5x + 11)$ **c)** $6(x - 2) + x$

d) $2(x + 3) + 4(2x - 1)$ **e)** $2(x + 3) - 4(2x - 1)$ **f)** $-2(x + 1) + 7(3x - 2)$

g) $5(-x + 12) + 5(x - 8)$ **h)** $(2 - x) - 2(2x - 10)$ **i)** $6(-x + 4) - (x - 15)$

6. Identify the errors in the following and provide the correct simplification.

a) $3x(2x + y) = 6x + 3xy$ **b)** $x^2(x^3 - 2x + 7) = x^6 - 2x^3 + 7x^2$

c) $4(x - 2) - 2(x - 3)$
$= 4x - 8 - 2x - 6$
$= 2x - 14$

d) $2(2t - 3) - 4(t + 5)$
$= 4t - 3 - 4t - 5$
$= -8$

e) $5(a + b) - (a + b)$
$= 5a + 5b - a + b$
$= 4a + 6b$

7. Expand and simplify.

a) $2a(a + 3) - 4a(2a - 1)$ **b)** $4(x^2 + 3) - (2x^2 - 1)$ **c)** $2(x + 3) - x - 1$

d) $z(z^3 + 3) - (3z + 7)$ **e)** $5(8x - 3y) + 2(4y + x)$

f) $-2x(x^4 + 3x^3) - 7x(2x^4 - x^3)$ **g)** $3a(2a^2b - ab + b^2) - 6b(a^3 + 3ab - 5b^2)$

h) $3x(x - 3) - 2x(x - 1) + x(2x - 2)$ **i)** $(p^2 - 3p)(4p) - (3 + 5p)(-2p^2)$

j) $a(b - c) + b(c - a) + c(a - b)$ **k)** $20x^3y^3 - 4x^3y^2(3x + 5y - xy)$

8. Determine a simplified expression for the area of the given shape.

a)

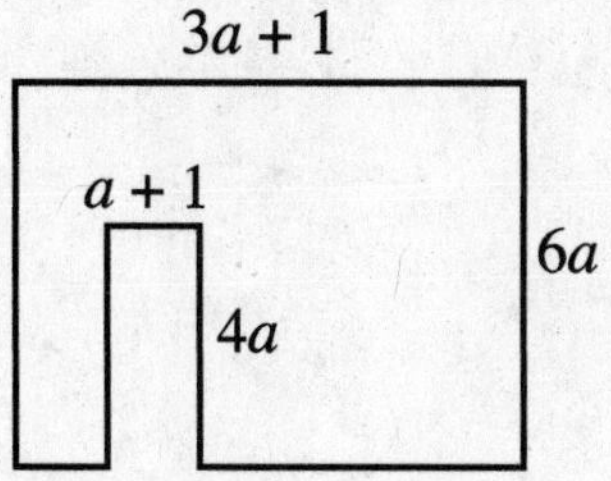

b)

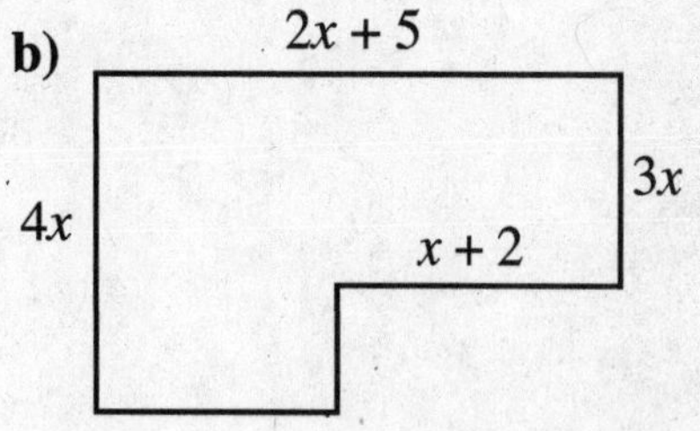

Multiple Choice

9. The algebra tile diagram represents the expansion of:

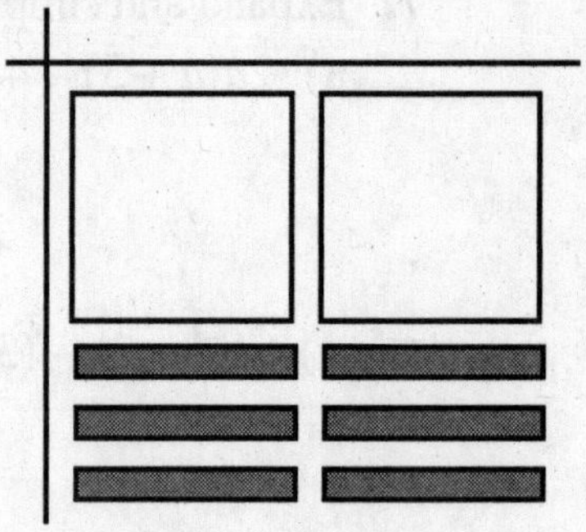

A. $2x(x + 3)$
B. $-2x(x + 3)$
C. $2x(x - 3)$
D. $-2x(x - 3)$

10. Which of the following expansions is incorrect?

A. $-2x^2(3x + 2) = -6x^3 - 4x^2$
B. $-4x(2 - x) = -8x + 4x^2$
C. $-5x(x^2 - 3) = -5x^3 - 15x$
D. $7x^2(x^2 + 3) = 7x^4 + 21x^2$

Numerical Response

11. The expression $2x(4 - 3x) + 5x(2x - 1) - 3(4x + 2)$ can be written in the form $ax^2 + bx + c$. The value of $a + b - c$ is ______.

(Record your answer in the numerical response box from left to right)

Answer Key

1. a) $3(2x + 1) = 6x + 3$ **b)** $x(x + 2) = x^2 + 2x$ **c)** $-2(x - 1) = -2x + 2$
d) $(x + 1)(x) = x^2 + x$ **e)** $-3x(2 - x) = -6x + 3x^2$

2. a) $x(x + 1) = x^2 + x$ **b)** $3(x - 1) = 3x - 3$ **c)** $(x - 1)(x) = x^2 - x$
d) $x(2x + 1) = 2x^2 + x$ **e)** $2x(x - 2) = 2x^2 - 4x$ **f)** $(x - 2)(2x) = 2x^2 - 4x$

3. a) i)

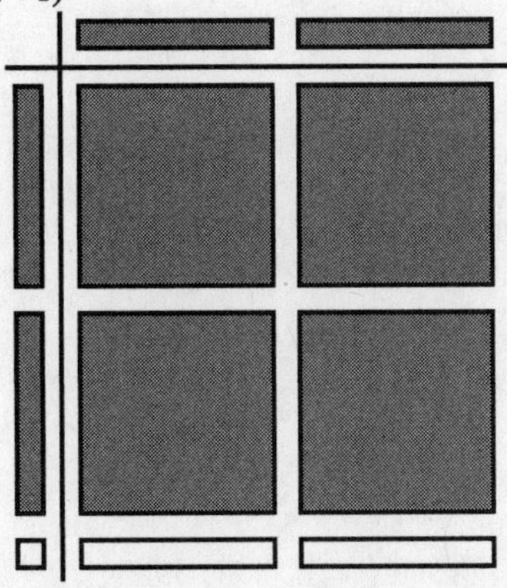

ii) $2x(2x - 1) = 4x^2 - 2x$

iii)

Left Side	Right Side
(2 x 4) ((2 x 4) – 1)	4 (4²) – 2(4)
= (8) ((7)	= 64 – 8
= 56	= 56

b) i)

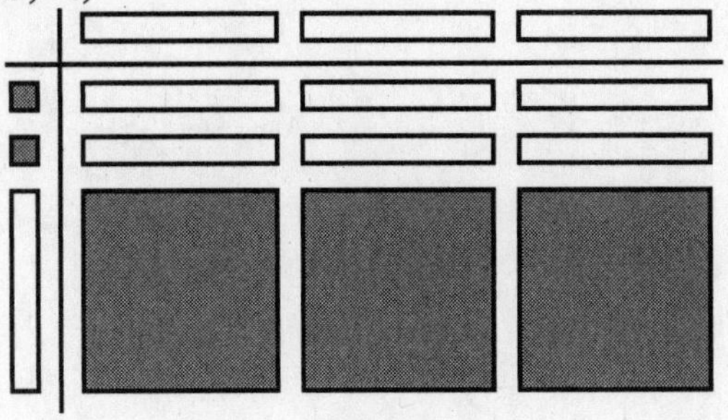

ii) $-3x(2 - x) = -6x + 3x^2$

iii)

Left Side	Right Side
(–3 x 4) (2 – 4)	(–6 x 4) + 3(4²)
= (–12) ((–2)	= –24 + 48
= 24	= 24

4. a) $42x - 18$ **b)** $-16x - 36$ **c)** $8xy + 32xz$
d) $-x^2 + 5xy$ **e)** $3x - 6y + 9z$ **f)** $-2ab + 2ac - 10ad$
g) $3x^2 + 9x$ **h)** $2x^2 - 10xy + 8xz$ **i)** $x^2 - 2x^3 + 3x^4$ **j)** $-8x^3 - 4x^2 + 24x$

5. a) $3x + 8$ **b)** $-10x - 14$ **c)** $7x - 12$
d) $10x + 2$ **e)** $-6x + 10$ **f)** $19x - 16$
g) 20 **h)** $-5x + 22$ **i)** $-7x + 39$

6. a) $3x(2x) = 6x^2$, not $6x$. $3x(2x + y) = 6x^2 + 3xy$
b) $x^2(x^3) = x^5$ not x^6. $x^2(x^3 - 2x + 7) = x^5 - 2x^3 + 7x^2$
c) $-2(-3) = 6$, not -6. $4(x - 2) - 2(x - 3) = 4x - 8 - 2x + 6 = 2x - 2$
d) The monomials 2 and –4 multiply <u>both</u> terms in the binomials.
$2(2t - 3) - 4(t + 5) = 4t - 6 - 4t - 20 = -26$.
e) The negative multiplies both a and b. $5(a + b) - (a + b) = 5a + 5b - a - b = 4a + 4b$.

7. a) $-6a^2 + 10a$ **b)** $2x^2 + 13$ **c)** $x + 5$ **d)** $z^4 - 7$
e) $42x - 7y$ **f)** $-16x^5 + x^4$ **g)** $-3a^2b - 15ab^2 + 30b^3$ **h)** $3x^2 - 9x$
i) $14p^3 - 6p^2$ **j)** 0 **k)** $-12x^4y^2 + 4x^4y^3$

8. a) $14a^2 + 2a$ **b)** $7x^2 + 18x$ **9.** D **10.** C **11.**

1			

Polynomial Operations Lesson #3:
Multiplication of Two Binomials

Multiplying Two Binomials using Area Diagrams

In the last lesson, we multiplied a monomial by a polynomial. In this lesson, we extend the process to the product of two binomials.

Class Ex. #1

Complete the algebra tile diagrams and determine the binomial products.

a) $(x + 3)(x + 2)$ =

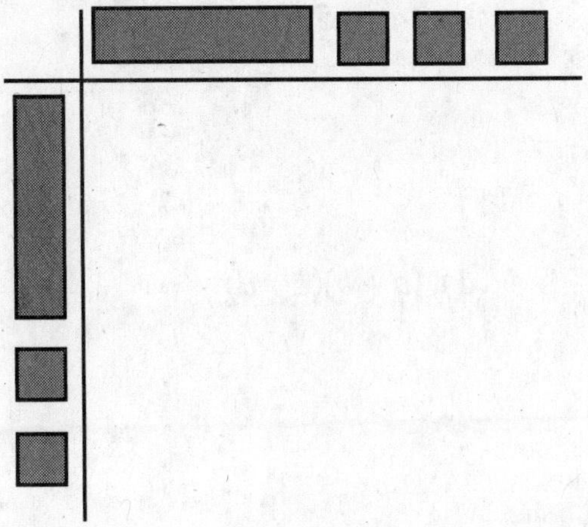

b) ( )( ) =

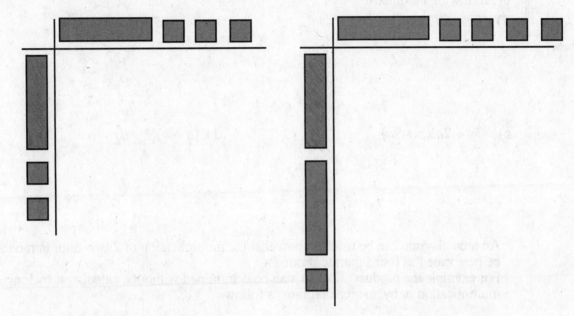

c) ($x - 3$)($x - 2$) = $x^2 - 5 + 6$

d) ($2x - 1$)($x + 2$) =

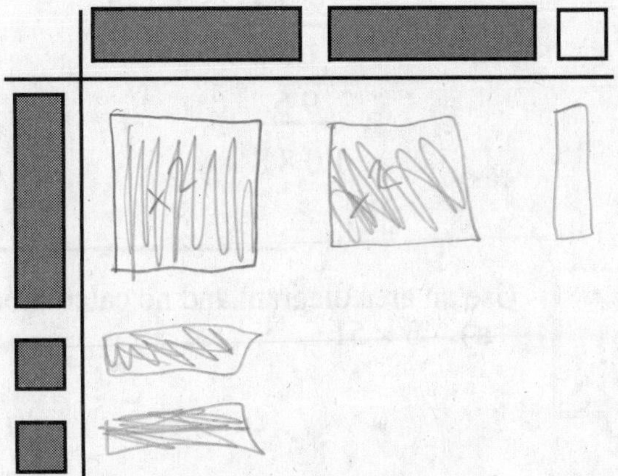

In class example 1a), we used an algebra tile diagram to show that the product $(x + 3)(x + 2)$ could be expressed in simplified expanded form as $x^2 + 5x + 6$.

The algebra tile diagram used to model $(x + 3)(x + 2)$ can be modified into the following area diagram which shows that the product of two binomials is equivalent to four monomial products.

	x	3
x	x^2	$3x$
2	$2x$	6

$(x + 3)(x + 2)$
$= x^2 + 5x + 6$

Class Ex. #2 Use an area diagram like the one above to determine the product of each of the following binomials.

a) $(5x - 6)(2x + 1)$

b) $(a^2 - 5)(a^2 - 8)$

	$5x$	-6
$2x$	$10x^2$	$-12x$
$+1$	$5x$	-6

$= 10x^2 - 7x - 6$

numerical
– variables
using exp. rule

c) $(3p + 2q)(p + 9q)$

d) $(a + b)(c + d)$

final = sum of total products

An area diagram can be used to show that the multiplication of 2 two-digit numbers can be performed as four separate products.
For example the product 32×34 can be determined without a calculator, by long multiplication or by an area diagram as follows:

Long Multiplication

$$\begin{array}{r} 3\,2 \\ \times\ 3\,4 \\ \hline 1\,2\,8 \\ 9\,6\ \ \ \\ \hline 1\,0\,8\,8 \end{array}$$

32×34
$30 \times 30 =$
$90 +$
$4 + 2 =$
96

Area Diagram

	30	2
30	900	60
4	120	8

32×34
$= 900 + 120 + 60 + 8$
$= 1088$

Class Ex. #3 Use an area diagram and no calculator to determine the following products.
a) 43×51 **b)** 76×82

Complete Assignment Questions #1 - #3

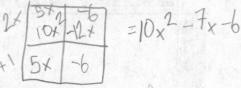

Multiplying Two Binomials using the Distributive Property

In the area diagram modelling $(x + 3)(x + 2)$, we noted that there were four separate monomial products involved in the expansion.

These products are simply the extension of the distributive property to binomial products.

Distributive property $(a + b)(c + d) = a(c + d) + b(c + d) = ac + ad + bc + bd$
for binomials

Class Ex. #4 Use the distributive property to determine the following products.

a) $(x + 3)(x + 2)$ **b)** $(a - 7)(2a - 1)$ **c)** $(p - 8)(q - 8)$

$$x(x+2)+3(x+2),$$

d) $(x + 4y)(x - 5y)$ **e)** $(9a^2 - 1)(5a^3 + 6)$

The method used in the distributive property can be simplified by noticing that the four monomial products $(a + b)(c + d) = ac + ad + bc + bd$ can be memorized using the acronym FOIL .

F – first term in each bracket ie ac
O – outside terms ie ad
I – inside terms ie bc
L – last term in each bracket ie bd

foil - first
- outside
- inside

Class Ex. #5 Use FOIL to determine each product.

a) $(x + 6)(x + 4)$ **b)** $(y - 7)(y + 2)$

c) $(3x + 1)(x - 5)$ **d)** $(6a - 5b)^2$

$$(6a - 5b)(6a - 5b)$$

$$= 36a^2 - 60ab^2$$

Complete Assignment Questions #4 - #9

Assignment

1. Complete the algebra tile diagrams and determine the binomial products.

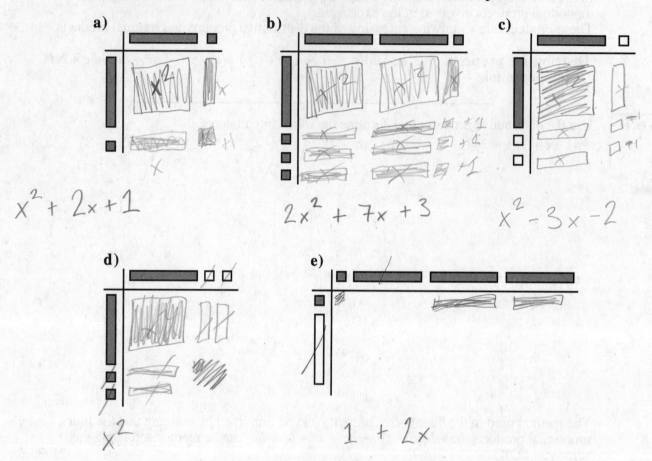

a)

$x^2 + 2x + 1$

b)

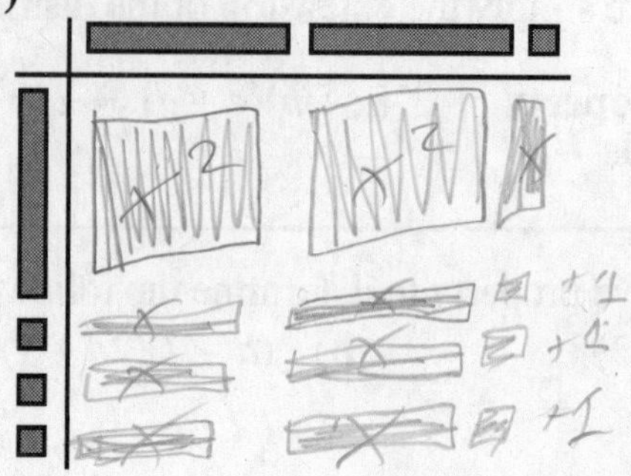

$2x^2 + 7x + 3$

c)

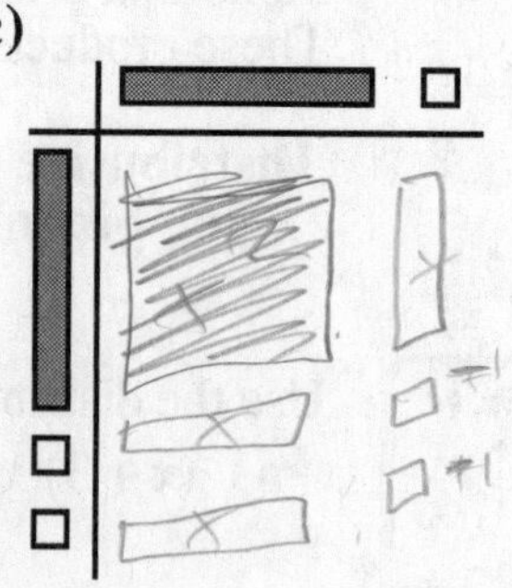

$x^2 - 3x - 2$

d)

x^2

e)

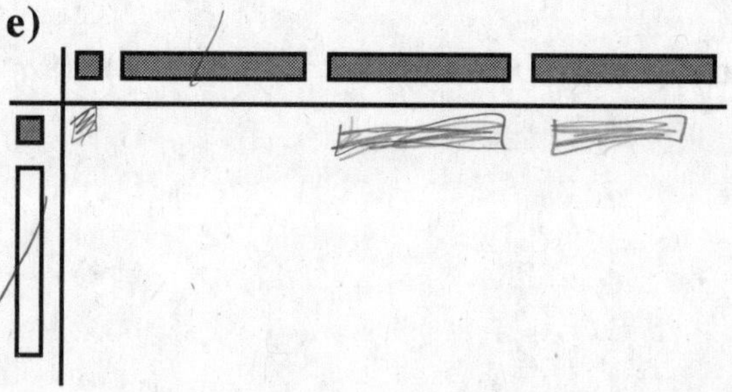

$1 + 2x$

2. Use an area diagram to determine the product of each of the following binomials.

a) $(x + 6)(x - 2)$ **b)** $(2x + 3)(2x + 7)$ **c)** $(y - 3)(4y + 1)$

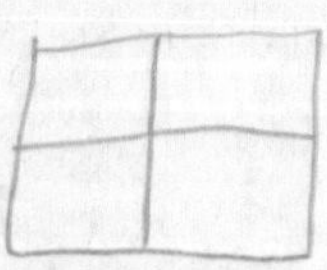

d) $(3d - 5)(6d - 9)$ **e)** $(2x - y)(4x + y)$ **f)** $(3p - 8q)(p - 5q)$

g) $(a^2 + 8)(a^2 - 8)$ **h)** $(t^3 + 2s)(t^3 + 2s)$ **i)** $(a + b)(a + c)$

3. Use an area diagram and no calculator to determine the following products.

a) 23×21

	20	3
20	400	60
1	20	3

400+60+20+3 =483

b) 34×12

	10	2
30	300	60
4	40	8

300+60+40+8 =408

c) 74×32

	70	4
30	2100	120
2	140	8

2100+120+140+8 =2368

d) 65×73 **e)** 49×55 **f)** 86×86

4. Use the distributive property to determine the following products.

a) $(x + 4)(x + 7)$

$x^2 + x7 + 28$

b) $(a + 7)(3a - 5)$ **c)** $(p - 2)(p - 8)$

d) $(x + 6y)(x - 2y)$ **e)** $(4a + 9b)(2a + 3b)$ **f)** $(6 - y)(1 + 4y)$

g) $(2a - 1)(6b - 1)$ **h)** $(7x^2 - 3)(7x^2 - 3)$ **i)** $(2y^2 - 3)(5y^5 + 1)$

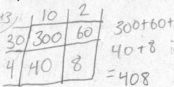

5. Use FOIL to determine each product.

a) $(x+3)(x+6)$ **b)** $(y+4)(y+9)$ **c)** $(x+1)(x-8)$ **d)** $(a-7)^2$

e) $(x+2)(5x+4)$ **f)** $(3y-5)(2y+9)$ **g)** $(6x+1)(x-6)$ **h)** $(6-5b)(6-5b)$

i) $(x+3y)(x+4y)$ **j)** $(a-7b)(3a+4b)$ **k)** $(5x+z)(5x-z)$ **l)** $(9-a^2)(5-a^2)$

6. A rectangle has length $(2a+5)$ cm and width $(a+4)$ cm.
Determine the area of the rectangle (in cm^2) by completing each of the following solutions.

Area = length × width = (   )(   )

(i) *use a diagram*

(ii) *use the distributive property*
$(2a+5)(a+4)$
$= 2a(a+\quad)+$

(iii) *use FOIL*
$(2a+5)(a+4)$

7. Expand and simplify where possible.

a) $(7x-2)(3x+5)$ **b)** $(2h-3)(2h-1)$ **c)** $(3z+4)(3z+5)$

d) $(4x-3)(3x-4)$ **e)** $(8x-3y)(2x+y)$ **f)** $(1+3b)^2$

g) $(x-2)(6y-1)$ **h)** $(1+3y^2)(1-3y^2)$ **i)** $(x^2+7y^2)(2x^2-5y^2)$

Numerical Response

8. The area of the rectangle shown can be written in the form $px^2 + qx + r$, where $p, q,$ and r are natural numbers.

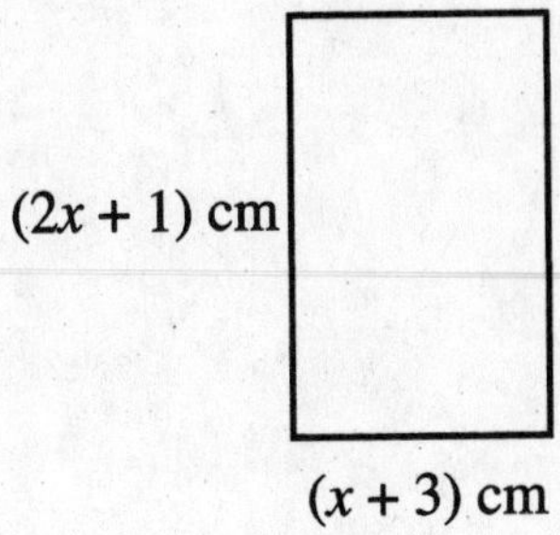

Write the value of p in the first box.
Write the value of q in the second box.
Write the value of r in the third box.

(Record your answer in the numerical response box from left to right)

9. The expansion of $(3x - c)(x - 3)$, where c is a whole number, results in a polynomial in x with a leading coefficient of 3 and a constant term of 12. The value of c is ______.

(Record your answer in the numerical response box from left to right)

Answer Key

1. **a)** $(x + 1)(x + 1) = x^2 + 2x + 1$ **b)** $(2x + 1)(x + 3) = 2x^2 + 7x + 3$
c) $(x - 1)(x - 2) = x^2 - 3x + 2$ **d)** $(x - 2)(x + 2) = x^2 - 4$
e) $(1 + 3x)(1 - x) = 1 + 2x - 3x^2$

2. **a)** $x^2 + 4x - 12$ **b)** $4x^2 + 20x + 21$ **c)** $4y^2 - 11y - 3$
d) $18d^2 - 57d + 45$ **e)** $8x^2 - 2xy - y^2$ **f)** $3p^2 - 23pq + 40q^2$
g) $a^4 - 64$ **h)** $t^6 + 4st^3 + 4s^2$ **i)** $a^2 + ab + ac + bc$

3. **a)** 483 **b)** 408 **c)** 2368 **d)** 4745 **e)** 2695 **f)** 7396

4. **a)** $x^2 + 11x + 28$ **b)** $3a^2 + 16a - 35$ **c)** $p^2 - 10p + 16$
d) $x^2 + 4xy - 12y^2$ **e)** $8a^2 + 30ab + 27b^2$ **f)** $6 + 23y - 4y^2$
g) $12ab - 2a - 6b + 1$ **h)** $49x^4 - 42x^2 + 9$ **i)** $10y^7 - 15y^5 + 2y^2 - 3$

5. **a)** $x^2 + 9x + 18$ **b)** $y^2 + 13y + 36$ **c)** $x^2 - 7x - 8$
d) $a^2 - 14a + 49$ **e)** $5x^2 + 14x + 8$ **f)** $6y^2 + 17y - 45$
g) $6x^2 - 35x - 6$ **h)** $36 - 60b + 25b^2$ **i)** $x^2 + 7xy + 12y^2$
j) $3a^2 - 17ab - 28b^2$ **k)** $25x^2 - z^2$ **l)** $45 - 14a^2 + a^4$

6. Area = $(2a + 5)(a + 4) = 2a^2 + 13a + 20$

7. **a)** $21x^2 + 29x - 10$ **b)** $4h^2 - 8h + 3$ **c)** $9z^2 + 27z + 20$
d) $12x^2 - 25x + 12$ **e)** $16x^2 + 2xy - 3y^2$ **f)** $1 + 6b + 9b^2$
g) $6xy - x - 12y + 2$ **h)** $1 - 9y^4$ **i)** $2x^4 + 9x^2y^2 - 35y^4$

8.

2	7	3	

9.

4			

Polynomial Operations Lesson #4:
Multiplication of Polynomials - Part One

Three Important Products

Complete the following using the distributive property (FOIL).

i) $(a+b)^2 = (a+b)(a+b)$ **ii)** $(a-b)^2 = (a-b)(a-b)$ **iii)** $(a-b)(a+b)$

$=$ $=$ $=$

$=$ $=$ $=$

1. **The square of a binomial can be found by squaring the first term, doubling the product of the two terms and squaring the last term.**

2. **The product of the sum and difference of the same two monomials results in the difference of the squares of the monomials.**
This important result will be considered in more detail in future lessons on factoring.

Expand each of the following.

a) $(x+7)^2$ **b)** $(3x-1)^2$ **c)** $(2m-3n)^2$

d) $(4-7x)(4+7x)$ **e)** $(5a+3b)(5a-3b)$ **e)** $(2p-9q)(2p-9q)$

Complete Assignment Question #1

Expand and simplify.

a) $5(2x - 3)(x - 6)$ **b)** $-8(7p + 3)^2$

Expand and simplify.

a) $(x + 5)(x - 5) - (x + 2)(x + 8)$ **b)** $(9a + 4)(4a - 9) - (6a - 5)^2$

Expand and simplify.

a) $5x(3x^2 - 7x + 1) - (4x + 3x^2)(5x - 8)$ **b)** $4(2x - 7)(3x + 2) - 8(x - 1)(3x - 1)$

Given that, for every value of x, the polynomial $x^2 + 20x + 50$ can be written in the form $(x + a)^2 + b$, determine the values of a and b.

Complete Assignment Questions #2 - #7

Assignment

1. Expand and simplify where possible.

a) $(x-8)^2$ **b)** $(x-9)(x+9)$ **c)** $(3x-y)^2$

d) $(5x+2y)^2$ **e)** $(3x-2)(3x+2)$ **f)** $(-2y+1)^2$

g) $(2p+7)^2$ **h)** $(4m+3n)(4m-3n)$ **i)** $(5a-6b)^2$

j) $(9-5x^2)(9+5x^2)$ **k)** $(6a-7b)(6a-7b)$ **l)** $(2a^3-7)(2a^3+7)$

2. Expand and simplify where possible.

a) $2(4x-3)(3x-4)$ **b)** $7(5x-2)(6x+1)$ **c)** $-3(a+8)(2a+9)$

d) $5(4x+1)^2$ **e)** $6(8x-3y)(2x+y)$ **f)** $-4(a+3b)(2a-5b)$

3. Expand and simplify where possible.

a) $(x-3)(x-6)+(x+2)(x+7)$ **b)** $(x-5)(x+4)-(x+1)(x-8)$

c) $(x-3)^2+(x+3)^2$ **d)** $(x-y)(x-4y)-(x+y)(x-y)$

4. Expand and simplify where possible.

a) $(3x-1)(x-3)-2x(x-1)$

b) $(4x+1)(2x+3)-(3x-7)(2x-5)$

c) $(9x-1)(x-4)-(3x+1)(3x-1)$

d) $8(5-3x)(2+5x)-3(1+x)^2$

e) $5(2x-3)(2x+5)+3(x+7)(x+2)$

f) $4(2p+3q)^2-(5p-q)(7p+11q)$

5. Expand and simplify where possible.

a) $(x+4)^2+(x+2)^2$

b) $(3a-b)^2-(2a+5b)^2$

c) $3(y-1)^2-2(2y-1)^2$

d) $9-2(x-1)(x+7)+(2x-5)(x-3)$

e) $3(1+3y)(4-y)-(3y-2)(3y-5)$

Use the following information to answer the next question .

A student provides the following expansions for four binomial products.

$(x+3)^2 = x^2 + 9$	$(3x - y)(3x - y) = 9x^2 - 6xy - y^2$
$(2x + y)(2x - y) = 2x^2 - y^2$	$(5x + 7)^2 = 25x^2 + 35x + 49$

Multiple Choice **6.** How many of the student's expansions are incorrect?

A. One
B. Two
C. Three
D. Four

Numerical Response **7.** Given that for every value of x, $x^2 - 10x + 39 = (x - a)^2 + b$, then the value of b must be ______.

(Record your answer in the numerical response box from left to right)

Answer Key

1. a) $x^2 - 16x + 64$ **b)** $x^2 - 81$ **c)** $9x^2 - 6xy + y^2$
d) $25x^2 + 20xy + 4y^2$ **e)** $9x^2 - 4$ **f)** $4y^2 - 4y + 1$
g) $4p^2 + 28p + 49$ **h)** $16m^2 - 9n^2$ **i)** $25a^2 - 60ab + 36b^2$
j) $81 - 25x^4$ **k)** $36a^2 - 84ab + 49b^2$ **l)** $4a^6 - 49$

2. a) $24x^2 - 50x + 24$ **b)** $210x^2 - 49x - 14$ **c)** $-6a^2 - 75a - 216$
d) $80x^2 + 40x + 5$ **e)** $96x^2 + 12xy - 18y^2$ **f)** $-8a^2 - 4ab + 60b^2$

3. a) $2x^2 + 32$ **b)** $6x - 12$ **c)** $2x^2 + 18$ **d)** $-5xy + 5y^2$

4. a) $x^2 - 8x + 3$ **b)** $2x^2 + 43x - 32$ **c)** $-37x + 5$
d) $77 + 146x - 123x^2$ **e)** $23x^2 + 47x - 33$ **f)** $-19p^2 + 47q^2$

5. a) $2x^2 + 12x + 20$ **b)** $5a^2 - 26ab - 24b^2$ **c)** $-5y^2 + 2y + 1$
d) $-23x + 38$ **e)** $-18y^2 + 54y + 2$

6. D **7.**

1	4		

Polynomial Operations Lesson #5:
Multiplication of Polynomials - Part Two

In this lesson, we deal with more involved polynomial multiplication including multiplying a binomial by a trinomial and the product of three binomials.

Product of a Binomial and a Trinomial

Class Ex. #1

A rectangle has length $(5x + 2)$ cm. and width $(x^2 + 2x + 1)$ cm.
Determine the area of the rectangle (in cm^2) by completing each of the following solutions.

Area = length × width = ()()

i) *use a diagram* **ii)** *use the distributive property*

x^2	$+2x$	$+1$
$5x$	$5x^3$	$10x^2$	$5x$
$+2$	$2x^2$	$4x$	2

$5x^3 + 10x^2 + 2x^2$
$+5x + 4x + 2$
 $9x$

$5x^3 + 12x^2 + 9x + 2$

$(5x + 2)(x^2 + 2x + 1)$
$= 5x(x^2 + 2x + 1) + 2(x^2 + 2x + 1)$
$=$
$=$ sum

Class Ex. #2

Expand and simplify.

a) $(x^2 - 4)(2x^3 + x - 5)$ **b)** $(2y^2 - 3y - 7)(y - 6)$

	$2x^3$	x	-5
x^2	$2x^5$	x^3	$-5x^2$
-4	$-8x^3$	$-4x$	20

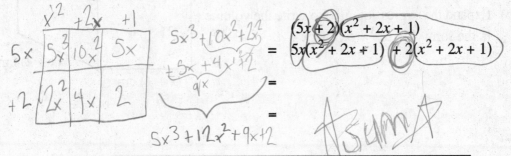

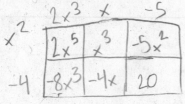

$2x^5 + x^3 - 5x^2 \quad -8x^3 - 4x + 20 \quad \rightarrow \quad 2x^5 - 8x^6 - 5x^2$

Class Ex. #3

Expand and simplify $4(a - 4)(a^2 - 3a - 6) - (4a - 3)(4a + 3)$. Later

in pairs

All products in brackets

$(4a - 8)(a^2 - 3a - 6)$

$4a^3 - 24a - 6$

Complete Assignment Questions #1 - #3

Product of Three Binomials

In this section, we extend the multiplication of binomials to consider three factors. This leads to applications involving the volume of a rectangular prism.

Consider the rectangular prism shown.

a) Write an expression which represents the volume of the prism in cm^3.

b) Expand the expression in a) to write the volume in the form $V = ax^3 + bx^2 + cx + d$.

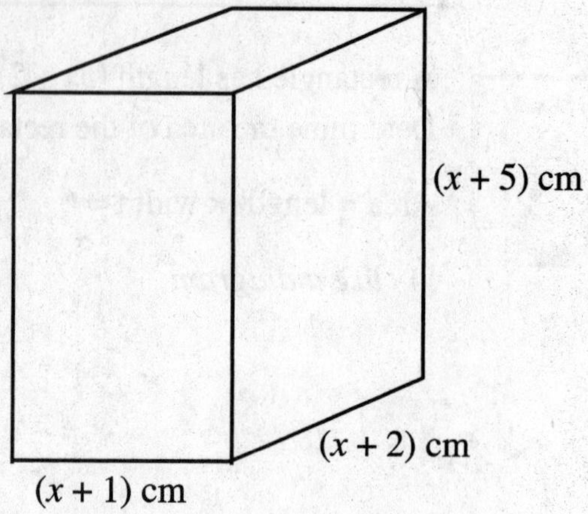

Expand and simplify.

a) $(x - 3)(x + 4)(2x - 1)$ **b)** $(2x - 1)(x - 3)(x + 4)$

$(x^2 - 12)(2x - 1)$

	$2x$	-1
x^2	$2x^3$	$-1x^2$
-12	$-24x$	$+12$

$2x^3 - 1x^2 - 24x + 12$

c) Comment on the results to a) and b).

Complete Assignment Questions #4 - #9

Assignment

1. Use a diagram to determine the expansion.

a) $(y - 5)(y^2 + 2y + 4)$

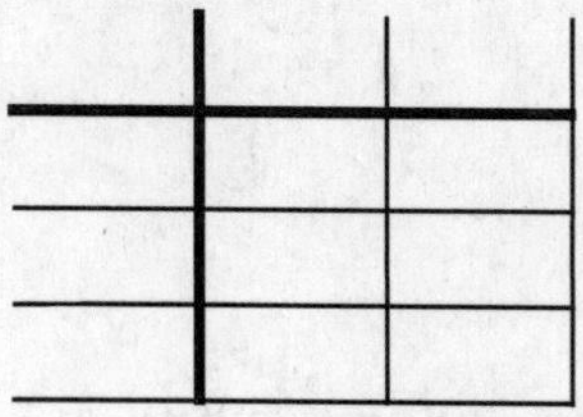

b) $(3m + 7)(m^2 - 3m + 6)$

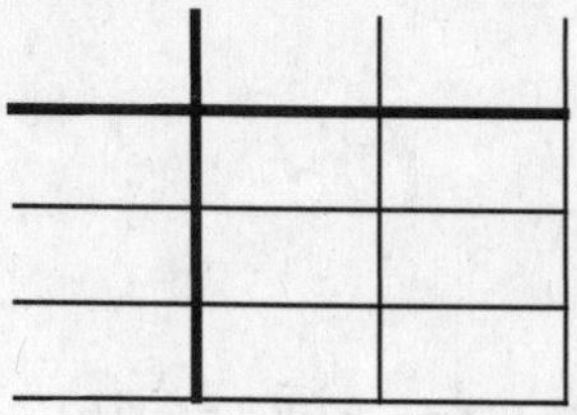

2. Use the distributive law to determine the expansion.

a) $(x - 4)(x^2 - 6x + 3)$

b) $(2a + 5)(a^2 - 7a - 9)$

3. Expand and simplify.

a) $(x^2 - 7)(2x^3 + 4x - 1)$

b) $(-m^2 - m + 1)(m + 1)$

c) $(a - 3b)(4a^2 - 3ab - 2b^2)$

d) $2(5x + 2)(3x^2 + x - 4)$

4. Expand and simplify.

a) $(x + 1)(x + 2)(3x + 5)$

b) $(h - 4)(2h - 3)(3h - 1)$

c) $(a + 3b)(2a - 5b)(2a + 5b)$

d) $(3x + 7y)(4x - 3y)(x - 4y)$

5. Calculate the volume of the cube shown below.

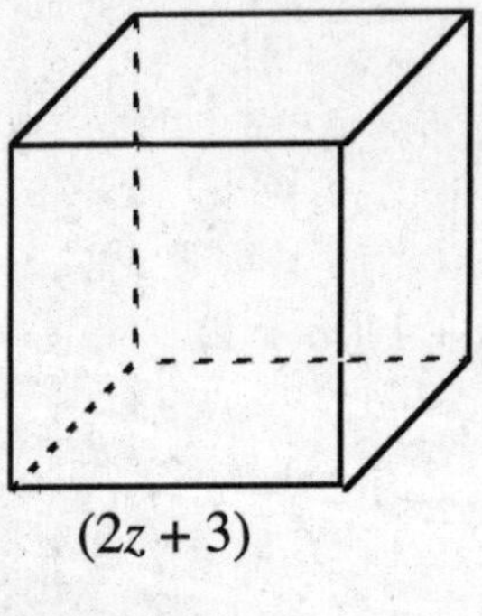

6. Calculate the volume of the rectangular prism illustrated.

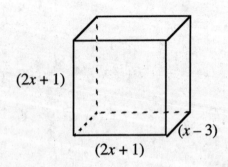

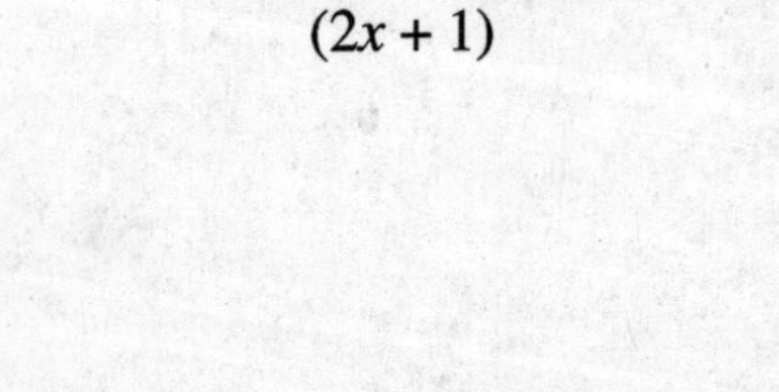

7. Simplify

a) $-3(a^2 + 2)(3a^2 - a - 1)$

b) $(-2x^2 - 3x + 1)(x^2 - x - 3)$

c) $2(4x - 1)^2 - (3x - 2)^3$

Use the following information to answer the next question.

A student attempts to expand $(a + 2)^3$.
His work is shown below.

$(a+2)^3$

$= (a+2)(a+2)(a+2)$	Line 1
$= (a+2)(a^2+4)$	Line 2
$= a^3 + 2a^2 + 4a + 8$	Line 3

Multiple Choice **8.** Which of the following statements is true?

A. The student made an error in Line 1.
B. The student made an error in Line 2.
C. The student made an error in Line 3.
D. The student's expansion is correct.

Numerical Response **9.** Subtracting the product of $(3x - 1)$ and $(2x^2 - 4x + 3)$ from the sum of $(2x^3 - 7x^2 - 6)$ and $(x^2 + 6x - 3)$ results in a polynomial of the form $ax^3 + bx^2 + cx + d$. The value of $b - 2c$ is _____ .

(Record your answer in the numerical response box from left to right)

Answer Key

1. a) $y^3 - 3y^2 - 6y - 20$ **b)** $3m^3 - 2m^2 - 3m + 42$

2. a) $x^3 - 10x^2 + 27x - 12$ **b)** $2a^3 - 9a^2 - 53a - 45$

3. a) $2x^5 - 10x^3 - x^2 - 28x + 7$ **b)** $-m^3 - 2m^2 + 1$
c) $4a^3 - 15a^2b + 7ab^2 + 6b^3$ **d)** $30x^3 + 22x^2 - 36x - 16$

4. a) $3x^3 + 14x^2 + 21x + 10$ **b)** $6h^3 - 35h^2 + 47h - 12$
c) $4a^3 + 12a^2b - 25ab^2 - 75b^3$ **d)** $12x^3 - 29x^2y - 97xy^2 + 84y^3$

5. $8z^3 + 36z^2 + 54z + 27$

6. $4x^3 - 8x^2 - 11x - 3$

7. a) $-9a^4 + 3a^3 - 15a^2 + 6a + 6$ **b)** $-2x^4 - x^3 + 10x^2 + 8x - 3$
c) $-27x^3 + 86x^2 - 52x + 10$

8. B **9.**

2	2		

Polynomial Operations Lesson #6:
Problem Solving with Polynomial Products

a) The area of the given figure can be written as a trinomial in the form $ax^2 + bx + c$. Determine the values of a, b, and c.

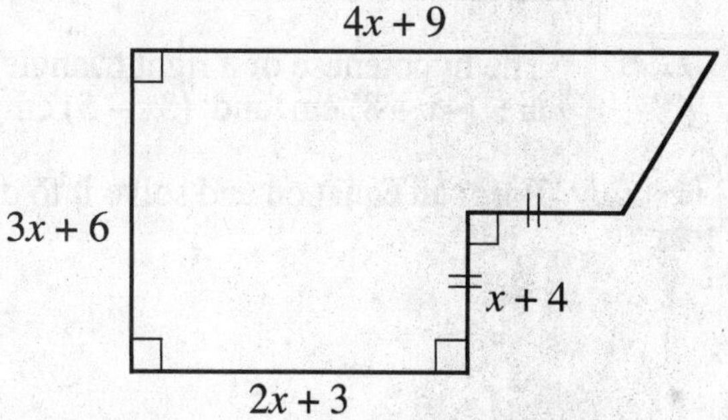

b) Calculate the area if $x = 2.5$.

A rectangular garden with length of $(8 - 3a)$ m and width $(a + 8)$ m contains three square flower beds each with a side length of $(2a + 5)$ m. The remainder of the garden is grass.

a) Draw a diagram to illustrate this information.

b) Write and simplify an expression for the area of grass in the garden.

c) Determine the area of grass if $a = -1.5$.

Equation Solving

Class Ex. #3

The hypotenuse of a right triangle is $(5x + 5)$ cm long and the lengths of the other two sides are $(4x + 8)$ cm and $(3x - 5)$ cm.

Form an equation and solve it to determine the lengths of the three sides of the triangle.

Complete Assignment Questions #1 - #15

Assignment

1. In each case, the figures consist of a series of horizontal and vertical lines. The area of each figure can be written as a trinomial in the form $ax^2 + bx + c$. Determine the values of a, b, and c, and calculate the area when $x = 2.4$.

a)

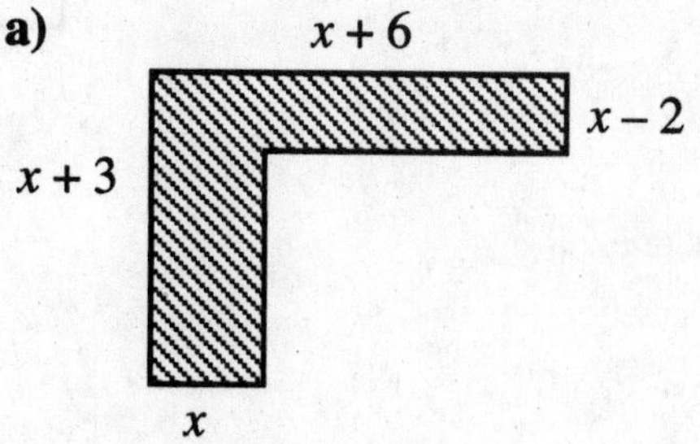

b)

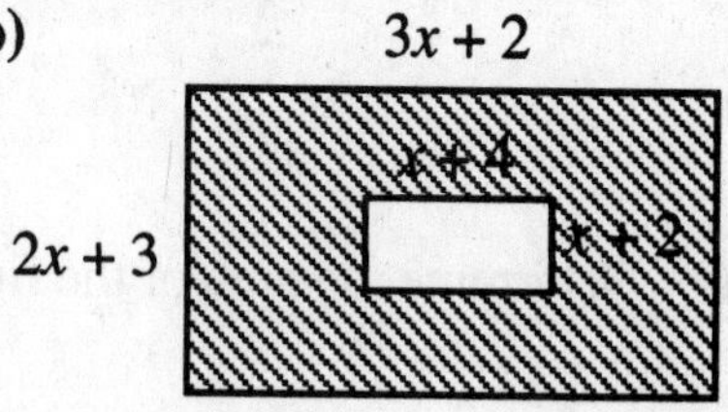

2. The figure consists of a rectangle within a rectangle.

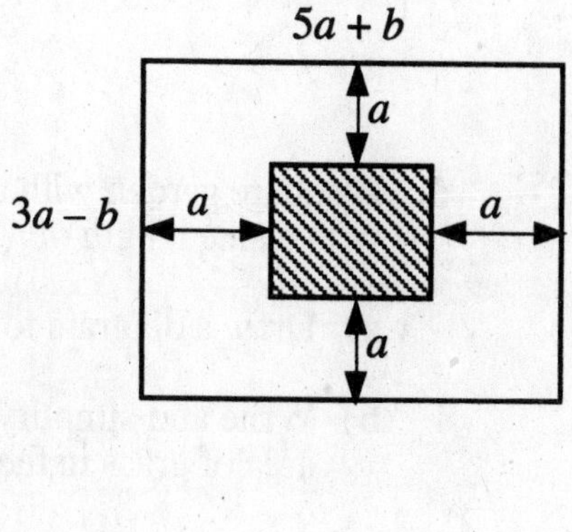

a) Determine a simplified expression of the shaded area in terms of a and b.

b) Calculate the area when $a = 2.8$ and $b = -3.5$.

3. a) Determine the area of the figure in the form $ay^2 + by + c$.

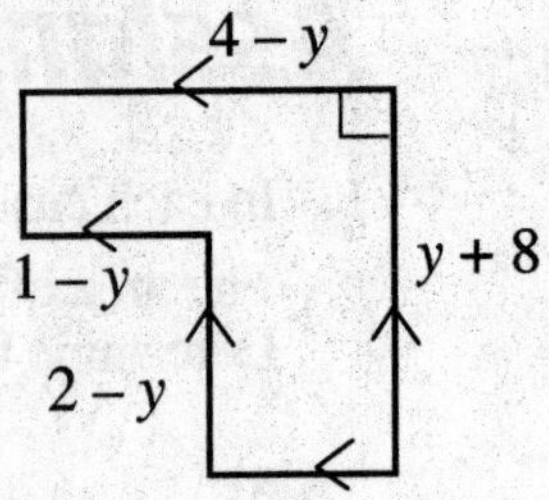

b) Determine the area of the figure when $y = -2$.

4. A square metal plate of side 25 cm is heated so that each side increases in length by x cm.

a) Write and simplify an expression for the area of the heated plate.

b) Write and simplify an expression for the increase in area of the plate.

c) If $x = 0.2$, calculate the increase in area.

5. A square garden with a side length of $(3x + 1)$ m contains two square flower beds each with a side length of $(x + 1)$ m. The remainder of the garden is grass.

a) Draw a diagram to illustrate this information.

b) Write and simplify an expression for the area of grass in the garden.

6. A metal washer has internal radius r mm and width w mm as shown.

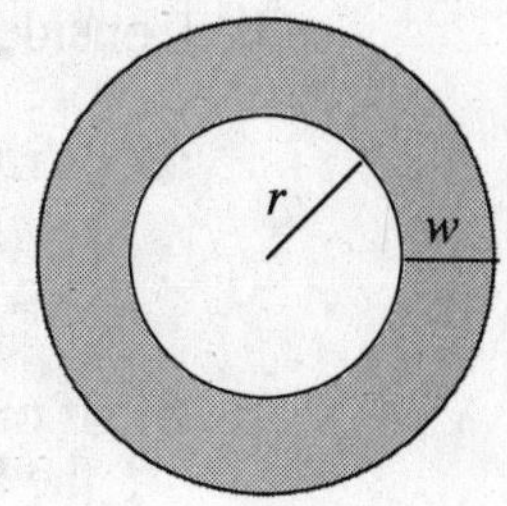

a) Write an expression for the outer radius of the washer.

b) Show that the area of the washer, A mm^2, is given by $A = 2\pi rw + \pi w^2$.

7. Solve the following equations where the variable is on the set of real numbers.

a) $(3x - 1)(x - 1) = 3x(x + 1)$

b) $(y + 2)^2 = y^2 + 2$

c) $t^2 - (t - 9)^2 = 9$

d) $2a^2 - (a - 3)^2 = (a + 2)(a - 1)$

8. The hypotenuse of a right triangle is $(5x - 6)$ cm long and the lengths of the other two sides are $(4x - 7)$ cm and $(3x - 1)$ cm. Form an equation and solve it to determine the value of x and the lengths of the three sides of the triangle.

9. Consider a set of rectangles with sides $(4a - 3)$ cm and $(2a + 7)$ cm.

a) Write and simplify an expression in a for the area of one of these rectangles.

b) If one of these rectangles has a perimeter of 50 cm, determine the length and width of this rectangle.

c) If another of these rectangles is a square, determine the length of each side.

10. A rectangle has length $(x^2 + 4x - 1)$ cm and width $(3x - 2)$ cm.

a) Write and simplify an expression for the area of the rectangle in cm^2.

b) If $x = 2.5$, calculate the area of the rectangle.

11. Dice for a children's board game are cubes with an edge length of $(3x - 2)$ mm.

a) Write and simplify an expression for the volume of a die in mm^3.

b) The manufacturer packages dice in cubic containers containing 64 dice. Determine the volume of the container in cm^3 if $x = 4$.

12. A rectangular prism has length $(5x - 2)$ cm, width $(3x - 1)$ cm, and height $(3x + 1)$ cm.

a) Write and simplify an expression for the volume of the rectangular prism in cm^3.

b) Write and simplify an expression for the surface area of the rectangular prism in cm^2.

c) If $x = 4$, calculate the volume and surface area of the rectangular prism.

Multiple Choice

13. A box is in the shape of a rectangular prism. The length of the box is y cm. The width is 2 cm less than the length, and the height is 2 cm more than the length. If the volume of the box can be written in the form $V = ay^3 + by^2 + cy + d$ where $a, b, c,$ and d are integers, then how many of the parameters a, b, c, and d are equal to zero?

A. 0
B. 1
C. 2
D. 3

14. The square and the rectangle in the diagram are equal in area.
The value of x, to the nearest tenth, is ______.

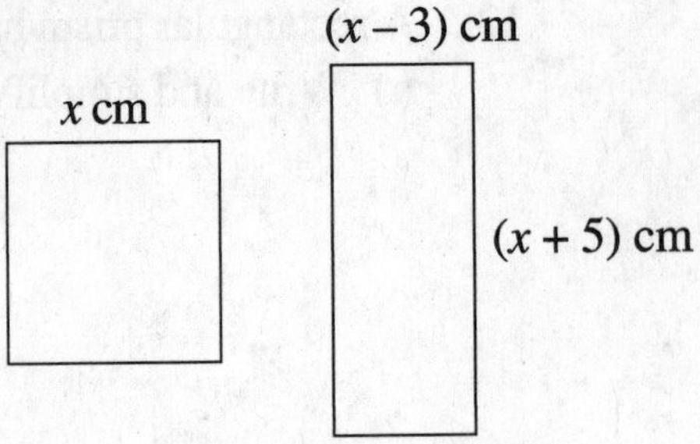

(Record your answer in the numerical response box from left to right)

15. The diagram shows the lengths of the sides of right triangle *ABC*.

The perimeter (to the nearest tenth of a cm) of triangle *ABC* is ______.

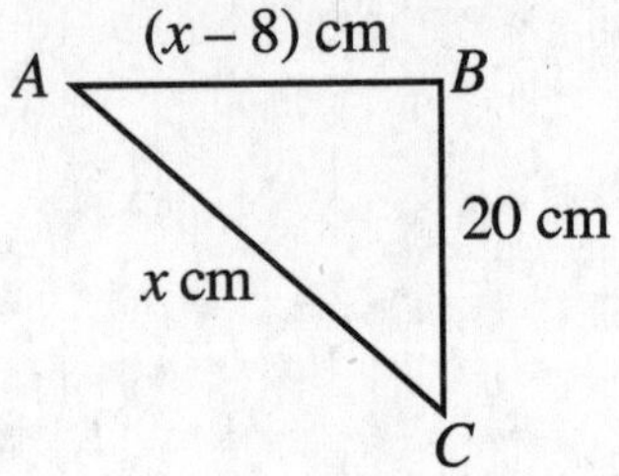

(Record your answer in the numerical response box from left to right)

Answer Key

1. a) $a = 1,\ b = 9,\ c = -12$, area = 15.36 units^2 **b)** $a = 5,\ b = 7,\ c = -2$, area = 43.6 units^2

2. a) $3a^2 - 2ab - b^2$ **b)** 30.87 units^2 **3. a)** $30 - y - 2y^2$ **b)** 24 units^2

4. a) $625 + 50x + x^2$ cm^2 **b)** $50x + x^2$ cm^2 **c)** 10.04 cm^2

5. b) $(3x + 1)^2 - 2(x + 1)^2 = 7x^2 + 2x - 1$ m^2 **6. a)** $(r + w)$ *mm*

7. a) $\frac{1}{7}$ **b)** $-\frac{1}{2}$ **c)** 5 **d)** $\frac{7}{5}$

8. $(5x - 6)^2 = (4x - 7)^2 + (3x - 1)^2$; $x = 7$; 29 cm, 21 cm 20 cm

9. a) $(4a - 3)(2a + 7) = 8a^2 + 22a - 21$ cm^2 **b)** 11 cm by 14 cm **c)** 17 cm

10. a) $(x^2 + 4x - 1)(3x - 2) = 3x^3 + 10x^2 - 11x + 2$ cm^2 **b)** 83.875 cm^2

11. a) $(3x - 2)^3 = 27x^3 - 54x^2 + 36x - 8$ mm^3 **b)** 64 cm^3

12. a) $(5x - 2)(3x - 1)(3x + 1) = 45x^3 - 18x^2 - 5x + 2$ cm^3

b) $2(3x - 1)(3x + 1) + 2(3x - 1)(5x - 2) + 2(3x + 1)(5x - 2) = 78x^2 - 24x - 2$ cm^2

c) volume = 2574 cm^3, surface area = 1150 cm^2

13. C **14.** | 7 | . | 5 | | **15.** | 7 | 0 | . | 0 |

Polynomial Operations Lesson #7:
Practice Test

1. Which of the following could not be classified as a monomial?

A. $9x^4$ **B.** $x + 1$ **C.** 7 **D.** $-6x$

2. The degree of the polynomial $a^3b + 2c^2$ is

A. 3 **B.** 4 **C.** 5 **D.** 6

3. Which of the following is a polynomial of degree 5?

I $5x$ **II** $3x^5 - 2x^6$ **III** $2x^4 - 3x^{-2} + 5x^5$ **IV** $3x^2y^3$

A. IV only **B.** III and IV only **C.** I, II, III, and IV

D. some other combination of **I, II, III,** and **IV**

Numerical Response

1. The polynomial $2x^3 - 9 + 8x^4$ has leading coefficient P, degree Q, and constant term R. The value of $P - Q - R$ is _____.

(Record your answer in the numerical response box from left to right)

Use the following diagram to answer the next question.

Dark tiles represent positive quantities and light tiles represent negative quantities.

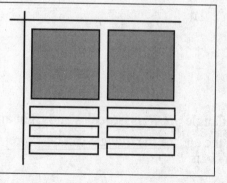

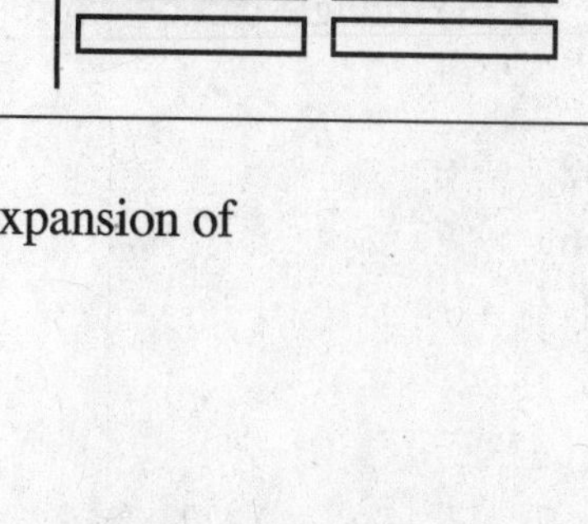

4. The algebra tile diagram represents the expansion of

A. $2x^2(x^2 - 3x)$

B. $x^2(x - 3)$

C. $2x(x - 3)$

D. $2x(x + 3)$

5. When $(x + y)(x - y)$ is expanded, how many terms are in the simplified product?

A. 1 **B.** 2

C. 3 **D.** 4

6. The area (in mm^2) of a rectangle with length $6 - a$ mm and width $8 - a$ mm is

A. $48 + a^2$
B. $48 - 14a - a^2$
C. $48 - 2a + a^2$
D. $48 - 14a + a^2$

7. Which of the following expansions is correct?

A. $-2x^2(3x^3 + 5) = -6x^6 - 10x^2$
B. $-7x(2 - 3x) = -14x - 21x^2$
C. $-5x^3(4 + x) = -20x^3 - 5x^3$
D. $-9x^2(1 - x) = -9x^2 + 9x^3$

Numerical Response **2.** The expression $6x(4 - 3x) - 5x(x - 4) - (9x + 2)$ can be written in the form $ax^2 + bx + c$. The value of abc is ______.

(Record your answer in the numerical response box from left to right)

8. Triangle PQR is isosceles and right angled at Q. Side PQ measures $2x + 8$ cm. If the area of the triangle can be expressed in the form $ax^2 + bx + c\ \text{cm}^2$, then the value of b is

A. 32
B. 16
C. 8
D. 6

Numerical Response

3. If $(x - a)^2 + a = x^2 - 12x + c$, then the value of c is ______.

(Record your answer in the numerical response box from left to right)

Use the following information to answer the next question.

The rectangle has length $4x + 3$ mm and width $2x + 4$ mm.

The square has side length $x + 3$ mm.

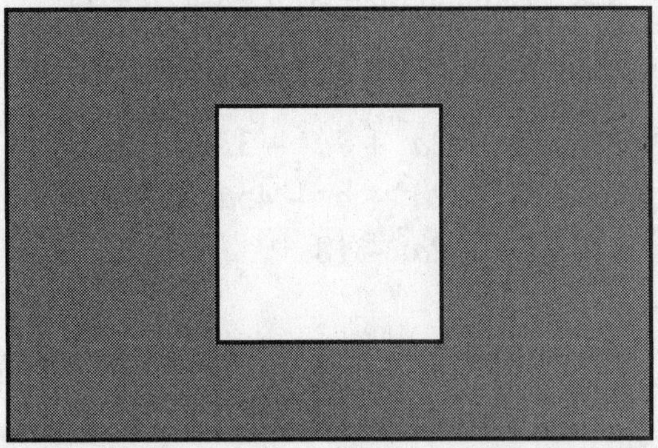

9. The area, in mm^2, of the shaded region is

A. $7x^2 + 22x + 21$
B. $7x^2 + 28x + 21$
C. $7x^2 + 16x + 3$
D. $7x^2 + 22x + 3$

10. The expansion $(6t - 1)(2t^2 - 7t - 1)$ is

A. $12t^3 - 44t^2 + t + 1$
B. $12t^3 - 40t^2 - 13t + 1$
C. $12t^3 - 44t^2 - t + 1$
D. $12t^3 - 44t^2 - 13t - 1$

11. Subtracting the product of $(2x - 3)$ and $(3x + 2)$ from the sum of $(3x^2 + 3x - 2)$ and $(3x^2 + 2x - 4)$ results in a polynomial of the form $px^2 + qx + r$. How many of the parameters p, q, r are equal to zero?

A. 0
B. 1
C. 2
D. 3

12. Expand $(a + 3)(a - 6)(2a + 1)$

A. $2a^3 - 5a^2 - 39a - 18$
B. $2a^3 + 7a^2 - 33a - 18$
C. $2a^3 + a^2 - 45a - 18$
D. $2a^3 - 18$

In questions #13 and #14 four responses are given.

Answer *A* if response 1 and response 2 only are correct

***B* if response 1 and response 3 only are correct**

***C* if response 2 and response 4 only are correct**

***D* if some other response or combination of the responses is correct.**

13. Which of the following are binomials of degree 6?

Response 1: $x^6 + x$
Response 2: $6x^3 + 6y^3$
Response 3: $4a^2b^4 + 2a^3$
Response 4: y^5z

14. Which of the following polynomial products contains a term of degree one?

Response 1 $(x - 3)(x - 2)$
Response 2 $(x - 3)(x - 3)$
Response 3 $(x - 3)(x + 3)$
Response 4 $(x - 3)(x - 6)(x + 2)$

Use the following information to answer questions #15 and Numerical Response #5.

A sheet of paper measures 17 cm by 11 cm. Squares of side x cm are cut out from each corner as shown. The paper is folded along the dotted lines to form a rectangular prism.

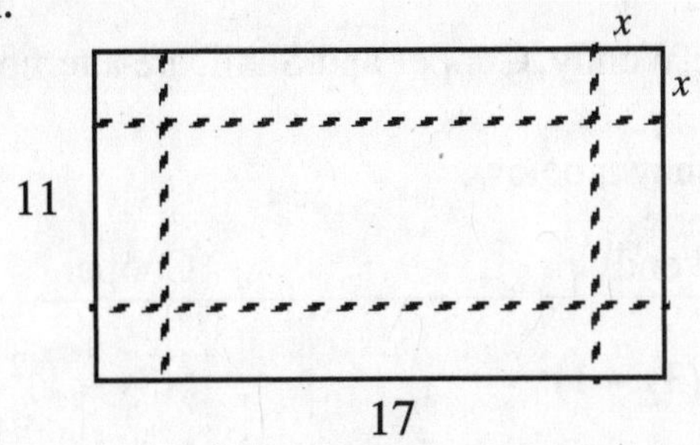

15. The length and width (in cm) of the rectangular prism are respectively

A. $17 - x$ and $11 - x$

B. $17 - 2x$ and $11 - 2x$

C. $17 + x$ and $11 + x$

D. $17 + 2x$ and $11 + 2x$

Numerical Response 4. The volume of the rectangular prism can be written as the polynomial expression $ax^3 + bx^2 + cx$ where a, b, and c are integers. The value of $a + c$, to the nearest whole number, is _____.

(Record your answer in the numerical response box from left to right)

Numerical Response 5. The trinomial $x^2 - 14x + 52$ can be expressed in the form $(x - p)^2 + q$.

Write the value of p in the first box.
Write the value of q in the second box.

(Record your answer in the numerical response box from left to right)

Written Response - 5 marks

Use the following information to answer the next question.

1. Three students, Wendy, Cooper and Sahil, are attempting to expand the polynomial $5(3y-1)^2$.
Their work is shown below.

	Wendy	Cooper	Sahil
	$5(3y-1)^2$	$5(3y-1)^2$	$5(3y-1)^2$
Line 1	$(15y-5)^2$	$5(6y^2-6y+1)$	$5(9y^2-3y+1)$
Line 2	$225y^2-150y+25$	$30y^2-30y+5$	$45y^2-15y+5$

- Wendy's work contains one mathematical error. Describe in detail the error she made.

- Cooper's work contains one mathematical error. Describe in detail the error he made.

- Sahil's work contains one mathematical error. Describe in detail the error he made.

- Determine the correct expansion of $5(3y-1)^2$.

- Verify the expansion by substituting $y=-4$ in the original expression and in your expansion and confirming the same numerical value.

Answer Key

1. B	2. B	3. A	4. C	5. B
6. D	7. D	8. B	9. C	10. A
11. C	12. A	13. B	14. A	15. B

Numerical Response

1. | 1 | 3 | | |

2. | 1 | 6 | 1 | 0 |

3. | 4 | 2 | | |

4. | 1 | 9 | 1 | |

5. | 7 | 3 | | |

Written response

- In line 1 Wendy distributed the 5 before squaring. BEDMAS tells us to do exponents before multiplication.
- In line 1 Cooper expanded $(3y-1)^2$ incorrectly. The first term should be $(3y)(3y) = 9y^2$.
- In line 1 Sahil also expanded $(3y-1)^2$ incorrectly. The middle term should be $(3y)(-1)(2) = -6y$.
- $5(3y-1)^2 = 5(9y^2 - 6y + 1) = 45y^2 - 30y + 5$
- $LS = 5[3(-4)-1]^2 = 5[-12-1]^2 = 5(-13)^2 = 5(169) = 845$

  $RS = 45(-4)^2 - 30(-4) + 5 = 45(16) + 120 + 5 = 720 + 120 + 5 = 845$

  $LS = RS$ so the expansion is verified.

Factoring Polynomial Expressions Lesson #1:
Common Factors - Part One

Overview of Unit

In this unit, we introduce the process of factoring. This includes factoring by removing a common factor (monomial, binomial, and grouping), factoring a trinomial (inspection and decomposition) and factoring a difference of squares. These techniques are illustrated concretely, pictorially, and symbolically. We express a polynomial as a product of its factors and include, for enrichment, polynomial equation solving.

Expanding and Factoring

In the previous unit, we were concerned with multiplying polynomial expressions.
In particular we multiplied

i) a monomial by a polynomial e.g. $2x(x+5) =$ __________

ii) a binomial by a binomial to form a trinomial e.g. $(x+1)(x+3) =$ __________

$(2x+3)(x+4) =$ __________

iii) a binomial by a binomial to form a binomial e.g. $(x-5)(x+5) =$ __________

In these examples, we have **expanded** a product of polynomials to form a sum or difference of monomials.

In this unit, we are concerned with the opposite process. We want to write a sum or difference of monomials as a product of polynomials. This process is called **factoring**.

We will be studying the following three major types of factoring.

Complete the following using the results obtained above.

i) factoring by removing a common factor e.g. $2x^2 + 10x =$ __________

ii) factoring a trinomial. e.g. $x^2 + 4x + 3 =$ __________

$2x^2 + 11x + 12 =$ __________

iii) factoring a difference of squares e.g. $x^2 - 25 =$ __________

Greatest Common Factor

In the unit on number, we met the concept of the greatest common factor of whole numbers. The GCF of 48 and 72 was found by using prime factorization.

$$48 = 2 \times 2 \times 2 \times 2 \times 3 \quad \text{and} \quad 72 = 2 \times 2 \times 2 \times 3 \times 3 \qquad \boxed{24} = GCF$$

To determine the greatest common factor of 48 and 72, we found the product of each prime factor (including repeats) which is <u>common</u> to each prime factorization.

GCF of 48 and 72 is $2 \times 2 \times 2 \times 3 =$ ___24___.

The same process can be used to determine the greatest common factor of two monomials like $6a^3$ and $9a^2b$.

$$6a^3 = 2 \times 3 \times a \times a \times a \quad \text{and} \quad 9a^2b = 3 \times 3 \times a \times a \times b$$

$$\text{GCF of } 6a^3 \text{ and } 9a^2b \text{ is} \quad \times \quad \times \quad = \underline{\quad\quad}.$$

Class Ex. #1 Write the prime factorization of $8x^2y^2$ and $20xy^3$ and determine the greatest common factor of $8x^2y^2$ and $20xy^3$. 8,1,4,2 20,1,10,2,5,4

easy peasy

$$4xy^2(2x + 5y)$$

Note • The greatest common factor of two simple monomials can be determined by <u>inspection</u>, by taking the GCF of any numerical coefficients and multiplying by each common variable to the lowest common exponent.

The greatest common factor of $10p^3q$ and $15p^2q^2$ is determined by multiplying 5 by p^2 by q, i.e. $5p^2q$.

• If all the monomials are negative, the GCF is usually considered to be negative (see example d) below).

Class Ex. #2 In each case, state the greatest common factor of the following sets of monomials.

a) $12ab, 15a^2b^3$
$$3ab(4 + 5ab^2)$$

b) $18x^4y^2, -24x^3y^5$
$$6x^2y^2(3x^2 - 4xy^3)$$

c) $a^3bc^2, 2ac^7$
$$ac^2(a^2b + 2c^5)$$

d) $-40a^3b, -20a^2b^3, -10a^2b^2$
$$-10a^2b(4a + 2b^2 + b)$$

Complete Assignment Question #1 - #3

Factoring a Polynomial by Removing the Greatest Common Factor

Factoring is a process in which a sum or difference of terms is expressed as a product of factors.

A polynomial like $8x^2y^2 + 20xy^3$ can be factored by a process called removing (or taking out, or dividing out) the greatest common factor from each term.

We know that $4xy^2 \quad 4xy^2 \quad 3-2=1$

$4xy^2(2x + 5y)$ can be expanded to give $8x^2y^2 + 20xy^3$.

It follows that

$8x^2y^2 + 20xy^3$ can be factored to give $4xy^2(2x + 5y)$.

In this case, the greatest common factor $4xy^2$ has been removed from each term.

Class Ex. #3

In each case, complete the factoring.

a) $21x + 14y =$ ____ $(3x + 2y)$ **b)** $5x^4 + 15x^3 + 5x^2 =$ ____ $(x^2 + 3x + 1)$

Class Ex. #4

In each case, the greatest common factor has been removed. Complete the factoring.

a) $5a^2 + 25a = 5a(a + \quad)$ **b)** $18p - 16q = 2(\quad - 8q)$

c) $-4mn - 6m^2 = -2m($ **d)** $18x^2y^2 - 45xy + 9x = 9x($

Class Ex. #5

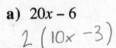

Factor each polynomial by removing the greatest common factor.

a) $20x - 6$ **b)** $16x^4 + 4x^2$ **c)** $10a^3b^2 + 8ab^3 + 2ab^4$

$2(10x - 3)$ $4x^2(4x^2 + 1)$ $2ab^2(5a^2 + 4b + b^2)$

d) $12p^3 - 6p^2 + 15p$ **e)** $25xy^2z^3 - 20x^2y^4z^2 + 30x^4y^2z^5$

$3p(4p^2 - 2p + 5)$ $5xy^2z^2(5z - 4xy^2 + 6x^3z^3)$

? CAN I FACTOR AGAIN?

Class Ex. #6

The surface area of a cone is given by the formula $A = \pi r^2 + \pi rs$, where r is the radius of the base of the cone and s is the slant height.

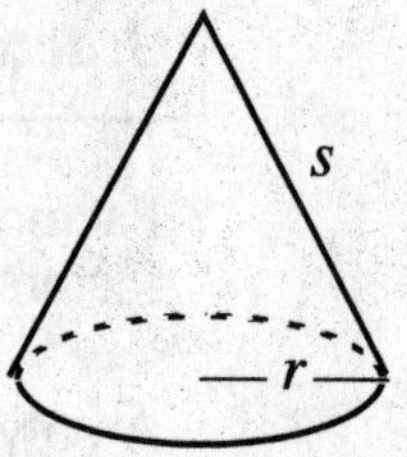

i) Determine the surface area of a cone, to the nearest 0.01 cm^2, which has slant height 7.40 cm and base radius 2.60 cm.

$\pi r(r+s)$

ii) Write the formula for A in factored form.

iii) Calculate the surface area of the cone, to the nearest 0.01 cm^2, using the factored form of A.

iv) Which method i) or iii) is simpler to use?

Complete Assignment Questions #4 - #16

Assignment

1. Write the prime factorization of $12a^3$ and $30a^2$ and determine the greatest common factor of $12a^3$ and $30a^2$.

2. Write the prime factorization of $10xy^4$ and $25x^2y^3$ and determine the greatest common factor of $10xy^4$ and $25x^2y^3$.

3. In each case, state the greatest common factor of the following sets of monomials.

a) $7m,\ 14m$ **b)** $6x^2,\ 9x$ **c)** $bc^2,\ bc^7$

d) $ab,\ a^2b^2$ **e)** $4x^4,\ 8x^3$ **f)** $3xyz,\ 9rst,\ 12def$

g) $-8pq^3,\ 18p^2q$ **h)** $-10x^5z^6,\ -15x^5z^4$ **i)** $8ab^2,\ 9ab,\ 6a^2b$

j) $10xy,\ 16xz,\ 20xyz$ **k)** $-2x^3y,\ -4x^3y^4,\ -4x^2y^4$ **l)** $-28pqr^3,\ -56p^2q,\ -64q^2r$

4. Complete the factoring in each case.

a) $12a + 24b =$ ___ $(a + 2b)$ **b)** $4p^2 - 7p =$ ___ $(4p - 7)$

c) $2xy + 3xz =$ ___ $(2y + 3z)$ **d)** $5x^2 + 10x + 15 =$ ___ $(x^2 + 2x + 3)$

e) $6cde - 4cd =$ ___ $(3e - 2)$ **f)** $3y^3 - 9y =$ ___ $(y^2 - 3)$

5. In each case, the greatest common factor has been removed. Complete the factoring.

a) $3a^2 + 15a = 3a(a +$ **b)** $20p - 10q = 10(\quad - q)$

c) $6x^3 - 9x^2 = 3x^2($ **d)** $4a^2b + 8a^3b^2 = 4a^2b($

e) $-15x^2y - 10x^2y^2 = -5x^2y($ **f)** $16xm^2n^3 - 12mn^2 - 4mn = 4mn($

6. Factor the following polynomials by removing the greatest common factor.

a) $6m + 6n$ **b)** $7xy^2 + 49$ **c)** $15pq - 5$ **d)** $8c + 12d$

e) $xy + y$ **f)** $6x^2 - 9x$ **g)** $9ab - 12ac$ **h)** $48y^2 - 72y^5$

7. Factor the following polynomials

a) $12x - 8y + 16z$ **b)** $9pq + 6pr - 15p$ **c)** $t^3 + t^2 + t$

d) $5x^2 - 10xy - 20xz$ **e)** $4abc - 2abd + 8abe$ **f)** $14a^2b^2 + 21a^3b^2 - 35a^2b^3$

8. In each of the following:
i) simplify the expression by combining like terms.
ii) factor the resulting polynomial.

a) $5x^2 - 2x + 7 - 2x^2 + 8x - 7$

b) $6 - 2y + 5y^2 - 10y + 3y^2 - 12$

c) $xy^3 - 2x^3y + 6x^2y^2 - 5xy^3 + 8x^3y$

d) $2(x^3 - 3x) - 4x(x - 6) + 5x^2(x - 2) - 4x$

9. Factor the following polynomials. Expand your answer to verify the factoring.

a) $24x^3 - 60x^2$

b) $-8p^3 - 32p^2 - 8p$

10. The surface area of a cylinder is given by the formula $A = 2\pi r^2 + 2\pi rh$, where r is the radius of the base and h is the height of the cylinder.

a) Calculate the surface area, to the nearest 0.01 cm^2, of a cylinder which has vertical height 14.5 cm and base diameter 11 cm.

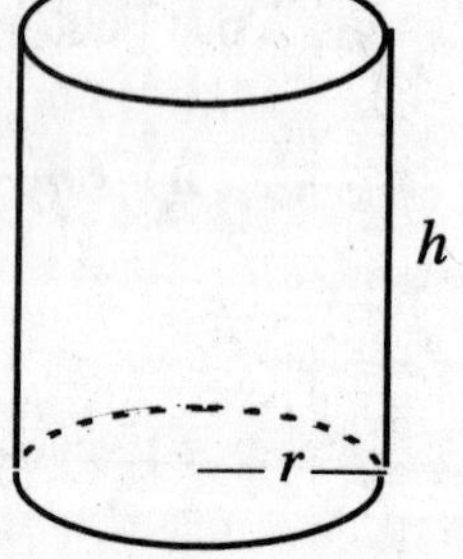

b) Write the formula for A in factored form.

c) Calculate the surface area of the cylinder, to the nearest 0.01 cm^2, using the factored form of A.

d) Which method a) or c) is simpler to use?

11. An archer standing on the ground fires an arrow vertically upward into the air at a speed of 30m/s .
The height (h metres) of the arrow above the ground after t seconds can be approximated by the formula $h = 30t - 5t^2$.

a) Write h in factored form.

b) Use the factored form of h to calculate the height for each of the times in the table. Record your answer in the table.

Time (t seconds)	0	1	2	3	4	5	6
Height (h metres)							

c) Explain why the height of the arrow after two seconds is the same as the height of the arrow after four seconds.

d) Calculate h when $t = 7$. Explain why this has no meaning in the context of the question.

12. A square of side $2r$ cm has semicircles drawn externally on each of two opposite sides.

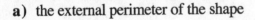

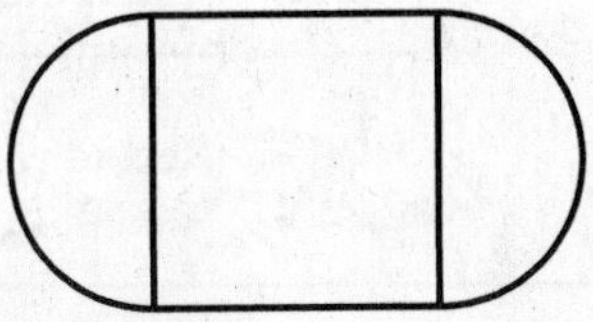

Find expressions in factored form for

a) the external perimeter of the shape

b) the area of the shape

Multiple Choice

13. $\pi r^3 + 3\pi r$ is equivalent to

A. $3\pi^2 r^4$
B. $3\pi(r^2 + r)$
C. $\pi r(2r + 3)$
D. $\pi r(r^2 + 3)$

14. One factor of $9x^4 - 6x^3 + 3x^2$ is

A. $9x^4$
B. $3x^2 - 2x$
C. $3x^2 - 6x + 3$
D. $3x^2 - 2x + 1$

Numerical Response

15. When $x^4y^3 - x^2y^3 + x^6y$ is factored, the greatest common factor has degree A and the remaining trinomial factor has degree B. The value of $A + 2B$ is _____.

(Record your answer in the numerical response box from left to right)

16. When the greatest common factor is removed from the binomial $98x^2 - 28x$, the binomial can be written in the form $ax(bx + c)$. The value of $a + b + c$ is _____.

(Record your answer in the numerical response box from left to right)

Answer Key

1. $12a^3 = 2 \cdot 2 \cdot 3 \cdot a \cdot a \cdot a.$ $30a^2 = 2 \cdot 3 \cdot 5 \cdot a \cdot a.$ $GCF = 2 \cdot 3 \cdot a \cdot a = 6a^2$

2. $10xy^4 = 2 \cdot 5 \cdot x \cdot y \cdot y \cdot y \cdot y.$ $25x^2y^3 = 5 \cdot 5 \cdot x \cdot x \cdot y \cdot y \cdot y.$ $GCF = 5 \cdot x \cdot y \cdot y \cdot y = 5xy^3$

3. a) $7m$ b) $3x$ c) bc^2 d) ab e) $4x^3$ f) 3 g) $2pq$ h) $-5x^5z^4$ i) ab j) $2x$ k) $-2x^2y$ l) $-4q$

4. a) 12 b) p c) x d) 5 e) $2cd$ f) $3y$

5. a) $a + 5$ b) $2p - q$ c) $2x - 3$ d) $1 + 2ab$ e) $3 + 2y$ f) $4xmn^2 - 3n - 1$

6. a) $6(m + n)$ b) $7(xy^2 + 7)$ c) $5(3pq - 1)$ d) $4(2c + 3d)$
e) $y(x + 1)$ f) $3x(2x - 3)$ g) $3a(3b - 4c)$ h) $24y^2(2 - 3y^3)$

7. a) $4(3x - 2y + 4z)$ b) $3p(3q + 2r - 5)$ c) $t(t^2 + t + 1)$ d) $5x(x - 2y - 4z)$
e) $2ab(2c - d + 4e)$ f) $7a^2b^2(2 + 3a - 5b)$

8. a) $3x^2 + 6x = 3x(x + 2)$ b) $8y^2 - 12y - 6 = 2(4y^2 - 6y - 3)$
c) $6x^3y + 6x^2y^2 - 4xy^3 = 2xy(3x^2 + 3xy - 2y^2)$ d) $7x^3 - 14x^2 + 14x = 7x(x^2 - 2x + 2)$

9. a) $12x^2(2x - 5)$ b) $-8p(p^2 + 4p + 1)$

10. a) 691.15 cm^2 b) $A = 2\pi r(r + h)$ c) 691.15 cm^2 d) c) is simpler

11. a) $h = 5t(6 - t)$ b) 0, 25, 40, 45, 40, 25, 0
c) At 2 sec. the arrow is on the way up and at 4 sec. the arrow is on the way down.
d) $h = -35$. The arrow has already hit the ground at $t = 6$. It does not travel 35m below the ground.

12. a) $2r(\pi + 2)$ cm. b) $r^2(\pi + 4)\text{ cm}^2$. **13.** D **14.** D

15.

1	1		

16.

1	9		

Factoring Polynomial Expressions Les
Common Factors - Part Two

Binomial Common Factors

In certain circumstances, the greatest common factor may be a binomial rath[er than]
monomial. This particular type of factoring will be part of a process for factoring
trinomials of the form $ax^2 + bx + c$, where $a \neq 1$, in a later lesson.

Class Ex. #1 Factor the following polynomials by removing the greatest common factor.

a) $(4x)(x + 7) - (3)(x + 7)$ **b)** $7(3 - 2y) + 2y(3 - 2y)$ **c)** $9a(4a + 1) + (4a + 1)$

Class Ex. #2 Factor the following and write the answer in simplest factored form.

a) $(3y + 2)(5y + 1) + (3y + 2)(4y)$ **b)** $3a(a - 6) - 9(a - 6)$

c) $2x(x - 5) + 5(5 - x)$ **d)** $20x(x - 3) - 4(3 - x)$

$$-1(x + 5) = (5 - x)$$

Complete Assignment Question #1

Factoring by Grouping

Sometimes polynomials in four terms can be factored by removing the greatest common
factor from a pair of terms followed by a binomial common factor. This method is called
factoring by grouping. The method of grouping is a component of the method used to factor
trinomials of the form $ax^2 + bx + c$, where $a \neq 1$, in a later lesson.

Class Ex. #3 Factor the following polynomials by grouping.

a) $x^2 + 3x + 6x + 18$ **b)** $8x^2 - 2x + 12x - 3$ **c)** $8a^2 - 4a - 10a + 5$

$x(x+3) + 6(x+3) \to GCF$

$(x+3)(x+6) \to x^2 + 6x + 3x + 18$

$9x$

d) $6a^2 - 9a - 2a + 3$ **e)** $pq + pr - sq - sr$ **f)** $5x^2 + 18y^2 - 15xy^2 - 6x$

Complete Assignment Questions #2 - #4

Monomial Common Factors involving Fractions

In polynomials involving fractional coefficients, it is useful to include a fraction as part of the monomial common factor so that the remaining factor is an integral polynomial with no common factor

$$\text{eg.} \quad \frac{1}{2}x^2 - 3x = \frac{1}{2}x(x-6)$$

Such a technique will prove useful in future math courses.

Class Ex. #4

In each case, a common factor has been removed so that the remaining factor is an integral binomial. Complete the factoring and check mentally by expanding the factored form.

a) $\frac{1}{3}x^2 + 4x = \frac{1}{3}x(\quad + \quad)$

b) $\frac{1}{4}a^2 - 4a = \frac{1}{4}a(\quad - \quad)$

c) $6x + \frac{2}{3} = \frac{2}{3}(\quad + \quad)$

d) $\frac{1}{2}a^2 - \frac{3}{4}b^2 = \frac{1}{4}(\quad - \quad)$

Class Ex. #5

Complete the factoring and check mentally by expanding the factored form.

a) $a - \frac{1}{6}a^2 = \_\_\_(6 - a)$

b) $\frac{1}{2}\pi r^2 - 2\pi r = \_\_\_(r - 4)$

c) $4x^2 + 2x + \frac{2}{5} = \_\_\_(10x^2 + \_\_\_ + \_\_\_)$

Class Ex. #6

In each case, remove a common factor so that the remaining factor is an integral polynomial.

a) $2a + \frac{1}{4}a^3$

b) $x^3 + \frac{1}{3}x^2 - \frac{1}{6}x$

Complete Assignment Questions #5 - #13

Assignment

1. Factor the following polynomials by removing the greatest common factor.

a) $(3x)(x + 5) - (7)(x + 5)$ **b)** $7y(x + 4) + 2(x + 4)$ **c)** $x(x - 1) - (x - 1)$

d) $(a + b)(x) - (a + b)(y)$ **e)** $4x(a + b) - 8y(a + b)$ **f)** $2a(a + 9) - 4(a + 9)$

g) $21a(b+c) + 7d(b+c)$ **h)** $x(5x - 3) - 4(3 - 5x)$ **i)** $2(4 - 7p) + 3p(-4 + 7p)$

2. Factor the following polynomials by grouping.

a) $x^2 + 2x + 6x + 12$ **b)** $x^2 + 3x + 15x + 45$ **c)** $m^2 - 5m + 2m - 10$

d) $a^2 - 9a - 5a + 45$ **e)** $x^2 - 15x - 4x + 60$ **f)** $t^2 + 7t - 3t - 21$

3. Factor the following polynomials by grouping.

a) $2x^2 + 2x + 3x + 3$ **b)** $3x^2 + x + 6x + 2$ **c)** $3m^2 + 9m + 5m + 15$

d) $6b^2 - 9b - 4b + 6$ **e)** $2a^2 - 6a - a + 3$ **f)** $5x^2 + 2x - 25x - 10$

g) $16 + 4p + 4p + p^2$ **h)** $15 - 3y - 5y + y^2$ **i)** $a^2 + ax + ay + xy$

4. Factor the following polynomials by grouping.

a) $ab + x^2 - ax - bx$ **b)** $4b^2 + 3a - 12b - ab$ **c)** $4x^2 + 15y^2 - 12xy^2 - 5x$

5. In each case, a common factor has been removed so that the remaining factor is an integral binomial. Complete the factoring and check mentally by expanding the factored form.

a) $\frac{1}{2}x - x^2 = \frac{1}{2}x(\quad - \quad)$ **b)** $3a^2 + \frac{2}{3}a = \frac{1}{3}a(\quad + \quad)$ **c)** $-\frac{1}{4}y^2 - y = -\frac{1}{4}y(\qquad)$

6. Complete the factoring and check mentally by expanding the factored form.

a) $\frac{1}{5}n - \frac{2}{5} = \_(n - 2)$ **b)** $\frac{1}{2}x^3 + \frac{1}{4}x = \_\_\_(2x^2 + 1)$ **c)** $0.2a^3 - 0.5a = \_\_\_(2a^2 - 5)$

7. In each case, remove a common factor so that the remaining factor is an integral polynomial.

a) $\frac{1}{2} + \frac{1}{2}x$ **b)** $\frac{1}{2}m - \frac{3}{2}$ **c)** $\frac{3}{4}ah - \frac{1}{2}bh$ **d)** $\frac{2}{3}x + 6$

e) $\frac{3}{2}x^2 - 1$ **f)** $z^2 - \frac{1}{5}z + \frac{2}{5}$ **g)** $\frac{4}{3}\pi r^3 - 4\pi r^2$ **h)** $\frac{1}{3}Ah + \pi r^2 h$

8. An object is thrown down from a high building. The distance, s metres, travelled by the object in t seconds is given by the formula $s = vt + \frac{1}{2}at^2$.

a) Express s in factored form.

b) Use the factored form to calculate the distance travelled in 0.1 seconds if $v = 5$ and $a = 9.8$.

9. Identify and explain the error in each of the following polynomial factorizations.

a) $\frac{1}{2}x^2 - \frac{1}{4}x = \frac{1}{2}x(x - 2)$

b) $\frac{1}{6}\pi r^2 - \frac{1}{2}\pi r = \frac{1}{6}\pi r(r - 3\pi)$

c) $t^2 - 4t - 24 + 6t = t(t - 4) - 6(4 - t) = (t - 4)(t - 6)$

Multiple Choice

10. One factor of $xy - 4xz - 12tz + 3ty$ is

A. $(4t + x)$
B. $(3t - x)$
C. $(y - 4z)$
D. $(3x + t)$

11. How many of the following three statements are true?

i) $p^2 + pq + p = p(p + q)$

ii) $\frac{2}{3}\pi r^3 + \pi r^2 h = \frac{2}{3}\pi r^2(r + 2h)$

iii) $t^2 + t^4 + t^6 = t^2(1 + t^2 + t^3)$

A. 0
B. 1
C. 2
D. 3

12. $x(x - 2) + y(2 - x)$ is equivalent to

A. $(x - 2)(x + y)$
B. $(x - 2)(x - y)$
C. $(2 - x)(x - y)$
D. $(2 - x)(x + y)$

13. Consider the polynomial $3a^2 + 4a + 9a + c$, where c is a constant. If $a + 3$ is a factor, then the other factor must be

A. $a + 4$
B. $3a + 4$
C. $3a + 9$
D. $a + 12$

Numerical Response **14.** The polynomial $2x^2 + 3x + 8x + p$ has a factor of $(2x + 3)$. The value of p is ______.

(Record your answer in the numerical response box from left to right)

Answer Key

1. a) $(x + 5)(3x - 7)$ **b)** $(x + 4)(7y + 2)$ **c)** $(x - 1)(x - 1) = (x - 1)^2$
d) $(a + b)(x - y)$ **e)** $4(a + b)(x - 2y)$ **f)** $2(a + 9)(a - 2)$
g) $7(b + c)(3a + d)$ **h)** $(5x - 3)(x + 4)$ **i)** $(4 - 7p)(2 - 3p)$

2. a) $(x + 2)(x + 6)$ **b)** $(x + 3)(x + 15)$ **c)** $(m - 5)(m + 2)$
d) $(a - 9)(a - 5)$ **e)** $(x - 15)(x - 4)$ **f)** $(t + 7)(t - 3)$

3. a) $(x + 1)(2x + 3)$ **b)** $(3x + 1)(x + 2)$ **c)** $(m + 3)(3m + 5)$
d) $(2b - 3)(3b - 2)$ **e)** $(a - 3)(2a - 1)$ **f)** $(5x + 2)(x - 5)$
g) $(4 + p)^2$ **h)** $(5 - y)(3 - y)$ **i)** $(a + x)(a + y)$

4. a) $(b - x)(a - x)$ or $(x - a)(x - b)$ **b)** $(b - 3)(4b - a)$ **c)** $(x - 3y^2)(4x - 5)$

5. a) $\frac{1}{2}x(1 - 2x)$ **b)** $\frac{1}{3}a(9a + 2)$ **c)** $-\frac{1}{4}y(y + 4)$

6. a) $\frac{1}{5}(n - 2)$ **b)** $\frac{1}{4}x(2x^2 + 1)$ **c)** $0.1a(2a^2 - 5)$

7. a) $\frac{1}{2}(1 + x)$ **b)** $\frac{1}{2}(m - 3)$ **c)** $\frac{1}{4}h(3a - 2b)$ **d)** $\frac{2}{3}(x + 9)$
e) $\frac{1}{2}(3x^2 - 2)$ **f)** $\frac{1}{5}(5z^2 - z + 2)$ **g)** $\frac{4}{3}\pi r^2(r - 3)$ **h)** $\frac{1}{3}h(A + 3\pi r^2)$

8. a) $s = \frac{1}{2}t(2v + at)$ **b)** 0.549 m

9. a) $\frac{1}{2} \times 2 \neq \frac{1}{4}$ The common factor is $\frac{1}{4}x$ Answer is $\frac{1}{4}x(2x - 1)$

b) The second factor in the binomial should not contain π since π is part of the common factor. Answer is $\frac{1}{6}\pi r(r - 3)$

c) The last step does not follow from the previous one. $t - 4$ is not a common factor unless the sign in the middle of the second step is changed. Answer is $(t - 4)(t + 6)$.

10. C **11.** A **12.** B **13.** B **14.**

1	2		

Factoring Polynomial Expressions Lesson #3:
Factoring Trinomials of the Form $x^2 + bx + c$ - Part One

Factoring Trinomials using Algebra Tiles

Consider the algebra tile diagram shown.

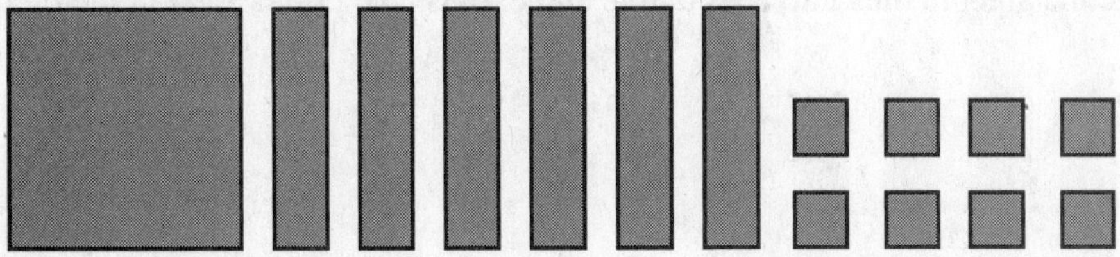

• Write the polynomial expression which is represented by the algebra tiles.

• The algebra tiles can be rearranged into a rectangular form as shown below.

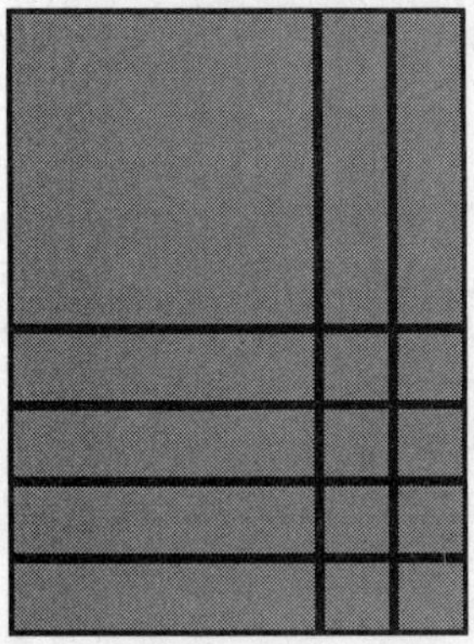

i) Write an expression for the length of the rectangle.

ii) Write an expression for the width of the rectangle.

iii) Write the area of the rectangle as a product of two binomials.

iv) Write the area of the rectangle in expanded form.

• The work above provides a method for factoring the trinomial $x^2 + 6x + 8$ into the product of two binomials $(x + 2)(x + 4)$: i.e. $x^2 + 6x + 8 = (x + 2)(x + 4)$.

a) Write the polynomial expression which is represented by the algebra tiles.

b) Arrange the algebra tiles into a rectangle and write an expression for the length and width of the rectangle.

c) Use the results above to express the polynomial in factored form.

Class Ex. #2

a) Write the polynomial expression which is represented by the algebra tiles.

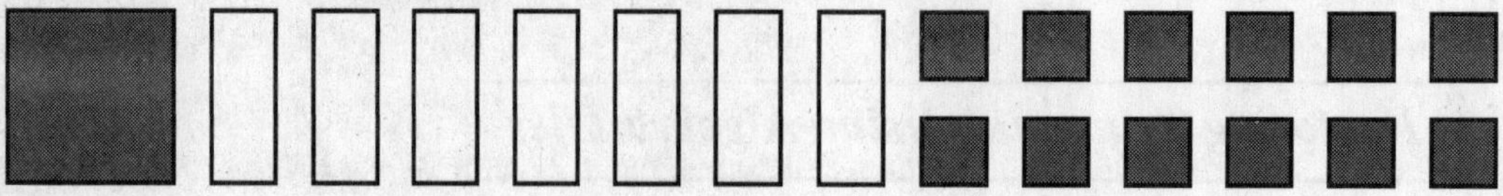

b) Arrange the algebra tiles into a rectangle and express the polynomial in factored form.

Complete Assignment Questions #1 - #3

Investigation: Factoring Trinomials by Inspection

- Expand the following binomials.

$(x + 2)(x + 4) = x^2 + 4x + 2x + 8 = x^2 + 6x + 8.$

$(x + 3)(x + 3) =$

$(x + 1)(x + 7) =$

$(x + 5)(x + 2) =$

$(x - 5)(x - 2) =$

$(x + 8)(x - 6) =$

- Consider the expansion $(x + p)(x + q) = x^2 + bx + c$.

In each of the examples above what is the connection between

i) the value of b and the values of p and q? $b =$ ________

ii) the value of c and the values of p and q? $c =$ ________

Class Ex. #3

Use FOIL to show that $(x + p)(x + q)$ can be written in the form $x^2 + (p + q)x + pq$.

Factoring $x^2 + bx + c$ by Inspection

In order to factor $x^2 + bx + c$ by inspection we need to find two integers which have a product equal to c and a sum equal to b. If no two such integers exist, then the polynomial cannot be factored.

In order to factor $x^2 + 8x + 12$ we need to find two numbers which multiply to ___ and add to ____ .

In order to factor $x^2 - 13x + 12$ we need to find two numbers which multiply to ___ and add to ____ .

The next example practices this skill.

Class Ex. #4

Complete the tables to find two numbers with the given sum and the given product..

Sum	Product	Integers
12	20	2, 10
9	20	
4	4	
–9	18	

Sum	Product	Integers
–15	14	
–1	–6	
2	–15	
–26	48	

Note

Notice that:

- if the product is **positive**, then the two integers must be either **both positive** or **both negative.**
- if the product is **negative**, then one integer is **positive** and the other is **negative**.

Note

For the remainder of this lesson, we will only deal with examples where the product is positive. In the next lesson we will include examples where the product is negative.

Class Ex. #5

Factor the following trinomials where possible.

a) $x^2 + 8x + 12$ **b)** $x^2 + 13x + 12$ **c)** $x^2 - 13x + 12$

d) $a^2 - 11a + 10$ **e)** $y^2 + 3y + 4$ **f)** $x^2 + 27x + 50$

Class Ex. #6

Factor the polynomial expressions by first removing a common factor.

a) $4x^2 - 32x + 48$ **b)** $3x^3 + 21x^2 + 30x$

Note In this example there were two steps in the factoring process - a common factor followed by a trinomial. If we are asked to factor a polynomial expression, it is understood this means to continue factoring until no further factoring is possible. This is sometimes written as "factor completely ...". The operation "factor" means "factor completely".

Complete Assignment Questions #4 - #15

Assignment

1. a) Write the polynomial expression which is represented by the algebra tiles.

b) Arrange the algebra tiles into a rectangle and write an expression for the length and width of the rectangle.

c) Use the results above to express the polynomial in factored form.

2. a) Write a polynomial expression for the group of algebra tiles shown.

b) Arrange the algebra tiles into a rectangle.

c) State the length and width of the rectangle and hence express the polynomial in factored form.

3. Use algebra tiles to factor the following trinomials.

a) $x^2 + 5x + 6$ **b)** $x^2 + 6x + 5$ **c)** $x^2 - 6x + 8$

4. Complete the tables to find two numbers with the given sum and the given product.

	Sum	Product	Integers
a)	5	6	
b)	8	7	
c)	11	30	
d)	−11	30	

	Sum	Product	Integers
e)	11	10	
f)	−8	15	
g)	−15	56	
h)	−18	56	

5. Complete the following.

a) $x^2 + 7x + 12 = (x + 3)(x + \quad)$ **b)** $x^2 + 9x + 8 = (x + \quad)(x + \quad)$

c) $x^2 - 7x + 10 = (x - 2)(x - \quad)$ **d)** $t^2 - 14t + 24 = (t - \quad)(t - \quad)$

e) $z^2 + 8z + 15 = (z + 5)(\quad\quad)$ **f)** $b^2 - 12b + 20 = (b - 2)(\quad\quad)$

6. Factor the following.

a) $x^2 + 3x + 2$ **b)** $x^2 - 3x + 2$ **c)** $x^2 + 9x + 18$

d) $x^2 + 8x + 12$ **e)** $x^2 - 10x + 21$ **f)** $x^2 - 11x + 24$

7. Factor where possible.

a) $x^2 + 11x + 10$ **b)** $x^2 + 10x + 11$ **c)** $n^2 + 12n + 32$

d) $y^2 - 11y + 28$ **e)** $y^2 + 17y + 42$ **f)** $f^2 - 10f + 21$

g) $p^2 - 16p + 28$ **h)** $x^2 + 24x + 80$ **i)** $c^2 - 32c + 60$

j) $a^2 - 12a + 24$ **k)** $d^2 + 18d + 45$ **l)** $p^2 - 29p + 100$

m) $m^2 + 22m + 121$ **n)** $n^2 - 23n + 102$ **o)** $q^2 - 28q + 115$

8. a) The expression $x^2 + bx + 12$ can be factored over the integers. Determine all possible values of b.

b) If the expression $x^2 + 6x + c$, where $c > 0$, can be factored over the integers, determine all possible values of c.

9. A volleyball court has an area of $x^2 + 15x + 36$ square metres.

a) Factor $x^2 + 15x + 36$ to find binomials that represent the length and width of the court.

b) If $x = 3$, determine the length and width of the court.

10. Factor.

a) $2x^2 + 6x + 4$ **b)** $4x^2 - 48x + 128$ **c)** $-2a^2 - 30a - 108$

d) $5x^2 - 20x + 15$ **e)** $ax^2 - 14ax + 45a$ **f)** $-10a^4 + 100a^3 - 240a^2$

11. Consider the following in which each letter represents a whole number.

$x^2 + 5x + 6 = (x + A)(x + B)$ $x^2 + 10x + 21 = (x + B)(x + G)$

$x^2 - 9x + 20 = (x - T)(x - L)$ $2x^2 - 16x + 32 = 2(x - T)^2$

$x^3 + 10x^2 + 9x = x(x + S)(x + E)$ $6x^2 - 54x + 48 = 6(x - I)(x - S)$

Determine the value of each letter and hence name the famous person represented by the following code.

(3) (8) (5) (5) (7) (2) (4) (9) (1)

_ _ _ _ _ _ _ _ _

Multiple Choice

12. Which of the following is **not** a factor of $3m^2 - 27m + 54$?

A. $m - 3$

B. $m - 6$

C. $m - 9$

D. 3

13. For which of the following trinomials is $a + 5$ **not** a factor?

A. $a^2 + 6a + 5$

B. $a^2 + 11a + 30$

C. $a^2 + 10a + 50$

D. $a^2 + 10a + 25$

14. The expression $t^2 + kt + 12$ **cannot** be factored if k has the value

A. -13 **B.** -8 **C.** 7 **D.** 11

Numerical Response

15. The largest value of b for which $x^2 + bx + 32$ can be factored over the integers is ____.

(Record your answer in the numerical response box from left to right)

Answer Key

1. a) $x^2 + 4x + 3$ **b)** $x + 3,\ x + 1,$ **c)** $x^2 + 4x + 3 = (x + 3)(x + 1)$

2. a) $x^2 - 7x + 10$ **c)** $x - 2, x - 5,$ $x^2 - 7x + 10 = (x - 2)(x - 5)$

3. a) $(x + 2)(x + 3)$ **b)** $(x + 1)(x + 5)$ **c)** $(x - 4)(x - 2)$

4. a) 2, 3 **b)** 1, 7 **c)** 5, 6 **d)** –5, –6
e) 1, 10 **f)** –3, –5 **g)** –7, –8 **h)** –4, –14

5. a) $(x + 3)(x + 4)$ **b)** $(x + 1)(x + 8)$ **c)** $(x - 2)(x - 5)$
d) $(t - 2)(t - 12)$ **e)** $(z + 5)(z + 3)$ **f)** $(b - 2)(b - 10)$

6. a) $(x + 1)(x + 2)$ **b)** $(x - 1)(x - 2)$ **c)** $(x + 3)(x + 6)$
d) $(x + 2)(x + 6)$ **e)** $(x - 3)(x - 7)$ **f)** $(x - 3)(x - 8)$

7. a) $(x + 1)(x + 10)$ **b)** not possible **c)** $(n + 4)(n + 8)$
d) $(y - 4)(y - 7)$ **e)** $(y + 3)(y + 14)$ **f)** $(f - 3)(f - 7)$
g) $(p - 2)(p - 14)$ **h)** $(x + 4)(x + 20)$ **i)** $(c - 2)(c - 30)$
j) not possible **k)** $(d + 3)(d + 15)$ **l)** $(p - 4)(p - 25)$
m) $(m + 11)(m + 11)$ OR $(m + 11)^2$ **n)** $(n - 6)(n - 17)$ **o)** $(q - 5)(q - 23)$

8. a) 7, 8, 13,–7, –8, –13 **b)** 5, 8, 9 **9. a)** $(x + 12)(x + 3)$ **b)** 15m, 6m

10. a) $2(x + 1)(x + 2)$ **b)** $4(x - 4)(x - 8)$ **c)** $-2(a + 6)(a + 9)$
d) $5(x - 1)(x - 3)$ **e)** $a(x - 5)(x - 9)$ **f)** $-10a^2(a - 4)(a - 6)$

11. BILLGATES **12.** C **13.** C **14.** D **15.**

3	3		

Factoring Polynomial Expressions Lesson #4:
Factoring Trinomials of the Form $x^2 + bx + c$ - Part Two

Review of Factoring By Inspection

In order to factor $x^2 + bx + c$ by inspection, we need to find two integers which have a product equal to c and a sum equal to b. If no two such integers exist, then the polynomial cannot be factored.

In order to factor $x^2 + 6x + 9$, we need to find two numbers whose product is ___ and whose sum is ____ .

In order to factor $x^2 + x - 12$, we need to find two numbers whose product is ___ and whose sum is ____ .

Recall the following points from the previous lesson.

- If the product is **positive**, then the two integers must be either **both positive** or **both negative.**
- If the product is **negative**, then one integer is **positive** and the other is **negative**.

Factor the following trinomials by inspection.

a) $x^2 - x - 12$ **b)** $x^2 + 3x - 18$ **c)** $a^2 - 7a - 8$

Factor where possible.

a) $a^2 + 6a - 27$ **b)** $2t^2 - 14t + 20$

c) $x^2 - 3x - 6$ **d)** $4x^4 - 16x^3 - 20x^2$

Factoring Trinomials of the form $x^2 + bxy + cy^2$

Complete the following statements:

i) $(x + 2)(x + 4)$ can be expanded to $x^2 + 6x + 8$,

so $x^2 + 6x + 8$ can be factored to ()() .

ii) $(x + 2y)(x + 4y)$ can be expanded to _____ ,

so _____ can be factored to ()() .

Class Ex. #3

Factor.

a) $x^2 + 13xy + 30y^2$ **b)** $x^2 + 71xy - 72y^2$ **c)** $3a^2 - 15ab - 252b^2$

Complete Assignment Questions #1 - #11

Assignment

$\frac{15}{3,5,15,1}$

$\frac{24}{12,2,24,1,}$
$4,6,3,8$

1. Complete the table to find two numbers with the given sum and the given product.

	Sum	Product	Integers
a)	8	−20	
b)	−8	−20	
c)	−1	−20	

	Sum	Product	Integers
d)	3	−70	
e)	−11	28	
f)	0	−16	

2. Factor the following trinomials.

a) $x^2 - 2x - 15$

$(x - 5)(x + 3) \rightarrow x^2 + 3x - 5x - 15$
$\qquad\qquad\qquad -2x$

b) $x^2 - 2x - 24$

$(x - 6)(x + 4) \rightarrow x^2 + 4x - 6x - 24$
$\qquad\qquad\qquad -2x$

c) $x^2 + 2x - 24$

$(x + 6)(x - 4)$

d) $x^2 + 2x - 3$

e) $x^2 + x - 30$

f) $x^2 - 3x - 10$

3. Factor where possible.

a) $x^2 + 10x + 16$ **b)** $x^2 - 11x + 18$ **c)** $x^2 - 2x - 8$ **d)** $x^2 + 3x - 18$

e) $x^2 - 4x + 12$ **f)** $x^2 - 4x - 12$ **g)** $x^2 - 10x + 25$ **h)** $x^2 + x - 20$

i) $m^2 + 21m + 38$ **j)** $a^2 - 17a + 42$ **k)** $p^2 - 10p - 9$ **l)** $p^2 - 9p - 10$

4. Factor.

a) $2x^2 + 14x + 24$ **b)** $4x^2 - 28x - 32$ **c)** $5x^2 - 20x + 15$

d) $-2a^2 + 2a + 220$ **e)** $b^2x^2 - 4b^2x - 45b^2$ **f)** $2x^3 + 2x^2 - 40x$

5. Consider the following in which the each letter represents a whole number.

$x^2 + 4x - 5 = (x + A)(x - O)$ $x^2 - 3x - 54 = (x - E)(x + I)$

$x^3 + 2x^2 - 8x = x(x - Y)(x + P)$ $3x^2 - 48x + 192 = T(x - R)^2$

$-5x^2 + 20x + 105 = -5(x + T)(x - H)$

Determine the value of each letter and hence name the fictional character represented by the following code.

(7) (5) (8) (8) (2) (4) (1) (3) (3) (9) (8)

_ _ _ _ _ _ _ _ _ _ _

6. Factor.

a) $x^2 + 18xy + 45y^2$ **b)** $x^2 + 10xy - 24y^2$ **c)** $a^2 - 12ab + 36b^2$

d) $p^2 - 12pq + 11q^2$ **e)** $x^2 + xy - 72y^2$ **f)** $x^2 - 54xy - 112y^2$

7. Factor completely.

a) $4x^2 - 80xy + 144y^2$ **b)** $3b^2 - 15bv - 72v^2$ **c)** $2c^2 + 66cd - 140d^2$

Multiple Choice

8. When factored, the trinomials $x^2 - 10x + 21$ and $x^2 - 4x - 21$ have one binomial factor in common. This factor is

A. $x - 7$ **B.** $x + 7$
C. $x - 3$ **D.** $x + 3$

9. One factor of $-m^3 - m^2 + 6m$ is

A. $m - 2$ **B.** $m + 2$
C. $m - 3$ **D.** $m - 6$

10. One factor of $3x^2 - 6xy - 9y^2$ is

A. $3x$ **B.** $x + 2y$
C. $x + 3y$ **D.** $x + y$

11. The expression $x^2 - 4x + c$ **cannot** be factored if c has the value

A. -5
B. 0
C. 4
D. 5

Answer Key

1. a) $-2, 10$ **b)** $-10, 2$ **c)** $-5, 4$ **d)** $-7, 10$ **e)** $-4, -7$ **f)** $-4, 4$

2. a) $(x - 5)(x + 3)$ **b)** $(x - 6)(x + 4)$ **c)** $(x + 6)(x - 4)$ **d)** $(x + 3)(x - 1)$ **e)** $(x + 6)(x - 5)$ **f)** $(x - 5)(x + 2)$

3. a) $(x + 8)(x + 2)$ **b)** $(x - 9)(x - 2)$ **c)** $(x + 2)(x - 4)$ **d)** $(x + 6)(x - 3)$ **e)** not possible **f)** $(x - 6)(x + 2)$ **g)** $(x - 5)^2$ **h)** $(x + 5)(x - 4)$ **i)** $(m + 2)(m + 19)$ **j)** $(a - 14)(a - 3)$ **k)** not possible **l)** $(p - 10)(p + 1)$

4. a) $2(x + 3)(x + 4)$ **b)** $4(x - 8)(x + 1)$ **c)** $5(x - 3)(x - 1)$ **d)** $-2(a - 11)(a + 10)$ **e)** $b^2(x - 9)(x + 5)$ **f)** $2x(x + 5)(x - 4)$

5. HARRY POTTER

6. a) $(x + 15y)(x + 3y)$ **b)** $(x - 2y)(x + 12y)$ **c)** $(a - 6b)^2$ **d)** $(p - q)(p - 11q)$ **e)** $(x - 8y)(x + 9y)$ **f)** $(x + 2y)(x - 56y)$

7. a) $4(x - 18y)(x - 2y)$ **b)** $3(b - 8v)(b + 3v)$ **c)** $2(c + 35d)(c - 2d)$

8. A **9.** A **10.** D **11.** D

Factoring Polynomial Expressions Lesson #5:
Difference of Squares

Investigation

a) Complete the following using the trinomial factoring method from the previous lessons.

	Sum	Product	Integers	Polynomial	Factored Form
i)	–6	–16		$x^2 - 6x - 16$	
ii)	–15	–16			
iii)	0	–16		$x^2 + 0x - 16 = x^2 - 16$	
iv)	0	–64			
v)	0	–25			

b) The third row in a) shows that the factored form of $x^2 - 16$ is $(x - 4)(x + 4)$.
Use the pattern from the last three rows to factor the following.

i) $x^2 - 9 =$ **ii)** $x^2 - 49 =$ **iii)** $x^2 - 36 =$

iv) $x^2 - 1 =$ **v)** $a^2 - 100 =$

c) Extend the procedure from above to factor $m^2 - n^2$.
Verify your answer by expanding the factored form.

d) Consider the expansion $(x - y)(x + y) = x^2 + bx + c$.

i) Explain why the value of b is zero.

ii) Express c in terms of y.

Difference of Squares

The examples on the previous page are trinomials of the form $x^2 + bx + c$, where $b = 0$ and c is the negative of a square number.

This results in a **difference of squares** such as $x^2 - 25$, $x^2 - 100$, etc.

To factor a difference of squares we can use the identity:

$$a^2 - b^2 = (a - b)(a + b)$$

The identity $a^2 - b^2 = (a - b)(a + b)$ can be illustrated in the following diagram.

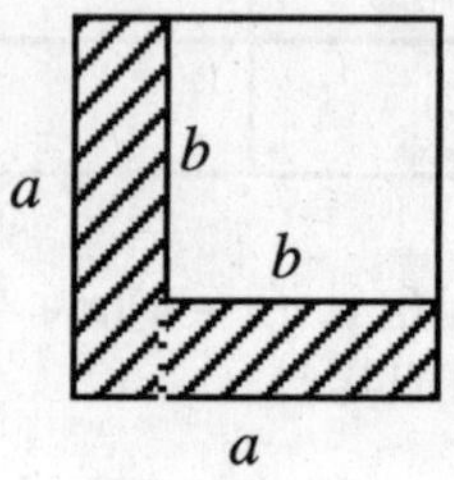

Shaded area = $a^2 - b^2$

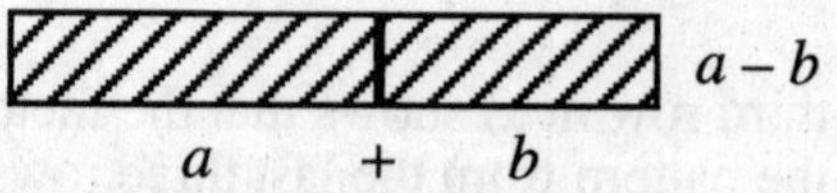

Shaded area = $(a - b)(a + b)$

The shaded area on the left is cut along the dotted line and rearranged to form the diagram on the right.

The shaded area on the left is represented by $a^2 - b^2$ *and the shaded area on the right is represented by* $(a - b)(a + b)$.

Factor the following polynomials using the difference of squares method.

a) $a^2 - 4$

b) $t^2 - 144$

c) $x^2 - y^2$

d) $p^2 - 7^2$

Note that it is not possible to factor a sum of squares like $x^2 + 4$, i.e. $x^2 + 0x + 4$.
It is not possible to find two integers whose product is positive and whose sum is zero.

In the identity $a^2 - b^2 = (a - b)(a + b)$ we can replace a and/or b by numbers, variables, monomials and even polynomials.

For example, $4x^2 - 25$ can be written as $(2x)^2 - (5)^2$ and can be factored using the above identity with $a = 2x$ and $b = 5$.

$$4x^2 - 25 = (\qquad)(\qquad)$$

$9m^2 - 4n^2$ can be written as $(3m)^2 - (2n)^2$, and can be factored using the above identity with $a = 3m$ and $b = 2n$.

$$9m^2 - 4n^2 = (\qquad)(\qquad)$$

The factoring above can be verified by expanding the product of the factors.

Factor, if possible, using the difference of squares method.

a) $16t^2 - 49$ **b)** $81a^2 - 1$ **c)** $100 - y^2$

d) $36p^2 - 25q^2$ **e)** $4x^2 + 25$ **f)** $64 - 9a^2b^2$

The floor of an international doubles squash court is rectangular with an area of $25a^2 - b^2$ square feet.

a) Write expressions for the length and width of the floor.

b) The perimeter of the floor is 140 feet. Determine the length and width of the floor if the length is 1.8 times the width.

Difference of Squares involving a Common Factor

The first step in factoring any polynomial expression should be to determine if we can remove a common factor.

Factor the following polynomials by first removing the greatest common factor.

a) $2a^2 - 50$ **b)** $3x^2 - 12y^2$ **c)** $144p^2q^2 - 4$ **d)** $3x^3 - 27x$

Complete Assignment Questions #1 - #14

Assignment

1. Complete the following by determining the missing factor.

a) $x^2 - 36 = (x - 6)(\quad)$ **b)** $c^2 - 121 = (c + 11)(\quad)$ **c)** $j^2 - k^2 = (j - k)(\quad)$

2. Factor the following polynomials using a difference of squares.

a) $x^2 - 49$ **b)** $x^2 - 1$ **c)** $x^2 - 15^2$ **d)** $x^2 - 400$

3. Explain how factoring a difference of squares in one variable can be regarded as a special case of factoring trinomials by inspection.

4. Factor where possible.

a) $m^2 - n^2$ **b)** $c^2 - 7^2$ **c)** $1 - k^2$ **d)** $g^2 - 64h^2$

e) $25x^2 - 144$ **f)** $16a^2 - 9b^2$ **g)** $4x^2 + z^2$ **h)** $121a^2 - 36b^2$

i) $49 - 4h$ **j)** $100 - 81b^2$ **k)** $1 - 25z^2$ **l)** $225a^2 - b^2$

m) $169z^2 - 4q^2$ **n)** $256 - y^2$ **o)** $t^2 + 36z^2$ **p)** $49a^2 - 400$

5. The floor of a classroom is rectangular with an area of $81m^2 - 4n^2$ square metres.

a) Write expressions in m and n for the length and width of the floor.

b) If the perimeter of the floor is 72 metres, form an equation in m and n and solve for m.

c) Determine the length and width of the floor if the length is 25% greater the width.

6. Factor.

a) $8x^2 - 32$ **b)** $4a^2 - 100y^2$ **c)** $3t^2 + 27s^2$

d) $7x^2 - 7y^2$ **e)** $9a^2b^2 - 36$ **f)** $8 - 50p^2q^2$

g) $xy^2 - x^3$ **h)** $20a^2b^2 - 5a^4b^4$

7. Factor.

a) $a^2b^2 - 9$ **b)** $c^2 - d^2e^2$ **c)** $100x^2 - y^2z^2$

d) $p^2q^2 - r^2s^2$ **e)** $25x^2y^2 - 1$ **f)** $c^2d^2 - 4f^2$

g) $4x^2a^2 - 49z^2t^2$ **h)** $16a^2c^2 - 225b^2d^2$

8. The diagram shows a circle of radius R with a circle of radius r removed.

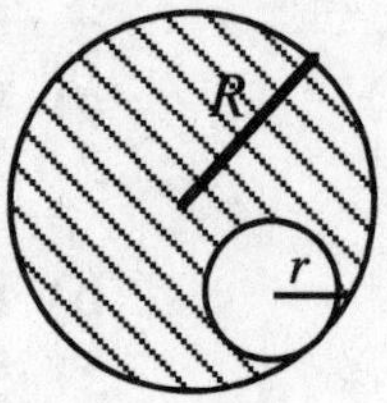

a) Write an expression for the shaded area.

b) Write the expression in a) in factored form.

c) Determine the shaded area (as a multiple of π) if $R = 8.5$ and $r = 1.5$. Do not use a calculator.

9. The expression $\frac{1}{2}mv^2 - \frac{1}{2}mu^2$ occurs in physics.

a) Write the expression in factored form.

b) Determine the value of the expression when $m = 10$, $v = 75$, and $u = 25$. Do not use a calculator.

10. Consider the following in which each letter represents a whole number.

$64x^2 - y^2 = (Hx - y)(Hx + y)$ $\quad$ $16x^2 - 4 = C(Ix + 1)(Ix - 1)$

$7x^2 - 252y^2 = P(x - Ey)(x + Ey)$ $\quad$ $Lx^2 - Ny^2 = (3x - 5y)(Sx + Ay)$

Determine the value of each letter and hence name the country represented by the following code.

(4) (8) (2) (9) (6)

_ _ _ _ _

11. Susan was showing Rose how the difference of squares method can be used to multiply certain numbers without using a calculator. She showed Rose the following:

$$38 \times 42$$
$$= (40-2)(40+2) \quad = (40^2 - 2^2) \quad = (1600-4) \quad = 1596$$

a) Use the above process to evaluate:

i) 27×33 ii) 61×59

b) Explain why this process cannot be used to determine the product 66×72.

c) Make up your own multiplication question which can be answered using this process.

Multiple Choice

12. One factor of $16 - 4m^2$ is

A. $4 - m$
B. $8 - 2m$
C. $4 + m$
D. $2 + m$

13. Given that $x^2 - y^2 = 45$ and $x + y = 9$, the value of x is

A. 2
B. 5
C. 7
D. impossible to determine

Numerical Response

14. $3x + 2y$ is a factor of the binomial $a^2x^2 - b^2y^2$.
The value of $a^2 + b^2$ is _____ .
(Record your answer in the numerical response box from left to right)

Answer Key

1. a) $(x + 6)$ **b)** $(c - 11)$ **c)** $(j + k)$

2. a) $(x - 7)(x + 7)$ **b)** $(x - 1)(x + 1)$ **c)** $(x - 15)(x + 15)$ **d)** $(x - 20)(x + 20)$

3. A difference of squares can be regarded as a trinomial of the form $x^2 + bx + c$ in which $b = 0$ and c is negative. We need to find two numbers which multiply to c and add to zero.

4. a) $(m - n)(m + n)$ **b)** $(c - 7)(c + 7)$ **c)** $(1 - k)(1 + k)$
d) $(g - 8h)(g + 8h)$ **e)** $(5x - 12)(5x + 12)$ **f)** $(4a - 3b)(4a + 3b)$
g) not factorable **h)** $(11a - 6b)(11a + 6b)$ **i)** not factorable using whole number exponent.
j) $(10 - 9b)(10 + 9b)$ **k)** $(1 + 5z)(1 - 5z)$ **l)** $(15a + b)(15a - b)$
m) $(13z - 2q)(13z + 2q)$ **n)** $(16 - y)(16 + y)$ **o)** not factorable **p)** $(7a + 20)(7a - 20)$

5. a) $(9m + 2n)$ metres, $(9m - 2n)$ metres **b)** $2(9m + 2n) + 2(9m - 2n) = 72$, $m = 2$
c) Length = 20 metres, Width = 16 metres.

6. a) $8(x - 2)(x + 2)$ **b)** $4(a - 5y)(a + 5y)$ **c)** $3(t^2 + 9s^2)$ **d)** $7(x - y)(x + y)$
e) $9(ab - 2)(ab + 2)$ **f)** $2(2 - 5pq)(2 + 5pq)$ **g)** $x(y - x)(y + x)$ **h)** $5a^2b^2(2 - ab)(2 + ab)$

7. a) $(ab - 3)(ab + 3)$ **b)** $(c - de)(c + de)$ **c)** $(10x - yz)(10x + yz)$
d) $(pq - rs)(pq + rs)$ **e)** $(5xy - 1)(5xy + 1)$ **f)** $(cd - 2f)(cd + 2f)$
g) $(2xa - 7zt)(2xa + 7zt)$ **h)** $(4ac - 15bd)(4ac + 15bd)$

8. a) $A = \pi R^2 - \pi r^2$ **b)** $\pi(R - r)(R + r)$ **c)** 70π

9. a) $\frac{1}{2}m(v - u)(v + u)$ **b)** 25 000 **10.** CHILE

11. a) **i)** 891 **ii)** 3599
b) 66×72 expressed as a difference of squares $(69^2 - 3^2)$ cannot easily be evaluated without a calculator or long multiplication.

12. D **13.** C **14.**

1	3		

Factoring Polynomial Expressions Lesson #6:
Factoring $ax^2 + bx + c$ (where $a \neq 1$)

In this lesson we learn a method for factoring polynomials of the form $ax^2 + bx + c$ where $a \neq 1$. This is one of the most important processes in this course and has a large number of applications in almost every math course you will meet in high school or further education.

NOTE: This lesson requires more than one period of class time.

Binomial Products

Complete the following

$(2x + 1)(3x + 4)$ = ____________________ so ____________________ factors to $(2x + 1)(3x + 4)$

$(3x - 2)(4x + 3)$ = ____________________ so ____________________ factors to $(3x - 2)(4x + 3)$

Consider the following problem: What are the factors of $2x^2 + 7x + 6$?
We need to find two binomials whose product is $2x^2 + 7x + 6$. The first method we will consider is to use algebra tiles.

Factoring $ax^2 + bx + c$ using Algebra Tiles

a) Write a polynomial expression for the group of algebra tiles shown.

b) Arrange the algebra tiles into a rectangle and state the length and width of the rectangle.

c) Use the algebra tile diagram to express the polynomial in factored form.

Factor $5x^2 + 7x + 2$ using algebra tiles.

Complete Assignment Questions #1 - #2

Factoring using algebra tiles will work for all trinomials of the form $ax^2 + bx + c$ which have binomial factors. However, it can get rather tedious if the values of a, b, c are large.

The second method we will consider uses, as part of its process, factoring by grouping. We will review this concept first.

Review of Factoring by Grouping

Factor the following polynomials by grouping.

i) $6x^2 + 3x + 8x + 4$ **ii)** $12x^2 + 9x - 8x - 6$

Factoring $ax^2 + bx + c$ using the Method of Decomposition

In Reviw part i) above, we factored

$6x^2 + 3x + 8x + 4$ or $6x^2 + 11x + 4$ to get $(2x + 1)(3x + 4)$.

In order to factor $6x^2 + 11x + 4$, we must first split $11x$ into $3x$ and $8x$ and then group.

But how do we know to split $11x$ into $3x$ and $8x$ rather than $2x$ and $9x$ or $5x$ and $6x$ etc.?

We will provide the answer to this on the next page.

In Reviw part ii) above, we factored

$12x^2 + 9x - 8x - 6$ or $12x^2 + x - 6$ to get $(4x + 3)(3x - 2)$.

In order to factor $12x^2 + x - 6$, we must first split $1x$ into $9x$ and $-8x$ and then group.

But how do we know to split $1x$ into $9x$ and $-8x$ rather than $5x$ and $-4x$ or $3x$ and $-2x$?

In Reviw part i), how are the numbers 8 and 3 connected to the value of a (i.e. 6), the value of b (i.e. 11) and the value of c (i.e. 4)?

In Reviw part ii), how are the numbers 9 and –8 connected to the value of a (i.e. 12), the value of b (i.e. 1) and the value of c (i.e. – 6)?

The method of factoring $ax^2 + bx + c$ by splitting the value of b into two integers whose product is ac and whose sum is b is called the **method of decomposition**.

Class Ex. #3

Factor, using the method of decomposition, and compare the answers with Class Examples #1 and #2.

a) $2x^2 + 7x + 6$

b) $5x^2 + 7x + 2$

Class Ex. #4

Factor.

a) $6x^2 + 17x - 3$

b) $3n^2 - 2n - 8$

c) $12x^2 - 8x + 1$

Class Ex. #5

Factor.

a) $15 - 7y - 2y^2$

b) $15k^2 + 5k - 10$

Factoring Trinomials of the form $ax^2 + bxy + cy^2$

The method of decomposition can be applied to trinomials of the form $ax^2 + bxy + cy^2$.

Factor.

a) $2x^2 - 5xy + 2y^2$ **b)** $2n^2 - 7nm - 15m^2$

Complete Assignment Questions #3 - #14

Assignment

1. a) Write a polynomial expression for the group of algebra tiles shown.

b) Arrange the algebra tiles into a rectangle and state the length and width of the rectangle.

c) Use the algebra tile diagram to express the polynomial in factored form.

2. Factor the following expressions using algebra tiles.

a) $2x^2 + 5x + 3$

b) $2x^2 + 7x + 3$

c) $6x^2 + 7x + 2$

d) $4x^2 + 13x + 3$

3. Factor the following expressions.

a) $10x^2 + 17x + 3$

b) $9x^2 + 6x + 1$

c) $3x^2 + 14x + 15$

d) $3a^2 - 23a - 8$

e) $3a^2 + a - 2$

f) $5x^2 - 23x - 10$

g) $2p^2 - 19p + 9$

h) $6x^2 - 13x + 6$

4. Factor.

a) $6x^2 + 5x - 6$

b) $2x^2 + x - 1$

c) $3x^2 - 2x - 1$

d) $8y^2 + 2y - 3$

e) $9t^2 - 24t + 16$

f) $12m^2 - 11m - 5$

g) $12p^2 + 13p - 4$

h) $9x^2 - x - 10$

5. A rectangular garden has an area of $2a^2 + 3a - 5$ m^2.

a) Write the area as the product of two binomials.

b) The garden is to be completely enclosed by a path 1m wide. Find and simplify an expression for the area of the path.

c) The path is concrete, poured to a depth of 12 cm. Calculate the volume (in m^3) of concrete used if $a = 7$.

6. Factor the following expressions.

a) $12 + 8x + x^2$

b) $6 - 7x - 20x^2$

c) $3 + a - 10a^2$

d) $10a^2 + 25a - 15$

e) $12z^2 + 66z + 30$

f) $4x^3 - 7x^2 - 2x$

7. Consider the following in which each letter represents a whole number.

$10x^2 + 13x - 3 = (Ax + M)(Cx - P)$

$7x^2 + 64x + 9 = (x + S)(Ox + P)$

$24x^2 - 90x + 54 = B(x - M)(Kx - M)$

$64x^2 - 1 = (Lx - 1)(Lx + 1)$

Determine the value of each letter and hence name the place in Canada represented by the following code.

(4) (2) (3) (8) (7) (7) (1) (9) (6) (5)

_ _ _ _ _ _ _ _ _ _

8. A tank in the shape of a rectangular prism has dimensions $2x$, $3x+1$, and $5x+3$ metres.

A wooden block is dropped into the tank and the tank is then filled with water.

The volume of water is $22x^3 + 18x^2 + 3x$ cubic metres.

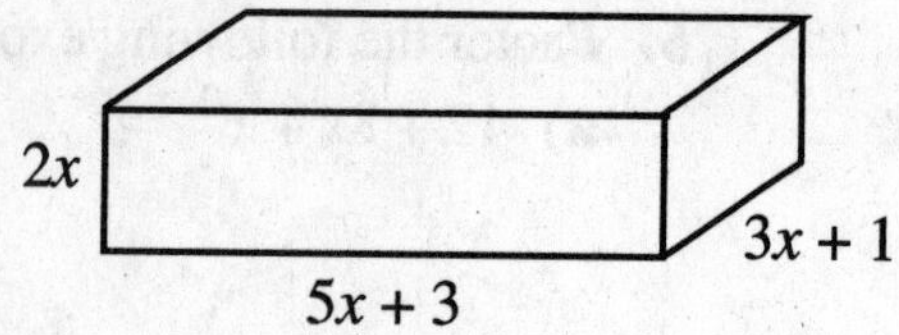

a) Determine a polynomial expression for the volume of the wooden block.

b) Factor the expression in a) to determine the dimensions of the wooden block.

9. Factor.

a) $8x^2 + 22xy + 5y^2$

b) $6x^2 + 11xy - 7y^2$

c) $4a^2 - 9ab - 9b^2$

d) $2m^2 - 19mn + 9n^2$

e) $9x^2 + xy - 10y^2$

f) $8x^2 + 7xy - 15y^2$

Multiple Choice

10. One factor of $12x^2 + 10x - 8$ is

A. $3x + 4$
B. $3x - 4$
C. $2x + 1$
D. $6x - 1$

11. The polynomials $4x^2 + 8x - 5$ and $12x^2 - 3$ have in common a factor of

A. $4x + 1$
B. $4x - 1$
C. $2x + 1$
D. $2x - 1$

Numerical Response

12. The factored form of $3x^2 + 19x - 14$ is $(x + a)(bx + c)$ where a, b, and c are integers. The value of b^c, to the nearest hundredth, is ________.
(Record your answer in the numerical response box from left to right)

13. The expression $15x^2 + 11x - 56$ can be written in the form $(ax - b)(cx + d)$ where a, b, c, and d are all positive integers.

Write the value of a in the first box. Write the value of b in the second box.
Write the value of c in the third box. Write the value of d in the fourth box.

(Record your answer in the numerical response box from left to right)

Extension **14.** Given that $(\sin x)^2$ is written as $\sin^2 x$ and $(\cos x)^2$ is written as $\cos^2 x$, factor

a) $6 \sin^2 x + \sin x - 2$ **b)** $4 \cos^2 x - 7 \cos x + 3$

Answer Key

1. a) $3x^2 + 7x + 2$ **b)** $3x + 1, x + 2$ **c)** $3x^2 + 7x + 2 = (3x + 1)(x + 2)$

2. a) $(2x + 3)(x + 1)$ **b)** $(2x + 1)(x + 3)$ **c)** $(3x + 2)(2x + 1)$ **d)** $(4x + 1)(x + 3)$

3. a) $(5x + 1)(2x + 3)$ **b)** $(3x + 1)^2$ **c)** $(3x + 5)(x + 3)$ **d)** $(3a + 1)(a - 8)$
e) $(3a - 2)(a + 1)$ **f)** $(5x + 2)(x - 5)$ **g)** $(2p - 1)(p - 9)$ **h)** $(3x - 2)(2x - 3)$

4. a) $(3x - 2)(2x + 3)$ **b)** $(2x - 1)(x + 1)$ **c)** $(3x + 1)(x - 1)$ **d)** $(2y - 1)(4y + 3)$
e) $(3t - 4)^2$ **f)** $(3m + 1)(4m - 5)$ **g)** $(4p - 1)(3p + 4)$ **h)** $(9x - 10)(x + 1)$

5. a) $(2a + 5)(a - 1)$ **b)** $6a + 12$ m^2 **c)** 6.48 m^3

6. a) $(6 + x)(2 + x)$ **b)** $(3 + 4x)(2 - 5x)$ **c)** $(3 - 5a)(1 + 2a)$
d) $5(2a - 1)(a + 3)$ **e)** $6(2z + 1)(z + 5)$ **f)** $x(4x + 1)(x - 2)$

7. KAMLOOPS BC **8. a)** $8x^3 + 10x^2 + 3x$ m^3 **b)** $4x + 3$, $2x + 1$, and x m

9. a) $(2x + 5y)(4x + y)$ **b)** $(2x - y)(3x + 7y)$ **c)** $(4a + 3b)(a - 3b)$
d) $(2m - n)(m - 9n)$ **e)** $(9x + 10y)(x - y)$ **f)** $(8x + 15y)(x - y)$

10. A **11.** D **12.**

0	.	1	1

13.

5	8	3	7

14. a) $(3 \sin x + 2)(2 \sin x - 1)$ **b)** $(4 \cos x - 3)(\cos x - 1)$

Factoring Polynomial Expressions Lesson #7:
Further Factoring

Perfect Square Trinomials

A **perfect square trinomial** is formed from the product of two identical binomials. Perfect square trinomials can be factored by considering the pattern displayed when squaring binomials.

$\nearrow (+)$ Middle # $\nearrow (-)$ middle #

Complete the following: $(p + q)^2 = \underline{p^2 + pq + pq + q^2}$ $(p - q)^2 = \underline{p^2 + pq - pq + q^2}$

$\hookrightarrow p^2 + 2pq + q^2$ $\hookrightarrow p^2 - 2pq + q^2$

From the above we can see that :

. The first term in the trinomial is the square of the _____ term in the binomial.

. The last term in the trinomial is the square of the _____ term in the binomial.

. The middle term in the trinomial is _____ the _____ of the first and last terms in the binomial.

$2(5x) = \Rightarrow =$ perfect

Note In a perfect square trinomial, e.g. $x^2 + 10x + 25$, the **first and last terms must be perfect squares** and the **middle term must be twice the product of the square roots of the first and last terms.**

Class Ex. #1 Which of the following are perfect square trinomials?

a) $a^2 + 4a + 4$ b) $x^2 - 9x + 6$ c) $4x^2 - 36x + 81$ d) $y^2 + 8y - 16$

$(a+2)(a+2)$ NO $2(9 \cdot 2x) -18 \times \cdot 2 = 36$ NO

$= (a+2)^2$ negatre

Class Ex. #2 Fill in the blank so that each of the following is a perfect square trinomial.

a) $x^2 + \underline{20}x + 100$ b) $x^2 - \underline{20}x + 100$ c) $25x^2 + \underline{60}x + 36$ d) $9m^2 + 24m + \underline{16}$

$2(10x) = 20x$ $2(-10x)$ $2(6 \cdot 5x)$ $12 \cdot 5x = 60x$ $2(3m \cdot 4)$

$6m \cdot 4 = 24m$

$\sqrt{\frac{1}{9}} = \frac{1}{3}$

Class Ex. #3 Factor.

a) $49x^2 - 14x + 1$ b) $16 + 40x + 25x^2$ c) $\frac{1}{9}a^2 - 2ab + 9b^2$ ($\sqrt{}$ both top and bottom

$2(-7x \cdot 1) = \sqrt{}$ $2(4 \cdot 5x) =$ check by $(\frac{1}{3}a \cdot 3b) = \frac{6ab}{3} = 2ab$

$(7x -1)(7x -1)$ $(5x \cdot 4)(5x \cdot 4)$ expanding $(\frac{1}{3}a - 3b)(\frac{1}{3}a - 3b)$

Complete Assignment Questions #1 - #3

Note The remaining sections in this lesson are used to introduce a process which will be extended in the next course.

Factoring Trinomials of the form $f^2 + bf + c$ where f is a Monomial

The method of inspection can be extended to factor polynomial expressions of the form $f^2 + bf + c$, where f itself is a polynomial. In this section we will restrict f to be a monomial; in the next course we will consider f to be a binomial or trinomial.

In the trinomial $x^2 + bx + c$, the degrees of the terms are 2, 1, and 0 respectively. The method of inspection can also be used when the terms have degrees 4, 2, and 0 or 6, 3, and 0 etc.

In all cases, we make a substitution which results in a trinomial with terms of degree 2, 1, and 0.

The following example to factor $x^4 + 5x^2 + 6$ illustrates the process.

$x^4 + 5x^2 + 6$ can be written $(x^2)^2 + 5(x^2) + 6$.

Make the substitution $A = x^2$ so the expression becomes $A^2 + 5A + 6$ which factors to $(A + 2)(A + 3)$.

Replace A by x^2 to get $(x^2 + 2)(x^2 + 3)$

$x^4 + 5x^2 + 6 = (x^2 + 2)(x^2 + 3)$

With experience this process can be done by inspection.

Class Ex. #4 Factor completely.

a) $a^4 - 5a^2 - 14$ b) $x^4 + 4x^2 - 5$ c) $x^6 - 9x^3 + 14$

① $(x+2)(x+2)$ 4

$= x^2 + 2x + 2x + 4$ → $4x$

→ $x^2 + 4x + 4$

② $(x-3)(x-3)$ 9

$= x^2 - 3x - 3x + 9$ → $-6x$

→ $x^2 - 6x + 9$

$(x+2)$ = double = 4

ex. $\sqrt{x^2} = x$ → $(-3x)$ → Double = $2(-3x) = -6x$

$\sqrt{9} = -3$

Factoring Trinomials of the form $af^2 + bf + c$ where f is a monomial

The method of decomposition can be extended to factor polynomial expressions of the form $af^2 + bf + c$ where f itself is a polynomial. In this section we will restrict f to be a monomial; in the next course we will consider f to be a binomial or trinomial.

In the trinomial $ax^2 + bx + c$, the degrees of the terms are 2, 1, and 0 respectively. The method of decomposition can also be used when the terms have degrees 4, 2, and 0 or 6, 3, and 0 etc.

The expression $4y^4 - 11y^2 - 3$ can be factored using the method of decomposition by substituting $A = y^2$ or by splitting $-11y^2$ into two terms in y^2.

Complete the work started below.

Method 1

$4y^4 - 11y^2 - 3 = 4(y^2)^2 - 11(y^2) - 3$

Let $A = y^2$ $\qquad 4A^2 - 11A - 3$

$=$

Method 2

$4y^4 - 11y^2 - 3 = 4y^4 - 12y^2 + 1y^2 - 3$

Class Ex. #5

Factor completely.

a) $4x^4 - 5x^2 - 6$ **b)** $y^{10} + 4y^5 - 12$ **c)** $2a^2b^2 - 31ab + 99$

Class Ex. #6

Factor completely. $8x^4 + 10x^2 - 3$.

More Complex Differences of Squares

The method of difference of squares in which $a^2 - b^2 = (a - b)(a + b)$ can also be extended to include examples where a and b represent polynomials.

The following process can be used to factor $x^4 - 16$.

$x^4 - 16y^4$ can be written $(x^2)^2 - (4y^2)^2$.

Make the substitution $A = x^2$ and $B = 4y^2$ so the expression becomes $A^2 - B^2$ which factors to $(A - B)(A + B)$.

Replace A by x^2 and B by $4y^2$ to get $(x^2 - 4y^2)(x^2 + 4y^2)$ which factors further to $(x - 2y)(x + 2y)(x^2 + 4y^2)$.

Class Ex. #8

Factor completely.

a) $k^4 - 1$

b) $80 - 5x^4$

c) $2p^5q^4 - 162pt^4$

Complete Assignment Questions #4 - #13

Assignment

→ $4x \cdot 1 = 4x$

→ $8y \cdot 4 = 32y$

1. Which of the following are perfect square trinomials?

18.5 ?

a) $a^2 + 12a + 36$ **b)** $x^2 - 25x + 50$ **c)** $4x^2 - 4x + 1$ **d)** $16y^2 + 32y + 16$

$2(6a) = 12a$ ✓ ✗ not perfect $2(2x \cdot 1)$ ✓ $2(4y \cdot 4)$ ✓

$5 \cdot 8 = 40$
$5 \cdot 10 = 50$

e) $a^2 + 9a + 9$ **f)** $25x^2 - 90x + 81$ **g)** $1 - 16x + 64x^2$ **h)** $y^2 + 20y - 100$

$2(3a) = 9a$ ✓ $2(-9 \cdot 5x)$ ✓ $2(-1 \cdot 8x) =$ NOT

$40 + 50$ $↪ -18 \cdot 5x = -90x$ $↪ 2 \cdot 8x = 16x$ perfect ✗

$= 90$ ✓

2. Fill in the blanks so that each of the following is a perfect square trinomial.

$18 \cdot 5 = 90$

a) $x^2 + \underline{14x} + 49$ **b)** $x^2 - \underline{24x} + 144$ **c)** $9x^2 + \underline{36x} + 36$ **d)** $4m^2 + 24m + \underline{36}$

$2(7x) = 14x$ $2(12x) = 24x$ $2(6 \cdot 3x)$ $2(2m \cdot 6)$ $6^2 = 3$

 $↪ 12 \cdot 3x = 36x$ $↪ 4m \cdot 6 = 24m$

e) $\frac{1}{4}a^2 + \underline{} + 1$ **f)** $225x^2 - \underline{} + 16$ **g)** $100x^2 + \underline{} + y^2$ **h)** $\underline{} - 30y + 9y^2$

3. Factor.

a) $16x^2 - 8x + 1$

$2(4x \cdot -1) = -8x$

$(4x - 1)(4x - 1)$

b) $36 + 60x + 25x^2$

$2(6 \cdot 5x)$ $(6 + 5x)(6 + 5x)$

↳ $12 \cdot 5x = 60x$

c) $4a^2 - 12ab + 9b^2$

$2(2a \cdot 3b)$ $(2a - 3b)(2a - 3b)$

↳ $4a \cdot 3b = 12ab$

d) $4x^2 - 44x + 121$

e) $5x^2 + 10x + 5$

f) $\frac{4}{9}x^2 + \frac{2}{9}x + \frac{1}{36}$

4. Factor completely.

a) $x^4 + 9x^2 + 20$

b) $x^4 - 9x^2 + 20$

c) $a^4 - 17a^2 + 16$

d) $t^6 - 4t^3 - 21$

e) $3x^4 + 9x^2 - 30$

f) $2x^5 - 16x^3 + 32x$

5. Factor completely.

a) $6x^4 + 11x^2 + 5$

b) $2a^4 - 5a^2 + 2$

c) $5p^6 - 8p^3 - 4$

d) $16x^4 + 8x^2 - 3$

e) $4 - 9t^2 - 9t^4$

f) $4x^5 - 50x^3 + 126x$

g) $4x^2y^2 - xy - 14$

h) $4\pi^2r^2 - 9\pi r - 9$

6. Factor.

a) $x^4 - y^4$

b) $a^4 - 256b^4$

c) $2z^4 - 162$

d) $48x^4 - 3y^4$

e) $9a^4b^4 - 144c^4d^4$

f) $z^8 - 1$

7. Factor the polynomial expression $16a^8 - 65a^4 + 4$.

Multiple Choice

8. From the expressions below, the one which does **not** represent a perfect square trinomial is

A. $x^2 - 14x + 49$
B. $144 + 24x + x^2$
C. $4x^2 - 12x + 36$
D. $9x^4 + 30x^2 + 25$

9. When factored completely, the polynomial $k^4 + 16 - 17k^2$ is equal to

A. $(k^2 - 1)(k^2 - 16)$
B. $(k^2 + 1)(k^2 + 16)$
C. $k^2(k + 1)(k + 16)$
D. $(k + 1)(k - 1)(k + 4)(k - 4)$

10. One factor of $y^4 - 81$ is

A. $y + 9$
B. $y + 3$
C. $y^2 - 3$
D. $y^2 + 3$

11. One factor of $x^4 - 16x^2 + 15$ is

A. $x + 1$
B. $x^2 + 15$
C. $x + 15$
D. $x - 15$

Numerical Response

12. The polynomial expression $\frac{1}{16}x^2 + \frac{1}{3}x + \frac{4}{9}$ can be written in the form $(Ax + B)^2$. The value of the product AB, to the nearest one hundredth, is _____.

(Record your answer in the numerical response box from left to right)

13. Triangle PQR is right angled at P. The area of the triangle is $\frac{3}{2}x^2 + 10x + 16$ cm^2, where x is a positive integer. Given that the length of PQ is 12 cm more than the length of PR, the length of QR, to the nearest tenth of a cm, is _____.

(Record your answer in the numerical response box from left to right)

Answer Key

1. **a), c), d), f), g)** are all perfect square trinomials.

2. **a)** $14x$ **b)** $24x$ **c)** $36x$ **d)** 36 **e)** a **f)** $120x$ **g)** $20xy$ **h)** 25

3. **a)** $(4x - 1)^2$ **b)** $(6 + 5x)^2$ **c)** $(2a - 3b)^2$ **d)** $(2x - 11)^2$ **e)** $5(x + 1)^2$ **f)** $\left(\frac{2}{3}x + \frac{1}{6}\right)^2$

4. **a)** $(x^2 + 5)(x^2 + 4)$ **b)** $(x - 2)(x + 2)(x^2 - 5)$ **c)** $(a - 1)(a + 1)(a - 4)(a + 4)$
d) $(t^3 - 7)(t^3 + 3)$ **e)** $3(x^2 + 5)(x^2 - 2)$ **f)** $2x(x - 2)^2(x + 2)^2$

5. **a)** $(6x^2 + 5)(x^2 + 1)$ **b)** $(2a^2 - 1)(a^2 - 2)$ **c)** $(5p^3 + 2)(p^3 - 2)$
d) $(2x - 1)(2x + 1)(4x^2 + 3)$ **e)** $(4 + 3t^2)(1 - 3t^2)$ **f)** $2x(x - 3)(x + 3)(2x^2 - 7)$
g) $(4xy + 7)(xy - 2)$ **h)** $(4\pi r + 3)(\pi r - 3)$

6. **a)** $(x - y)(x + y)(x^2 + y^2)$ **b)** $(a - 4b)(a + 4b)(a^2 + 16b^2)$
c) $2(z - 3)(z + 3)(z^2 + 9)$ **d)** $3(2x - y)(2x + y)(4x^2 + y^2)$
e) $9(ab - 2cd)(ab + 2cd)(a^2b^2 + 4c^2d^2)$ **f)** $(z - 1)(z + 1)(z^2 + 1)(z^4 + 1)$

7. $(2a - 1)(2a + 1)(a^2 - 2)(a^2 + 2)(4a^2 + 1)$

8. C **9.** D **10.** B **11.** A

12.

0	.	1	7

13.

2	1	.	5

Factoring Polynomial Expressions Lesson #8:
Factoring Review

Guidelines for Factoring a Polynomial Expression

If we are asked to factor a polynomial expression, the following guidelines should help us to determine the best method.

1. Look for a common factor. If there is one, take out the common factor and look for further factoring.
2. If there is a binomial expression, look for a difference of squares.
3. If there is a trinomial expression of the form $x^2 + bx + c$, look for factoring by inspection.
4. If there is a trinomial expression of the form $ax^2 + bx + c$, look for factoring by decomposition. Watch out for perfect square trinomials.
5. If there is a polynomial with four terms, look for factoring by grouping.
6. After factoring, check to see if further factoring is possible.

The guidelines can be shown in a flowchart.

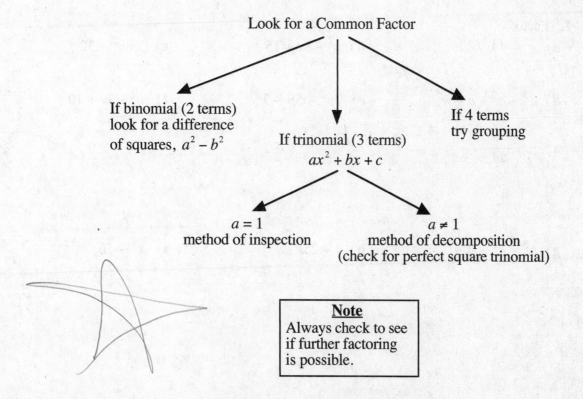

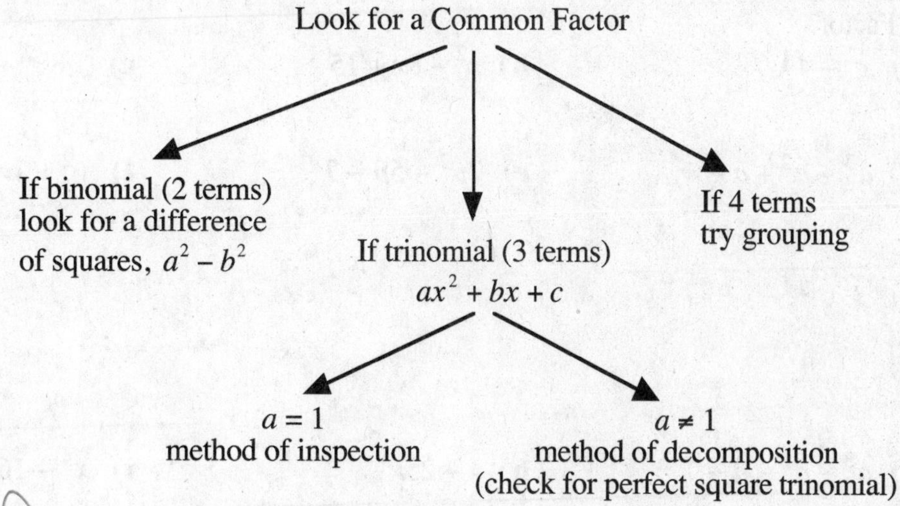

Look for a Common Factor
If binomial (2 terms) look for a difference of squares, $a^2 - b^2$
If trinomial (3 terms) $ax^2 + bx + c$
If 4 terms try grouping
$a = 1$ method of inspection
$a \neq 1$ method of decomposition (check for perfect square trinomial)

Note
Always check to see if further factoring is possible.

Factor the following.

a) $9x^2 - 36$ **b)** $x^2 - 16x - 36$ **c)** $-8x^2 + 26x + 15$

d) $24x^2 - 30x + 36x - 45$ **e)** $3 - 3x^2 - 36x^4$

Complete Assignment Questions #1 - #7

Assignment

1. Factor.

a) $x^2 - 49$ **b)** $x^2 - 8x + 15$ **c)** $8x^2 + 32$

d) $a^3 + a^2 + a + 1$ **e)** $2p^2 - 5p - 7$ **f)** $v^2 + 7v + 10$

g) $a^3 - a^2 - a + 1$ **h)** $4 - 25t^2$ **i)** $x^4 - 16$

2. Factor.

a) $7x^2 - 19x - 6$ **b)** $3 + x - 2x^2$ **c)** $a^2 - 64b^2$

d) $108 - 3z^2$ **e)** $x^4 + 5x^2 + 4$ **f)** $8v^2 - 32v - 96$

g) $625p^4 - 1$ **h)** $2y^4 - y^2 - 3$ **i)** $36 - 3x - 3x^2$

3. Factor.

a) $b^2 - 16 - 6b + 24$ **b)** $t^6 - t^3 - 6$ **c)** $36a^2 + 60a + 25$

d) $5 + 17g + 6g^2$ **e)** $x^5 - 81x$ **f)** $-256 + t^4$

g) $x^2 + y - x - xy$ **h)** $2x^4 - 15x^2 - 27$ **i)** $12a^2 + 32a - 12$

4. Factor.

a) $x^2 - 8xy - 33y^2$ **b)** $6a^2 + 19ab + 10b^2$ **c)** $15t^6 + t^3p^2 - 2p^4$

Multiple Choice

In questions #5 -#6 one or more of the four responses may be correct. Answer

A. if only 1 and 2 are correct
B. if only 1, 2, and 3 are correct
C. if only 3 and 4 are correct
D. if some other response or combination of responses is correct

5. The set of factors of $5x^2 - 10x - 15$ contains

(1) $x - 1$ (2) $x + 3$ (3) $x + 1$ (4) $x - 3$

6. $x + 4$ is a factor of

(1) $3x^2+7x - 20$ (2) $48 - 3x^2$ (3) $3x^2+ 12x$ (4) x^2+16

Numerical Response

7. If $9a^2 + ka + 16$ is a perfect square trinomial, then the value of k must be ______ .
(Record your answer in the numerical response box from left to right)

Answer Key

1. a) $(x - 7)(x + 7)$ **b)** $(x - 5)(x - 3)$ **c)** $8(x^2 + 4)$
d) $(a + 1)(a^2 + 1)$ **e)** $(p + 1)(2p - 7)$ **f)** $(v + 5)(v + 2)$
g) $(a + 1)(a - 1)^2$ **h)** $(2 - 5t)(2 + 5t)$ **i)** $(x - 2)(x + 2)(x^2 + 4)$

2. a) $(7x + 2)(x - 3)$ **b)** $(3 - 2x)(1 + x)$ **c)** $(a - 8b)(a + 8b)$
d) $3(6 - z)(6 + z)$ **e)** $(x^2 + 4)(x^2 + 1)$ **f)** $8(v + 2)(v - 6)$
g) $(5p - 1)(5p + 1)(25p^2 + 1)$ **h)** $(y^2 + 1)(2y^2 - 3)$ **i)** $3(4 + x)(3 - x)$

3. a) $(b - 2)(b - 4)$ **b)** $(t^3 - 3)(t^3 + 2)$
c) $(6a + 5)^2$ **d)** $(5 + 2g)(1 + 3g)$
e) $x(x - 3)(x + 3)(x^2 + 9)$ **f)** $-(4 - t)(4 + t)(16 + t^2)$ or $(t - 4)(t + 4)(t^2 + 16)$
g) $(x - 1)(x - y)$ **h)** $(x - 3)(x + 3)(2x^2 + 3)$ **i)** $4(3a - 1)(a + 3)$

4. a) $(x - 11y)(x + 3y)$ **b)** $(2a + 5b)(3a + 2b)$ **c)** $(5t^3 + 2p^2)(3t^3 - p^2)$

5. C **6.** B **7.**

2	4		

Factoring Polynomial Expressions Lesson #9
Enrichment Lesson - Solving Polynomial Equations

Solving Polynomial Equations

Complete the following.

The statement $x - 3 = 0$ is true only if $x =$ ______.

The statement $x + 1 = 0$ is true only if $x =$ ______.

The statement $(x - 3)(x + 1) = 0$ is true if $x =$ ______ or if $x =$ ______.

The statement $4(x - 3)(x + 1) = 0$ is true if ____________________.

All the above statements are polynomial equations in which the left side is a polynomial expression and the right side equals zero.

The **solution** to a polynomial equation is given by stating the value(s) of the variable which make(s) the left side and the right side equal. These values are said to **satisfy** the equation.

Consider the equation $x^2 - 2x - 3 = 0$. Factoring the left side leads to $(x - 3)(x + 1) = 0$. This is true if $x = 3$ or if $x = -1$. Since the equation is satisfied by both $x = 3$ and $x = -1$, the solutions to the equation are $x = 3$ **and** $x = -1$, sometimes written as $x = -1, 3$.

Complete the solution to the equation $x^2 - 9x + 20 = 0$.

$x^2 - 9x + 20 = 0$

$(x - \quad)(x - \quad) = 0$

$x - \quad = 0$ or $x - \quad = 0$

$x =$ ____ or $x =$ ____

The solutions are $x =$ ____ and $x =$ ____

or $x =$ ___ , ___

Solve the equation.

a) $x^2 - 81 = 0$ **b)** $4x^2 - 9 = 0$ **c)** $10x^2 - 90x = 0$ **d)** $10x^2 - 90 = 0$.

Solve the equation.

a) $3x^2 - 13x - 10 = 0$

b) $5x^2 + 30x = -25$

Complete Assignment Questions #1 - #4

Problem Solving with Polynomial Equations

Some problems in mathematics can be solved by the following procedure.

i) Introduce a variable to represent an unknown value.

ii) Form a polynomial equation from the given information.

iii) Solve the polynomial equation using the methods in this lesson.

iv) State the solution to the problem.

In this section we will consider fairly routine problems. This topic will be extended in a higher level math course.

The area of a rectangular sheet of paper is 300 cm^2. The length is 5 cm more than the width. Form a polynomial equation and solve it to determine the perimeter of the rectangular sheet.

Class Ex. #5

The diagram shows the cross-section of a water trough whose sloping sides AD and BC make an angle of $45°$ with the horizontal. The length $DC = 36$ cm.

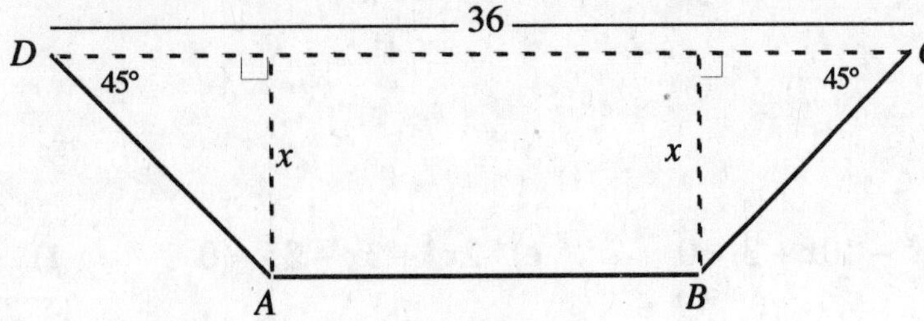

a) Show that the area of the cross-section is $x(36 - x)$ cm^2.

b) If the area of the cross-section is 260 cm^2, determine the value of x.

Complete Assignment Questions #5 - #10

Assignment

1. Solve the equation.

a) $(x - 2)(x + 7) = 0$ **b)** $(3x - 2)(2x + 5) = 0$ **c)** $5x(10 - x) = 0$

d) $x^2 + 2x = 0$ **e)** $x^2 - 121 = 0$ **f)** $9x^2 - 100 = 0$

g) $36x^2 = 25$ **h)** $9x - 4x^2 = 0$ **i)** $4(49 - x^2) = 0$

2. Solve the equation.

a) $x^2 - 3x + 2 = 0$ **b)** $x^2 + 13x + 30 = 0$ **c)** $x^2 + 2x - 15 = 0$

d) $3x^2 - 10x + 3 = 0$ **e)** $2x^2 + 3x - 35 = 0$ **f)** $15 - 2x - x^2 = 0$

3. Solve the equation.

a) $2x^2 + 5x = 7$ **b)** $6x^2 = 7x + 3$ **c)** $x(x + 4) = 32$

d) $(x - 3)(2x + 3) = 5$ **e)** $(2x - 3)^2 = 1$ **f)** $(x + 1)(x - 1) = 5(x + 1)$

4. Solve the equation.

a) $6a^2 - 7 - 19a = 0$ **b)** $21 - 8k - 2k^2 = 2k^2$

5. The diagram shows a piece of wood of uniform width x cm. $RS = 10$ cm and $ST = 7$ cm.

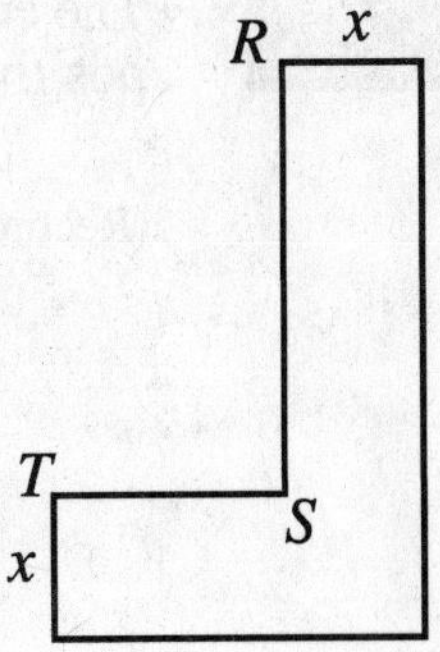

a) Find the area of the piece of wood in terms of x.

b) Find the value of x if the area is 60 cm^2.

6. The sum of the first n even numbers, starting with 0, is given by the formula $S = n(n - 1)$.

a) Determine the sum of the first 25 even numbers, starting with 0.

b) How many consecutive even numbers, starting with 0, add up to 870?

7. The height of a triangle is 8 mm more than the base. The area is 172.5 mm^2.

a) Write a polynomial equation to model this information.

b) Determine the height of the triangle.

Multiple Choice

8. The complete solution to the equation $x(x - 1) = 2$ is

A. $x = 0$ and $x = 1$
B. $x = 2$ and $x = 3$
C. $x = -1$ and $x = 2$
D. $x = -2$ and $x = 1$

Numerical Response

9. The equation $24x^2 + 2x = 15$ has solutions $x = a$ and $x = -b$, where a and b are positive rational numbers. The value of b, to the nearest hundredth, is _____.

(Record your answer in the numerical response box from left to right)

10. The sum of the first n natural numbers is given by the formula $S = \frac{1}{2}n(n+1)$. If the first k natural numbers have a sum of 496, the value of k is _____.

(Record your answer in the numerical response box from left to right)

Answer Key

1. a) 2, −7 **b)** $\frac{2}{3}, -\frac{5}{2}$ **c)** 0, 10 **d)** 0, − 2
e) ±11 **f)** $\pm\frac{10}{3}$ **g)** $\pm\frac{5}{6}$ **h)** $0, \frac{9}{4}$ **i)** ± 7

2. a) 1, 2 **b)** −10, −3 **c)** −5, 3 **d)** $\frac{1}{3}, 3$ **e)** $-5, \frac{7}{2}$ **f)** −5, 3

3. a) $-\frac{7}{2}, 1$ **b)** $-\frac{1}{3}, \frac{3}{2}$ **c)** −8, 4 **d)** $-2, \frac{7}{2}$ **e)** 1, 2 **f)** −1, 6

4. a) $-\frac{1}{3}, \frac{7}{2}$ **b)** $-\frac{7}{2}, \frac{3}{2}$ **5. a)** $x^2 + 17x$ cm^2 **b)** 3

6. a) 600 **b)** 30 **7. a)** $x^2 + 8x - 345 = 0$ **b)** 23 mm

8. C

9.

0	.	8	3

10.

3	1		

Factoring Polynomial Expressions Lesson #10:
Practice Test

1. One factor of $9x^4 - 6x^3 + 3x^2$ is

   A. $9x^4$
   B. $3x^2 - 2x$
   C. $3x^2 - 6x + 3$
   D. $3x^2 - 2x + 1$

2. When fully factored, the expression $x^3y^2 - x^2y^3$ is written

   A. $xy^2(x - xy)$
   B. $x^2y(xy - y)$
   C. $x^2y^2(x - y)$
   D. $x^3y^2(1 - xy)$

Numerical Response

1. When the greatest common factor is removed from the binomial $75x - 50x^2$, the binomial can be written in the form $ax(b + cx)$. The value of $a - b - c$ is _____ .

   (Record your answer in the numerical response box from left to right)

3. The expression $3ab^2 - 6a^3b + 3ab$, when fully factored, is written

   A. $ab(3b - 2a^2 + 3)$
   B. $3a(b^2 - 2a^2b + b)$
   C. $3ab(b - 2a^2)$
   D. none of these

4. The algebra tile diagram represents the factored form

   A. $(x^2 + 2x)(x^2 + 4x)$
   B. $8(x + 2)(x + 4)$
   C. $(x + 2)(x + 4)$
   D. $(x + 1)(x + 8)$

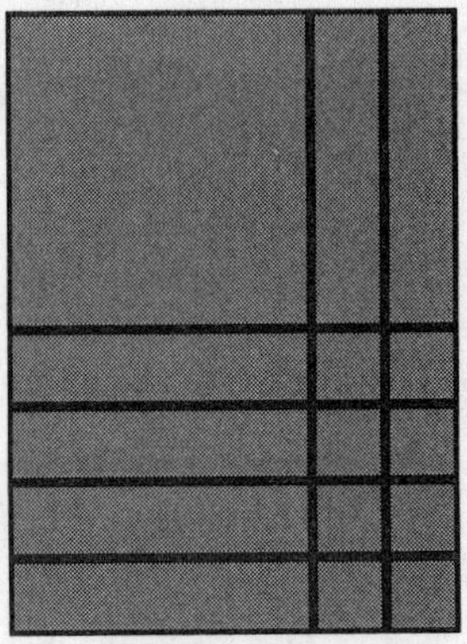

5. One factor of $a^2 - 10a - 24$ is

   A. $a - 2$
   B. $a - 4$
   C. $a - 6$
   D. $a - 12$

Use the following information to answer the next question.

An algebraic expression is represented by the algebra tiles shown.

Shaded tiles are positive.

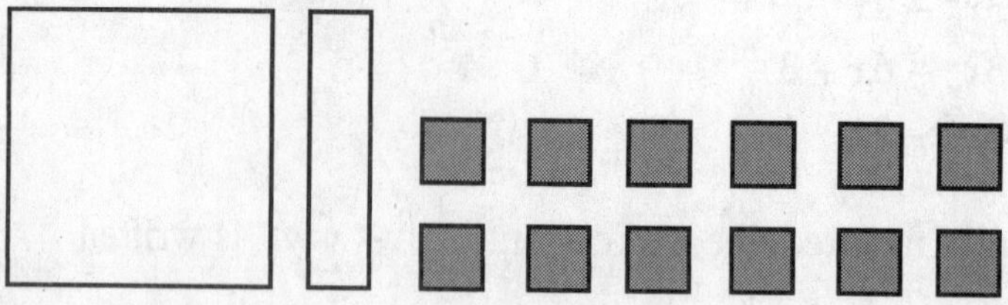

6. The factored form of the algebraic expression represented by the algebra tiles is

A. $(3 - x)(4 + x)$
B. $(3 - x)(4 - x)$
C. $(4 - x)(3 + x)$
D. $12 - x - x^2$

Use the following information to answer the next question.

Rectangle *ABCD* has been subdivided into four regions. The areas of two of these regions are a^2 and 144 as indicated. The combined area of the other two regions is $25a$.

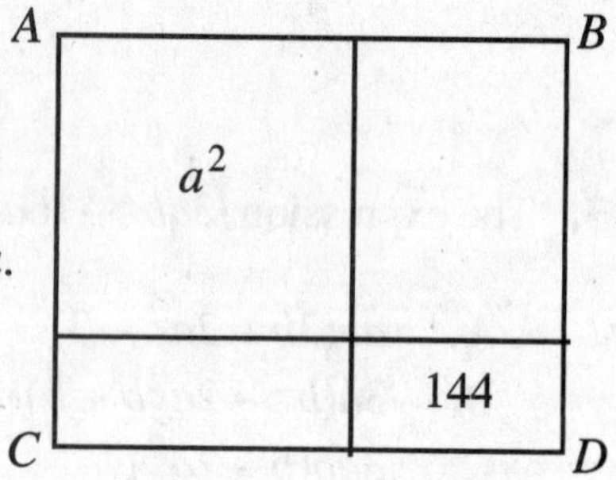

7. The perimeter of rectangle *ABCD* is

A. $a^2 + 25a + 144$
B. $4a + 48$
C. $4a + 50$
D. unable to be determined from the given information

8. For which of the following trinomials is $b + 3$ **not** a factor?
A. $b^2 + 3b$
B. $b^3 - 9b$
C. $b^2 + 2b - 15$
D. $b^2 - 6b - 27$

9. The expression $x^2 + px + 20$ **cannot** be factored over the integers if p has the value

A. -9
B. -12
C. 21
D. 20

Numerical Response **2.** The largest value of w for which $x^2 - wx + 48$ can be factored over the integers is ____ .

(Record your answer in the numerical response box from left to right)

10. One factor of $7a^2 - 28a^4$ is

A. $1 - 2a$
B. $28a^4$
C. $1 - 4a$
D. $1 - a$

11. Which of the following is a factor of $6y^2 - y - 1$?

A. $6y - 1$
B. $4y - 1$
C. $3y - 1$
D. $2y - 1$

Numerical Response **3.** The expression $2x^2 - 10x - 3x + c$ can be factored by grouping into the product of two binomials. If one of these binomials is $x - 5$, then the value of c is _____.

(Record your answer in the numerical response box from left to right)

In each of questions #12 - 14 four responses are given.

Answer *A* if response 1 and response 2 only are correct

_B_ if response 1 and response 3 only are correct

_C_ if response 2 and response 4 only are correct

_D_ if no response or some other response or combination of the responses is correct

12. Which of the following are factors of $2t^2 - 7t - 15$?

Response 1: $2t - 3$
Response 2: $t - 5$
Response 3: $t + 5$
Response 4: $2t + 3$

13. $x^2 + 25y^2$ has as a factor

Response 1 $x - 5y$
Response 2 $x - y$
Response 3 $x + 5y$
Response 4 $x + y$

14. The trinomial $ax^2 - 12x + c$ can be factored over the integers if

Response 1 $a = 1$ and $c = 36$
Response 2 $a = 36$ and $c = 1$
Response 3 $a = 1$ and $c = -36$
Response 4 $a = 36$ and $c = -1$

Numerical Response

4. If $4a^2 + 44a + c$ is a perfect square trinomial, then the value of c must be _______ .

(Record your answer in the numerical response box from left to right)

15. When fully factored, the expression $16a^4 - 1$ is written

A. $(4a^2 - 1)^2$

B. $(2a - 1)^2(2a + 1)^2$

C. $(4a^2 - 1)(4a^2 + 1)$

D. $(2a - 1)(2a + 1)(4a^2 + 1)$

Numerical Response **5.** Three algebraic expressions have been partially factored.

$$2x^2 - 3x - 14 = (2x - 7)(x + A)$$

$$x^4 - 7x^2 - 18 = (x^2 + 2)(x - B)(x + B)$$

$$5x^2 - 40x + 80 = C(x - D)^2$$

Write the value of A in the first box.
Write the value of B in the second box.
Write the value of C in the third box.
Write the value of D in the fourth box.
(Record your answer in the numerical response box from left to right)

Written Response - 5 marks

1. Students are investigating polynomials of the form $ax^2 + bx + c$, where a, b, and c are integers.

- State any polynomial with $a = 1$ and $c = 16$ which can be factored over the integers.

- State any polynomial with $a = 1$ and $c = 16$ which cannot be factored over the integers. **Explain** why factoring is not possible in this case.

- If $a = 1$ and $c = 16$, determine how many polynomials of this type are able to be factored over the integers.

- State a polynomial of the form $ax^2 + bx + c$ which can be factored over the integers and in which $a + b + c = 20$.

- If the trinomial $ax^2 + bx + c$ can be factored over the integers using the method of decomposition, explain why a, b, and c cannot **all** be **odd** integers.

Answer Key

1. D	2. C	3. D	4. C	5. D	6. A	7. C	8. C
9. D	10. A	11. D	12. C	13. D	14. A	15. D	

1. | 2 | 4 | | |

2. | 4 | 9 | | |

3. | 1 | 5 | | |

4. | 1 | 2 | 1 | |

5. | 2 | 3 | 5 | 4 |

Written Response.

Bullet 1 $x^2 + 10x + 16$ or any answer in bullet 3.

Bullet 2 Many answers are possible e.g. $x^2 + 3x + 16$ is not able to be factored because it is not possible to find two integers which multiply to 16 and add to 3.

Bullet 3 6 polynomials are possible $x^2 + 10x + 16$, $x^2 - 10x + 16$, $x^2 + 8x + 16$, $x^2 - 8x + 16$, $x^2 + 17x + 16$, $x^2 - 17x + 16$

Bullet 4 For example $x^2 + 10x + 9$ $x^2 + 7x + 12$

Bullet 5 If a, b, and c are all odd, then ac must be odd. To factor $ax^2 + bx + c$ using decomposition we need to find two integers which multiply to ac (which we know is odd) and add to b (which we also know is odd). It is not possible to find two numbers which multiply to an odd number and add to an odd number so a, b, and c cannot all be odd.

Relations and Functions Lesson #1:
Review & Preview

This lesson reviews some important concepts that will appear throughout the next three units.

The Cartesian Coordinate System

In mathematics "Cartesian" means relating to the French mathematician **René Descartes**. In 1637 he introduced the idea of specifying the position of a point on a surface using two intersecting axes as measuring guides.

The modern Cartesian coordinate system, in two dimensions, is defined by two axes at right angles to each other forming a plane (called the *xy* plane). The horizontal axis is labelled *x*, and the vertical axis is labelled *y*. All the points in a Cartesian coordinate system taken together form a **Cartesian plane**.

The point of intersection of the two axes is called the **origin**, usually labelled O. On each axis a unit length is chosen and units are marked off to form a grid. To specify a particular point on the grid we use a unique **ordered pair** of numbers called **coordinates**. The first number in the ordered pair, called the ***x*-coordinate**, identifies the position with regard to the *x*-axis, while the second number, called the ***y*-coordinate**, identifies the position with regard to the *y*-axis. The point $P(4, 3)$ is shown on the grid below. The intersection of the *x*-axis and *y*-axis creates four **quadrants**, numbered counterclockwise starting from the north-east quadrant.

a) Complete the following by writing the coordinates of the points represented by the letters on the grid.

A(*B*(*C*(

D(*O*(

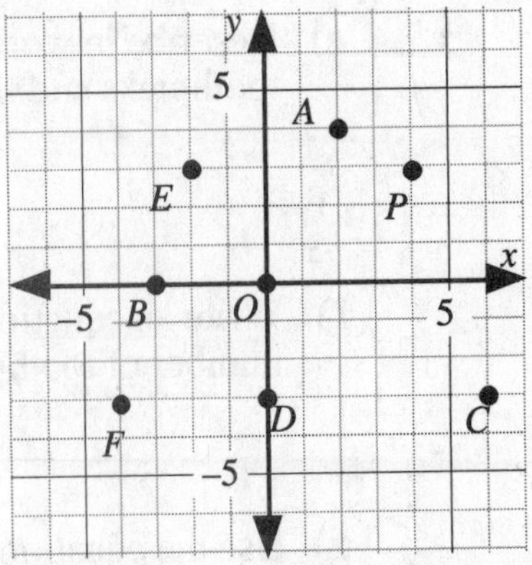

b) Write the coordinates of the point in the second quadrant.

c) Write the coordinates of the point in quadrant III.

d) Complete the following table using "positive" or "negative".

Quadrant	*x*-coordinate	*y*-coordinate
I		
II		
III		
IV		

Describing a Pictorial Pattern Using a Linear Relation

Use the following information to answer this Class Example.

Three toothpicks are used to form a triangle. A second triangle is formed by adding two more toothpicks. A third triangle is formed by adding another two more toothpicks, and the pattern continues.

Example of a toothpick →

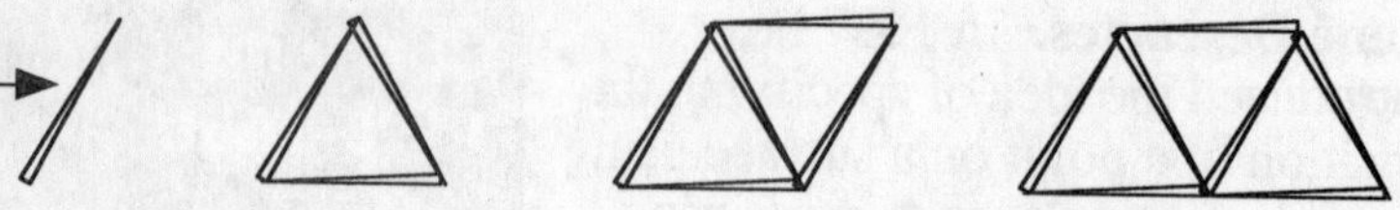

a) Draw the next two diagrams in the pattern.

b) Complete the table relating the number of toothpicks P, to the number of triangles, T.

Number of Triangles, T	1	2	3	4	5
Number of Toothpicks, P	3	5	7	9	11

c) Represent the data from the table of values on the grid.

d) Explain why it does not make sense to join the points in a straight line.

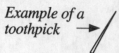

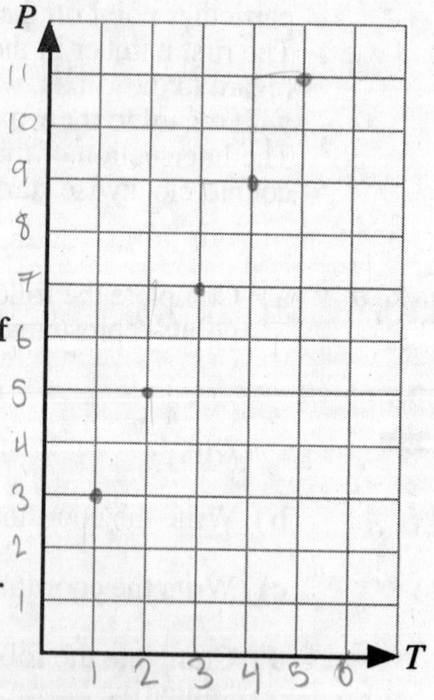

e) Describe in words the relationship between the number of toothpicks and the number of triangles.

f) Write an equation that can be used to determine the number of toothpicks if we know the number of triangles.

g) Use the equation to determine the number of toothpicks if there are 27 triangles.

h) Use the equation to determine the number of triangles if there are 83 toothpicks.

Class Ex. #3

Students in a Physics classroom determined the resistance in an electrical circuit by measuring the voltage (V volts) when a current (I amps) was passed through the circuit. The table below shows the results.

Current, (I) in amps	0.5	1.5	3	3.5	4
Voltage, (V) in volts	6	18	36	42	48

a) Represent the data from the table on the grid.

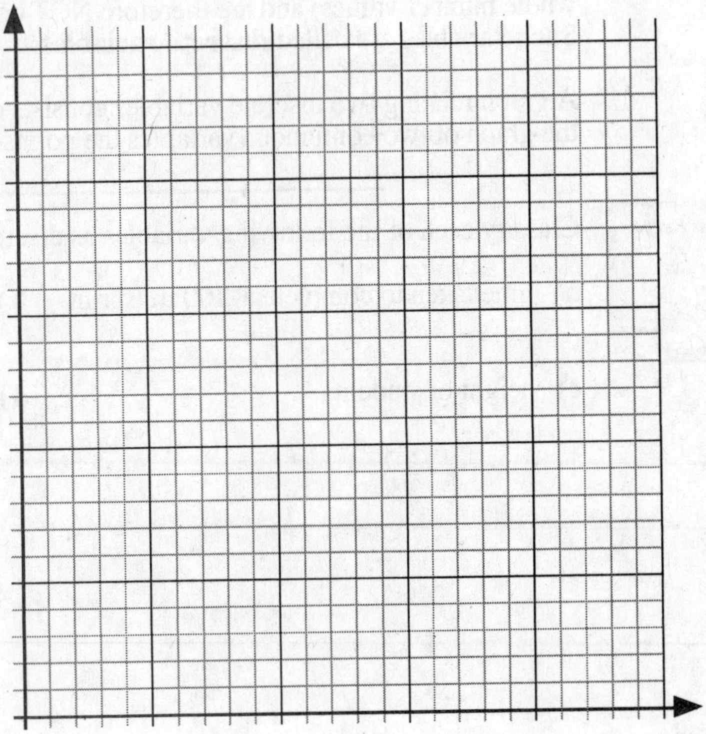

b) Does it make sense to join the points together with a straight line? Explain.

c) Use the graph to determine the voltage for a current of 2.5 amps.

d) Write an equation expressing V in terms of I.

e) Use the equation to determine the voltage when the current is 6.2 amps.

f) The resistance (R ohms) is calculated from the equation $V = IR$. State the resistance in this electrical circuit.

Discrete and Continuous Variables

In Class Example #3, the variables I and V are examples of **continuous variables** since they can take on every value within a particular interval, i.e. a variable for which it is possible to find an intermediate value between any two values. For the graph in this example, the current can take on any value between 0 and 5.

In Class Example #2, the variables P and T can only take on limited values (in this case whole number values) and are therefore NOT continuous variables. Such variables are called **discrete variables.**

A graph relating two discrete variables consists of a series of unconnected points, whereas in the graph of two continuous variables the points would be connected.

Classify each of the following variables as discrete or continuous.

a) time taken to complete a 100 m sprint

b) number of students who pass Math 10

c) height of students

d) shoe size

Complete Assignment Questions #1 - #12

Assignment

1. Complete the following statements.

a) The first coordinate of an ordered pair is called the _____ coordinate and the second coordinate is called the _____ coordinate.

b) X-axis, y-axis are used to locate or plot points on a Cartesian Plane.

c) The numbers of an ordered pair are called the ____________ of a point on the grid.

d) The *x*-axis and the *y*-axis intersect at the __________ .

e) The Cartesian plane is divided into four __________ .

2. The following questions refer to the grid on the right.

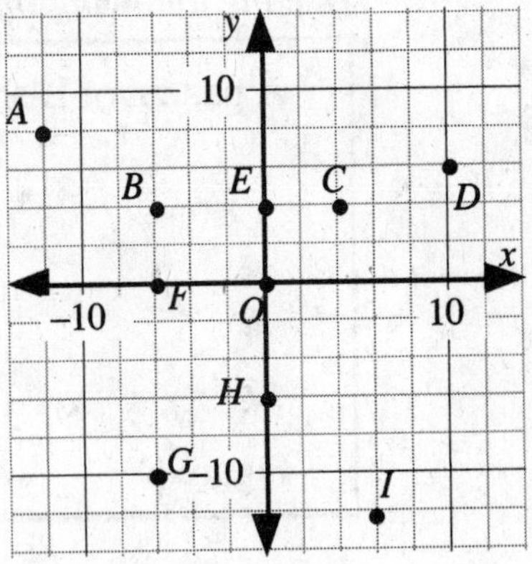

a) Name the points represented by the following coordinates.

i) (–6, 4) B **ii)** (6, –12) I **iii)** (0, 4) E

b) List the coordinates of each point.

i) *C* **ii)** *G* **iii)** *F* **iv)** *O* **v)** *H*

c) Which points are in

i) quadrant 1 **ii)** quadrant 2

iii) quadrant 3 **iv)** quadrant 4

d) Which points are inbetween quadrants?

e) Which points have the same *x*-coordinate? What visual check can be used?

f) Which points have the same *y*-coordinate? What visual check can be used?

3. The following is a scrambled message using ordered pairs. Plot the ordered pairs on the grid provided. Unscramble the letters, and find the message. The symbol • represents the beginning of a new letter.

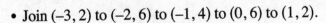

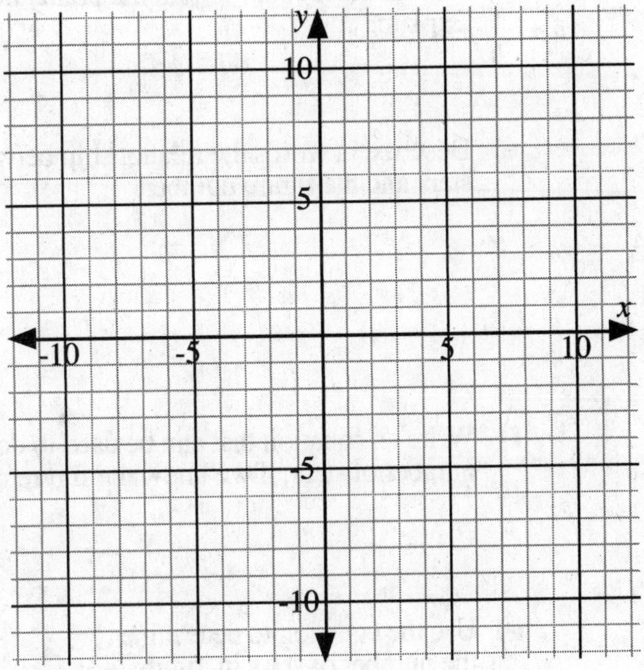

- Join (5, –9) to (5, –5). Join (7, –9) to (5, –7) to (7, –5).
- Join (–11, –2) to (–10, 0) to (–9, 2) to (–8, 0) to (–7, –2). Join (–8, 0) to (–10, 0).
- Join (0, –10) to (0, –6) to (2, –6) to (2, –8) to (0, –8) to (2, –10).
- Join (2, 0) to (0, 0) to (0, –2) to (2, –2) to (2, –4) to (0, –4).
- Join (8, 5) to (8, 9). Join (10, 5) to (10, 9). Join (8, 7) to (10, 7).
- Join (–3, 2) to (–2, 6) to (–1, 4) to (0, 6) to (1, 2).
- Join (3, 8) to (5, 8). Join (4, 8) to (4, 4).
- Join (6, 1) to (4, 1) to (4, –3) to (6, –3).
- Join (–6, –6) to (–6, –10) to (–4, –10) to (–4, –6) to (–6, –6).

Use the following information to answer the next question.

A pattern of L-shapes is shown

Figure 1 Figure 2 Figure 3

4.a) Draw the next two diagrams in the pattern.

b) Complete the table relating the number of stars, S, to the figure number, N.

Figure Number, N	1	2	3	4	5
Number of Stars, S	4	6	8	10	12

c) Represent the data from the table of values on the grid.

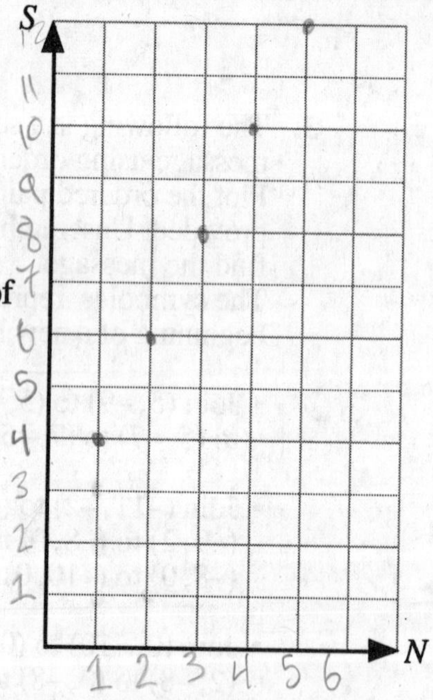

d) Does it make sense to join the points in a straight line? Explain.

e) Describe in words the relationship between the number of stars and the figure number.

f) Write an equation that can be used to determine the number of stars, if we know the figure number.

g) Use the equation to determine the number of stars in figure 43.

h) Use the equation to determine the figure number, if there are 140 stars.

Use the following information to answer the next question.

The boiling point of water varies according to the atmospheric pressure and the height above sea level. The table below shows the approximate boiling temperature of water in °C, relating to the height in metres above sea level.

Height Above Sea Level, *H*	0	2000	4000	6000	8000
Boiling Temperature, *T*	100	94	88	82	76

5.a) Represent the data from the table on the grid.

b) Does it make sense to join the points together with a straight line? Explain.

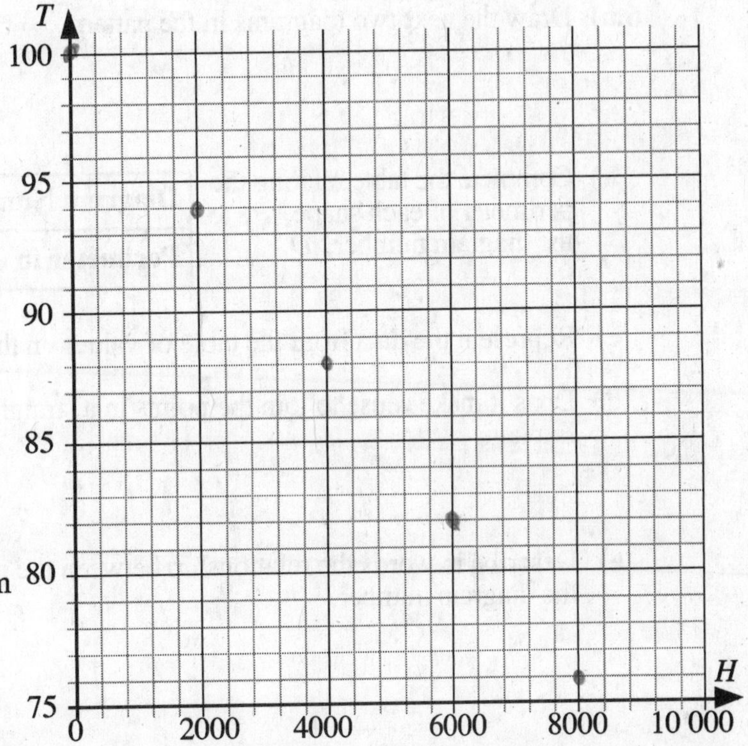

c) Use the graph to estimate the boiling temperature of water at a height of 3000 m above sea level.

d) Use the graph to estimate the height above sea level at which the boiling temperature of water is 85°C.

e) The equation relating T and H is $T = 100 - 0.003H$. Use the equation to check the accuracy of your estimates in **c)** and **d)**.

f) In the context of the question, what does the value 100 represent in the equation $T = 100 - 0.003H$?

Use the following information to answer the next question.

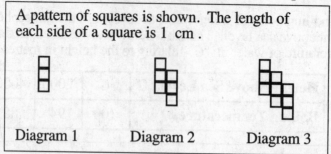

A pattern of squares is shown. The length of each side of a square is 1 cm .

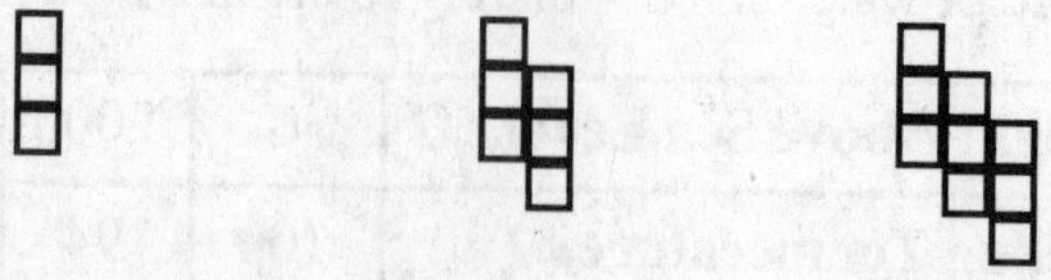

Diagram 1 Diagram 2 Diagram 3

6.a) Draw the next two diagrams in the pattern.

b) Complete the table relating the perimeter of each shape, P, to the diagram number, D.

Diagram Number, D	1	2	3	4	5
Perimeter in cm, P	8				

c) Represent the data from the table of values on the grid.

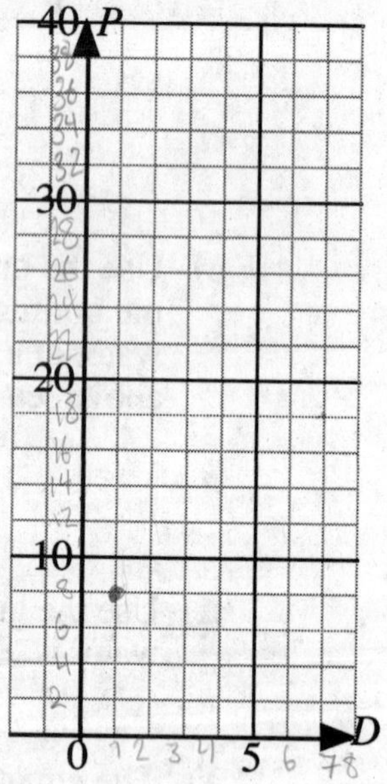

d) Does it make sense to join the points in a straight line? Explain.

e) Describe in words the relationship between the perimeter and the diagram number.

f) Write an equation that can be used to determine the perimeter, if we know the diagram number.

g) Use the equation to determine the perimeter of diagram 8.

h) Use the equation to determine the diagram number, if the perimeter is 56 cm.

7. Describe whether data points should or should not be connected on the graph of a relation in a given situation.

Multiple Choice

8. Which of the following variables is discrete?

A. temperature
B. weight
C. altitude
D. number of goals

9. Which of the following variables is continuous?

A. number of correct answers on a test.
B. number of letters in the alphabet.
C. number of grams of sugar in a pear.
D. number of students in a class.

10. Consider the following variables:

i) the age of a truck.
ii) the weight of a truck.
iii) the number of wheels on a truck.
iv) the number of litres of gas in the gas tank of a truck.

Which of the variables above is/are continuous?

A. ii) only
B. i) and ii) only.
C. i), ii), and iv) only
D. some other combination of i), ii), iii), and iv).

11. On a Cartesian Plane, the line segment joining the points $(-3,-2)$ and $(5,-5)$

A. intersects both the x-axis and y-axis.
B. intersects the y-axis but not the x-axis.
C. intersects the x-axis but not the y-axis.
D. does not intersect the x-axis or the y-axis.

Numerical Response

12. The relationship between degrees Celsius, C, and degrees Fahrenheit, F, is described by the equation $C = \frac{5}{9}(F - 32)$. The ignition temperature of paper is 451°F. To the nearest degree, the ignition temperature of paper in degrees Celsius is _____ .

(Record your answer in the numerical response box from left to right)

Answer Key

1. a) x y **b)** ordered pairs **c)** coordinates **d)** origin **e)** quadrants

2. a) **i)** B **ii)** I **iii)** E
b) **i)** (4, 4) **ii)** (–6, –10) **iii)** (–6, 0) **iv)** (0, 0) **v)** (0, –6)
c) **i)** C, D **ii)** A, B **iii)** G **iv)** I
d) E, F, H, O
e) $B, F, G,$ E, O, H They lie on the same vertical line.
f) B, E, C $F, O,$ They lie on the same horizontal line.

3. MATH ROCKS

4. a)

```
*           *
*           *
*           *
*           *
*           *
* * * * *   *
            * * * * * *
```

Figure 4 Figure 5

b)

Figure Number, N	1	2	3	4	5
Number of Stars, S	**4**	**6**	**8**	**10**	**12**

d) No, the variables are discrete.
Intermediate values have no meaning.
e) The number of stars is twice the figure number plus two.
f) $S = 2N + 2$ **g)** 88 **h)** 69

5. b) Yes. The data is continuous. Intermediate values have meaning.
c) 91 °C **d)** 5 000 m **e)** 91 °C, 5 000 m
f) 100°C is the boiling temperature of water at sea level.

6. a) Diagram 4 Diagram 5

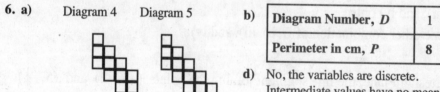

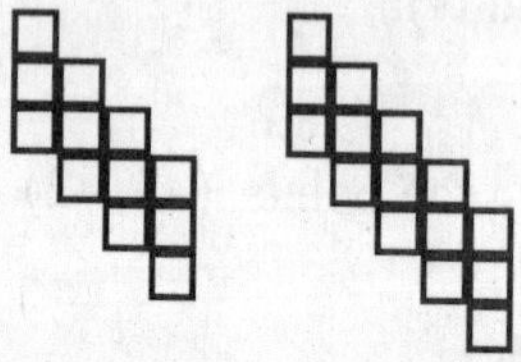

b)

Diagram Number, D	1	2	3	4	5
Perimeter in cm, P	**8**	**12**	**16**	**20**	**24**

d) No, the variables are discrete.
Intermediate values have no meaning.
e) The perimeter is 4 more than 4 times the diagram number.
f) $P = 4D + 4$ **g)** 36 cm **h)** Diagram 13

7. If the data is continous, i.e. all intermediate values have meaning, then the data points should be connected. If the data is discrete, ie not all intermediate points have meaning, then the data points should not be connected.

8. D **9.** C **10.** C **11.** B **12.**

2	3	3	

Relations and Functions Lesson #2:
Relationships Between Two Quantities

Relations

Much of mathematics involves the search for patterns and relationships between sets of data. Many real life applications of mathematics investigate the relationship between two quantities.

For example:

- the value of a computer is related to its age
- the price of a watermelon is related to its weight
- the time taken for a person to walk to school is related to the distance to be walked.

In mathematics, a comparison between two sets of elements is called a **relation**.

List one more example of a relation.

Representing the Relationship Between Two Quantities

In this unit we will consider seven ways in which the relationship between two quantities can be represented. Some of these ways are already familiar to us.

- in words
- a table of values
- a set of ordered pairs
- a mapping (or arrow) diagram
- an equation
- a graph
- function notation (some relations can be represented in this way (see Lessons 8, 9, & 10)

We will use the relation below as an example.

Investigating a Relation

Consider the following relation:

"The cost, C (cents per km), of driving a car is related to the speed, s (km per hour), at which it is driven."

We will use this relation to introduce some ideas which will be developed throughout the course of this unit. Our task is to represent this relation in some form.

The example illustrates a relationship between two **variables**, C and s.

In the statement of the relation, the cost depends on the speed.

C is called the **dependent variable** and s is called the **independent variable**.

When representing a relation, we often regard the values of the independent variable as the **input** and the values of the dependent variable as the **output**.

Before considering how to represent this relation we need some data: we need input values and output values.

The input values make up the **domain** of the relation, and the output values make up the **range** of the relation. These concepts will be discussed in more detail later.

Obviously we would not attempt to collect data for <u>every</u> possible input value (i.e. for every possible speed at which the car can be driven). Suppose that we choose as input values speeds of 20, 30, 40, ...120 km/h. and that the output values are as given in the diagrams below.

The diagrams show how the information collected can be represented as ordered pairs, in a table of values, and as a mapping diagram. The ordered pairs can also be represented graphically.

Table of Values

Input (s)	Output (C)
20	10
30	9.1
40	8.4
50	7.9
60	7.6
70	7.5
80	7.6
90	7.9
100	8.4
110	9.1
120	10

Ordered Pairs

(s, C)

(20, 10)
(30, 9.1)
(40, 8.4)
(50, 7.9)
(60, 7.6)
(70, 7.5)
(80, 7.6)
(90, 7.9)
(100, 8.4)
(110, 9.1)
(120, 10)

Mapping Diagram

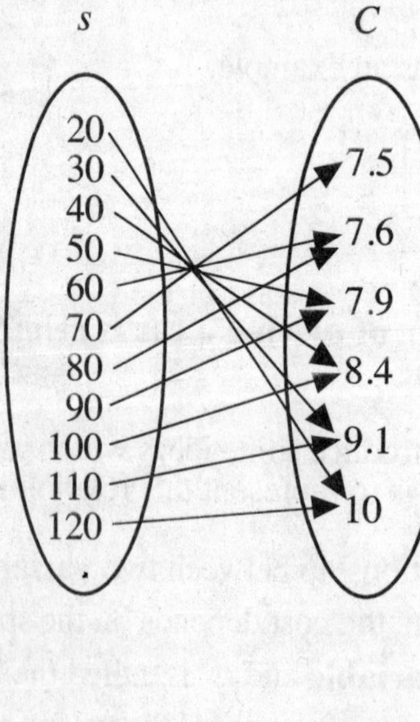

Graph

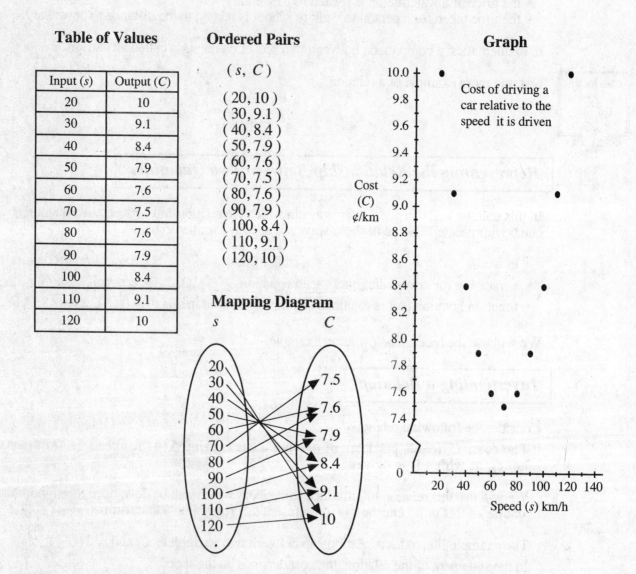

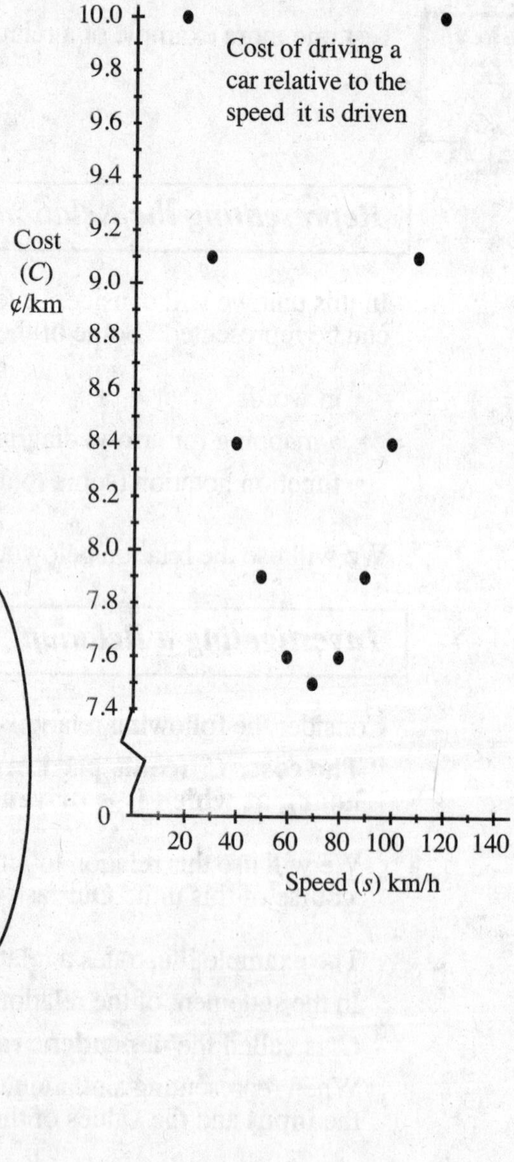

We have only chosen some of the possible input values. However it is obvious that an output value could have been determined for any input value greater than zero and up to the maximum speed of the car. It makes sense then to connect the points on the graph in some way.

Later we will learn how this can be done and how an equation can be determined that best represents the data.

The graph and equation for the relation are given below. Note that the equation is only valid for certain input values which make up the domain of the relation. For example, the equation would not be valid for $s = 5000$!

Equation

$$C = 0.001s^2 - 0.14s + 12.4$$

Graph

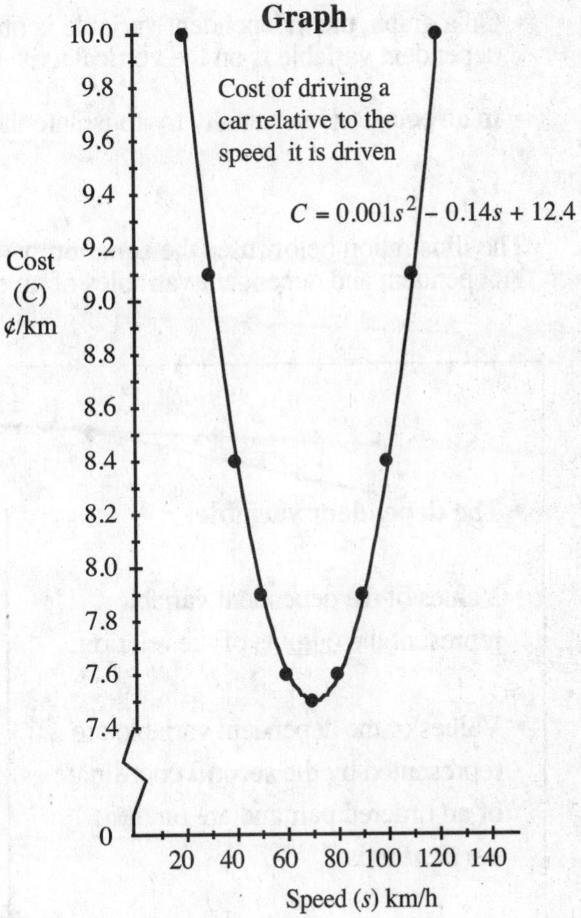

Independent and Dependent Variables in a Relation

The values of the independent variable represent the inputs, and the corresponding values of the dependent variable are the outputs.

- In an ordered pair, the values of the first coordinate are those of the independent variable, and the values of the second coordinate are values of the dependent variable.
- In a table of values, the independent variable is usually given first - either to the left or above the values of the dependent variable.
- In a mapping diagram, the arrows go from the independent variable to the dependent variable.
- On a graph, the independent variable is on the horizontal axis, often the x-axis, and the dependent variable is on the vertical axis, often the y-axis.
- In an equation, we usually try to isolate the dependent variable to the left side.

The illustration below uses the equation $y = 3x - 5$ as an example to illustrate the independent and dependent variables of an equation.

$$y = 3x - 5$$

• The **dependent variable.**	• The **independent variable.**
• Values of the dependent variable represent the <u>outputs</u> of the relation.	• Values of the independent variable represent the <u>inputs</u> of the relation.
• Values of the dependent variable are represented by the **second** coordinate of an ordered pair and are on the **vertical axis.**	• Values of the independent variable are represented by the **first** coordinate of an ordered pair and are on the **horizontal axis.**

Class Ex. #2

The diagrams show relations expressed in different ways. In each case

i) state the independent variable **ii)** state the dependent variable

iii) list the inputs **iv)** list the outputs

a)

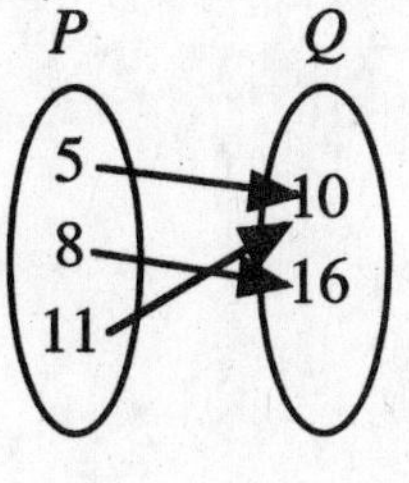

b)

V	A
4	15
10	12
25	15

c)

(B, c): $(3,7)$, $(4,11)$, $(5,15)$, $(6,19)$

Class Ex. #3

The diagrams show relations expressed in different ways. In each case

i) state the independent variable **ii)** state the dependent variable

a) $C = 2\pi r$

b)

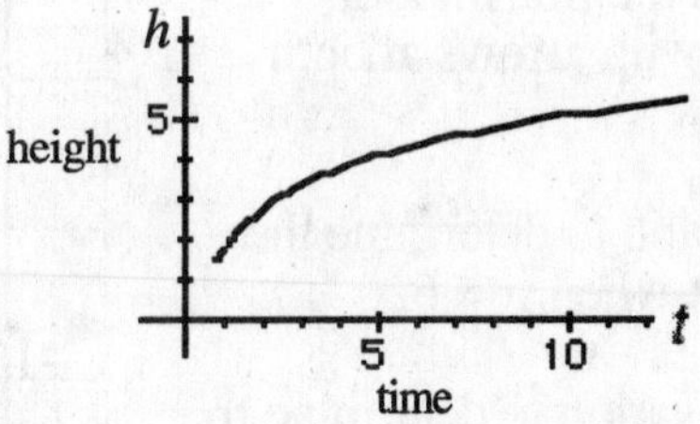

c) The amount of sap, s, obtained from a maple tree is dependent on the time, t, a container is left attached to the maple tree.

Complete Assignment Questions #1 - #4

Investigating Relationships by Plotting Ordered Pairs

In this section we will consider relations defined by an equation, and sketch a graph by plotting ordered pairs.

- Make a table of inputs by choosing replacements for the independent variable.
- For each of the input values, calculate the corresponding value (the output) of the dependent variable.
- Plot the ordered pairs on a Cartesian plane.

Class Ex. #4

Consider the relation described by the equation $y = 2x - 5$.

a) Complete the first five rows of the following table of values which shows some of the possible input values.

Input (x)	Output (y)	Ordered pair (x, y)
–2		
–1		
0		
1		
2		

b) Plot the ordered pairs in a) on the grid provided.

c) Connect the points on the grid, and extend the line in both directions with arrows at both ends.

d) Use the graph to determine the value of y when $x = 6$.

e) Use the equation to determine the value of y when $x = 6$, and verify the answer in d).

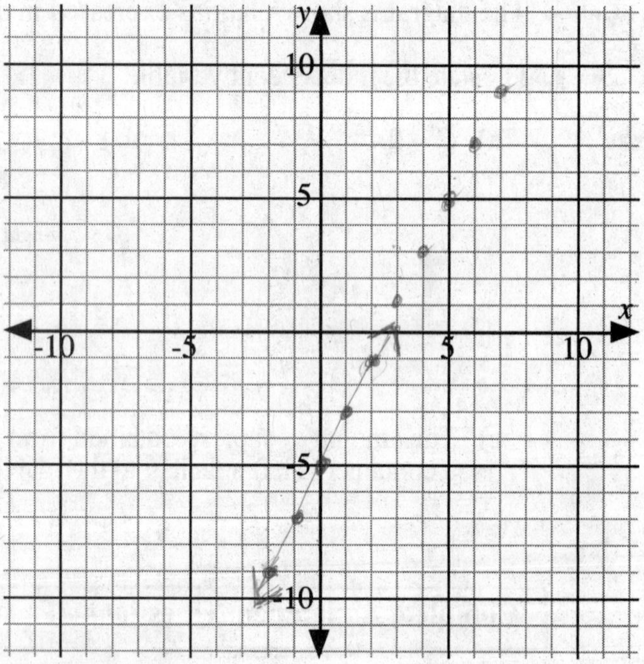

f) Write the value of y when $x = 6$ in the table of values using the first blank space in a).

g) Use the graph to determine the value of x when $y = 3$. Put this information in the last row in a).

h) Complete the following statement:

This relation is called a ______________ relation because the graph of the relation is a straight line.

Class Ex. #5

Consider the relation described by the equation $y = x^2 - 6$.

a) Complete the table of values to the right which show some of the possible input values.

$y = x^2 - 6$

$y = 4^2 - 6 = y = 10$

Input (x)	Output (y)	Ordered pair (x, y)
4	10	4,10
3	3	3,3
2	-2	2,-2
1	-5	1,-5
0	-6	0,-6
–1	-5	-1,-5
–2	-2	-2,-2
–3	3	-3,3
-4	10	-4,10

b) Plot the ordered pairs in a) on the grid provided.

c) Use the symmetry of the graph or table to predict the value of y when $x = -4$.

$y = 10$

d) Use the equation to determine the value of y when $x = -4$, and verify the answer in c).

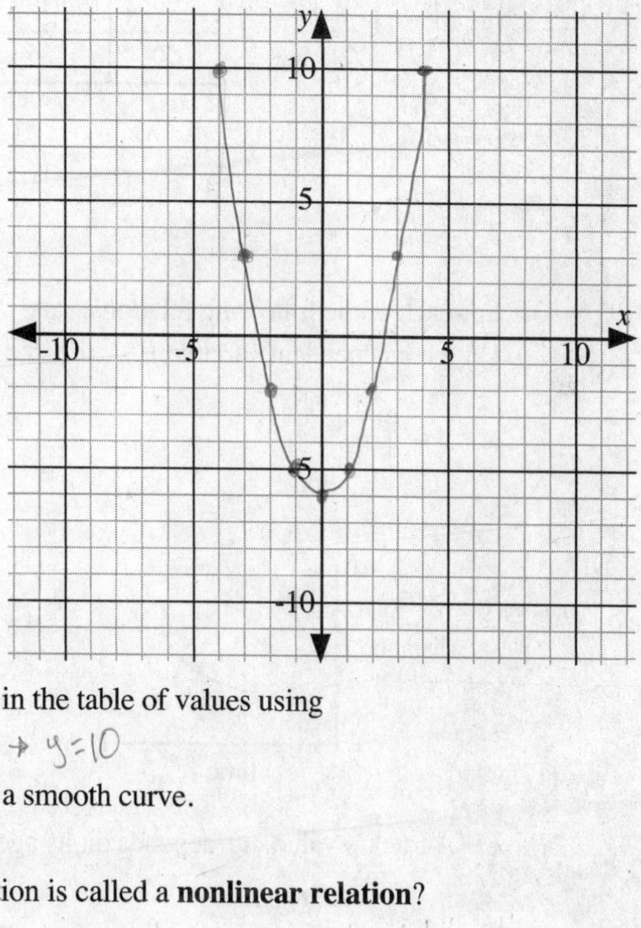

e) Write the value of y when $x = -4$ in the table of values using the first blank space in a).

$x = -4 \rightarrow y = 10$

f) Connect the points on the grid with a smooth curve.

g) Why do you think this type of relation is called a **nonlinear relation**?

Complete Assignment Questions #5 - #9

Assignment

1. Complete the following.

a) The mathematical relationship between two quantities is called a ____________.

b) The variable used for inputs in a relation is known as the ______________ variable.

c) The variable used for outputs in a relation is known as the ______________ variable.

d) In the equation $A = \pi r^2$, the independent variable is _____, and the dependent variable is _____.

2. The diagrams show relations expressed in different ways. In each case:

i) state the independent and dependent variables **ii)** list the inputs and outputs.

a)

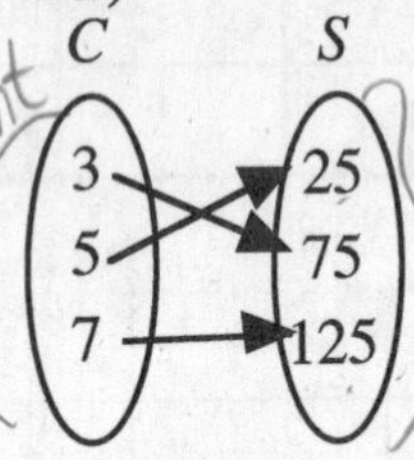

b)

C	n
8	22
20	19
50	35

c) (f, e): $(2, 3)$, $(-2, 19)$, $(8, 17)$, $(0, 2)$

3. For each of the following relations, state

i) the independent variable **ii)** the dependent variable

a) $V = \frac{4}{3}\pi r^3$

b) $C = \frac{5}{9}(F - 32)$

c)

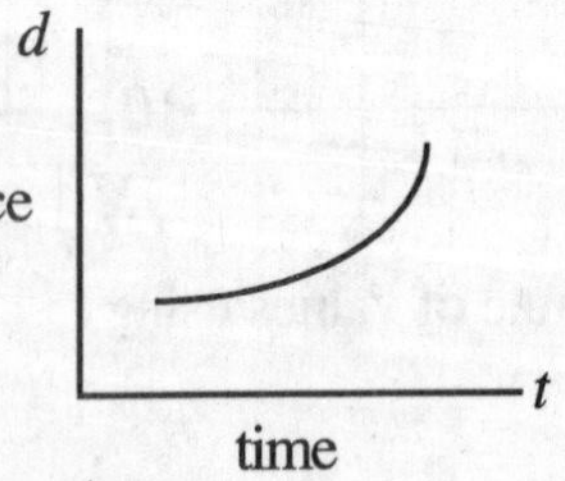

d)

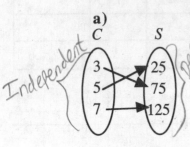

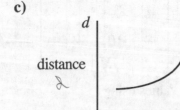

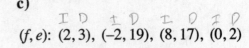

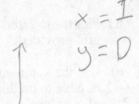

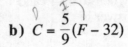

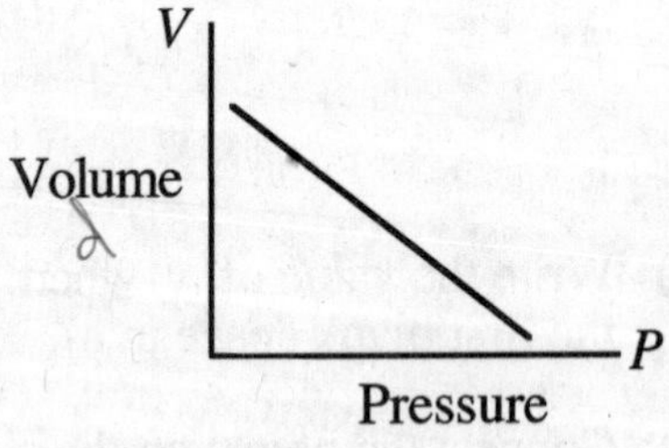

e) A truck's value, v, depends on its age, a.

f) The cost, C, of producing business cards is dependent on the number of cards, n, produced.

4. List the different ways a relation may be represented.

5. Consider the relation described by the equation $y = -x - 2$.

a) Identify the independent and dependent variables.

b) Complete the following table of values.

Input (x)	Output (y)	Ordered pair (x, y)
−3		
−1		
0		
1		

c) Plot the ordered pairs in b) on the grid provided.

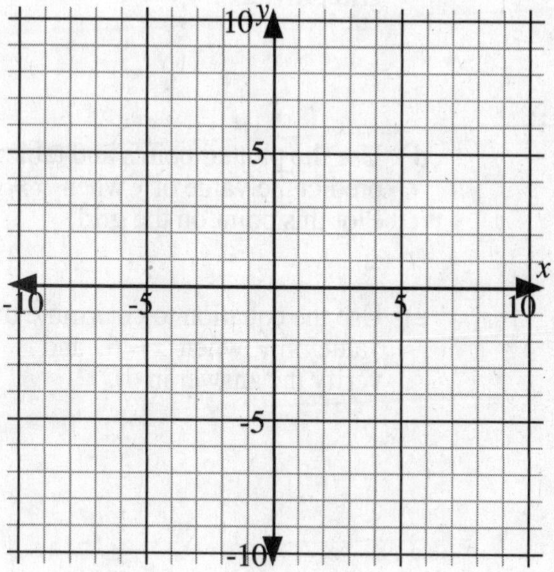

d) Connect the points on the grid, and then extend the line in both directions with arrows at both ends.

e) Use the graph to determine the value of y when $x = 5$.

f) Use the equation to determine the value of y when $x = 5$, and verify the answer in e).

g) Write the value of y when $x = 5$ in the table of values in b).

h) Use the graph to determine the value of x when $y = 0$. Include this ordered pair in the table of values.

i) Use the graph to determine the value of x when $y = 4$. Include this ordered pair in the table of values.

j) Verify the answer in i) using the equation.

k) Is this a linear or a nonlinear relation?

6. Consider the relation described by the equation $y = -0.5x^2 + 8$.

a) Identify the independent and dependent variables.

b) Complete the following table of values.

Input (x)	Output (y)	Ordered pair (x, y)
–6		
–4		
–2		
0		
2		
4		

c) Plot the ordered pairs in b) on the grid provided.

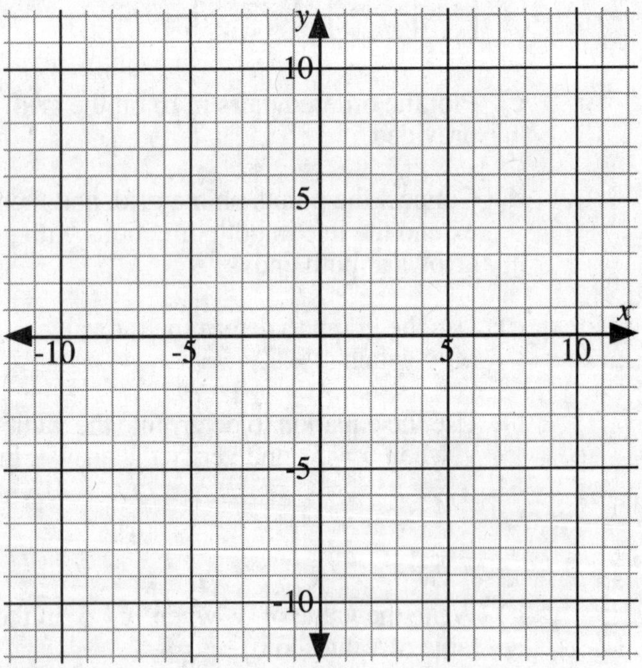

d) Use the plotted points and table to predict the value of y when $x = 6$. Plot this point on the grid.

e) Use the equation to determine the value of y when $x = 6$, and verify the answer in d).

f) Connect the points on the grid with a smooth curve.

g) Is this a linear or a nonlinear relation?

h) Use the graph to determine the values of x when $y = 3.5$. Verify your answer by using the equation.

7. For the following relations:

i) Complete the table of values choosing your own input values where necessary.
ii) Plot the ordered pairs on the grid, and sketch the graph of the relation.
iii) State whether the relation is linear or nonlinear.

a) $y = -2x + 3$

Input (x)	Output (y)	Ordered pair (x, y)
0		
3		

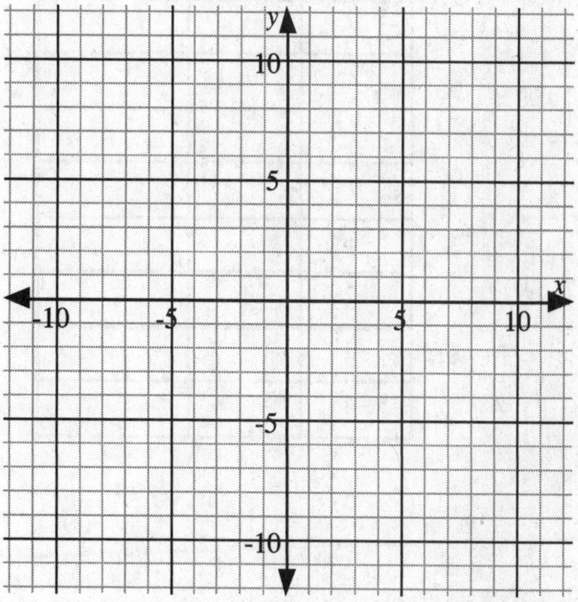

b) $y = 0.5x - 8$

Input (x)	Output (y)	Ordered pair (x, y)
–8		
0		
6		

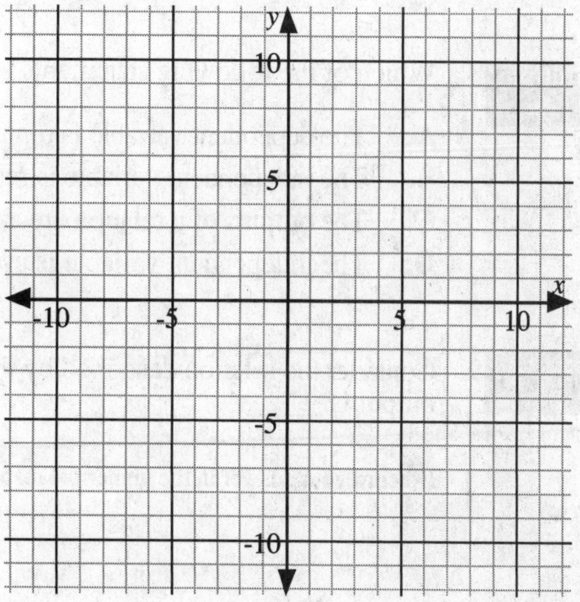

c) $y = -x^2 + 5$

Input (x)	Output (y)	Ordered pair (x, y)
4		
3		
2		
1		
0		
–1		
–2		
–3		
–4		

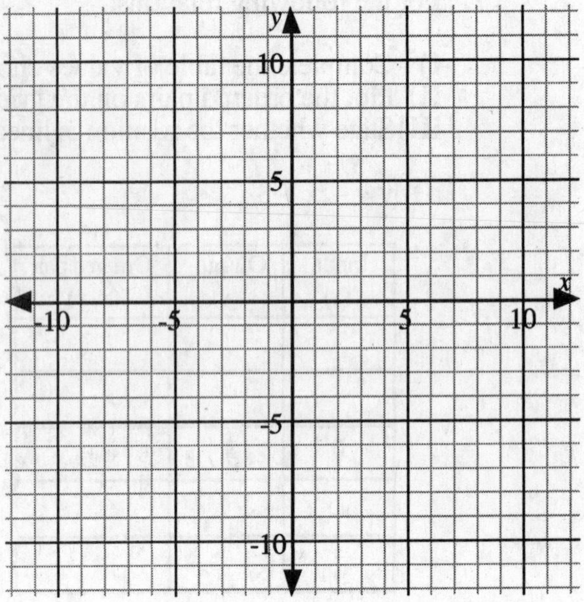

Multiple Choice **8.** Which of the following statements is false?

A. The dependent variable is represented on the vertical axis of a Cartesian Plane.
B. The independent variable is represented by the first coordinate of an ordered pair
C. The outputs of a relation are shown on the horizontal axis of a Cartesian Plane.
D. The independent variable is usually shown on the right side of an equation.

Numerical Response **9.** Consider the relation described by the equation $y = 1.5^{x-2}$. If the input is 4, then the output is ______.

(Record your answer in the numerical response box from left to right)

Answer Key

1. a) relation **b)** independent **c)** dependent **d)** r, A

2. a) i) independent - C dependent - S
ii) input - 3, 5, 7 output - 25, 75, 125

b) i) independent - C dependent - n
ii) input - 8, 20, 50 output - 22, 19, 35

c) i) independent - f dependent - e
ii) input - 2, –2, 8, 0 output - 3, 19, 17, 2

3. a) i) independent - r **ii)** dependent - V
b) i) independent - F **ii)** dependent - C
c) i) independent - time **ii)** dependent - distance
d) i) independent - pressure **ii)** dependent - volume
e) i) independent - a **ii)** dependent - v
f) i) independent - n **ii)** dependent - C

4. words, table of values, set of ordered pairs, mapping, equation, graph, function notation

5. a) Independent → x, Dependent → y
b) See table below **c), d)** See graph below **e)** –7 **f)** –7

	Input (x)	Output (y)	Ordered pair (x, y)
	–3	**1**	**(–3, 1)**
	–1	**–1**	**(–1, –1)**
	0	**–2**	**(0, –2)**
	1	**–3**	**(1, –3)**
g)	5	**–7**	**(5, –7)**
h)	**–2**	0	**(–2, 0)**
i)	**–6**	4	**(–6, 4)**

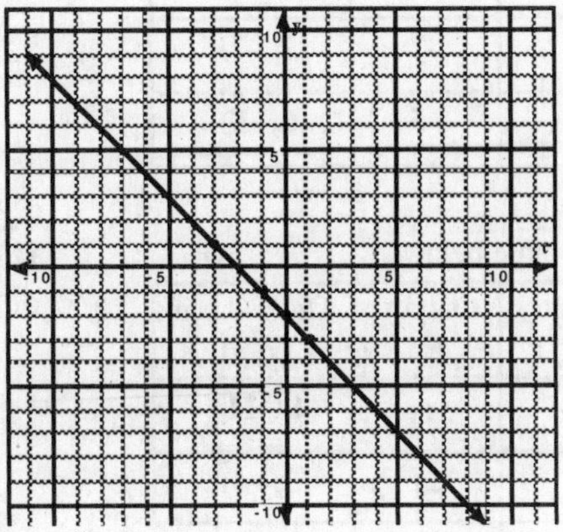

k) linear

6. a) Independent → x Dependent → y
b) See table below. **c), f)** See graph below. **d)** –10 **e)** $y = -0.5(6)^2 + 8$ $y = -10$ **g)** non-linear

Input (x)	Output (y)	Ordered pair (x, y)
–6	**–10**	**(–6, –10)**
–4	**0**	**(–4, 0)**
–2	**6**	**(–2, 6)**
0	**8**	**(0, 8)**
2	**6**	**(2, 6)**
4	**0**	**(4, 0)**

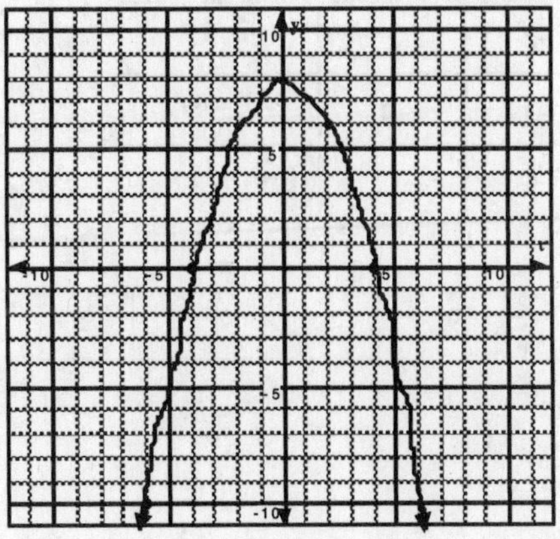

h) $x = \pm 3$

7. a) i) See table below. Inputs may vary.

Input (x)	Output (y)	Ordered pair (x, y)
–2	7	(–2, 7)
–1	5	(–1, 5)
0	3	(0, 3)
1	1	(1, 1)
3	–3	(3, –3)

ii) See grid below.

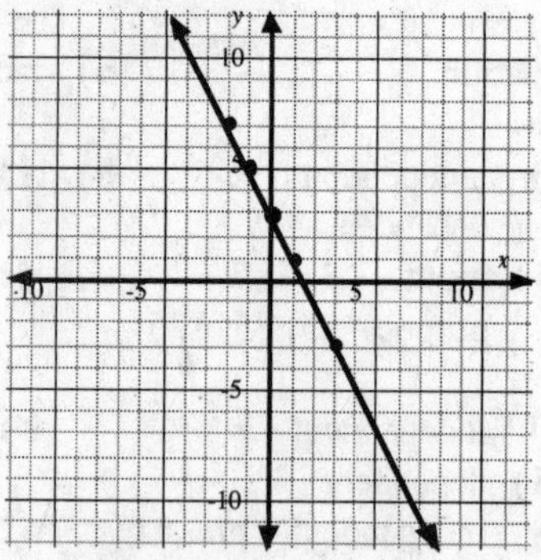

iii) linear

b) i) See table below. Inputs may vary.

Input (x)	Output (y)	Ordered pair (x, y)
–8	–12	(–8, –12)
–6	–11	(–6, –11)
0	–8	(0, –8)
2	–7	(2, –7)
6	–5	(6, –5)

ii) See grid below.

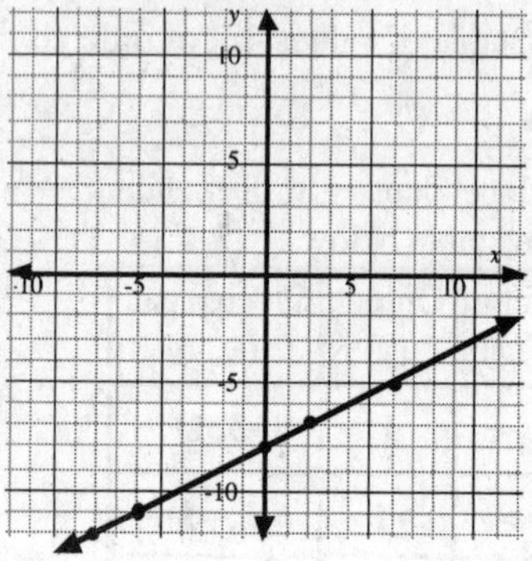

iii) linear

c) i) See table below.

Input (x)	Output (y)	Ordered pair (x, y)
4	–11	(4, –11)
3	–4	(3, –4)
2	1	(2, 1)
1	4	(1, 4)
0	5	(0, 5)
–1	4	(–1, 4)
–2	1	(–2, 1)
–3	–4	(–3, –4)
–4	–11	(–4, –11)

ii) See grid below.

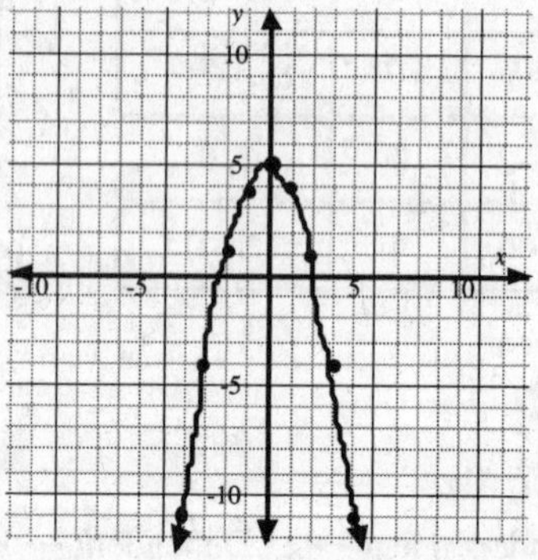

iii) non-linear

8. C

9.

2	.	2	5

Relations and Functions Lesson #3:
x- and y-intercepts and Interpreting Relations

Review

a) A **relation** is a connection between two quantities. A relation can be represented graphically by a set of ____________ ____________ .

b) The first component of a set of ordered pairs is the ___ coordinate, also known as the input. Values of the input are values of the________________ variable.

c) The second component of a set of ordered pairs is the ___ coordinate, also known as the output. Values of the output are values of the________________ variable.

Exploring x- and y-intercepts

Consider the following graphs.

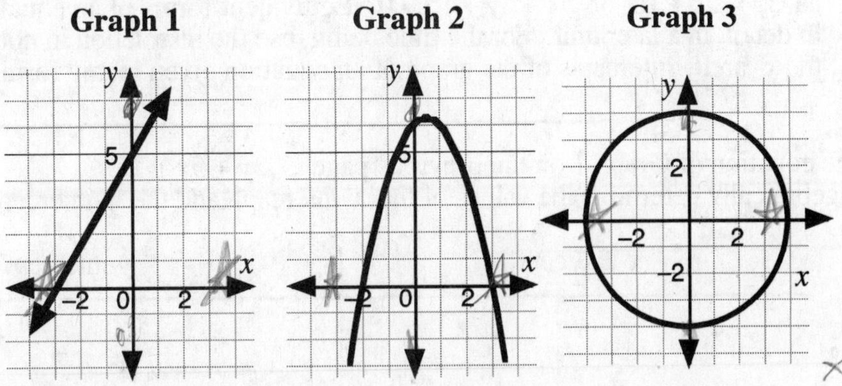

a) List the coordinates of the point(s) where each graph crosses the x-axis.

- Graph 1 crosses the x-axis at (,).
- Graph 2 crosses the x-axis at (,) and (,).
- Graph 3 crosses the x-axis at (,) and (,).

b) What do all the points in a) have in common?

c) List the coordinates of the point(s) where each graph crosses the y-axis.

- Graph 1 crosses the y-axis at (,).
- Graph 2 crosses the y-axis at (,).
- Graph 3 crosses the y-axis at (,) and (,).

d) What do all the points in c) have in common?

x- and y- intercepts of a Graph

The ***x*-intercept** of a graph is the *x*-coordinate of the ordered pair where the graph intersects the *x*-axis. An *x*-intercept occurs at a point on the graph where the *y*-coordinate is zero. The *x*-intercept can be given as a value or as an ordered pair.

The ***y*-intercept** of a graph is the *y*-coordinate of the ordered pair where the graph intersects the *y*-axis. A *y*-intercept occurs at a point on the graph where the *x*-coordinate is zero. The *y*-intercept can be given as a value or as an ordered pair.

1. Given the equation of the graph of a relation:
- to determine the *x*-intercept, set $y = 0$ and solve for x.
- to determine the *y*-intercept, set $x = 0$ and solve for y.

2. The equation of a graph can be written in different form;, all of which are equivalent.
The equation of Graph 1 on the previous page is $y = \frac{5}{3}x + 5$, which can be written as $3y = 5x + 15$ or $5x - 3y + 15 = 0$. Equivalent forms of an equation will be studied in detail, in a later unit. For the time being, use the instruction in note 1 to find the *x*- and *y*-intercepts of the graph of an equation given in any form.

The equation of Graph 1 on the previous page is $3y = 5x + 15$.
Algebraically determine the values of the *x*-intercept and the *y*-intercept of Graph 1.

x-intercept	*y*-intercept

The equation of Graph 3 on the previous page is $x^2 + y^2 = 16$.
Calculate the *x*-intercept and the *y*-intercept of the graph of $x^2 + y^2 = 16$. Give the answers as ordered pairs.

x-intercept	*y*-intercept

Complete Assignment Questions #1 - #3

Class Ex. #3 Lisa purchases a new car for $20 000. The value of the car can be represented by the formula $V = 20\,000 - 1250t$, where V is the value of the car in dollars, and t is the age of the car in years.

a) Complete the table of values and plot the ordered pairs on the grid.

Input (t)	Output (V)	Ordered pair (t, V)
0	20000	0, 20000
2	17500	2, 17500
4	15000	4, 15000
6	12500	6, 12500

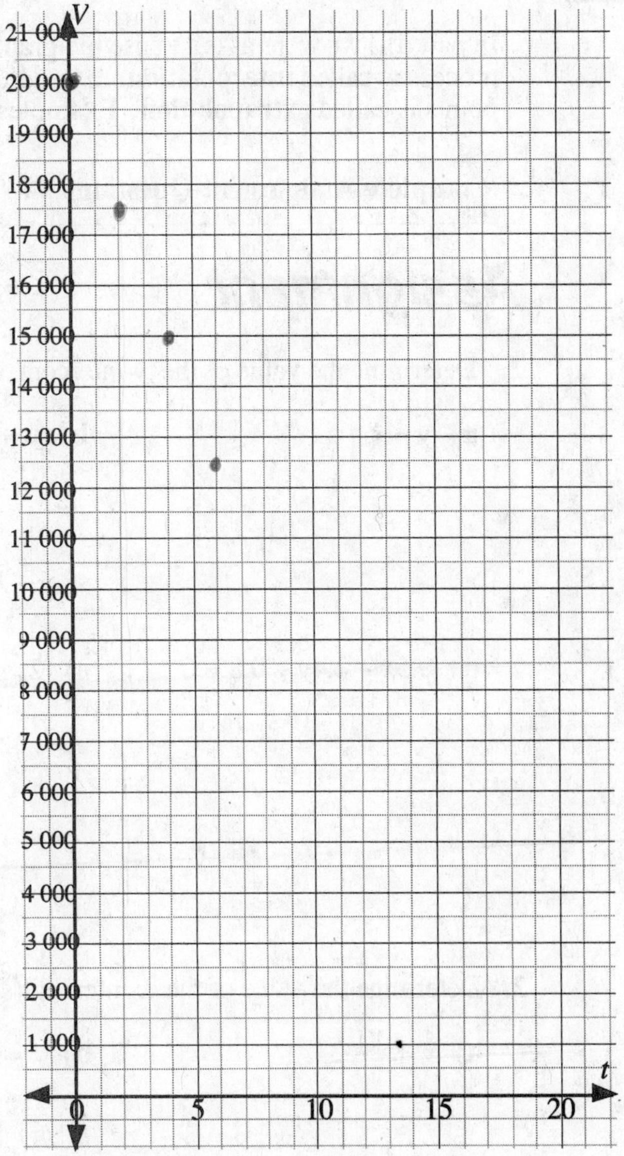

Connect the points with a straight line, and extend the line.

b) What does the ordered pair (0, 20 000) represent?

x = 0

c) Use the graph to estimate the t-intercept. What does the t-intercept represent?

d) Use the graph to estimate the value of the car after
i) 3 years **ii)** 10 years **iii)** 14 years.

16 250

e) Use the formula to verify d) ii).

20 000 − 1250 (3)

20 000 − 3750 = V = 16 250

f) Use the graph to estimate when the car will be worth
i) $5 000 t = 12 **ii)** half of the purchase price.

g) Use the formula to verify f) ii).

V = 20000 − 1250 t

V = 20000 − 1250 (12) → 5000 = V

20000 − 15000 = t = 12

h) Complete the following statement to describe the relation:

The original value of the car is __________ . It depreciates in value by ________ per year and has no value after ____________ years.

In this lesson, using algebra determines the **exact** values for intercepts, etc. whereas using graphs gives an **estimate** for intercepts, etc. In lesson 5 we use the features of a graphing calculator to determine more accurate results from a graph.

In part d)i) we were asked to use the graph to find values lying between given points. This process is called **interpolation**. Extending the graph to predict values outside the plotted points is called **extrapolation**. Examples of extrapolation are d)ii) and d)iii).

Complete Assignment Questions #4 - #9

Assignment

1. Determine the value of the *y*-intercept of the graph of each equation.

a) $y = x - 5$ **b)** $y = 3x - 15$ **c)** $2y + 3x - 12 = 0$

d) $0.5x - 2.4y + 0.8 = 0$ **e)** $2y = x^2 - 60$ **f)** $y = 0.001x^2 - 0.001x + 12.44$

2. Determine the value of the *x*-intercept(s) of the graph of each equation.

a) $y = x - 2$ **b)** $y = 2x - 8$ **c)** $3y + 2x - 12 = 0$

d) $0.6x - 2y + 0.5 = 0$ **e)** $y = x^2 - 9$ **f)** $y = 12 - 3x$

3. Determine the x- and y-intercepts of each equation. Answer as ordered pairs.

a) $y = 4x + 7$ **b)** $y = 15 - 6x$ **c)** $4x - 2y + 16 = 0$

d) $y = \frac{x^2}{2} - 18$ **e)** $x^2 + y^2 = 25$ **f)** $y = 3x$

g) $y = x^2 + 4$ **h)** $9x^2 + y^2 = 81$ **i)** $9x^2 - y^2 = 81$

4. Triple A Car Rental charges \$100 per rental plus 10¢ per km. The total cost, T, in dollars of renting the car can be represented by the formula, $T = 100 + 0.10n$, where n is the number of km travelled.

a) Complete the table of values, and plot the ordered pairs on the grid provided.

Number of km (n)	Total Rental Cost (T) dollars
0	
1000	
3500	
5000	

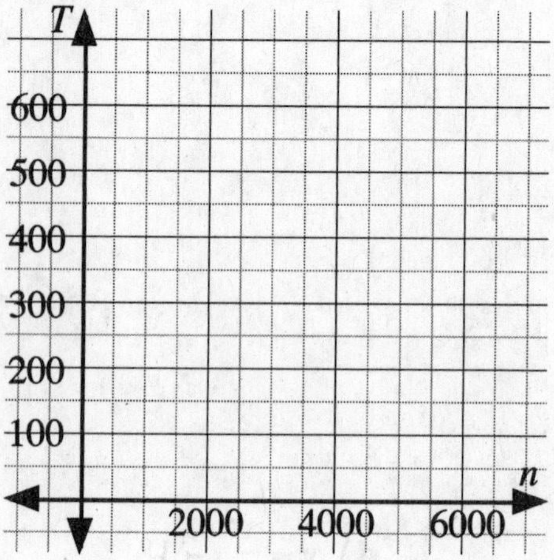

Connect the points with a straight line, and extend the line in both directions.

b) What does the ordered pair (0, 100) represent?

c) Determine the n-intercept of the graph. Explain why it is not applicable to this problem.

d) Interpolate from the graph to estimate the cost for a journey of:
i) 2000 km **ii)** 4500 km

e) Use the formula to verify the answers in d).

f) If the total cost of rental is \$650, use the graph to estimate the number of km travelled.

g) Verify the answer in f) using the formula.

5. An arrow is shot vertically into the air using a bow. The height, h metres, above the ground after t seconds, where $t \geq 0$ is approximated by the equation $h = -5t^2 + 20t + 25$.

a) The maximum height of the arrow is reached after 2 seconds. Calculate the maximum height.

b) Complete the table of values, and plot the points on the grid. Join the points with a smooth curve, and label the graph.

time (seconds)	height (metres)
0	
1	
2	
3	
4	
5	

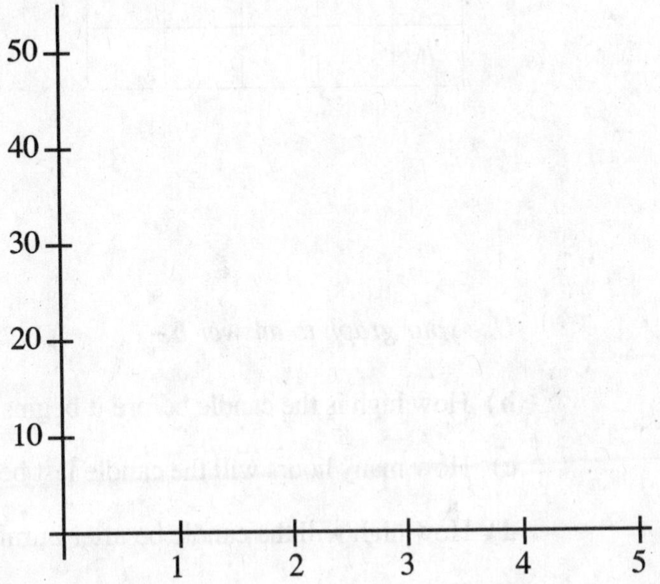

c) Is this a linear or nonlinear relation?

d) For how many seconds is the arrow in the air?

e) What does the h-intercept represent in the context of the question?

f) What does the t-intercept represent in the context of the question?

g) i) Use the graph to estimate the height of the arrow after 1.5 seconds.

ii) Use the equation to calculate the exact height of the arrow after 1.5 seconds.

h) Does it make sense to extend the graph of the relation $h = -5t^2 + 20t + 25$ further in a downward direction to the left or right? Explain.

6. A candle manufacturer determined that its "Long-Last" candles melted according to the formula $h = -2t + 12$, where h is the height of the candle, in cm, after t hours.

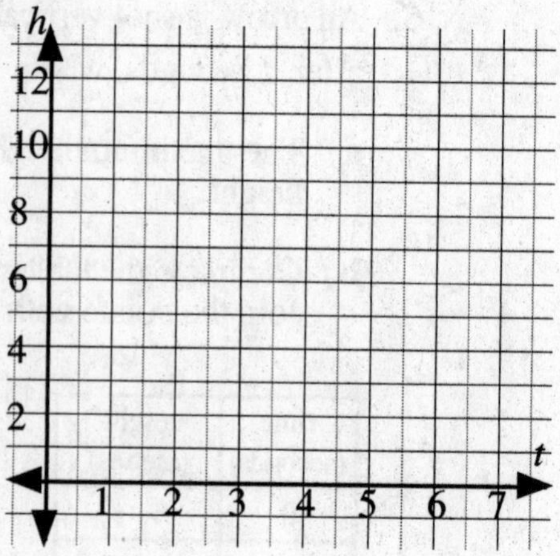

a) Make a table of values and use this to construct the graph of $h = -2t + 12$.

t				
h				

Use your graph to answer b – e.

b) How high is the candle before it begins to melt?

c) How many hours will the candle last before it will completely burn out?

d) How high will the candle be after burning for 5 hours?

e) How long will it take for the candle to burn down to a height of 7 cm?

f) Verify the answers from b) - e) using the formula.

7. A football is kicked by a student. The graph of the relation between the height of the football above the ground and time is shown. The formula that represents the relation is given by $h = -4.9t^2 + 19.4t + 0.6$, where h is the height in metres above the ground and t is the time in seconds the football is in the air.

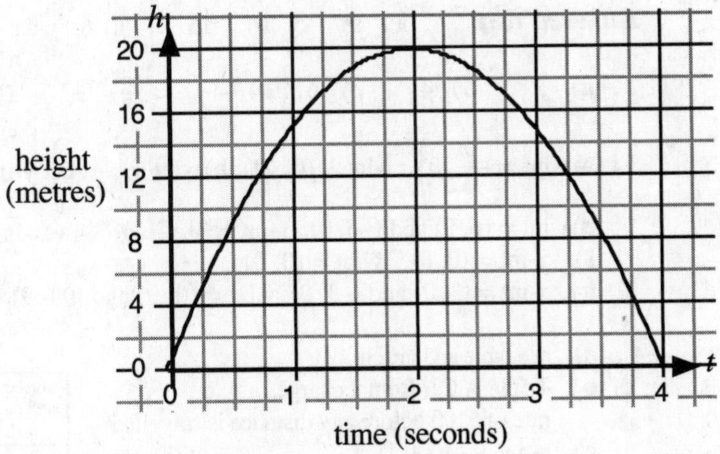

Use the graph to answer a – c:

a) Estimate, to the nearest metre, the maximum height of the football above the ground.

b) Estimate how long it takes for the football to reach the ground.

c) Estimate the height, to the nearest metre, of the football when it is in the air for 3 seconds.

d) Use the formula to calculate the exact answer to c).

e) Calculate the h-intercept, and describe what it represents in the context of the question.

Multiple Choice

8. In which of the following relations does the graph of the relation have x- and y-intercepts with equal values?

A. $y = x + 8$
B. $2x + 2y = 7$
C. $2x - 3y + 4 = 0$
D. none of the above

Numerical Response

9. The graph of the relation $4x^2 + 9y^2 - 36 = 0$ has x-intercepts a and b, and y-intercepts c and d. The value of the product $abcd$ is _____ .

(Record your answer in the numerical response box from left to right)

Answer Key **1.** **a)** −5 **b)** −15 c) 6 **d)** $\frac{1}{3}$ **e)** −30 **f)** 12.44

2. **a)** 2 **b)** 4 **c)** 6 **d)** $-\frac{5}{6}$ **e)** ±3 **f)** 4

3. **a)** x-int = $\left(-\frac{7}{4}, 0\right)$, y-int = (0. 7) **b)** x-int = $\left(\frac{5}{2}, 0\right)$ y-int = (0, 15) **c)** x-int = (−4, 0) y-int = (0, 8)

d) x-int = (6, 0) and (−6, 0), y-int = (0, −18) **e)** x-int = (5, 0) and (−5, 0) y-int = (0, 5) and (0, −5)

f) x-int = (0, 0), y-int = (0, 0) **g)** no x-int, y-int = (0, 4)

h) x-int = (3, 0) and (−3, 0) y-int = (0, 9) and (0, −9) **i)** x-int = (3,0) and (−3,0) no y-int

4. **a)** see table and graph
b) Triple A Car Rental charges a fixed rate of $100 before any distance is travelled
c) n–int = −1000, distance in this scenario cannot be represented by a negative value
d) **i)** $300 **ii)** $550
f) 5500 km

Number of km (n)	Total Rental Cost (T) dollars
0	100
1000	200
3500	450
5000	600

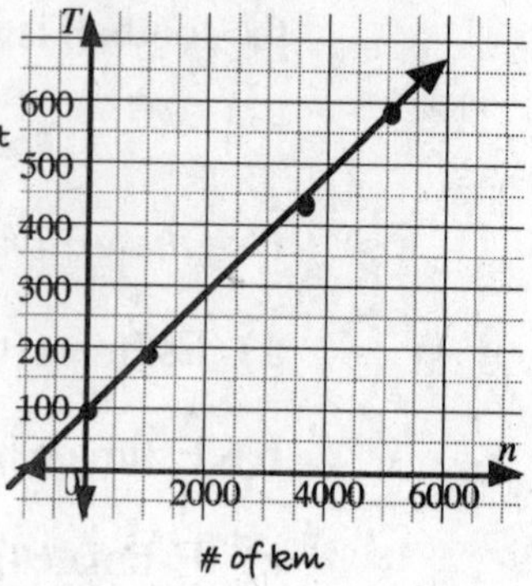

5. **a)** 45 m
b) see table and graph
c) non-linear
d) 5
e) The arrow was fired from a height of 25m above the ground
f) The number of seconds it takes to strike the ground.
g) **i)** approximately 44m
ii) 43.75
h) No to the left because time cannot be negative.
No to the right because the ground stops the arrow from going further.

time (seconds)	height (metres)
0	25
1	40
2	45
3	40
4	25
5	0

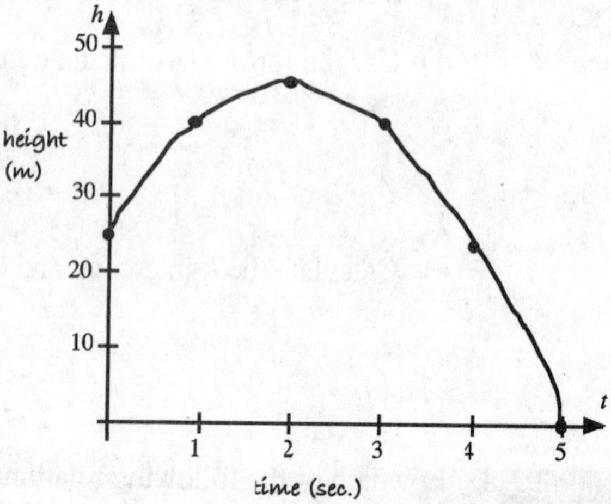

6. **a)** see table and graph
answers may vary
b) 12 cm
c) 6 hours
d) 2 cm
e) 2.5 hours

t	0	1	3	5
h	12	10	6	2

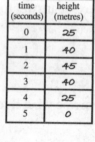

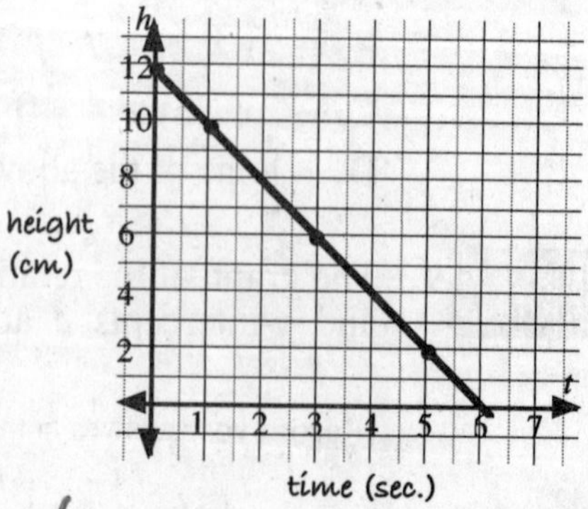

7. **a)** approx 20 m
b) approx 4 seconds
c) approx 15 m
d) 14.7 m
e) h–int is 0.6 m.
The football was punted 0.6 m above the ground.

8. B **9.**

3	6		

Relations and Functions Lesson #4:
Domain and Range

Review

Complete the following statements.

a) The x-intercept of a graph of a relation has a _____ coordinate with a value of zero.

b) The y-intercept of a graph of a relation has an _____ coordinate with a value of zero.

Domain and Range

The **domain** of a relation is the set of all possible values which can be used for the **input** of the **independent variable** (x).

The **range** of a relation is the set of all possible values of the **output** of the **dependent variable** (y).

In lesson 2 we described the relation in each of the following forms

- in words
- a table of values
- a set of ordered pairs
- a mapping (or arrow) diagram
- an equation
- a graph

In this lesson we will study the domain and range given in any of these forms.

Class Ex. #1

List the domain and range of the following set of ordered pairs.

a) (1, 2), (0, 5), (3, 8), (5, 9), (–3, 2)

b) (3, 3), (0, 3), (–3, 3), (2, 9), (–8, 3)

Class Ex. #2

In each case, state the domain and range of the relation represented by the graph.

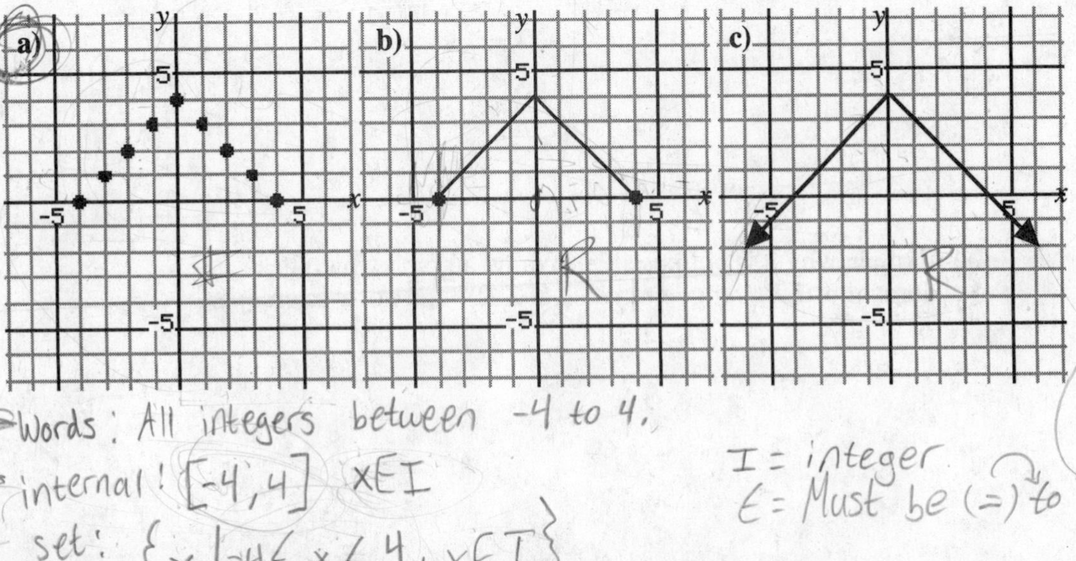

Class Ex. #3

State the domain and range of the following relations. R = Real I = integers.

a)

y [-3,

x ∈ R

y ≥ -3

$\{y \,|\, y \geq -3, y \in R\}$

b)

-2 +4

Radius = 7

$\{x \,|\, -2 \leq t \leq 4, x \in R\}$

c)

x y

1, 2, 3

2, 6

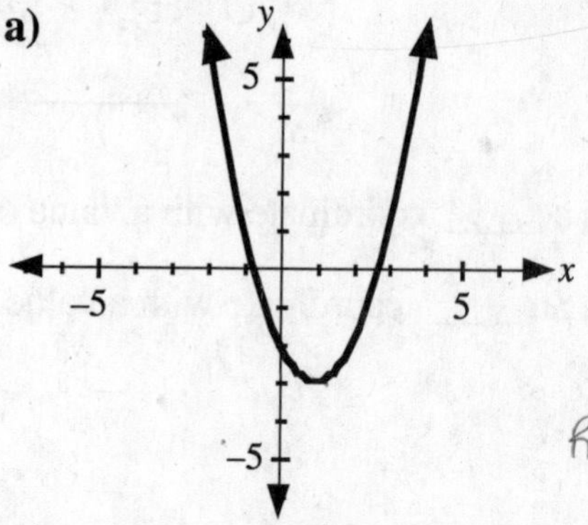

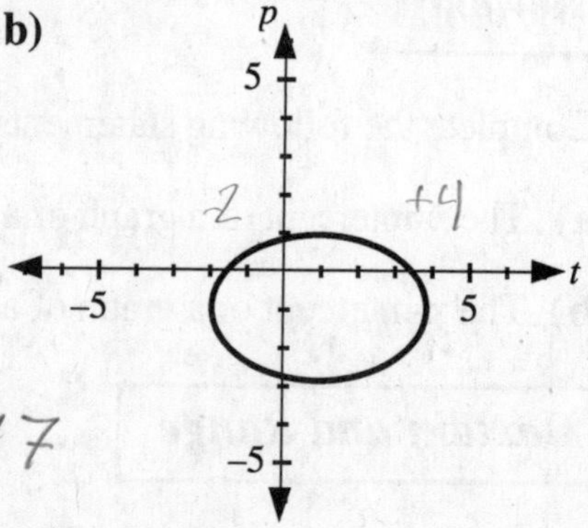

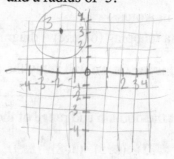

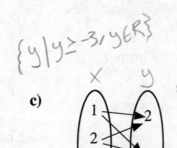

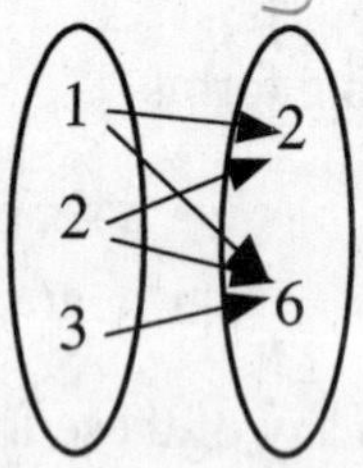

d) A circle with centre $(-2, 3)$ and a radius of 3.

Class Ex. #4

a) Draw the graph of a relation which has domain $x \in R$, range $\{y \,|\, y \leq 2, y \in R\}$ and

 i) only one x-intercept

 ii) two x-intercepts

b) Explain why it is not possible to draw a graph which has domain $x \in R$, range $\{y \,|\, y \leq 2, y \in R\}$ and no x-intercepts.

A high school football team is hosting a banquet to celebrate winning the championship.
The caterer charges a set up fee of $500 plus $20 per person.
The equation $C = 500 + 20n$ represents the cost of hosting the banquet for n people.

a) Make a table of values with 8 entries for a minimum of 100 and a maximum of 500 people.

n	C

b) Plot the eight ordered pairs from a) on the grid.

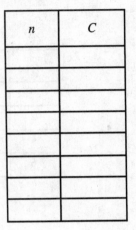

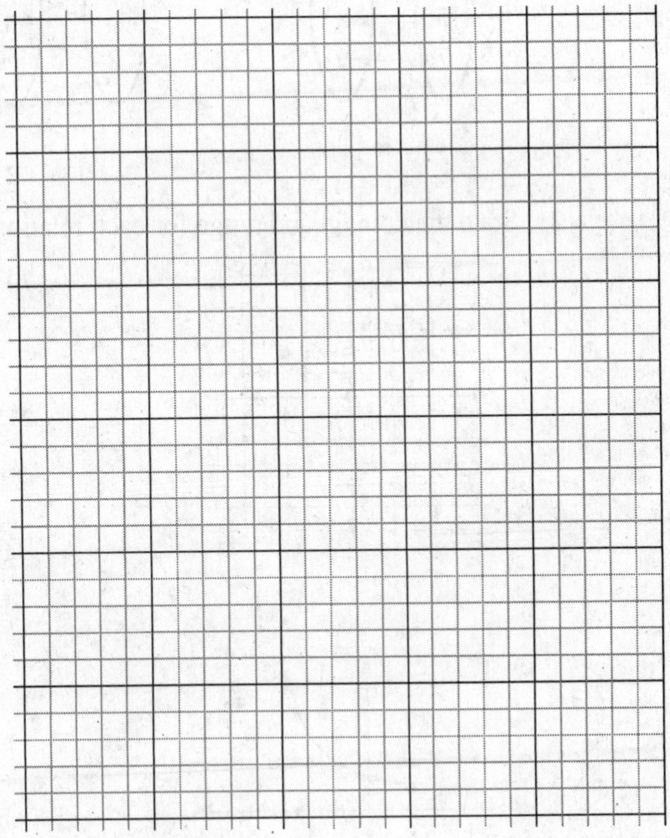

c) If all possible ordered pairs from b) were plotted on the grid, state the domain and range of the relation, and explain why there are restrictions on both.

Complete Assignment Questions #1 - #11

Assignment

1. State the domain and range of each relation.

a) (2, 3), (0, 2), (4, 8), (–1, 8), (–3, 1)

b) (–3, 3), (0, –5), (–3, 3), (5, –2), (–8, 1)

c)

Input (x)	Output (y)
0	3
2	4
4	5
6	3

d)

Input (x)	Output (y)
2	3
0	4
–3	5
2	6

e)

Input (x)	Output (y)
1	5
–1	5
3	5
7	5

f)

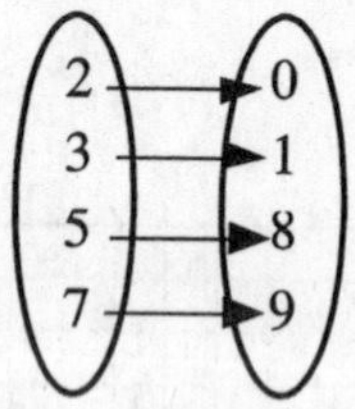

g)

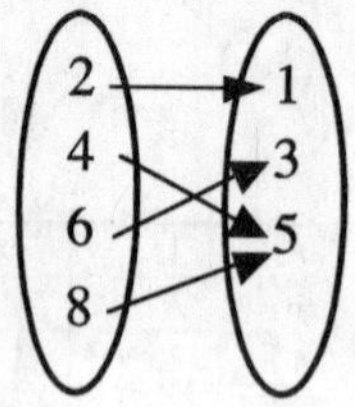

h)

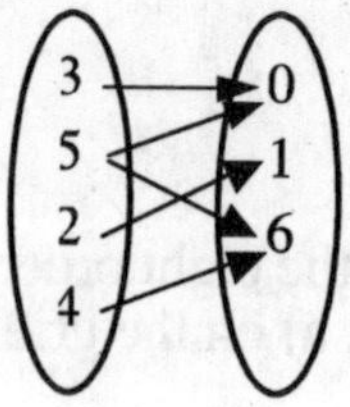

2. State the domain and range for each relation.

a)

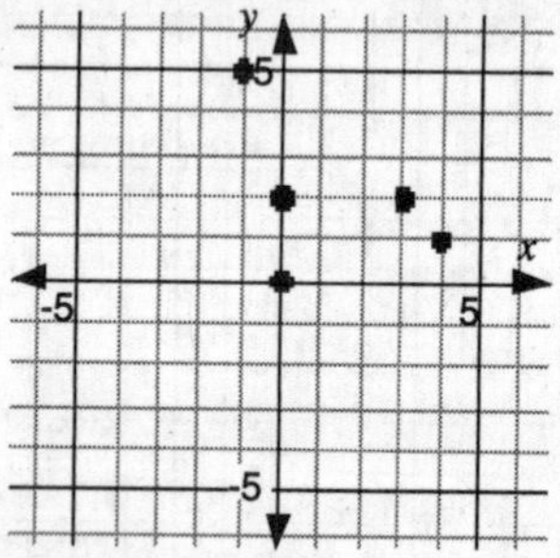

b)

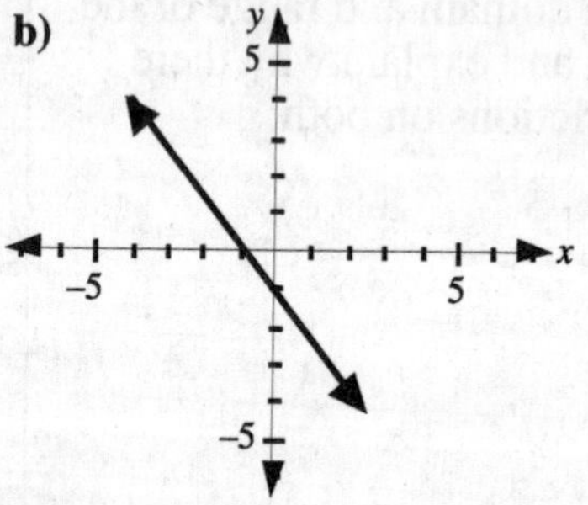

c)

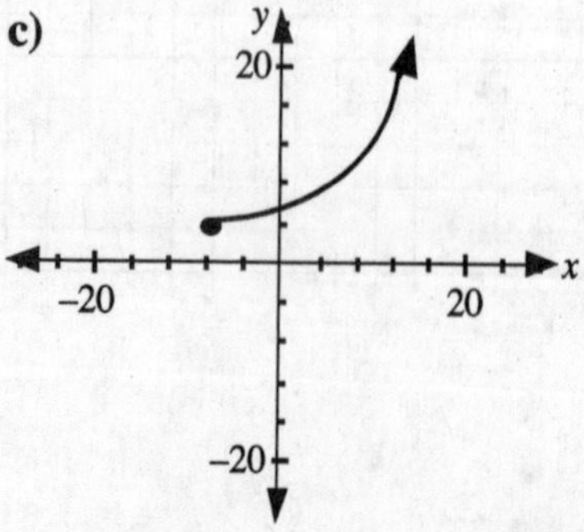

d)

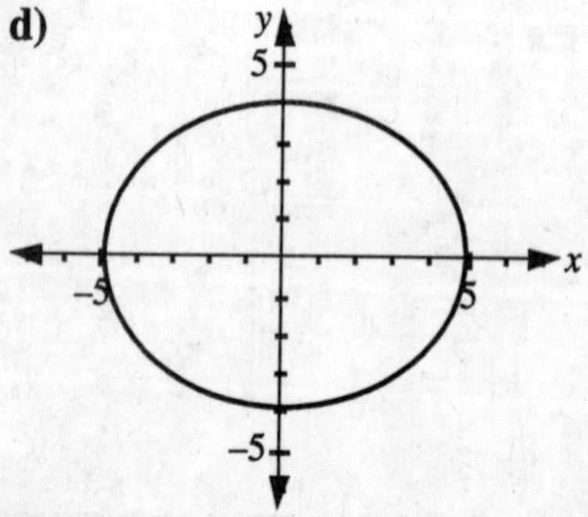

e)

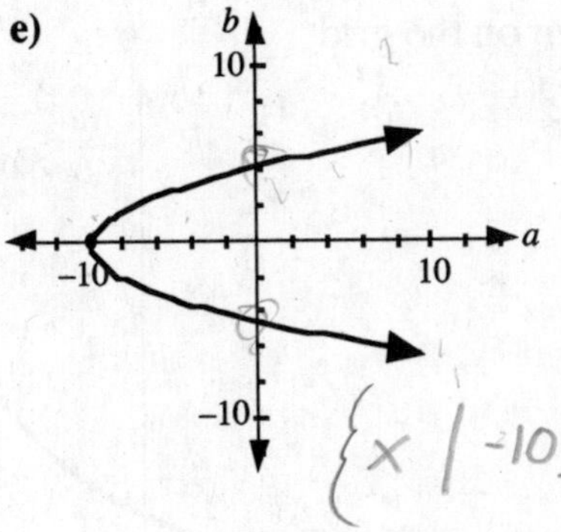

$\{x \mid -10 \leq x, x \in R\}$

$\{y \mid y \in R\}$

f)

$\{x \mid x \in R\}$

$\{y \mid 4 \geq y, y \in R\}$

g)

$\{y \mid 8 = y, y \in R\}$

$x \in R$

h)

$\{x \mid 5 > x, x \in R\}$

$\{y \mid 4 \geq y, y \in R\}$

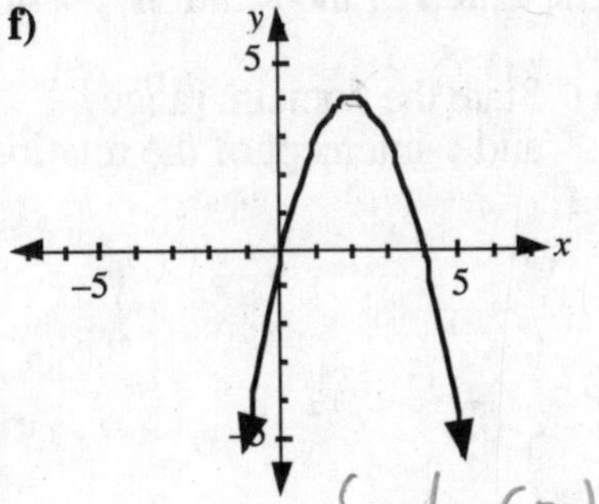

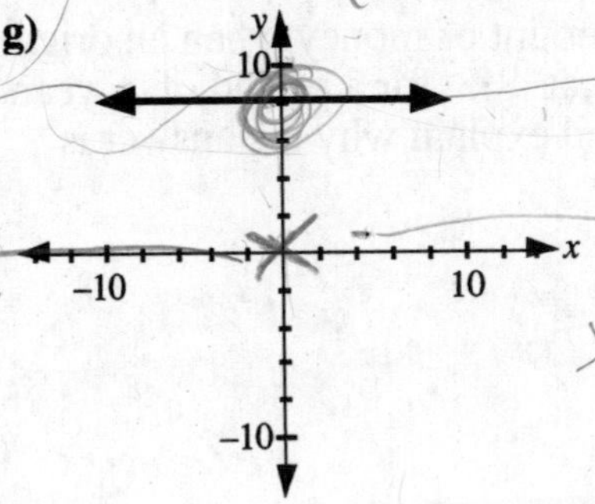

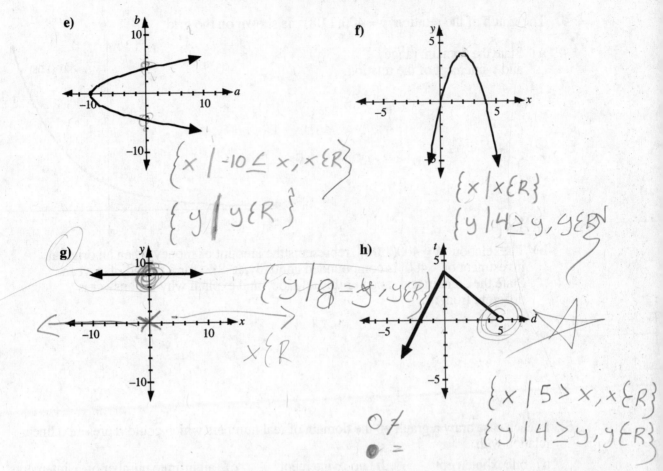

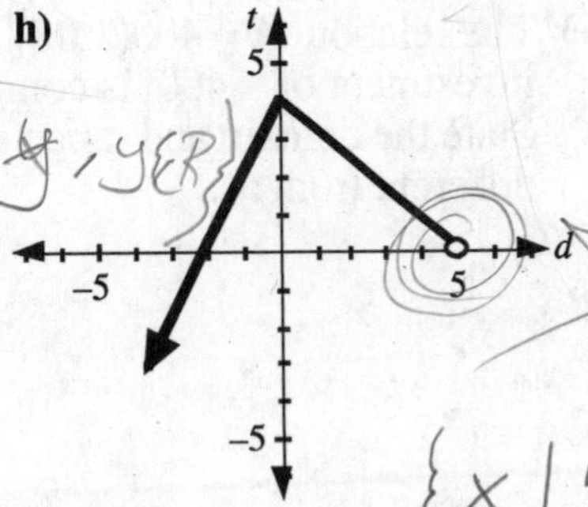

3. In each case a relation is graphed on a grid. State the domain and range of the relation if the graph is
 a) a circle whose centre is located at $(-1, 12)$ and has a radius of 5 units.

 b) a circle with centre $(-3, -5)$ and diameter 40 units.

 c) a rectangle with vertices $A(-8, 10)$, $B(-8, -2)$, $C(7, -2)$, and $D(7, 10)$.

 d) a triangle with vertices $T(-50, -75)$, $U(-35, -25)$, and $V(-65, -25)$.

4. The graph of the relation $y = 400(1.08)^x$ is shown on the grid.

a) State the domain, range, and y-intercept of the relation.

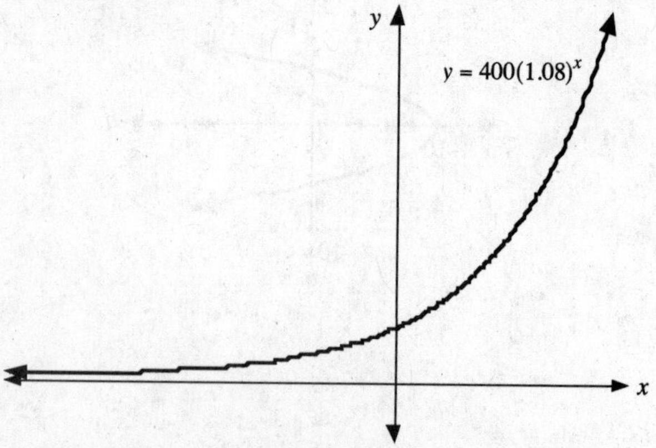

b) The relation $A = 400(1.08)^t$ represents the amount of money when an original investment of \$400 is compounded annually at 8% for a period of t years. State the domain and range of this relation, and explain why the answer is different from a).

5. In each case draw a graph on the domain of real numbers which could represent a linear relation with

a) one x-intercept

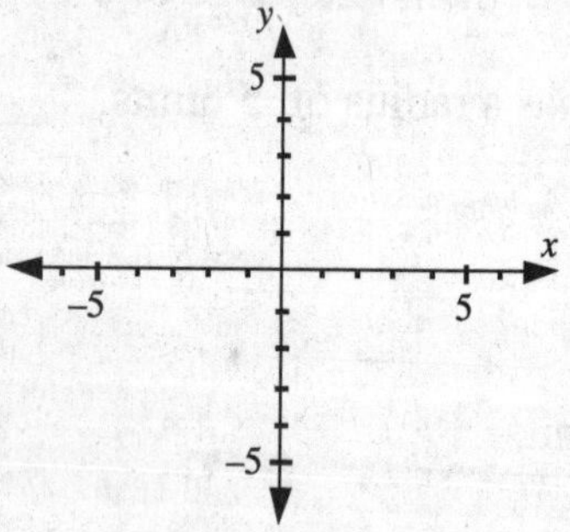

b) no x-intercept

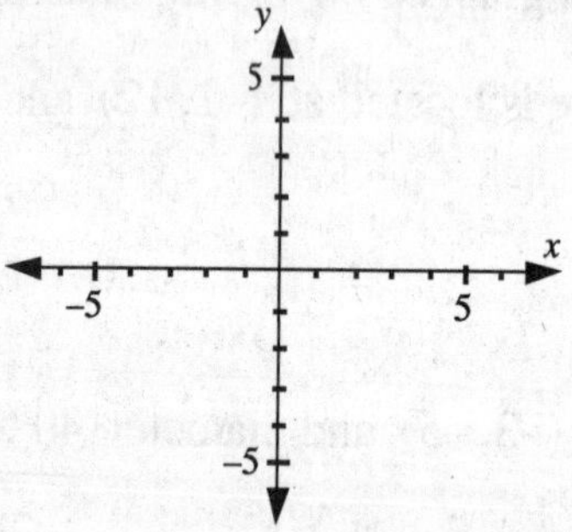

c) an infinite number of x-intercepts.

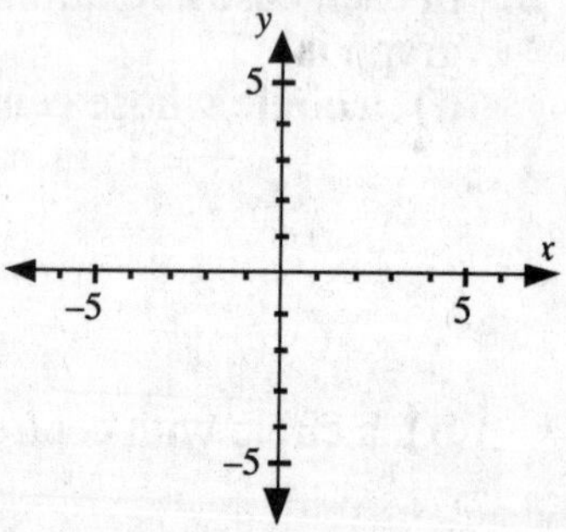

6. In each case draw a graph of a non linear relation with

a) domain $x \in R$, range $y \geq -3, y \in R$
two x-intercepts and one y-intercept

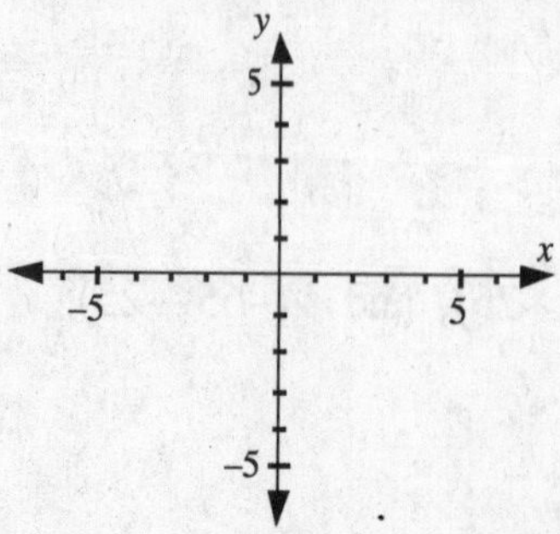

b) domain $x \in R$, range $y \geq -3, y \in R$
one x-intercept and one y-intercept.

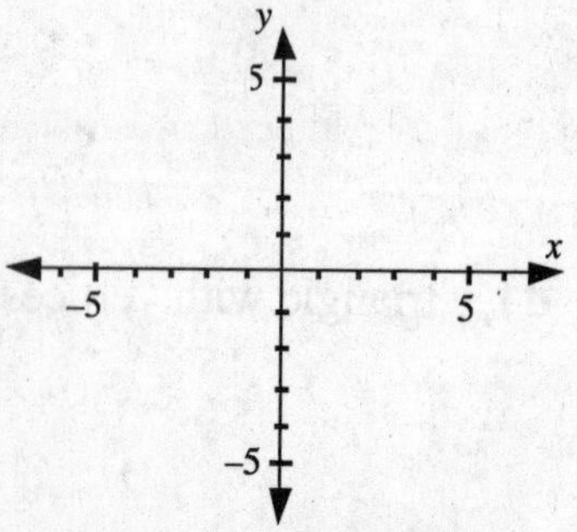

7. The graph shows the flight of Pamela's golf ball from the tee to a sand trap at the edge of the green.

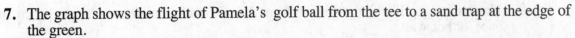

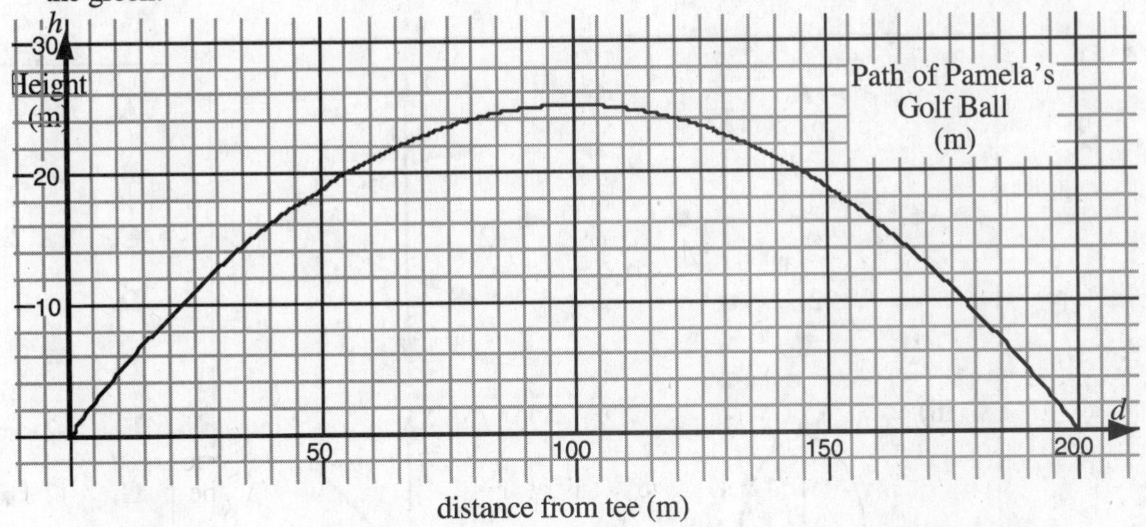

a) State the h-intercept and the d-intercepts of the graph, and explain their significance in relation to the question.

b) State the maximum height of the golf ball, and explain its relevance to the domain or range of the relation.

c) State the domain and range of the relation.

d) Estimate from the graph the horizontal distance the ball has travelled when it is 20 m in the air. Explain why there are two answers.

e) Estimate from the graph the height of the golf ball when the horizontal distance from the tee is 80 m.

f) Give a brief description of the relationship between the height of the golf ball and the horizontal distance from the tee.

8. Match each graph with the domain from A to F. Each domain may be used once, more than once, or not at all.

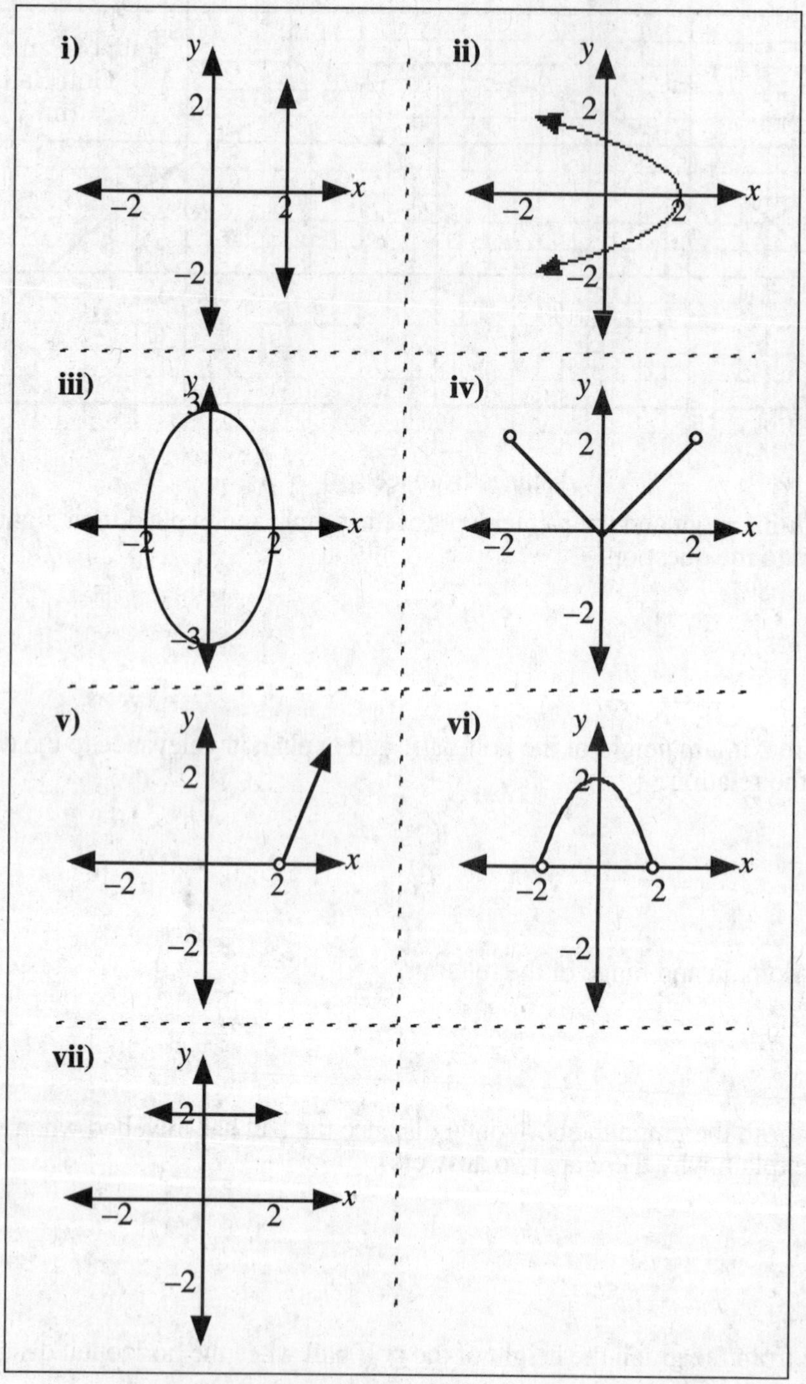

A. $x = 2$

B. $x < 2$

C. $x \leq 2$

D. $x > 2$

E. $x \geq 2$

F. $-2 < x < 2$

G. $-2 \leq x \leq 2$

H. $2 < x < -2$

I. $x \in R$

Multiple Choice **9.** The graphs of two relations are shown. Which of the following statements is true?

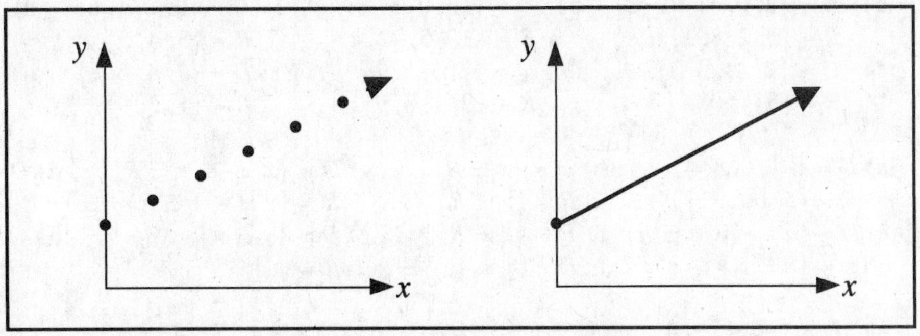

A. The domains are the same, but the ranges are different.
B. The ranges are the same, but the domains are different.
C. The domains are the same, and the ranges are the same.
D. The domains are different, and the ranges are different.

10. The graphs of two relations are shown. Which of the following statements is true?

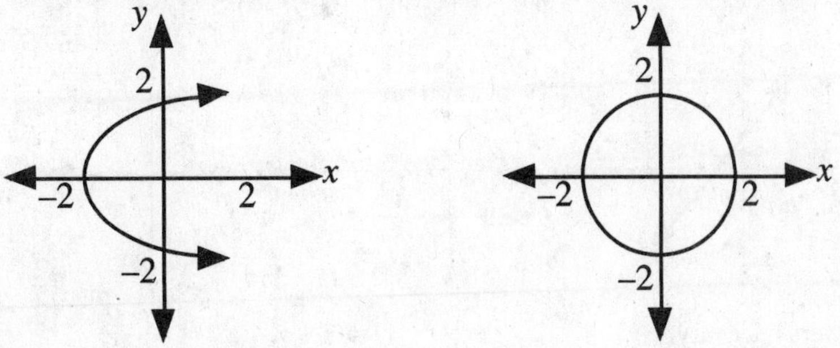

A. The range of each relation is $-2 \le y \le 2$.
B. The range of each relation is $y \in R$.
C. The domain of each relation is $-2 \le x \le 2$.
D. None of the above.

Numerical Response **11.** The relation between the distance travelled, d km, and the cost, C dollars, of renting a truck is given by the formula $C = 60 + 0.27d$. The domain of the relation can be expressed in the form $d \ge x$, and the range can be expressed in the form $C \ge y$. Write the value of y in the first two boxes and the value of x in the last two boxes.

(Record your answer in the numerical response box from left to right)

Answer Key

1. a) $D = \{2, 0, 4, -1, -3\}$ $R = \{3, 2, 8, 1\}$ b) $D = \{-3, 0, 5, -8\}$ $R = \{3, -5, -2, 1\}$ c) $D = \{0, 2, 4, 6\}$ $R = \{3, 4, 5\}$ d) $D = \{2, 0, -3\}$ $R = \{3, 4, 5, 6\}$
   e) $D = \{1, -1, 3, 7\}$ $R = \{5\}$ f) $D = \{2, 3, 5, 7\}$ $R = \{0, 1, 8, 9\}$ g) $D = \{2, 4, 6, 8\}$ $R = \{1, 3, 5\}$ h) $D = \{3, 5, 2, 4\}$ $R = \{0, 1, 6\}$

2. a) $D = \{-1, 0, 3, 4\}$ $R = \{5, 0, 2, 1\}$ b) $D = \{x \in R\}$ $R = \{y \in R\}$ c) $D = \{x \geq -8, x \in R\}$ $R = \{y \geq 4, y \in R\}$ d) $D = \{-5 \leq x \leq 5, x \in R\}$ $R = \{-4 \leq y \leq 4, y \in R\}$
   e) $D = \{a \geq -10, a \in R\}$ $R = \{b \in R\}$ f) $D = \{x \in R\}$ $R = \{y \leq 4, y \in R\}$ g) $D = \{x \in R\}$ $R = \{8\}$ h) $D = \{d < 5, d \in R\}$ $R = \{t \leq 4, t \in R\}$

3. a) $D = \{-6 \leq x \leq 4, x \in R\}$ $R = \{7 \leq y \leq 17, y \in R\}$ b) $D = \{-23 \leq x \leq 17, x \in R\}$ $R = \{-25 \leq y \leq 15, y \in R\}$
   c) $D = \{-8 \leq x \leq 7, x \in R\}$ $R = \{-2 \leq y \leq 10, y \in R\}$ d) $D = \{-65 \leq x \leq -35, x \in R\}$ $R = \{-75 \leq y \leq -25, y \in R\}$

4. a) $D = \{x \in R\}$ $R = \{y > 0, y \in R\}$, y–int is 400
   b) $D = \{t \geq 0, t \in R\}$ different from a) because time is never a negative value.
   $R = \{A \geq 400, A \in R\}$ different from a) because the amount of money can never be less than $400.

5. Answers may vary.

a)

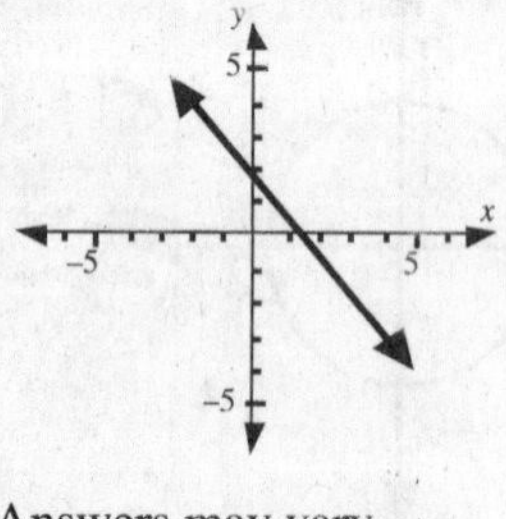

b)

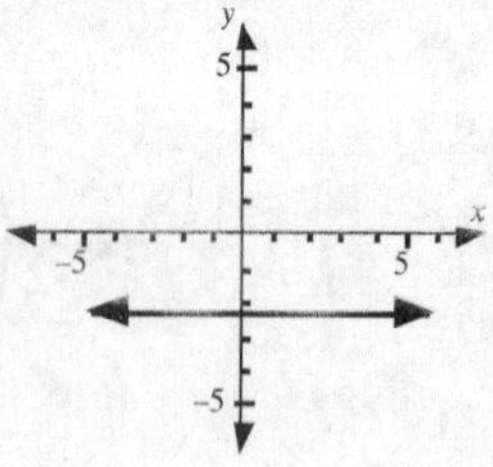

c)

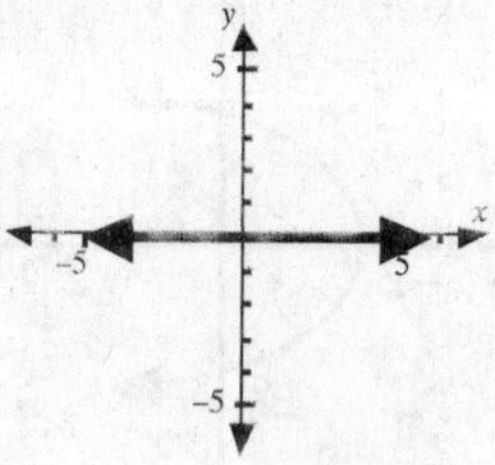

6. Answers may vary.

a)

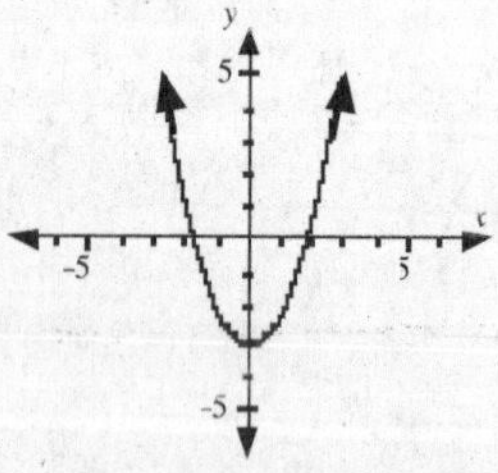

b)

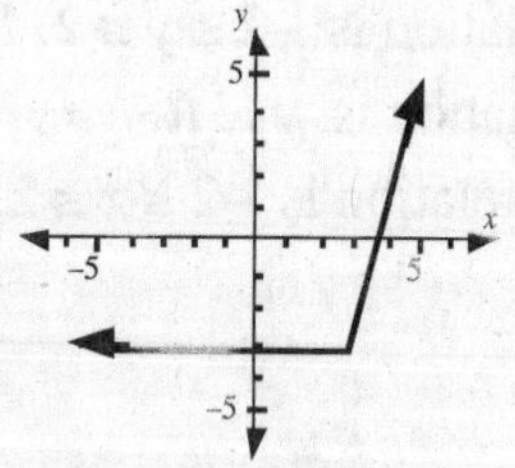

7. a) h–int = 0, d–int = 0 and 200. On the tee the ball is on the ground.
   It returns to ground level 200 m from the tee.
   b) max height = 25 m. The maximum height is the upper limit of the range.
   c) $D = \{0 \leq d \leq 200, d \in R\}$ $R = \{0 \leq h \leq 25, h \in R\}$
   d) 55 m from the tee when the ball is rising and 145m from the tee when the ball is descending.
   e) 24 m
   f) Starting from a height of 0 m at the tee, the golf ball increases in height to a maximum height of 25m, 100 m from the tee. Then the golf ball starts decreasing in height until it hits the ground 200 m from the tee.

8. i) A ii) C iii) G iv) F v) D vi) F vii) I

9. D 10. D 11.

6	0	0	0

Relations and Functions Lesson #5:
Relations and the Graphing Calculator

- Although features of different types of graphing calculators may be similar to each other, the instructions in this unit refer to the TI-83/TI-84 series of graphing calculators.
- This lesson takes more than one class to complete.

Preparing the Calculator to Graph

Confirm that the calculator is in "Function" mode as shown.
Press MODE and use the cursor keys to navigate to the proper settings, and then press ENTER .

```
Normal Sci Eng
Float 0123456789
Radian Degree
Func Par Pol Seq
Connected Dot
Sequential Simul
Real a+bi
Full Horiz G-T
```

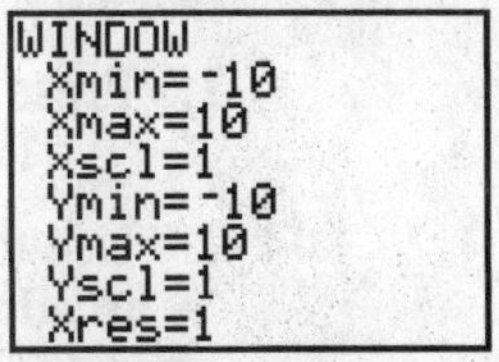

Set the display window of the calculator as shown.
Press WINDOW and use the cursor keys to navigate to the proper settings, and then press ENTER , or press ZOOM 6 .

```
WINDOW
Xmin=-10
Xmax=10
Xscl=1
Ymin=-10
Ymax=10
Yscl=1
Xres=1
```

Set the format of the calculator as shown.
Press 2nd ZOOM and use the cursor keys to navigate to the proper settings, and then press ENTER .

```
RectGC PolarGC
CoordOn CoordOff
GridOff GridOn
AxesOn AxesOff
LabelOff LabelOn
ExprOn ExprOff
```

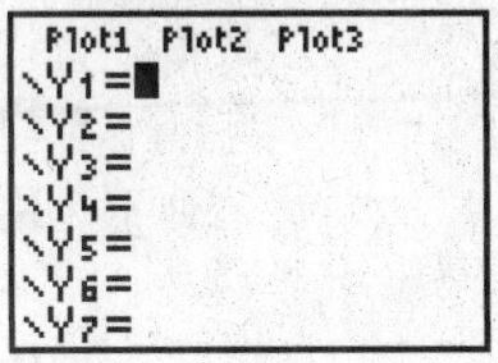

Press Y= to confirm that the "Y= editor" window is as shown.
If Plot1, Plot2, or Plot3 are highlighted in black, then you must turn them off by scrolling to Plot1, Plot2, or Plot3 and pressing ENTER .

```
Plot1 Plot2 Plot3
\Y1=
\Y2=
\Y3=
\Y4=
\Y5=
\Y6=
\Y7=
```

The relation with equation $y = -1.25x + 15$ is used throughout most of this lesson to illustrate some features of the graphing calculator.

Entering and Graphing a Relation using a Graphing Calculator

The following procedure may be used to display the graph of $y = -1.25x + 15$.

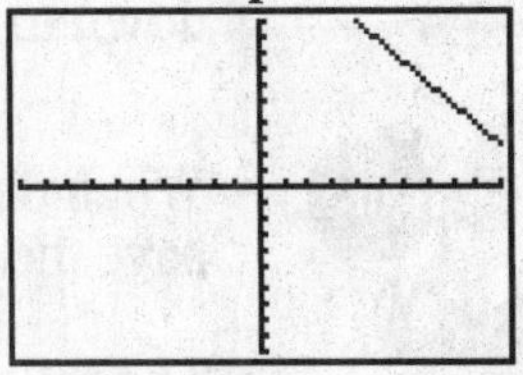

1. Access the "Y= editor" by pressing the Y= key.

2. Enter the equation in Y_1. (Write the equation in terms of the dependent variable if necessary).

3. Press the GRAPH key to display the graph.

Step 3
```
Plot1 Plot2 Plot3
\Y1=-1.25X+15
\Y2=
\Y3=
\Y4=
\Y5=
\Y6=
\Y7=
```

Step 4

Notice that the window we have chosen in this example does not allow us to see much of the graph. We need to alter the window setting to see the main features of the graph.

Using the Window and Zoom Features

Sometimes the standard display setting shown below does not allow us to see the behaviour of specific portions of a graph. For instance, if we wanted to see where the graph of $y = -1.25x + 15$ crosses the x-axis and the y-axis, we need to adjust the window settings of the calculator.

WINDOW	
Xmin=-10	**Minimum value** seen on the screen for x
Xmax=10	**Maximum value** seen on the screen for x
Xscl=1	**Scale for x-axis** - The increments of the tic marks for x
Ymin=-10	**Minimum value** seen on the screen for y
Ymax=10	**Maximum value** seen on the screen for y
Yscl=1	**Scale for y-axis** - The increments of the tic marks for y
Xres=1	**Resolution:** 1 is best screen resolution. Leave at 1

The following procedure may be used to adjust the window settings:

1. Press the `WINDOW` key.

2. Use the cursor to enter in appropriate values to adjust the Cartesian plane and press the `GRAPH` key.

```
WINDOW
 Xmin=-5
 Xmax=20
 Xscl=5
 Ymin=-10
 Ymax=25
 Yscl=5
 Xres=1
```

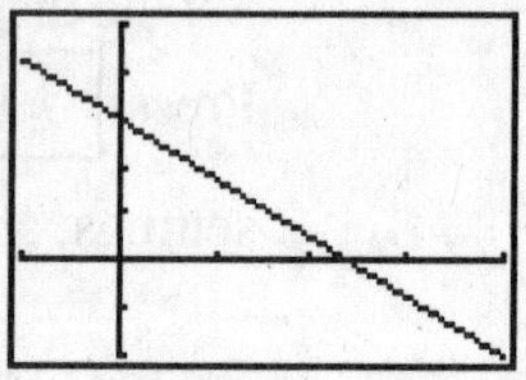

- An alternative method to "fit" the graph of an equation on the display screen is to use the `Zoom Out` feature of a graphing calculator. Although it may not give the exact window settings we would like, it can give a good first approximation.

  - Press the `ZOOM` `3` (or scroll down to `Zoom Out` and press `GRAPH`). Keep doing this until you see the graph.
  - Press `WINDOW` to see the new settings. Adjust the window.

- Another method to "fit" the graph of an equation on the display screen is to use the `ZoomFit` feature of a graphing calculator. Although it may not give the exact window settings we would like, it can also give a good first approximation.
- Press `ZOOM` `0` (or scroll down to `ZoomFit` and press `ENTER`).
- The standard display settings (as shown in the window at the top of this page) of a graphing calculator can be quickly entered by pressing `ZOOM` `6` (or scroll down to `ZStandard` and press `ENTER`).

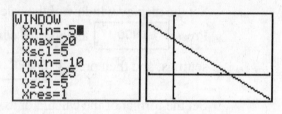

- When displaying a graph on the calculator, it is generally a good idea to have the x- and y- intercepts of the graph visible.

- The following notation is used to write a graphing calculator window.

  x:$[x_{min}, x_{max}, x_{scl}]$ y:$[y_{min}, y_{max}, y_{scl}]$

  For example, the window settings used above in step 1 can be written:

  x:$[-5, 20, 5]$ y:$[-10, 25, 5]$

Displaying the Table of Values for an Equation

The table of values feature may be used to display the ordered pairs of a relation defined by an equation. Before using this feature, we will need to set up the table using the table setup feature.

Accessing the Table Set Up Feature

- Press $\boxed{\text{2nd}}$ $\boxed{\text{WINDOW}}$ keys to access TBLSET. The illustration describes the features.

The value where the table starts.
The increments of the input.

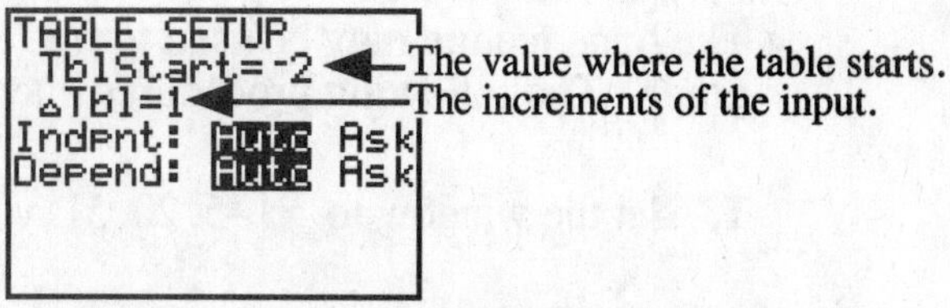

- This will lead us to a table of values starting with $x = -2$ and increasing in units of 1.

Accessing the Table of Values

- Press $\boxed{\text{2nd}}$ $\boxed{\text{GRAPH}}$ keys to access the table feature of the calculator.
We can use the cursor keys to scroll up and down the table to determine the value of y for any given value of x.

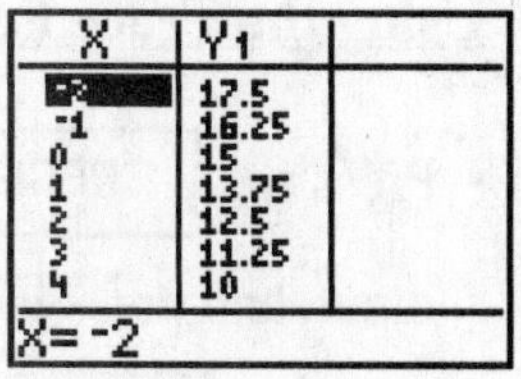

If a value of x which would require continous cursoring is used, for example $x = 400$, a quicker method of calculating the value of y is to use the following procedure.

- Access TBLSET feature and change Indpnt to Ask,
- Return to the table of values, type in 400, and press $\boxed{\text{ENTER}}$.

Accessing the Table of Values and the Graph Simultaneously

Return to Table Set Up as on the top of this page.

1. Press the $\boxed{\text{MODE}}$ key, scroll down and across to "G-T", and then press $\boxed{\text{ENTER}}$ and $\boxed{\text{GRAPH}}$.

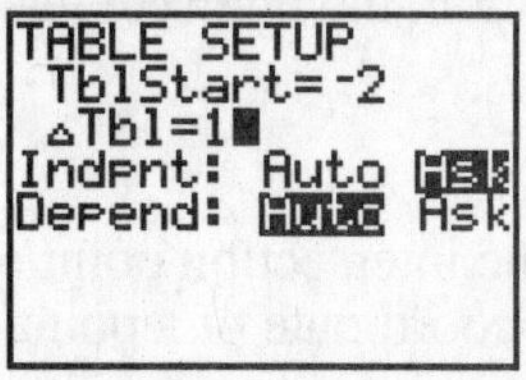

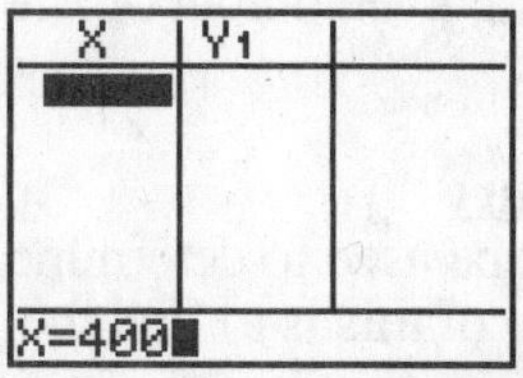

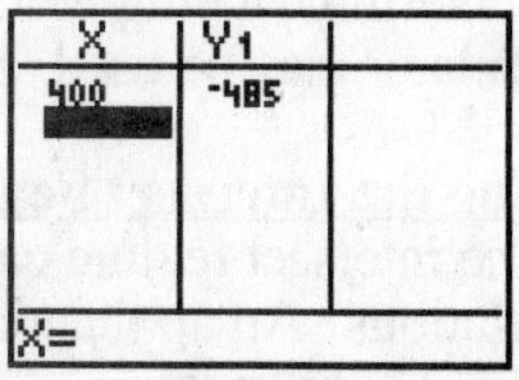

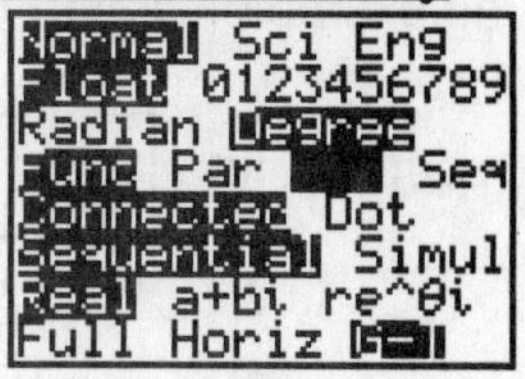

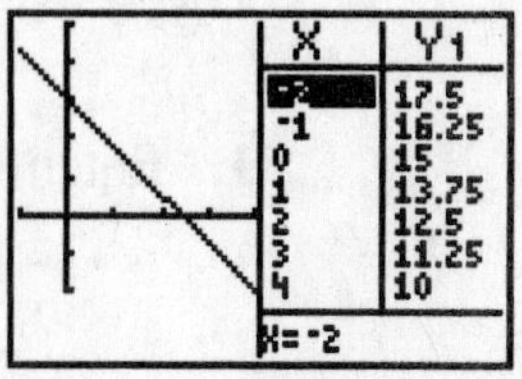

2. Switching between the graph and table of values can be done by pressing the $\boxed{\text{GRAPH}}$ key and the $\boxed{\text{2nd}}$ $\boxed{\text{GRAPH}}$ keys.

3. Using the $\boxed{\text{TRACE}}$ key in the G-T mode allows us to scroll along the graph and up and down the table of values at the same time (use the left and right arrow keys).

Complete Assignment Question #1

Finding the y- coordinate of a Point on the Graph of a Relation

To determine the output for a given input of a relation, the trace feature of a graphing calculator may be used.

Using the Trace Feature to Move Along the Graph

Return to Full screen.

The trace feature may be used to find the coordinates of points on the graph. The following procedures may be used.

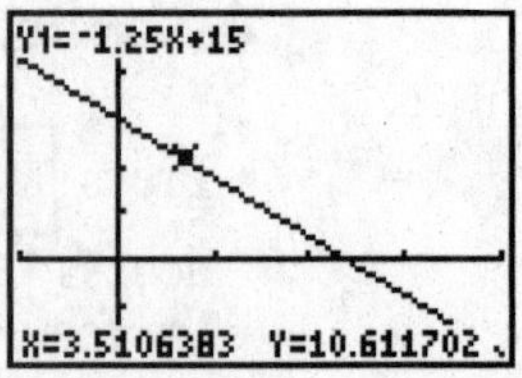

1. Set the window to x:[−5, 20, 5] y:[−10, 25, 5]

2. Press the `TRACE` key and use the scroll keys to move along the graph.

Using the Trace Feature to Determine the Value of *y* for a Given Value of *x*

- Press the `TRACE` key. Enter a value for the input, and press `ENTER`. For example, pressing `TRACE` `4` `ENTER` will calculate the value y when $x = 4$.
  The answer `Y = 10` will be displayed on the bottom right.

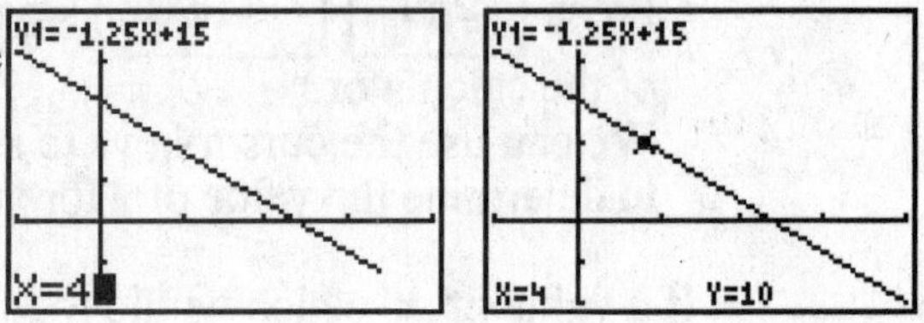

Finding the x- coordinate of a Point on the Graph of a Relation

To determine the input for a given output of a relation, the intersect feature of a graphing calculator may be used.

Using the Intersect Feature

- The intersect feature can be used to determine the intersection point of the graphs of two relations. An application of this is to find the *y*-coordinate of a point on a graph given the *x*-coordinate.

- As a working example we will find the *x*-coordinate of $y = -1.25x + 15$ when $y = 8$.

1. Enter the equation into `Y1`.

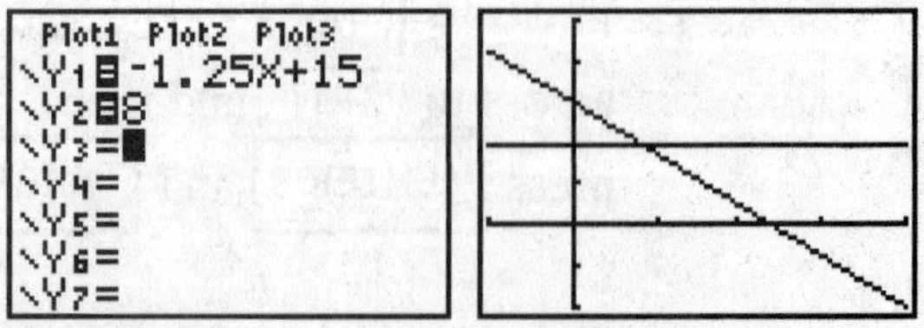

2. Enter the given value of *y* into `Y2`.

Press `GRAPH`, and adjust the window if necessary.

3. Access the CALC menu by entering `2nd` then `TRACE`.

4. Select the "`intersect`" feature.

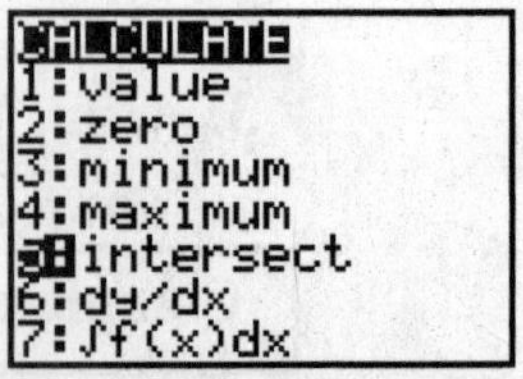

5. On the bottom left-hand side of the screen, the calculator will ask for the `First curve?` .

Scroll close to the intersection point, and press [ENTER] .

The values of x and y will vary depending on how close we scroll to the intersection point.

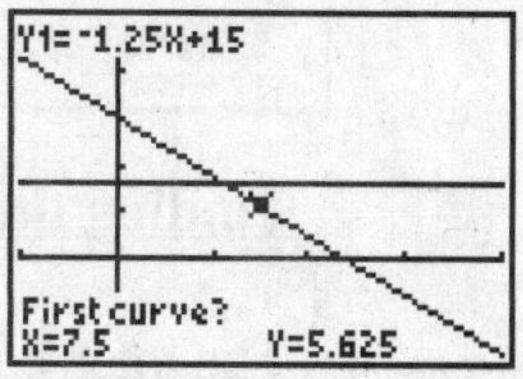

6. On the bottom left-hand side of the screen, the calculator will ask for a `Second curve?` .

Scroll close to the intersection point, and press [ENTER] .

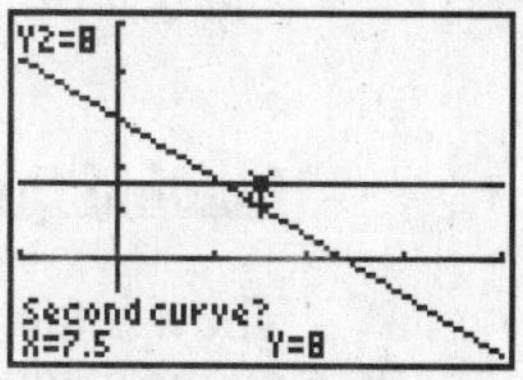

7. On the bottom left-hand side of the screen, the calculator will ask to `Guess?` .

Press [ENTER] .

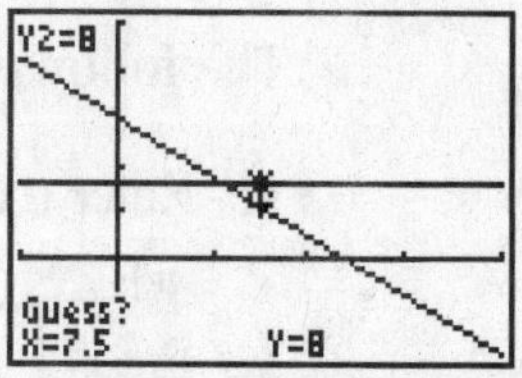

8. The x and y values of the intersection point will be displayed. In this example the intersection point is $(5.6, 8)$.

The answer to the question is $x = 5.6$.

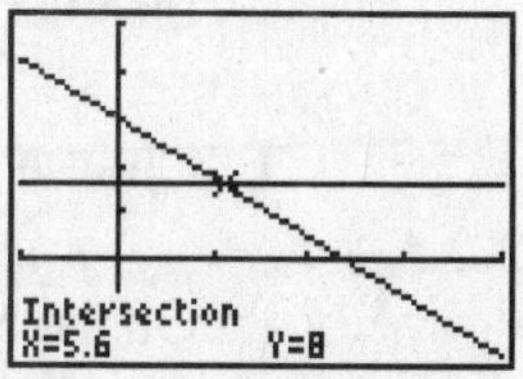

Class Ex. #1

Consider the equation $y = 2x - 25$.

a) Use a graphing calculator to sketch the graph on the grid provided. Write a suitable window.

x:[, ,] y:[, ,]

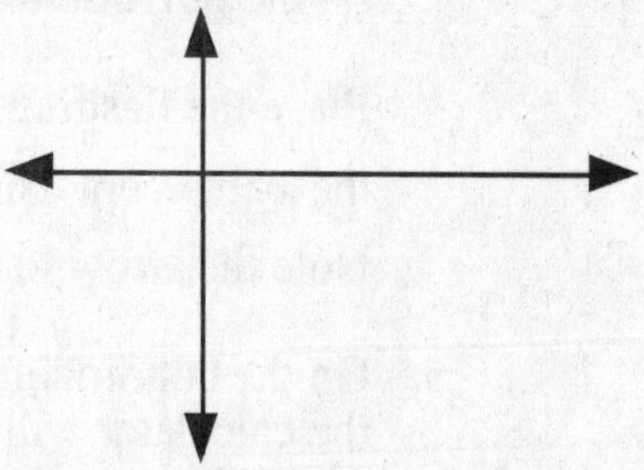

b) Use a graphing calculator to determine the value of y when $x = 4.5$.

c) Algebraically verify the answer in b).

d) Use a graphing calculator to determine the value of x when $y = -6.4$.

e) Algebraically verify the answer in d).

Complete Assignment Questions #2 - #5

Using a Graphing Calculator to Determine x-intercepts

Finding the *x*-intercept using the Intersect Feature

The intersect feature may be used to find the x-intercept by using the equation $y = 0$ for Y_2 and determining the intersection point of the graph and x-axis.

Finding the *x*-intercept using the Zero Feature

The x-intercept(s) on the graph of a relation can be determined using the **zero** feature on the calculator.

The following procedure may be used to determine the x-intercept on the graph .

1. Enter the equation in Y_1 ($y = -1.25x + 15$, x:[–5, 20, 5], y:[–10, 25, 5]).

2. Press [2nd] [TRACE] keys to access the CALCULATE (CALC) menu.

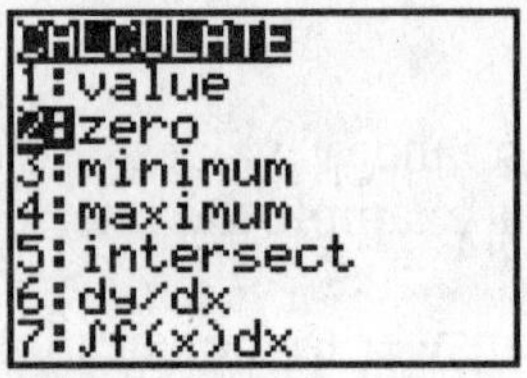

3. Choose 2:zero, and press [ENTER] .

4. On the bottom left-hand side of the screen, the calculator will ask for a LeftBound? . The calculator is asking us to put the cursor on the **left side of the *x*-intercept.**

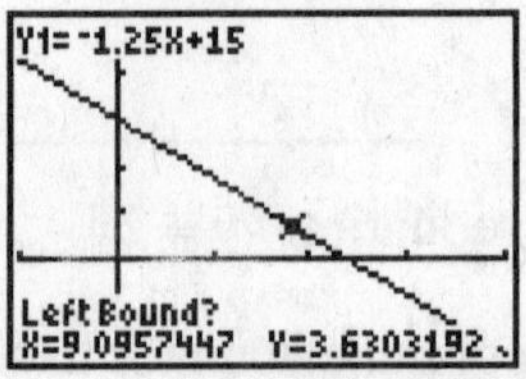

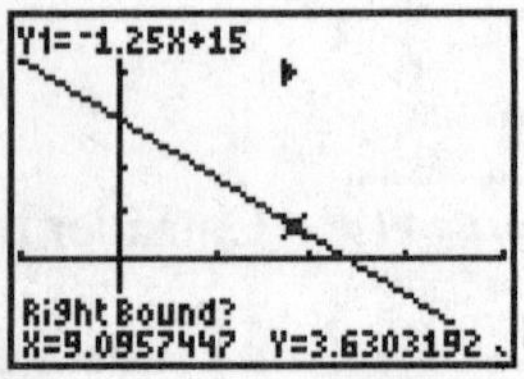

Place the flashing cursor on the left side of the x-intercept using the left and right cursor keys. Press [ENTER] . Note the arrow to the left and above the graph on the screen.

5. On the bottom left-hand side of the screen, the calculator will ask for a RightBound? . The calculator is asking us to put the cursor on the **right side of the *x*-intercept.**

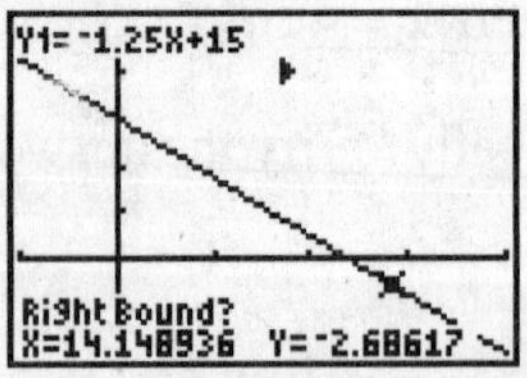

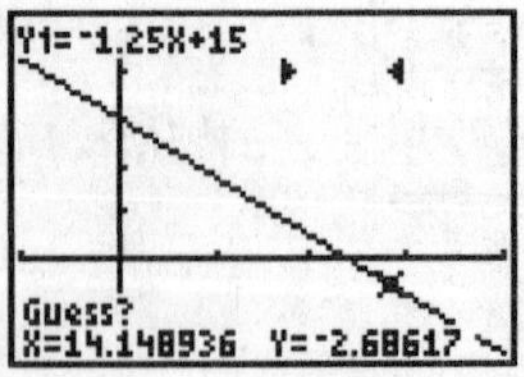

Place the flashing cursor on the right side of the x-intercept using the left and right cursor keys. Press [ENTER] . Note the second arrow to the right and above the graph on the screen.

6. On the bottom left-hand side of the screen, the calculator will ask to Guess? .

Press [ENTER] .

The x value will be the x-intercept.

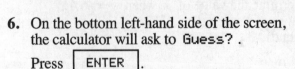

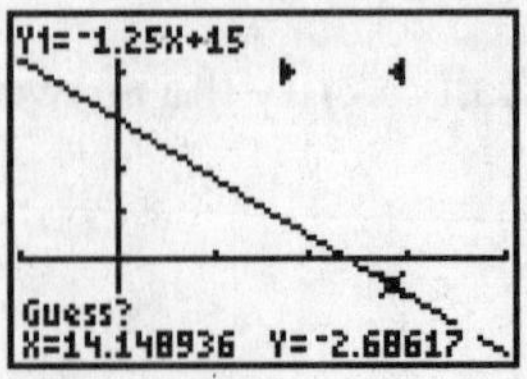

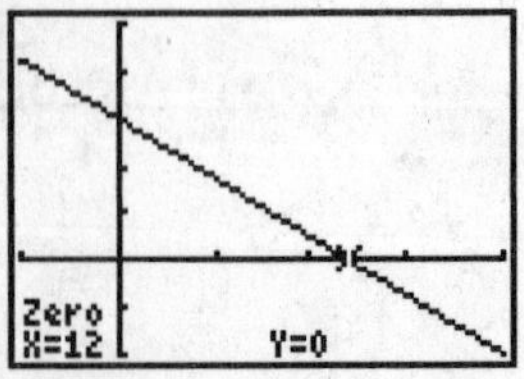

Using a Graphing Calculator to Determine y-intercepts

Finding the *y*-intercept using the Trace Feature

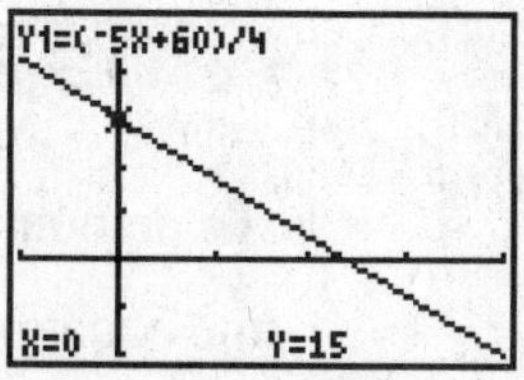

1. Enter the equation in Y_1, and adjust the window to appropriate settings to display the *x*- and *y*-intercepts.

2. Press the `TRACE` key. Press `0` for the input, and then press `ENTER` for the output.

Finding the *y*-intercept using the Value Feature

1. Enter the equation in Y_1, and adjust the window to appropriate settings to display the *x*- and *y*-intercepts.

2. Press `2nd` `TRACE` keys to access the `CALCULATE` (`CALC`) menu.

3. Choose `1:value`, and press `ENTER` `0` `ENTER`.

Finding the *y*-intercept using the Table Feature

Use the procedure described earlier to find y when $x = 0$.

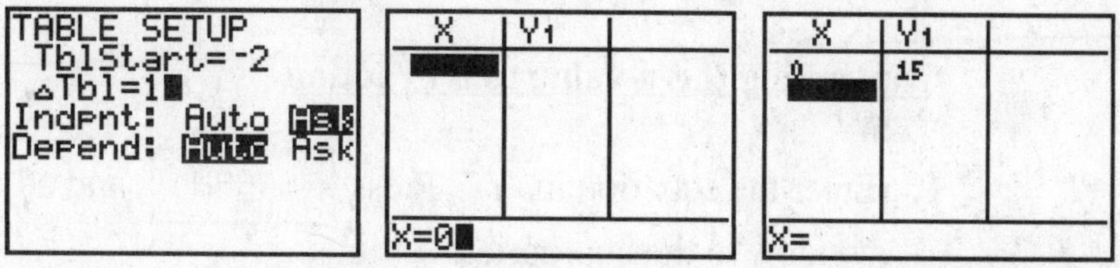

In each case use the features of a graphing calculator to calculate the *x*- and *y*-intercepts of the graphs of the relation.

a) $y = \dfrac{5x + 15}{3}$

b) $y = -x^2 + x + 6$

Converting a Decimal to a Fraction from a Graph Display

If the x- or y-intercept is not an integer, the graphing display will give the answer in decimal form. The following procedure may be used to write the decimal as an improper fraction (if applicable).

To demonstrate the procedure we will determine the x- and y-intercepts of the graph of the equation $y = \frac{(2x - 11)}{7}$.

Converting the x-value to a Fraction

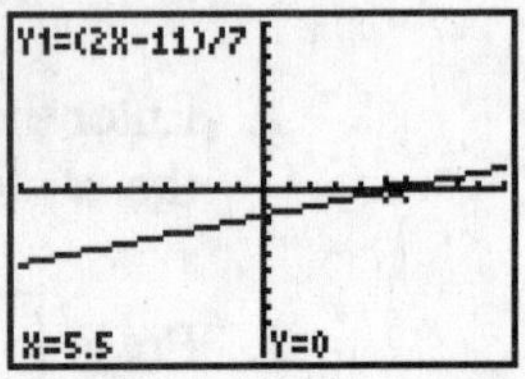

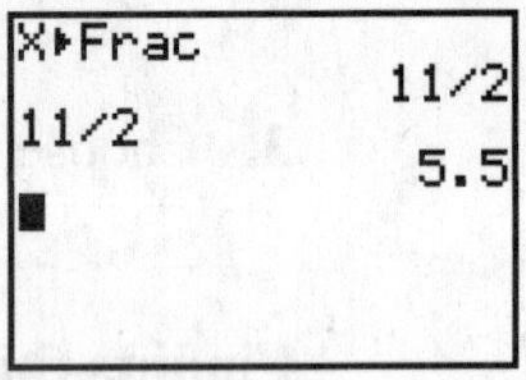

1. Enter the equation in Y_1. Press GRAPH , and adjust the window to the appropriate settings.
2. Find the x-intercept using the zero feature.
3. Press 2nd QUIT to exit the graph display.
4. Press X,T,θ,n MATH ENTER ENTER .
   The decimal value may be verified by dividing the fraction.

Converting the y-value to a Fraction

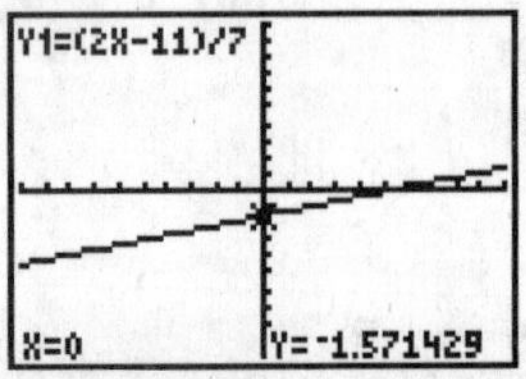

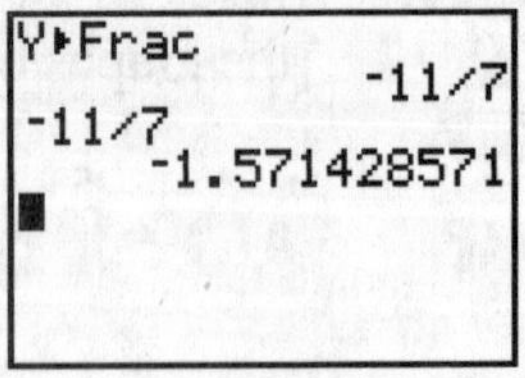

1. Enter the equation in Y_1. Press GRAPH , and adjust the window to the appropriate settings.
2. Find the y-intercept using the trace or value feature.
3. Press 2nd QUIT to exit the graph display.
4. Press ALPHA 1 to access the letter Y, and then press MATH ENTER ENTER .

The decimal value may be verified by dividing the fraction.

Complete Assignment Questions #6 - #7

Extension:Using a Graphing Calculator to Determine a Maximum Value

- The graphing calculator can be used to calculate the coordinates of the maximum or minimum points on a graph.
- The equation $y = -x^2 + 5x + 14$ will be used to illustrate the maximum features.

1. Enter the equation into [Y_1]; adjust the window to x: [–5, 10, 5] y: [–5, 30, 5], and press [GRAPH].

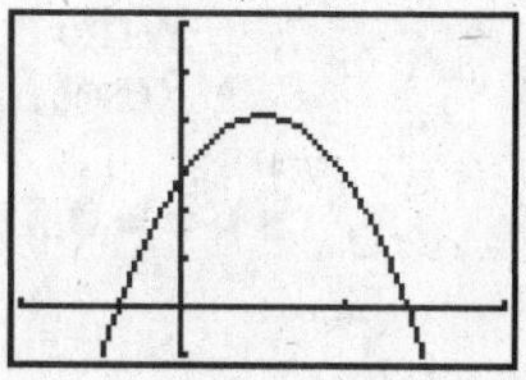

2. Access the CALC menu by entering [2nd] then [TRACE].

3. Select "maximum".

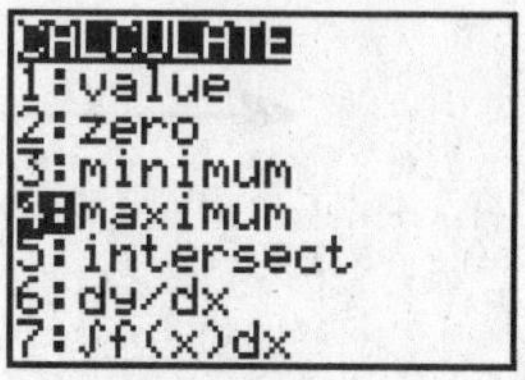

4. On the bottom left-hand side of the screen, the calculator will ask us for a LeftBound? . Select a value by scrolling to the left side of the maximum point and press [ENTER].

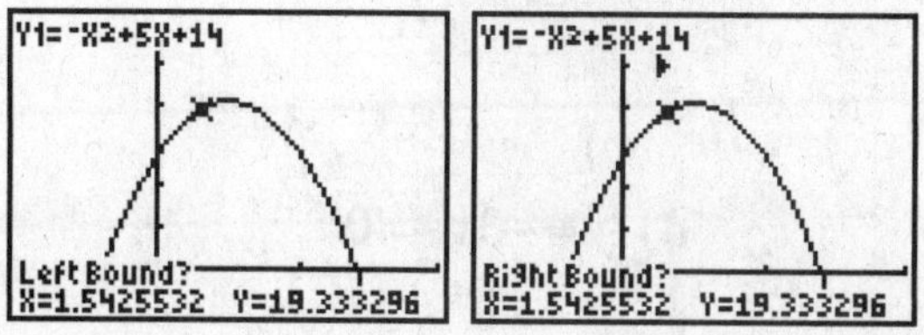

5. On the bottom left-hand side of the screen, the calculator will ask us for a RightBound ?. Select a value by scrolling to the right side of the maximum point and press [ENTER].

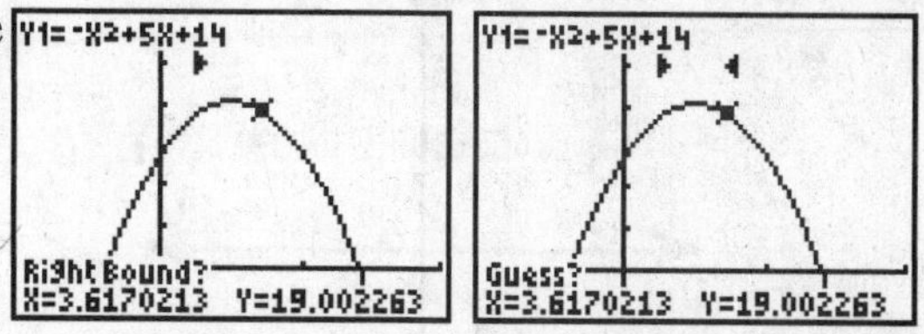

6. On the bottom left-hand side of the screen, the calculator will ask to Guess? . Press [ENTER].

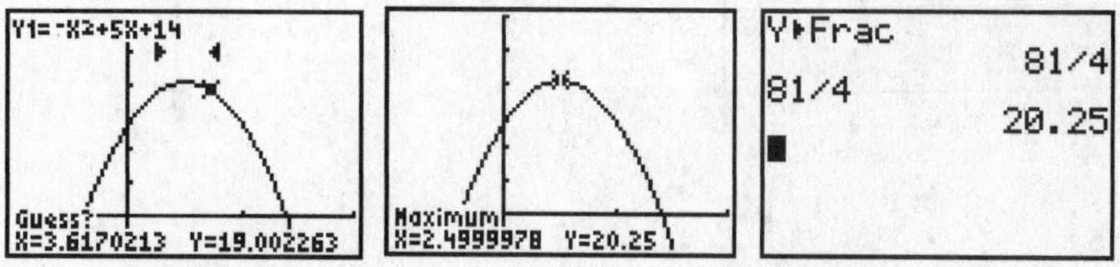

7. Due to the limitations of the calculator, the x value on the display may vary slightly from calculator to calculator. The answer obtained may depend on the window setting used and the bounds chosen. All the answers, however, should round to the exact answer; in this case 2.5. Test the point using the trace feature and entering $x = 2.5$.

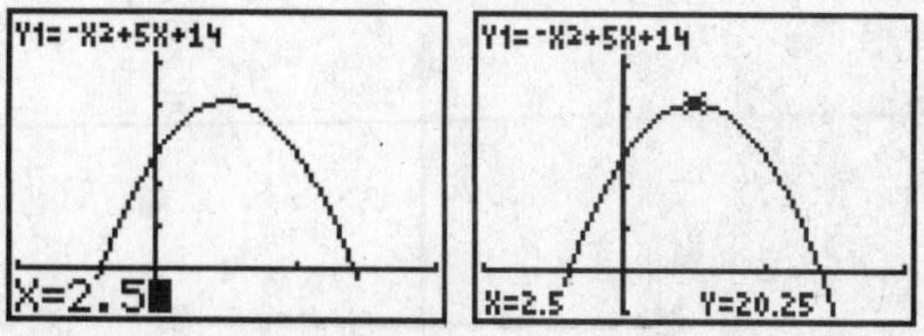

In this example the graph of $y = -x^2 + 5x + 14$ has a **maximum value** of 20.25 or $\frac{81}{4}$, and the **maximum point** has coordinates (2.5, 20.25).

Complete Assignment Questions #8 - #9

Assignment

1. For each relation represented by an equation:
   - Use a graphing calculator to graph the relation.
   - Adjust the window to an appropriate setting so that the x- and y- intercepts (where applicable) are visible.
   - Sketch the graph on the grid provided.
   - Write an appropriate window setting.
   - Reset the window to `ZStandard` before beginning a new graph.

a) $y = 0.5x - 8$

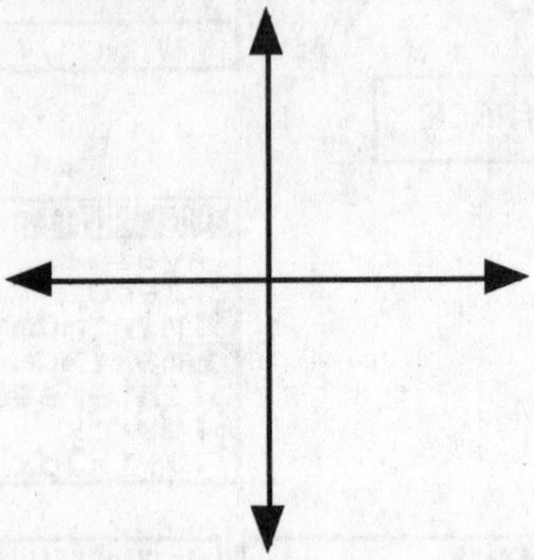

b) $y = 2x - 15$

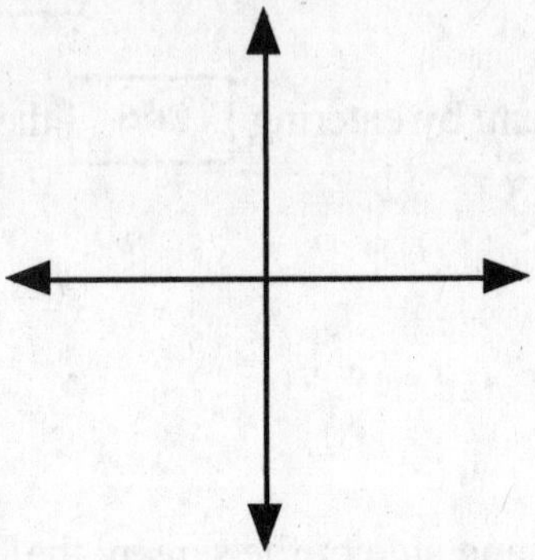

c) $y = -x + 25$

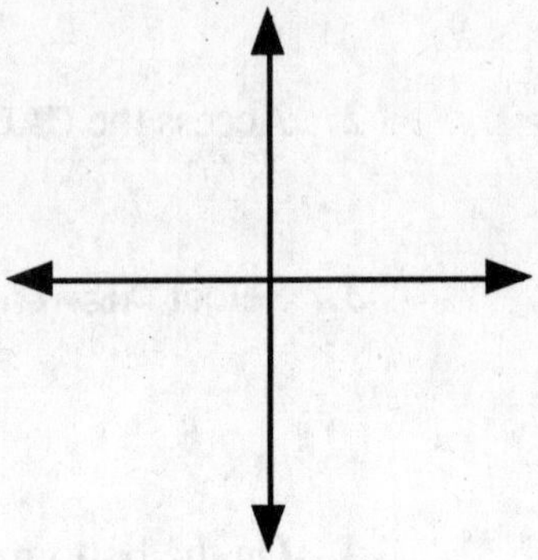

d) $y = -3x - 40$

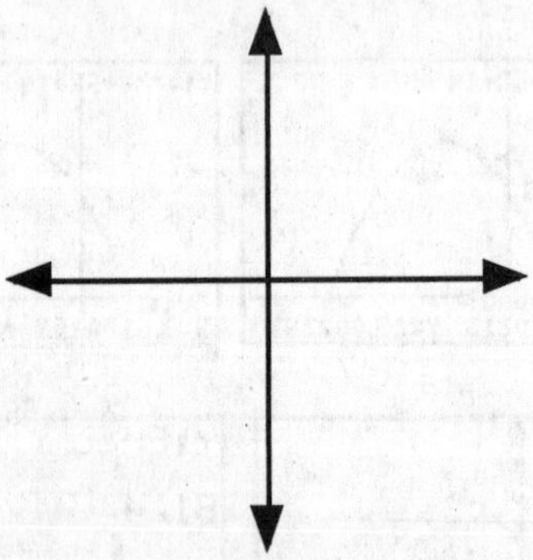

e) $y = -2x + 128$

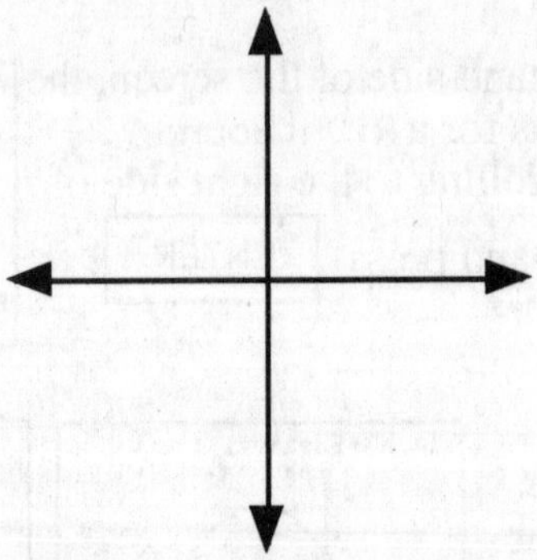

f) $y = x^2 - 15$

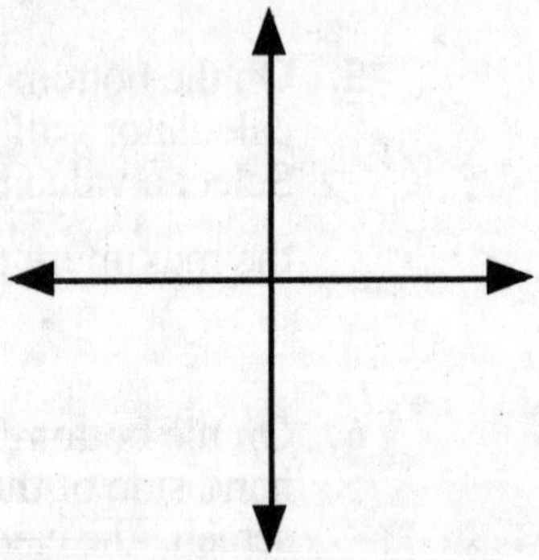

g) $y = x^2 + 20x$

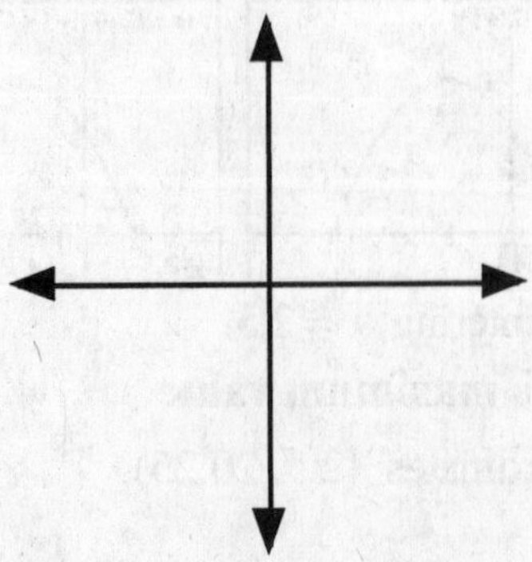

h) $y = 30$

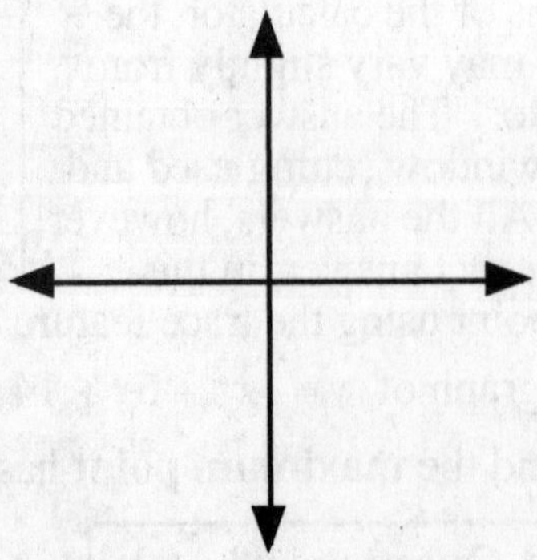

i) $y = 2^x$

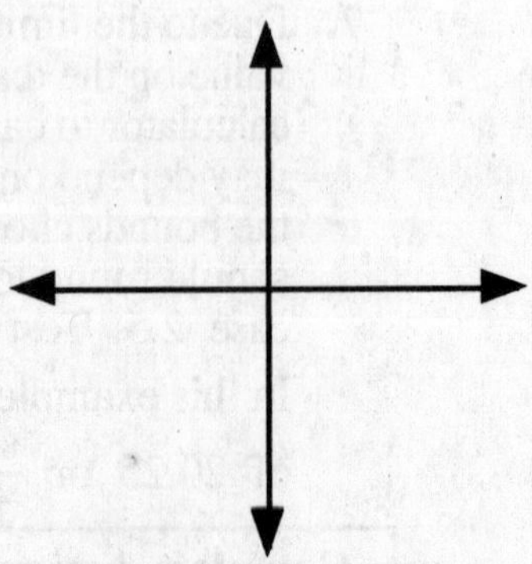

2. Consider the equation $y = -3x + 36$.

a) Use a graphing calculator to sketch the graph on the grid provided. Write an appropriate window so that the x- and y- intercepts are visible.

b) Use a graphing calculator to determine the value of y when $x = 5$.

c) Algebraically verify the answer in b).

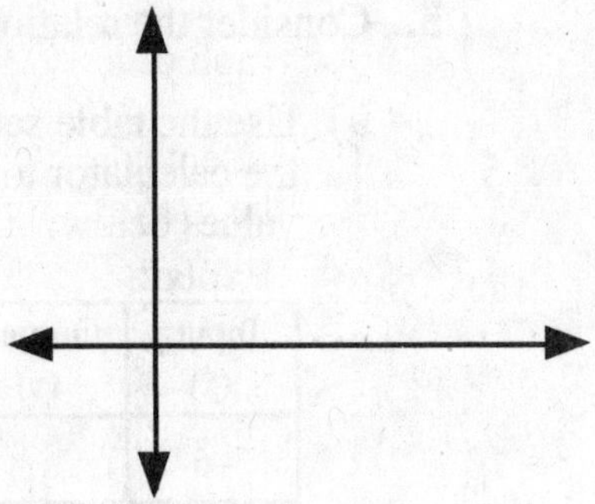

d) Use a graphing calculator to determine the value of x when $y = 12$.

e) Algebraically verify the answer in d).

3. Given the x-coordinate of each relation, determine the corresponding y-coordinate using the graphing features of a calculator.

a) $y = 8x - 5,\ x = 7,\ y =$

b) $y = 0.75x + 8,\quad x = 15,\ y =$

c) $y = -2x + 12,\ x = -17,\ y =$

d) $y = \frac{5}{3}x - 1,\ x = 0,\ y =$

e) $y = x^2 + 3x - 12,\ x = -5,\ y =$

f) $y = 2x^2 - 5x - 2,\ x = 3.5,\ y =$

g) $y = 2x^3 + 15,\ x = 2,\ y =$

h) $y = |x| - 7,\ x = -15,\ y =$

4. Given the y-coordinate of each relation, determine the corresponding x-coordinate using the graphing features of a calculator.
Write your answer to the nearest hundredth where necessary.

a) $y = 7x - 3,\ x =$, $y = 8$

b) $y = 5x + 8,\ x =$, $y = -3$

c) $y = -2x + 12,\ x =$, $y = 15$

d) $y = \frac{5}{3}x - 1,\ x =$, $y = -12$

e) $y = x^2 + 2x - 15,\ x =$ and , $y = 3$

f) $y = 2x^3 + 15,\ x =$, $y = 10$

g) $y = -x^2 - 10x - 21,\ x =$ and , $y = -15$

h) $y = |x| - 7,\ x =$, $y = 20$

5. Consider the relation given by the equation $y = -0.5x^2 + 8$.

a) Use the table set and table features of the calculator to complete the table of values below.

Input (x)	Output (y)
–6	
–4	
–2	
0	
2	
4	

b) Sketch the graph of the relation using an appropriate window.

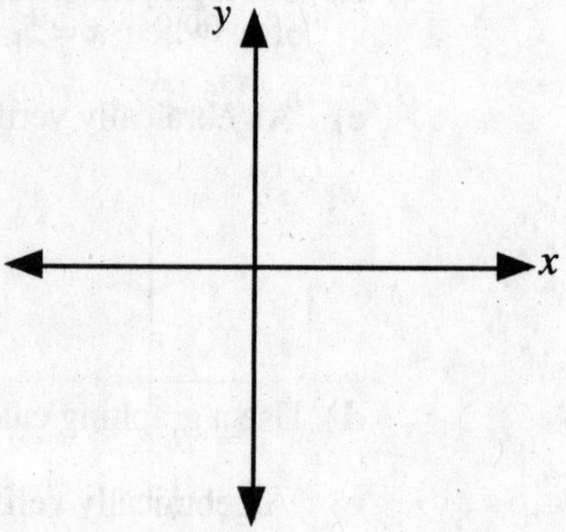

c) State the window setting x:[, ,] y:[, ,].

d) Use the appropriate features of a calculator to determine:

i) the value of y when $x = 10$

ii) the values of x when $y = 3.5$

e) Compare the answers to a), b), and d ii) with those from Lesson #2, assignment question #6.

6. For each equation use a graphing calculator to:

- sketch the graph of the relation on the grid provided
- **list** in the chart provided any x- and y-intercepts as **exact values**
- **write** the coordinates of the points representing the x- and y-intercepts on the graph of the relation.

a) $y = -3 - x$

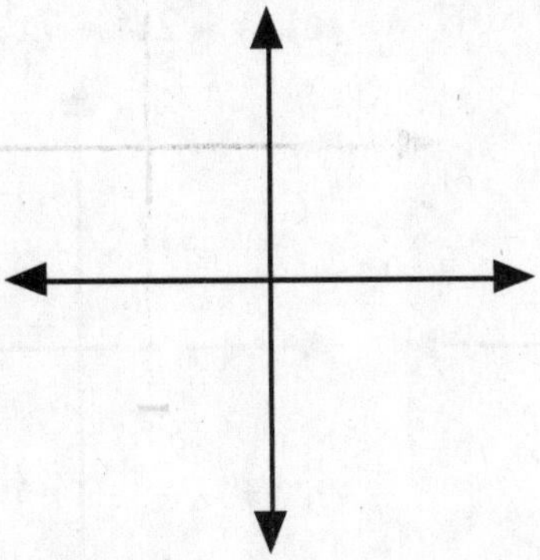

x-intercept	
y-intercept	

b) $y = -3x - 1$

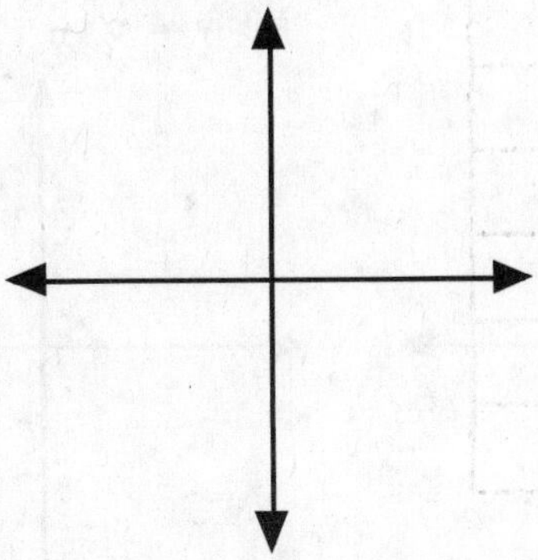

x-intercept	
y-intercept	

c) $y = 2x - 5$

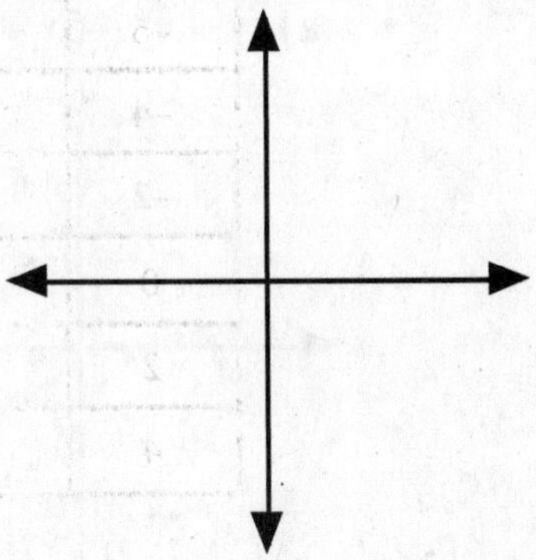

x-intercept	
y-intercept	

d) $y = -6x - 10$

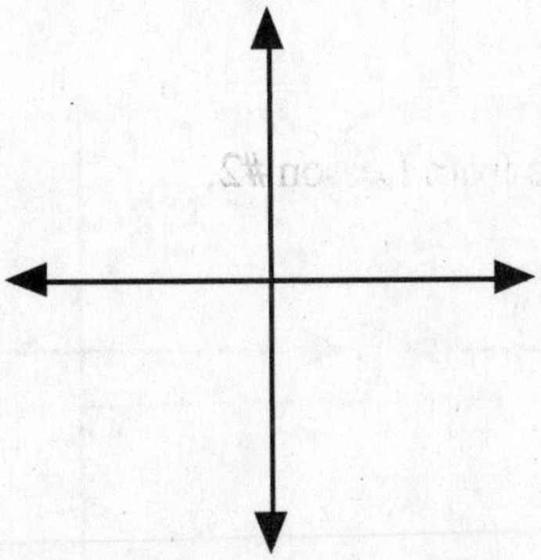

x-intercept	
y-intercept	

e) $y = \dfrac{-4x + 6}{3}$

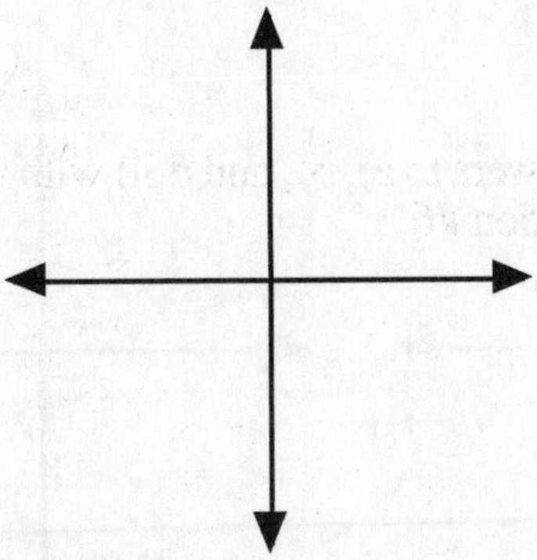

x-intercept	
y-intercept	

f) $y = 5$

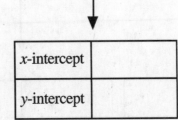

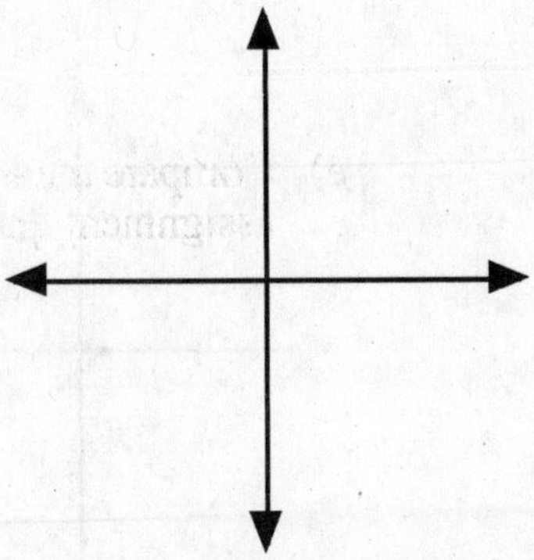

x-intercept	
y-intercept	

7. For each equation use a graphing calculator to:

- sketch the graph of the relation on the grid provided
- **list** in the chart provided any x- and y-intercepts as **exact values**
- **write** the coordinates of the points representing the x- and y-intercepts on the graph of the relation.

a) $y = x^2 - 5x - 6$

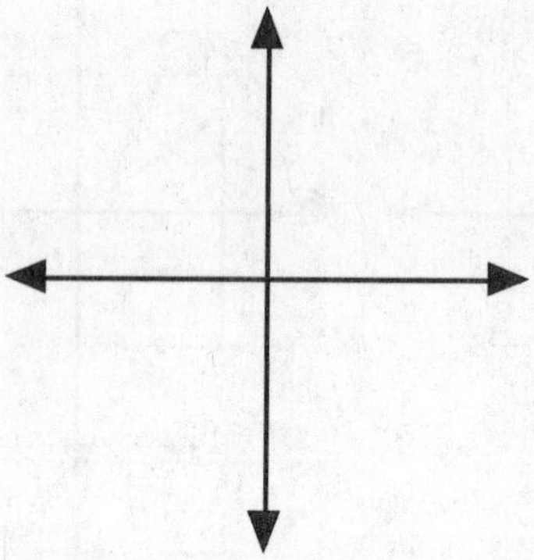

x-intercept(s)	
y-intercept	

b) $y = x^2 - 16$

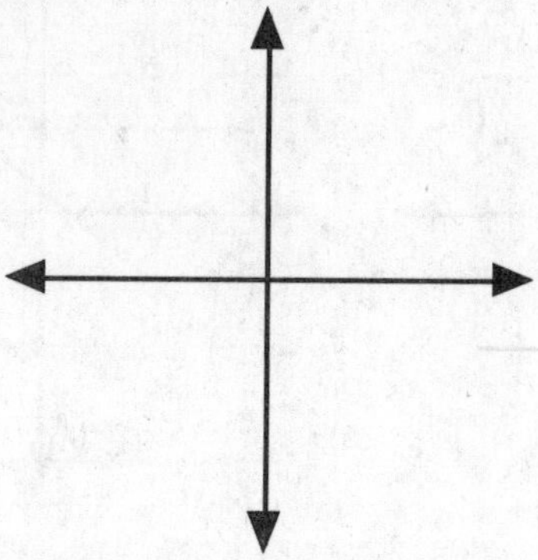

x-intercept(s)	
y-intercept	

c) $y = 2x^2 - 7x + 8$

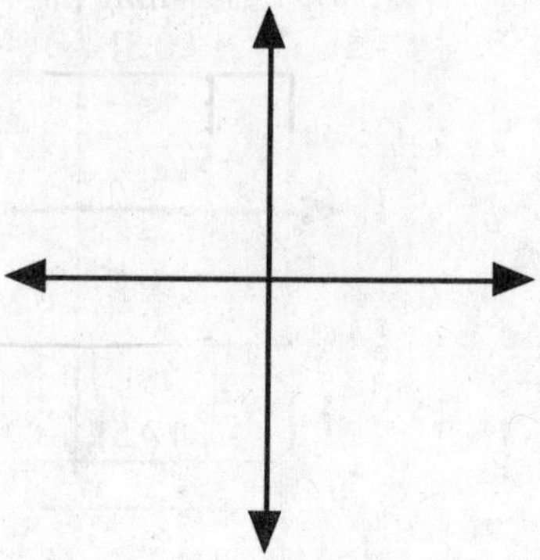

x-intercept(s)	
y-intercept	

d) $y = -x^2 + 3x + 18$

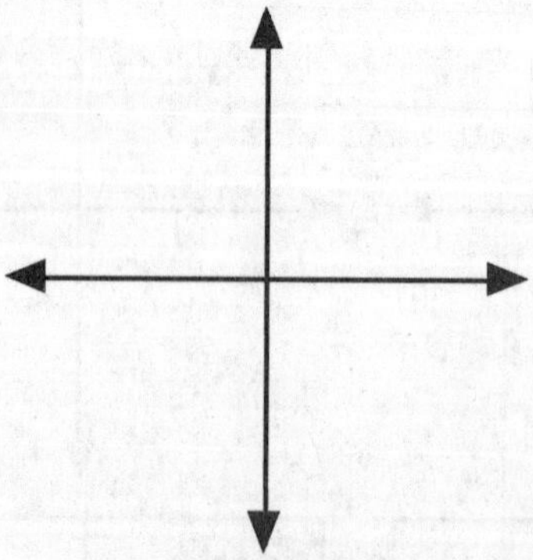

x-intercept(s)	
y-intercept	

e) $y = -2x^2 - 7x - 12$

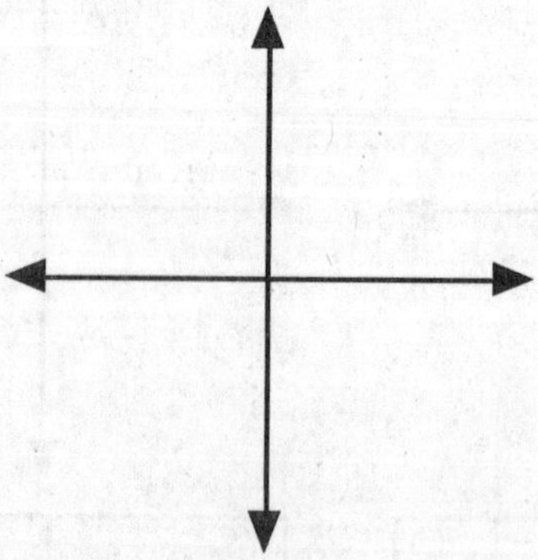

x-intercept(s)	
y-intercept	

f) $y = 2x^3 + x^2 - 16x - 15$

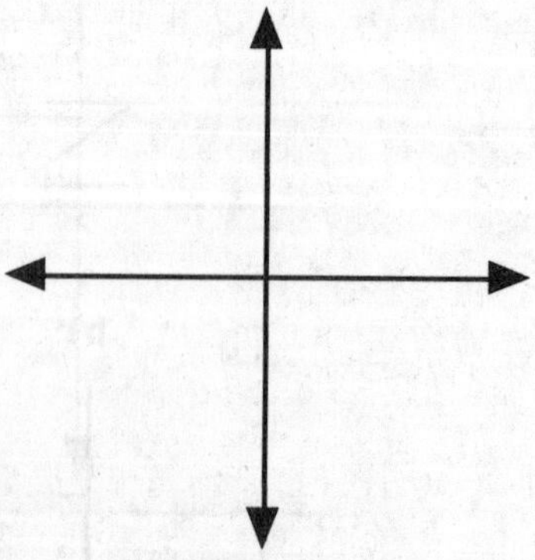

x-intercept(s)	
y-intercept	

8. Determine the coordinates of the maximum point of each graph. Answer using exact values.

a) $y = -0.3x^2 + 5x - 10$ **b)** $y = -0.1x^2 + 5x + 7$ **c)** $y = -9x^2 - 60x + 100$

9. Determine the coordinates of the minimum point of each graph. Answer using exact values.

a) $y = x^2 + 2x + 35$ **b)** $y = 0.15x^2 - 2x - 8$ **c)** $y = 0.5x^2 + 2x - 16$

Answer Key

1. *Window setting answers may vary.*

a) x: [-5,20,5], y: [-10,10,2]

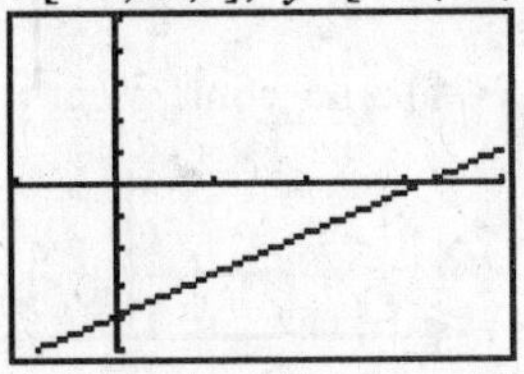

b) x: [-5,10,2], y: [-20,5,5]

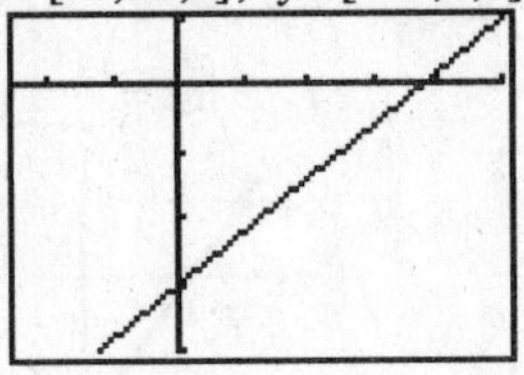

c) x: [-10,30,5], y: [-10,30,5]

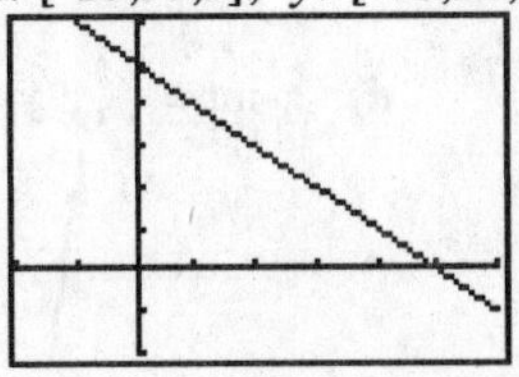

d) x: [-20,10,5], y: [-50,10,10]

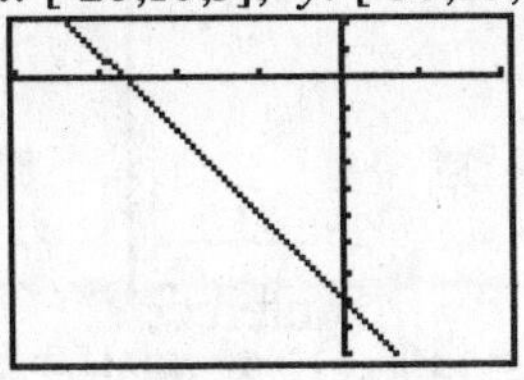

e) x: [-10,80,10], y: [-10,150,10]

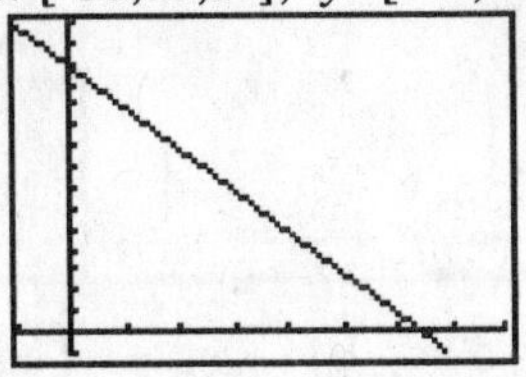

f) x: [-10,10,2], y: [–20,10,5]

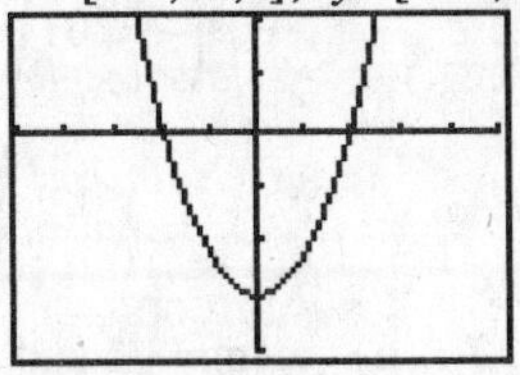

g) x: [-30,10,5], y: [-125,50,25]

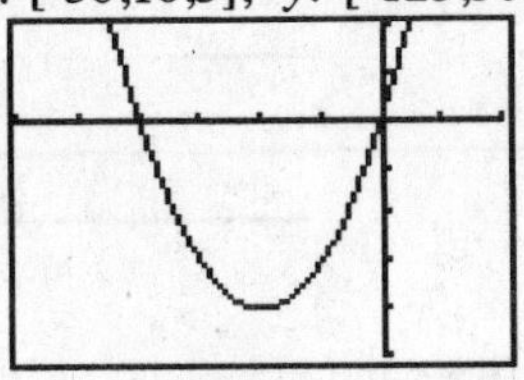

h) x: [-10,10,2], y: [-5,50,5]

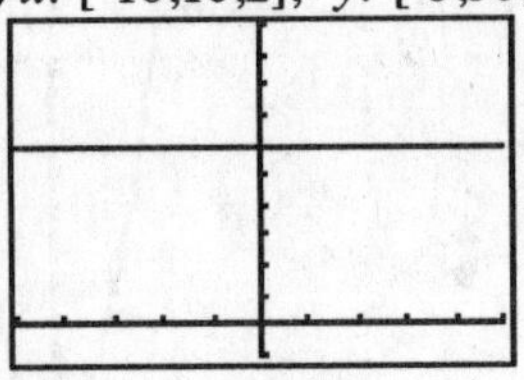

i) x: [-2,5,1], y: [-5,30,5]

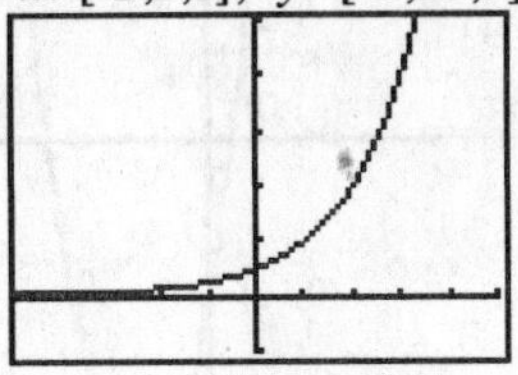

2. a) x: [-5,20,5], y: [-20,50,10] **b)** 21 **c)** 21 **d)** 8 **e)** 8

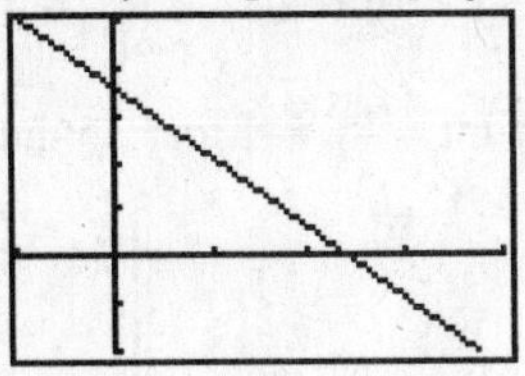

3. a) 51 **b)** 19.25 **c)** 46 **d)** –1
e) –2 **f)** 5 **g)** 31 **h)** 8

4. a) 1.57 **b)** –2.2 **c)** –1.5 **d)** –6.6
e) –5.36 and 3.36 **f)** –1.36 **g)** –9.36 and –0.64 **h)** ±27

5 a)

Input (x)	Output (y)
–6	-10
–4	0
–2	6
0	8
2	6
4	0

b)

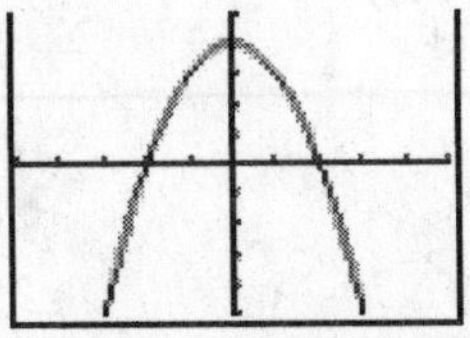

c) x:[–10, 10, 2] y:[–10, 10, 2]

d) i) –42 **ii)** –3 and 3

e) exactly the same

6. a) x-int = −3, y-int = −3 **b)** x-int = $-\frac{1}{3}$, y-int = −1 **c)** x-int = $\frac{5}{2}$, y-int = −5

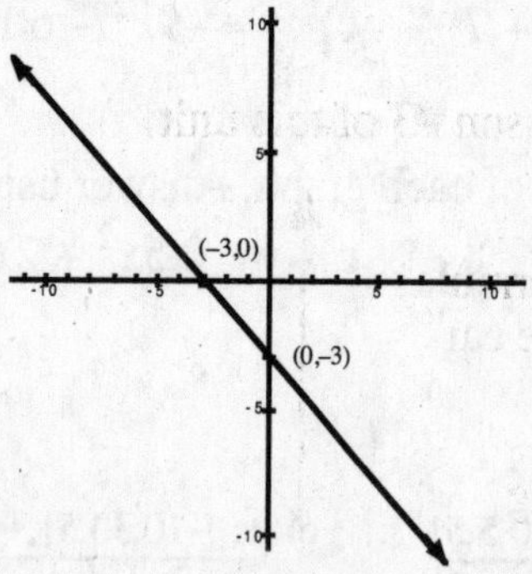

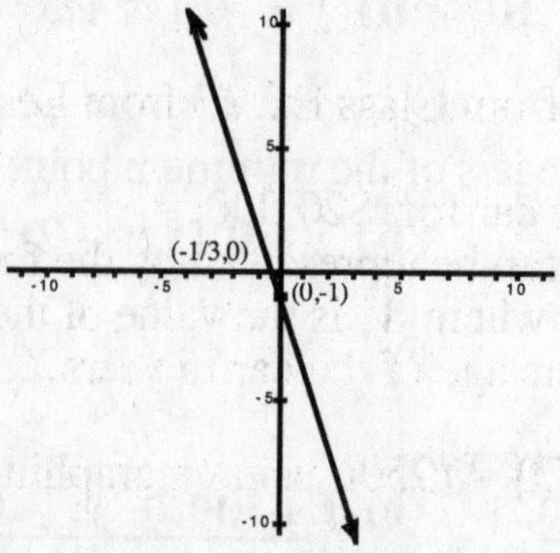

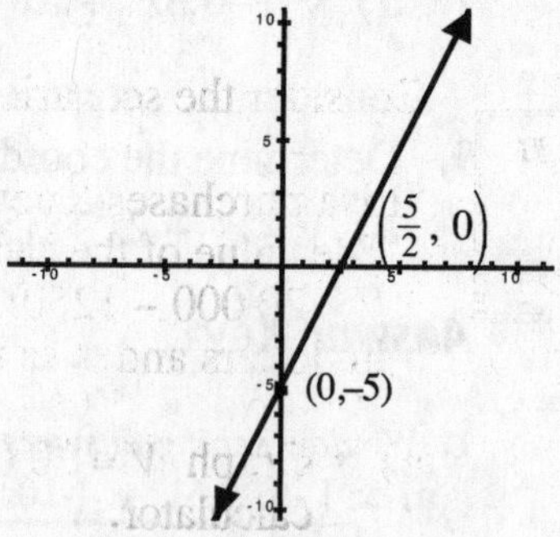

d) x-int = $-\frac{5}{3}$, y-int = −10 **e)** x-int = $\frac{3}{2}$, y-int = 2 **f)** no x-int, y-int = 5

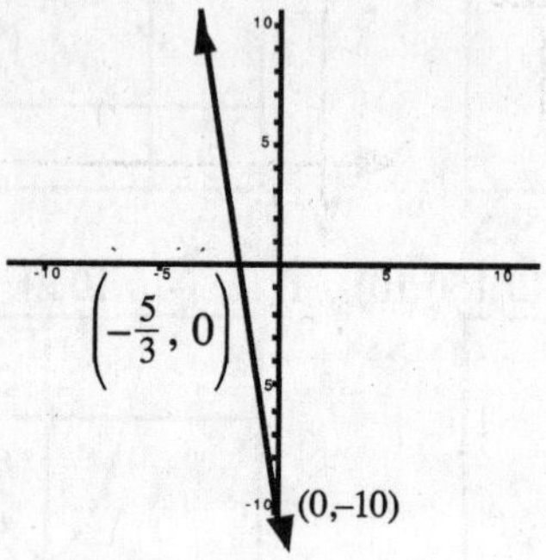

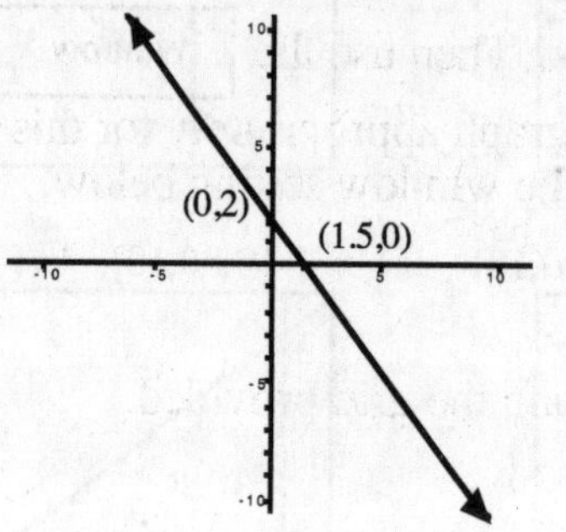

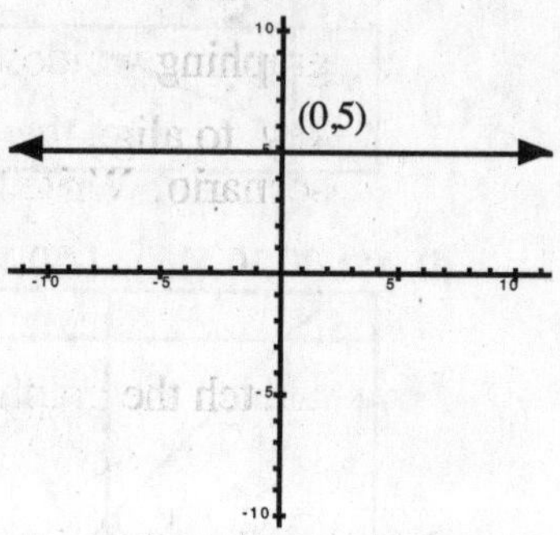

7. a) x-int = −1 and 6, y-int = −6 **b)** x-int = −4 and 4, y-int = −16 **c)** no x-int, y-int = 8

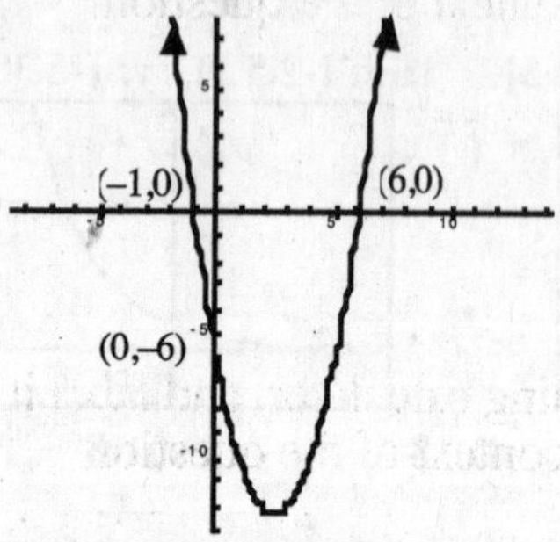

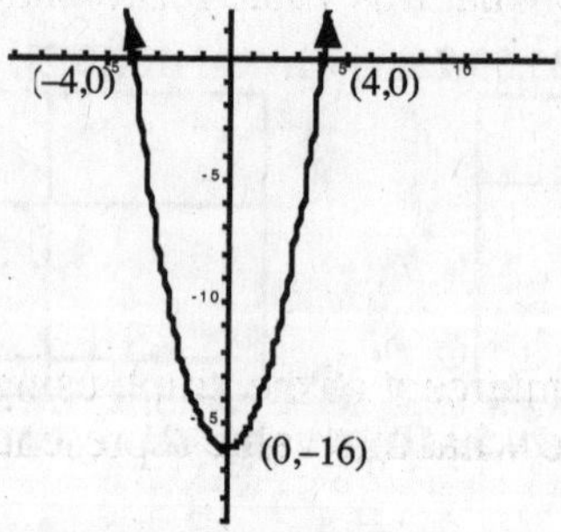

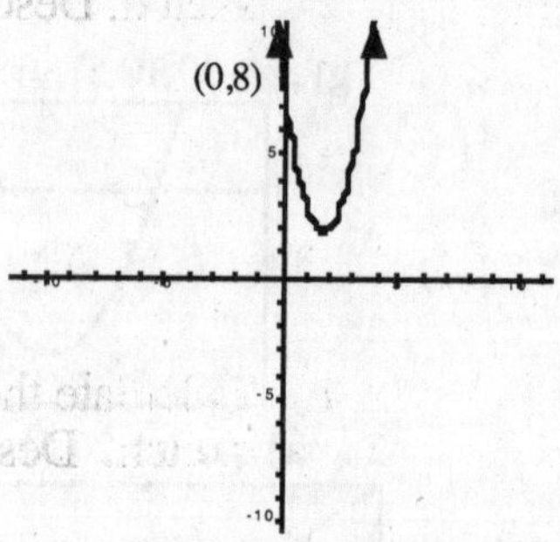

d) x-int = −3 and 6, y-int = 18 **e)** no x-int, y-int = −12 **f)** x-int = $-\frac{5}{2}$, −1 and 3 y-int = −15

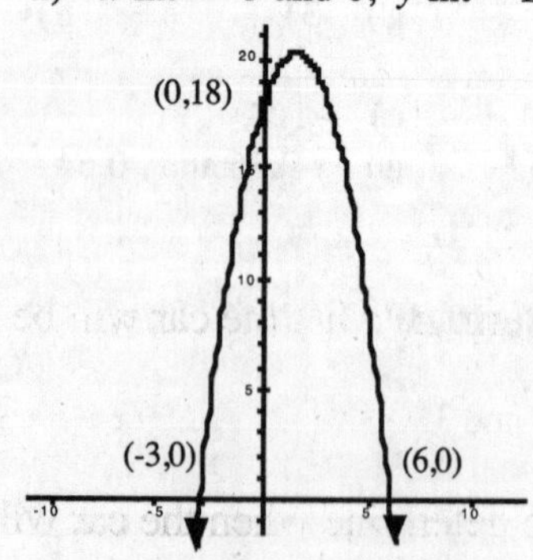

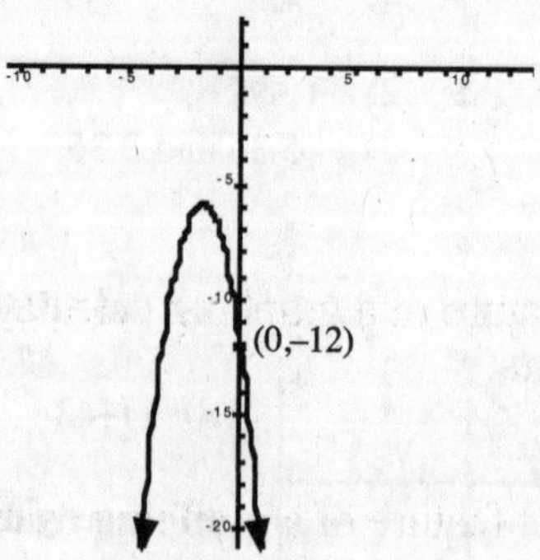

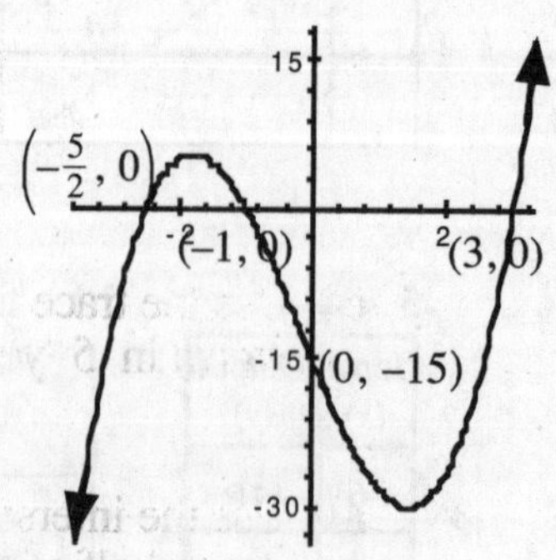

8. a) $\left(\frac{25}{3}, \frac{65}{6}\right)$ **b)** $\left(25, \frac{139}{2}\right)$ **c)** $\left(-\frac{10}{3}, 200\right)$

9. a) (−1, 34) **b)** $\left(\frac{20}{3}, -\frac{44}{3}\right)$ **c)** (−2, −18)

Relations and Functions Lesson #6:
Interpreting Relations Using a Graphing Calculator

Consider the scenario from Class Ex. #3 from Lesson #3 of this unit.

"Lisa purchases a new car for \$20 000.
The value of the car can be represented by the formula $V = 20\,000 - 1250t$, where V is the value of the car in dollars and t is the age of the car in years."

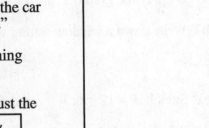

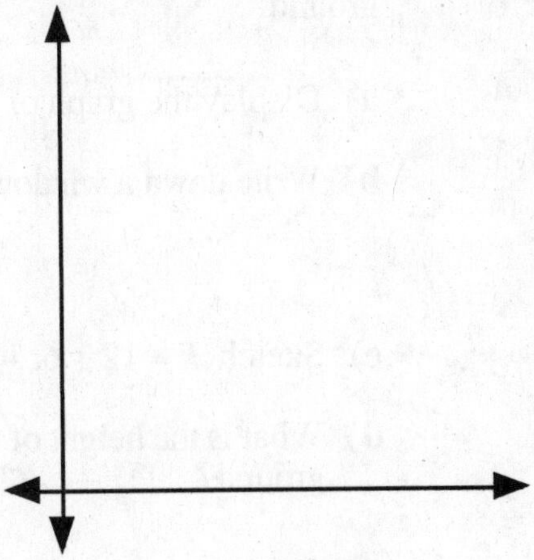

a) • Graph $V = 20\,000 - 1250t$ using a graphing calculator.

• Use the ZoomFit feature as a guide to adjust the graphing window. Then use the **Window** key to align the graph appropriately for this scenario. Write the window setting below.

• Sketch the graph on the grid provided.

b) Calculate the t-intercept of the graph using a graphing calculator, and label it on the sketch. Describe what this value represents in the context of the question.

c) Calculate the V-intercept of the graph using a graphing calculator, and label it on the sketch. Describe what this value represents in the context of the question.

d) Use the trace feature of a graphing calculator to determine what the car will be worth in 5 years.

e) Use the intersect feature of a graphing calculator to determine when the car will be worth half of the purchase price. Illustrate this on your sketch.

f) Write an appropriate domain and range for the function which describes the value of the car over time.

Class Ex. #2

The height of a human cannon ball, "Cano", can be described by the formula $h = 12 + 6t - t^2$, where h is the height in metres above ground level and t is the time in seconds. Cano is projected out of a cannon from the top of a building and lands on a soft mat. The mat is placed in a hole in the ground so that the top of the mat is level with the ground.

a) Display the graph of $h = 12 + 6t - t^2$ on a graphing calculator.

b) Write down a window setting which would be appropriate for this situation.

c) Sketch $h = 12 + 6t - t^2$ on the grid provided.

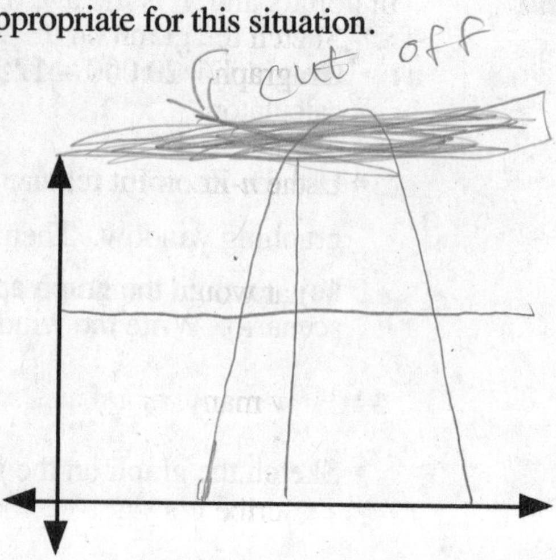

d) What is the height of the cannon above the ground?

e) What is the maximum height Cano reaches?

f) How many seconds does it take Cano to reach the highest point on the path he is travelling?

g) To the nearest hundredth of a second, how long does it take Cano to land on the mat?

h) How high is Cano one second after he is launched?

i) When will Cano be at the height in h) again?

j) In words, describe the relation connecting height and time.

k) Write an appropriate domain and range for the relation described in j).

Complete Assignment Questions #1 - #6

Assignment

In this assignment round answers to 2 decimal places unless otherwise stated.

1. Students at a senior high school produce an art literary magazine. The cost for this magazine can be modelled by the formula $C = 2n + 30$, where C is the total cost of the magazine in dollars and n is the number of magazines produced.

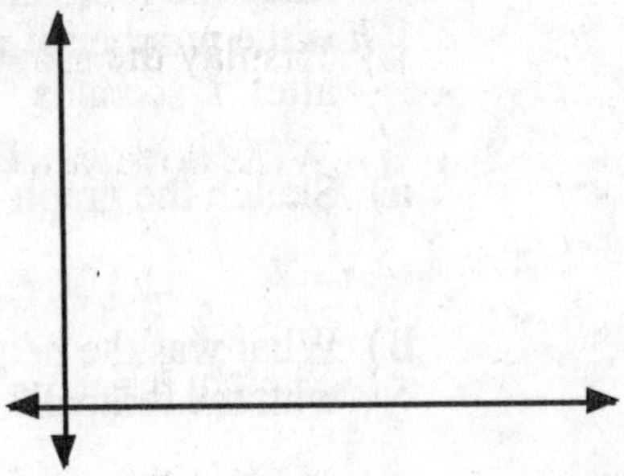

a) Sketch the graph on the grid provided. Explain why the graph is not continuous straight line.

b) Is the n-intercept relevant to the graph of this relation?

c) What would be the cost for 30 magazines?

d) How many magazines are produced if the total cost is $126?

e) Describe the significance of the C-intercept.

2. For a science experiment, a pot of water is heated to a certain temperature and then put in a freezer and allowed to freeze. The rate of freezing can be estimated by the formula $T = -0.4t + 50$, where the temperature, T, in degrees Celsius is recorded for each time, t in minutes.

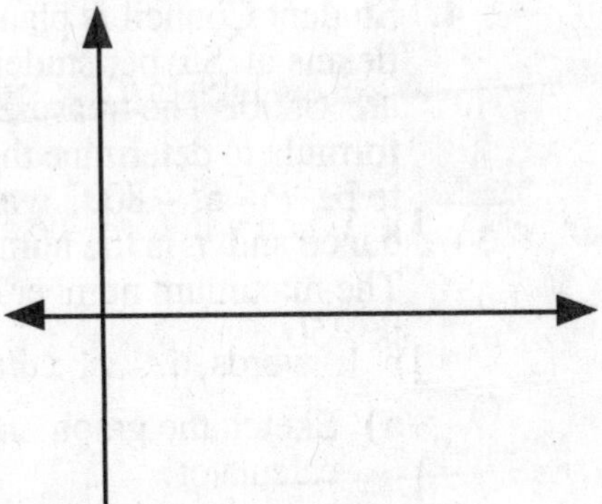

a) Sketch the graph on the grid using a graphing calculator.

b) What was the temperature of the water at 12 minutes?

c) How long did it take for the pot of water to cool down to 40°C?

d) Describe the significance of the t-intercept in this question.

e) Describe the relation in words.

3. During a high school football game, the height of a punt can be modelled by the relation

$$h = -5t^2 + 14t + 1$$

where
t is the number of seconds which have elapsed since the football was punted, and
h is the number of metres above the ground after t seconds

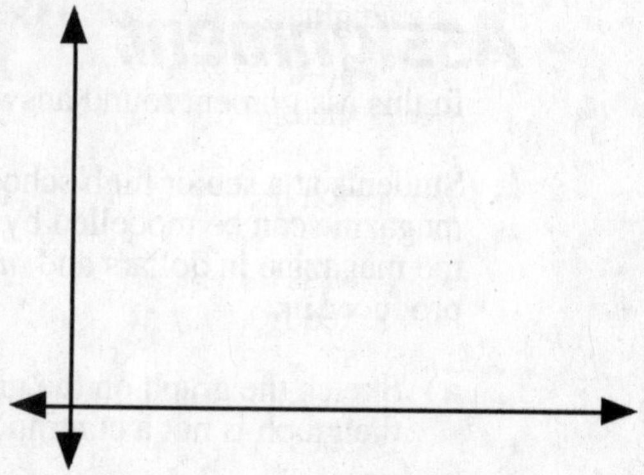

a) Sketch the graph on the grid.

b) What was the height of the football above the ground as the punter makes contact with the football?

c) What was the height of the football above the ground 1 second after contact?

d) What is the maximum height of the football above the ground?

e) How many seconds had elapsed when the football reached its maximum height?

f) The punt is not caught by the opposing team, and the football hits the ground. How many seconds, to the nearest hundredth, did it take for the football to hit the ground?

4. Student Council is planning a school dance and sells tickets at \$5 per student. The expenses for the dance are \$800. The treasurer of the council generates a formula to determine the potential profit for the dance to be $P = 5t - 800$, where P is the profit made on the dance and t is the number of tickets sold. The maximum number of tickets which can be sold is 450.

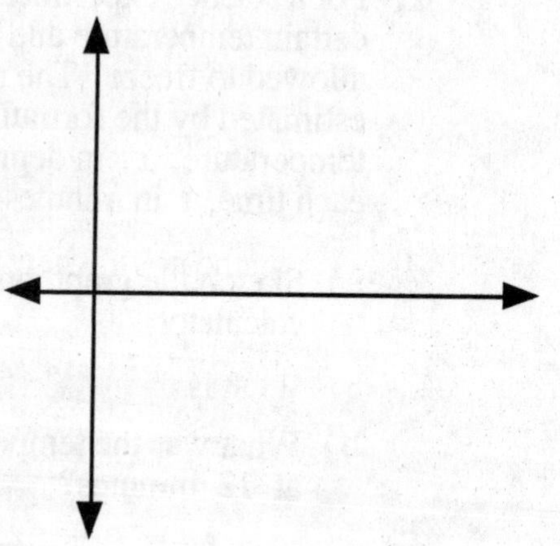

a) Sketch the graph on the grid using a graphing calculator.

b) Determine how many tickets need to be sold to break even.

c) How many tickets need to be sold to make a \$1250 profit?

d) How much profit is made if 200 tickets are sold?

e) Write the domain and range for this relation.

5. The height of a soccer ball after a free kick for the Hawks is given by the equation $h = 0.03(-d^2 + 40d)$, where h is the height in metres and d is the horizontal distance in metres the ball travels.

a) Sketch the graph on the grid.

b) What is the height that the soccer ball is kicked from?

c) What is the maximum height the soccer ball reaches?

d) How far down the field is the ball when it reaches its maximum height?

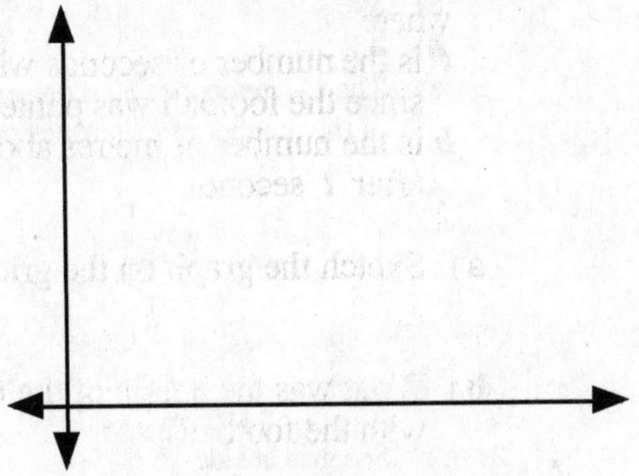

e) Before the ball strikes the ground, a defender heads the ball after it has travelled 38 m. What is the height of the ball above the ground when the defender heads it?

f) How high is the ball when it is 3 metres down the field?

6. In a soccer game the ball is passed back to the goal keeper, and she kicks the ball from ground level up the field. The height, h metres, of the ball above the ground can be modelled by the equation $h = -0.033d^2 + 1.6d - 10$, where d is the distance in metres from the goal line.

a) Sketch the graph on the grid.

b) What was the distance between the goal line and the point where the ball was kicked?

c) What is the maximum height the soccer ball reaches?

d) How far from the goal line is the ball when it reaches its maximum height?

e) What horizontal distance has the ball travelled when it hits the ground for the first time?

f) Write a domain and range for this relation.

g) At what distance from the goal line is the ball 5 metres in the air?

Assignment Key

1. a) See grid at side. The data is discrete so there are gaps in the line.
   b) No, since the number of magazines cannot be negative.
   c) \$90
   d) 48
   e) The C-intercept of 30 represents a fixed charge of \$30 irrespective of the number of magazines produced.

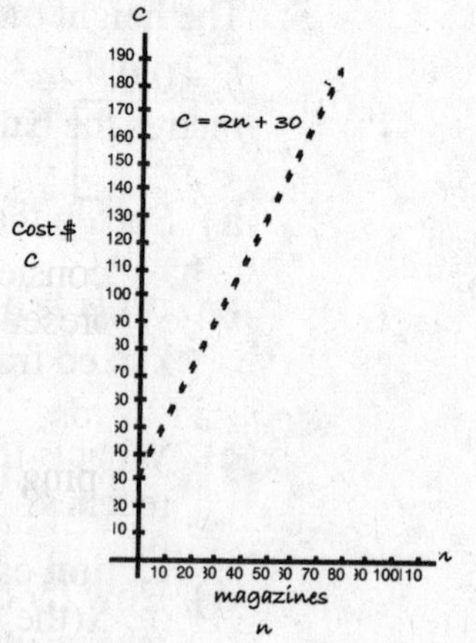

2. a) See grid at side
   b) 45.2° C
   c) 25 min.
   d) The t intercept of 125 represents the number of minutes it takes the water to freeze.
   e) A pot of water is heated to 50°C and placed in a freezer and allowed to freeze. It cools at a constant rate and after 125 min the water is frozen.

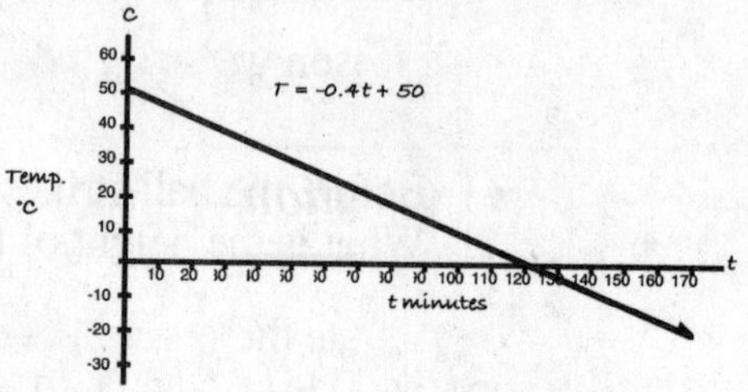

3. a) See grid below
   b) 1 m
   c) 10 m
   d) 10.8 m
   e) 1.4 sec.
   f) 2.87 sec.

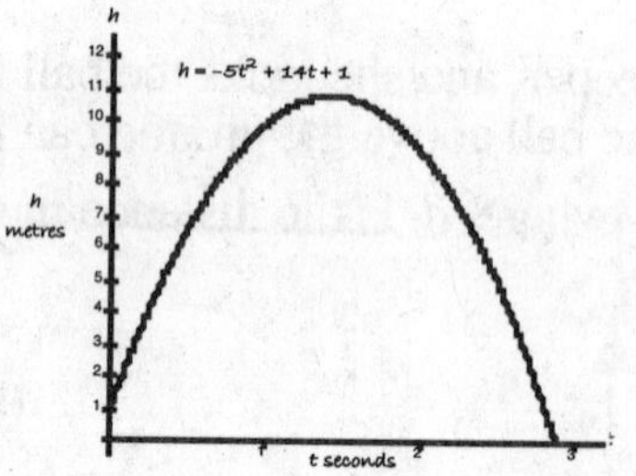

4. a) See grid below
   b) 160
   c) 410
   d) \$200
   e) domain: 0, 1, 2, 3 450
   range: –800, –795, –790, –785 1450
   (increasing in steps of 5)

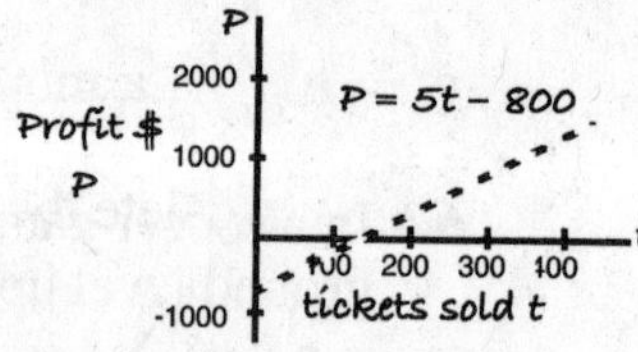

5. a) See grid at side
   b) 0 m c) 12 m
   d) 20 m e) 2.28 m
   f) 3.33 m

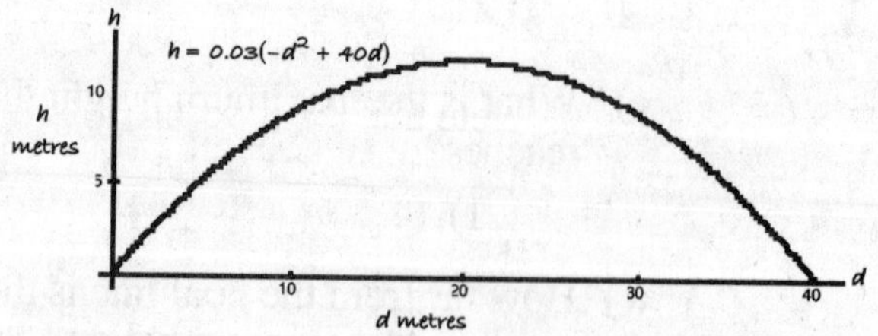

6. a) See grid at side
   b) 7.37 m c) 9.39 m
   d) 24.24 m e) 33.74 m
   f) domain: $\{7.37 \le d \le 41.11, d \in R\}$
   range: $\{0 \le h \le 9.39, h \in R\}$
   g) 12.70 m and 35.78 m

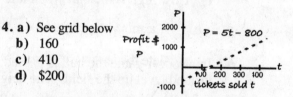

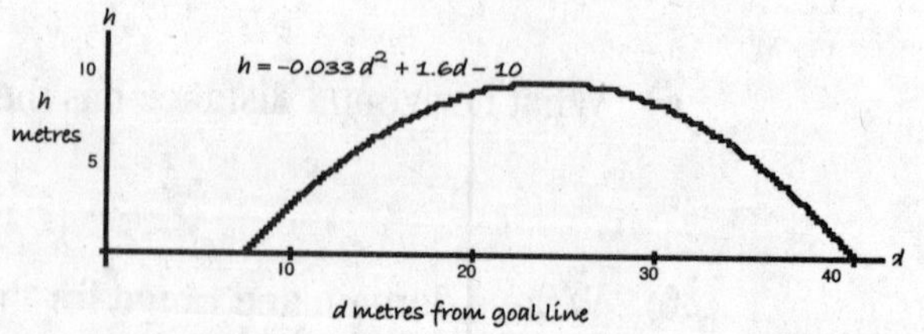

Relations and Functions Lesson #7:
Functions

Review

We have considered six ways in which the relationship between two quantities can be represented.

- in words
- a mapping (or arrow) diagram
- a table of values
- an equation
- a set of ordered pairs
- a graph

In a **relation** each element of the **domain** (the **input**) is related to an element or elements of the **range** (the **output**).

In this lesson we will study a special type of relation called a **function**.

Exploration

To illustrate the concept of function, we will look at two relations described in words with domain $D = \{1, 4, 9, 16\}$ and range $R = \{1, 2, 3, 4\}$.

i) "is a multiple of "

ii) "is the square of"

a) Complete the arrow diagrams.

i) "is a multiple of"

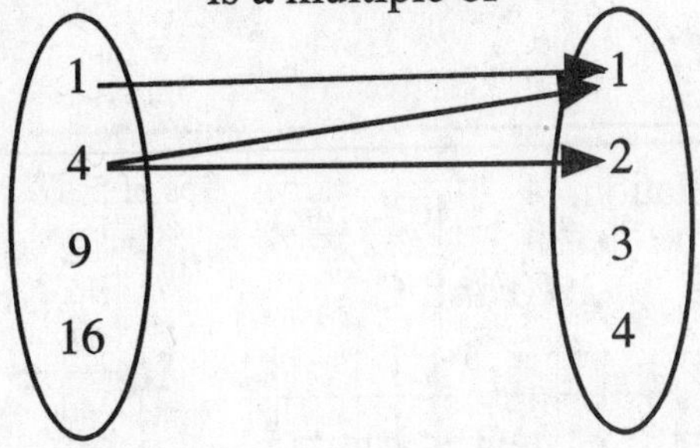

ii) "is the square of"

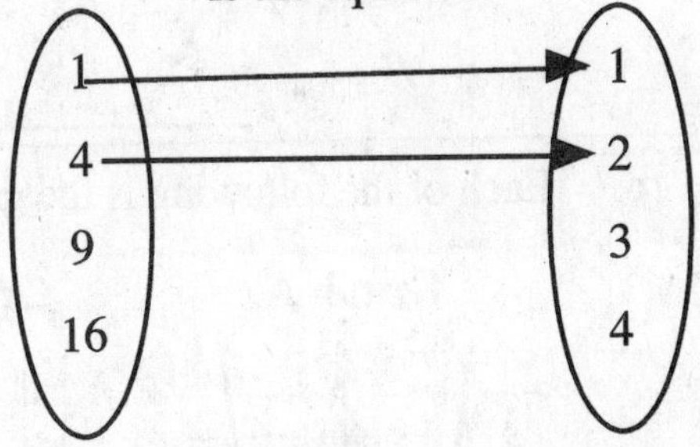

b) Complete the set of ordered pairs.

i) (1, 1), (4, 1), (

ii)

c) Plot the ordered pairs on the grid.

i)

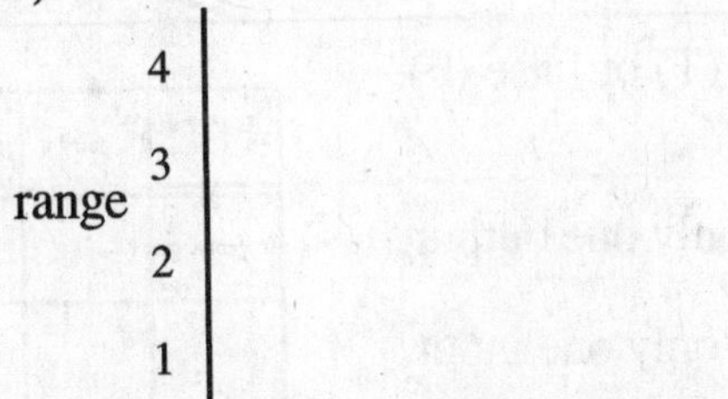

ii)

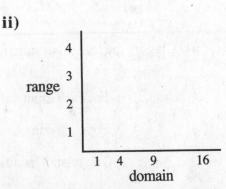

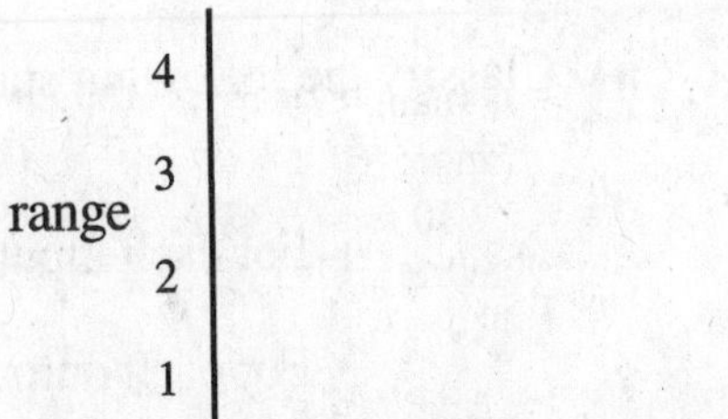

> ### Function

A functional relation, or **function**, is a special type of relation in which <u>each element of the domain is related to exactly one element of the range</u>. If any element of the domain is related to more than one element of the range, then the relation is not a function.

Class Ex. #1 In the exploration on the previous page, one of the relations is a function, and the other relation is not a function.

Explain how we can determine which relation is a function by looking at the following:

a) the arrow diagram

b) the ordered pairs

c) the graphs

↗Vertical line test.

Class Ex. #2 Each of the following is the graph of a relation.

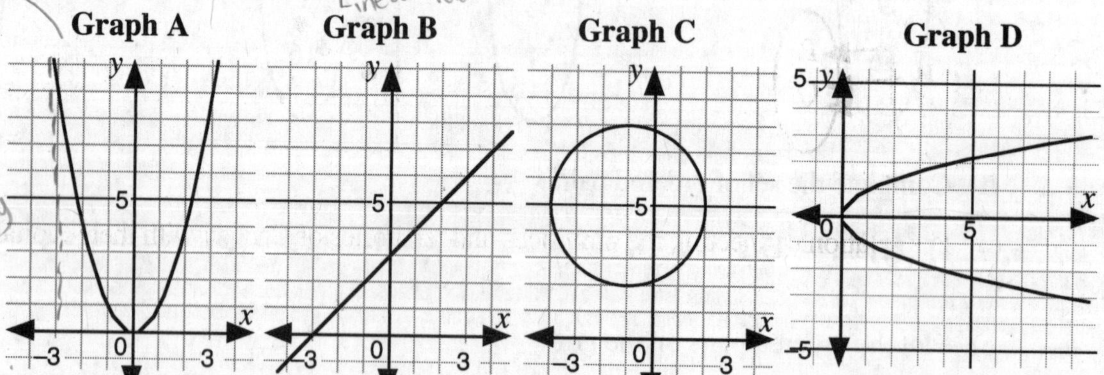

Linear relation

| Graph A | Graph B | Graph C | Graph D |

A= ~~No~~ Yes
- each x only
has 1 y

B = Yes
C = Not
D = Not

↗ One point for each

a) Classify the following statements as true (T) or false (F).

- For each input value there is only one output. *F*
- For each output value there is only one input. *F*
- The relation is a function. *T*

	A	B	C	D

b) From graph C, write two ordered pairs which show that the relation is not a function. Draw a line joining these points.

c) From graph D, write two ordered pairs which show that the relation is not a function. Draw a line joining these points.

d) On graphs A and B draw a series of vertical lines. Do any of these lines intersect the graph of the relation at more than one point?

Vertical Line Test

The vertical line test can be used on the graph of a relation to determine whether the relation is a function or not.

- If every vertical line, drawn on the domain of the relation, intersects the graph exactly once, then the relation is a function.
- If any vertical line intersects the graph more than once, then it is **not** a function.

Class Ex. #3

Determine which of the following are functions. Explain your answers.

a) (5, 8), (6, 7), (–5, 3), (2, 3), (6, 8)

Not a function

b) (3, 3), (2, 3), (4, 5), (–3, 2)

Function

c)

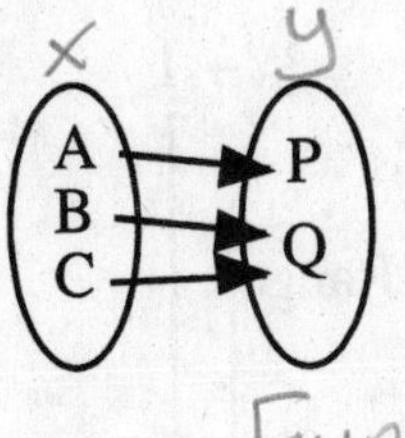

Function

d)

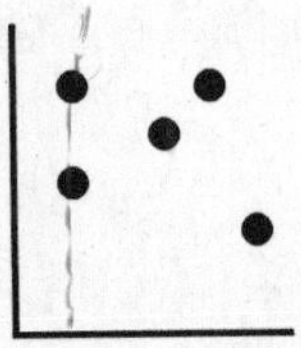

Not a function

e) The relation connecting the provinces and territories of Canada with their capital cities.

BC → Victoria
AB → Edmonton

f)

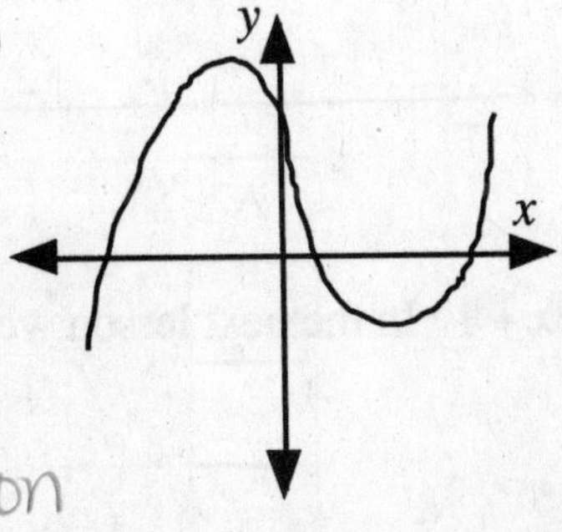

Function

g)

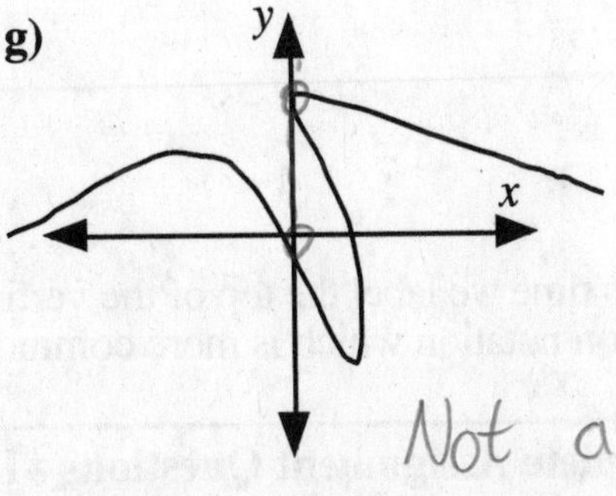

Not a function

A Function as a Mapping

A function from a set D, the domain, to a set R, the range, is a relation in which each element of D is related to exactly one element of R.

If the function f maps an element x in the domain to an element y in the range, we write $f: x \rightarrow y$.

Complete the following for the function "is the square of" on the first page of this lesson.

$1 \rightarrow$ $\qquad$ $4 \rightarrow$ $\qquad$ $9 \rightarrow$ $\qquad$ $\rightarrow$

Consider the function $f: x \rightarrow 3x + 1$, for domain $\{-1, 0, 1, 2\}$.

a) Complete $\quad -1 \rightarrow \quad 0 \rightarrow \quad \rightarrow \quad \rightarrow$

b) List the elements of the range of the function.

c) Show the function as:

i) an arrow diagram $\qquad$ **ii)** a set of ordered pairs $\qquad$ **iii)** a Cartesian graph.

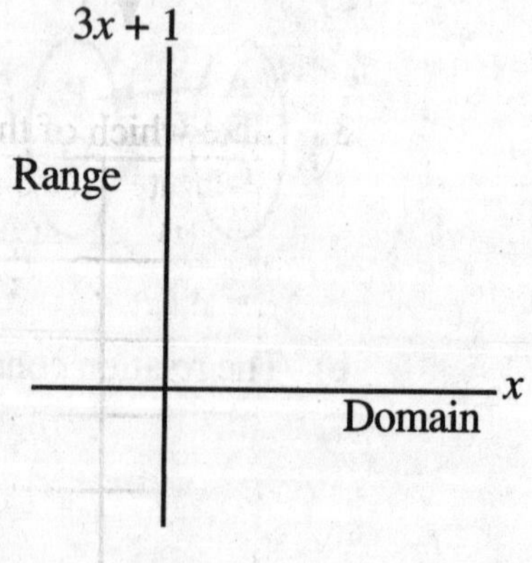

At this time we label the top of the vertical axis with $3x + 1$. In the next lesson we will learn function notation which is more commonly used.

Complete Assignment Questions #1 - #12

Assignment

1. Determine which of the following relations are functions. Give reasons for your answers.

a) (–1, 3), (–2, 1), (5, 2), (7, 3)

b)

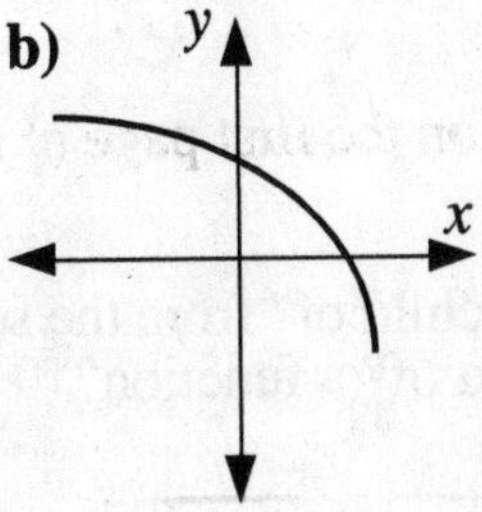

c)

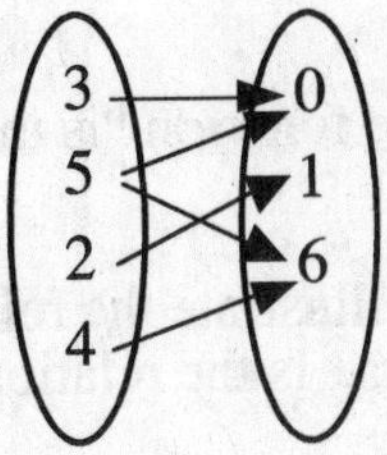

d)

Input (*x*)	Output (*y*)
2	3
0	4
–3	5
2	6

2. State which of the following relations are functions.

a) (0, 0), (1, 2), (2, 3), (3, 4), (4, 3)

b)

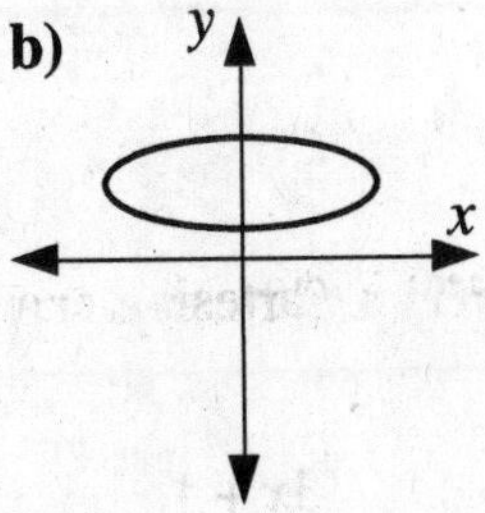

c)

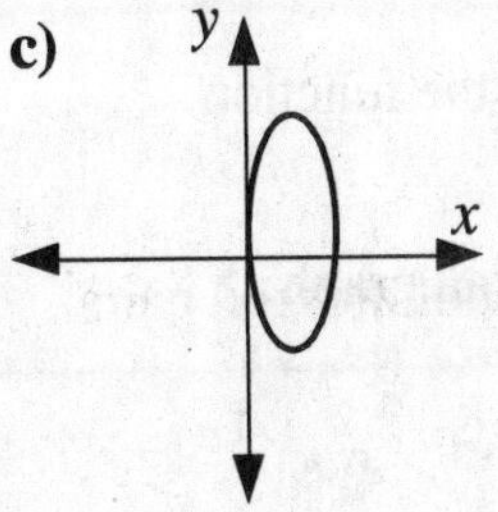

d)

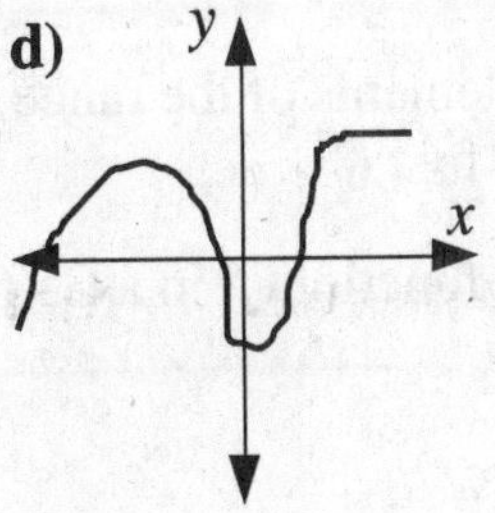

e)

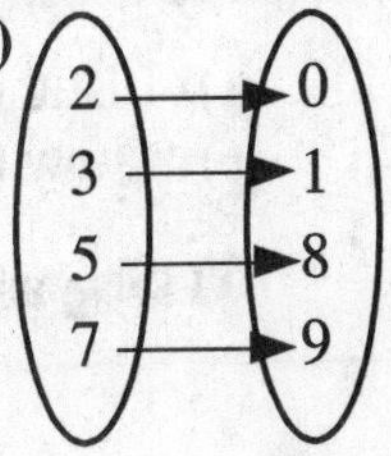

3. State which of the following relations are functions.

a)

Input (*x*)	Output (*y*)
0	3
2	4
4	5
6	3

b)

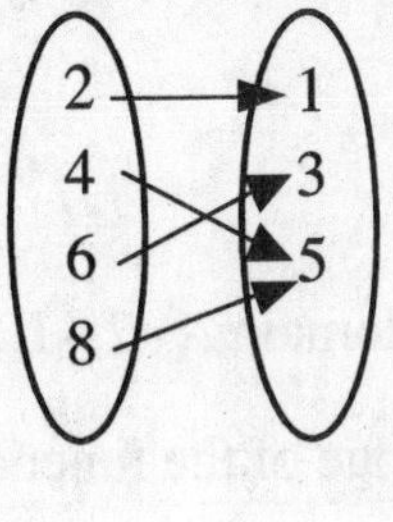

c)

Input (*x*)	Output (*y*)
1	5
–1	5
3	5
7	5

d)

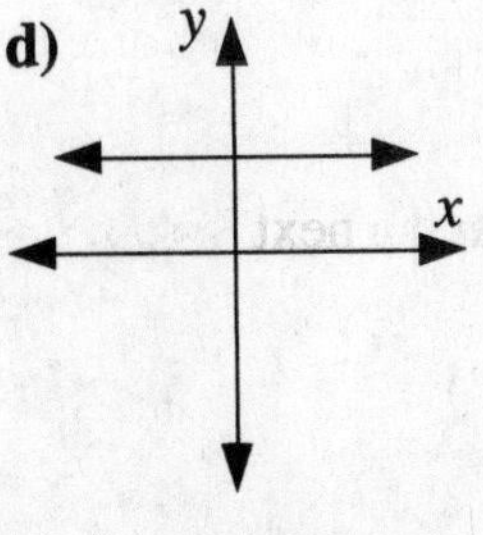

e)

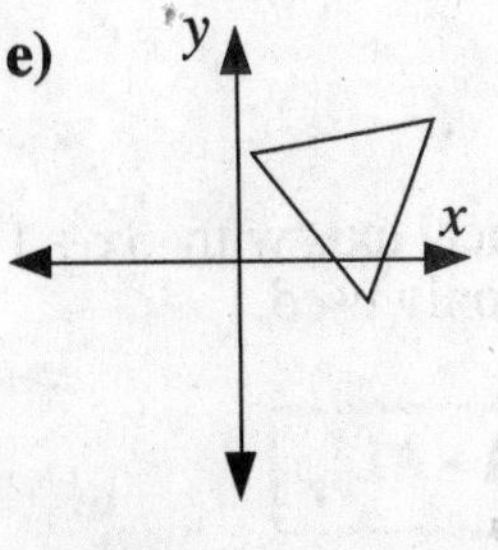

f)

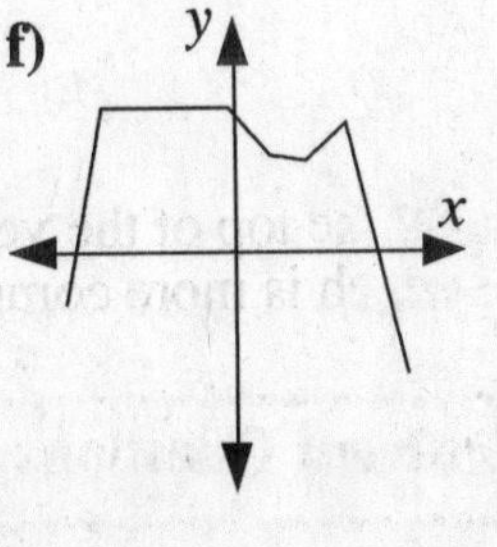

g)

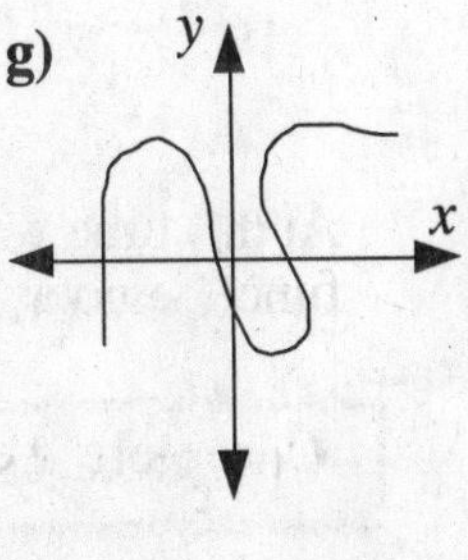

4. Mr. A has a son Jim and a daughter Kristen. Mr. B has three daughters, Lauren, Melanie, and Noreen.

a) Draw an arrow diagram to illustrate the relation "is the father of" from the set of fathers to the set of children. Is the relation "is the father of" a function?

b) Draw an arrow diagram to illustrate the relation "is the child of" from the set of children to the set of fathers. Is the relation "is the child of" a function?

5. The function $f: x \rightarrow 2x + 5$ has domain $\{0, 1, 2, 3\}$.

a) List the elements of the range of the function.

b) Show the function f in a Cartesian graph.

6. The function $g: x \rightarrow x^3$ has domain $\{-2, -1, 0, 1, 2\}$.

a) List the elements of the range of the function.

b) Show the function g in a Cartesian graph.

7. Consider the function $f: x \to x^2 - 4$.

a) Complete the following table of values.

Elements of Domain	3	2	1	–1	–2	–3
Elements of Range						

b) Plot the ordered pairs on a Cartesian graph.

c) Draw a smooth curve through the points to illustrate the function $f: x \to x^2 - 4,\ x \in R$.

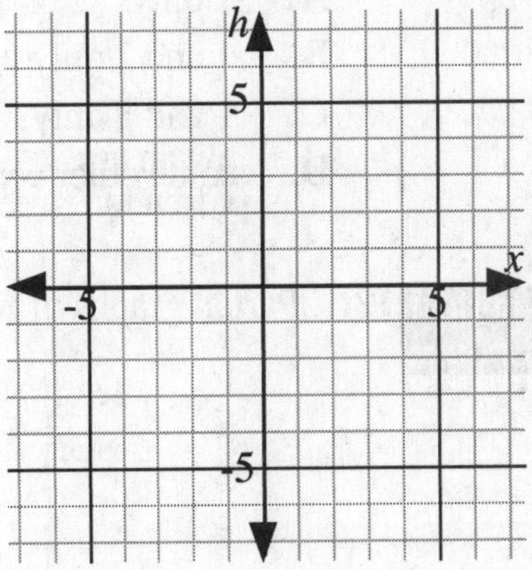

8. The domain of the function $h: x \to 6$ is $\{0, 10, 20\}$.

a) List the ordered pairs of the graph of the function.

b) Show the function h in a Cartesian graph.

Multiple Choice **9.** The function $f: x \to 6 - 2x$ has domain $\{0, 2, 4, 6, 8\}$.
Which of the following is **not** an element of the range of the function?

A. –10
B. 2
C. 4
D. -6

10. Which of the following statements is not always true for a function?

A. A function is a set of ordered pairs (x, y) in which for every x there is only one y.
B. A vertical line must not intersect the graph of a function in more than one point.
C. For every output there is only one input.
D. For every element in the domain, there is only one element in the range.

11. Which of the following represents a function?

1	"multiply the number by 3 and add 5."
2	$y = -x^2$
3	(9, 3), (4, 2), (1, 1), (0, 0). (1, –1), (4,–2), (9,–3)
4	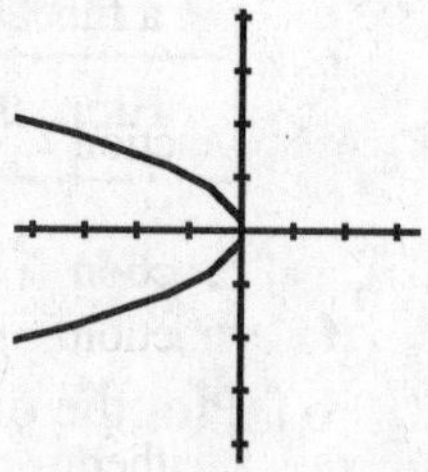

A. 1 only
B. 1 and 2 only
C. 1 and 3 only
D. some other combination of 1 - 4

Numerical Response **12.** Partial graphs of four functions are shown.

1.

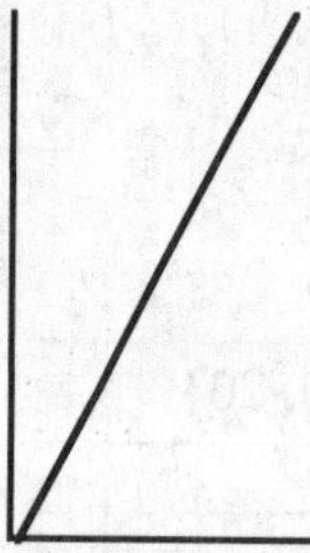

2.

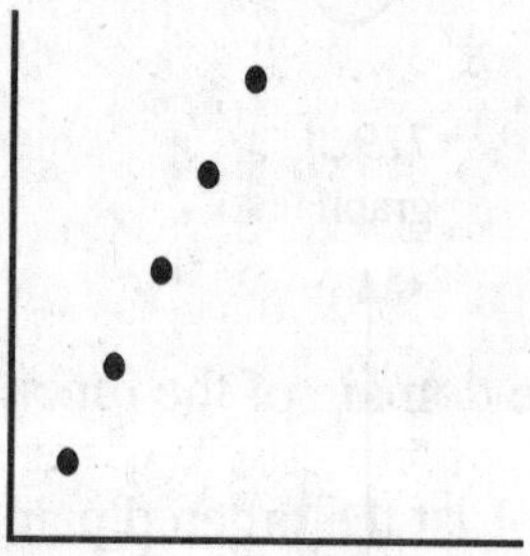

3.

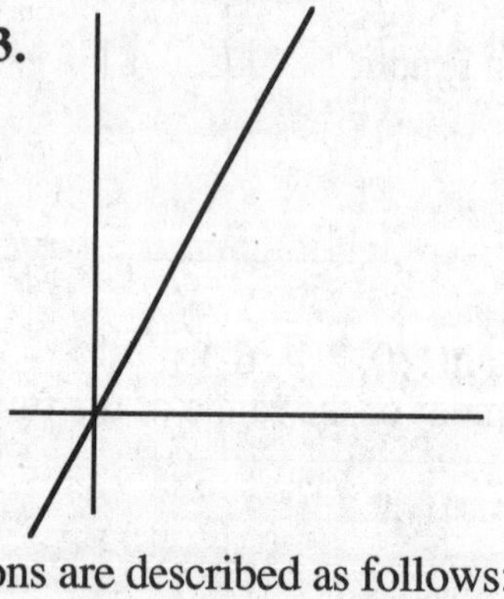

4.

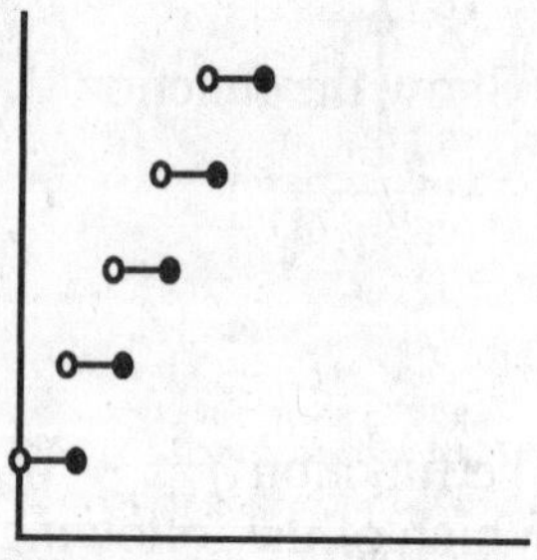

The functions are described as follows:

A: Coffee costs \$8 per jar. Graph cost as a function of the number of jars purchased.

B: Distance cycled at a constant speed of 8 km/h. Graph distance as a function of time.

C: Parking costs \$8 per hour (or part of an hour). Graph cost as a function of time.

D: Set of ordered pairs which satisfy the equation $y = 8x, x \in R$.
Graph y as a function of x.

Place the graph number for function A in the first box.
Place the graph number for function B in the second box.
Place the graph number for function C in the third box.
Place the graph number for function D in the last box.
(Record your answer in the numerical response box from left to right)

Answer Key

1. a) function: each first coordinate has only one second coordinate
b) function: vertical lines intersects the graph exactly once
c) not a function: the input 5 has two outputs
d) not a function: the input 2 has two outputs

2. a) function **b)** not a function **c)** not a function **d)** not a function **e)** function

3. a) function **b)** function **c)** function **d)** function **e)** not a function
f) function **g)** not a function

4. a) Neither mapping diagrams represents a function **b)** Both mapping diagrams represent functions

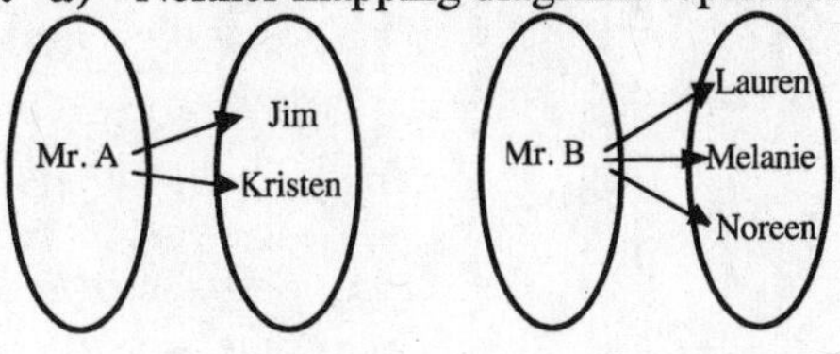

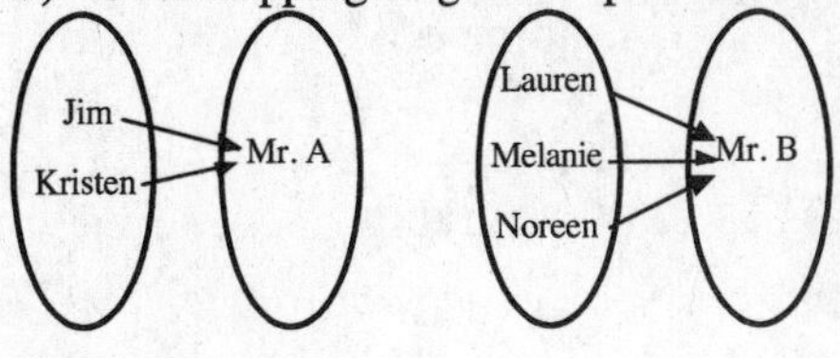

5. a) $\{5, 7, 9, 11\}$
b) see graph below

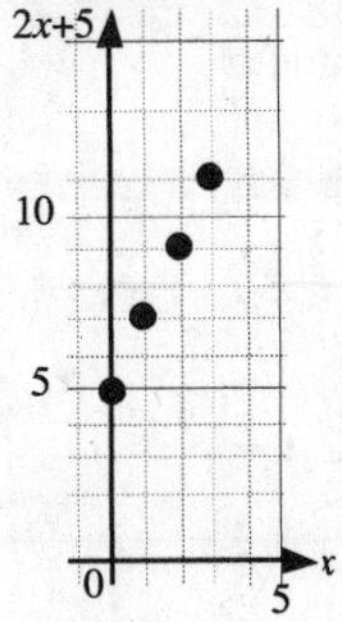

6. a) $\{-8, -1, 0, 1, 8\}$
b) see graph below

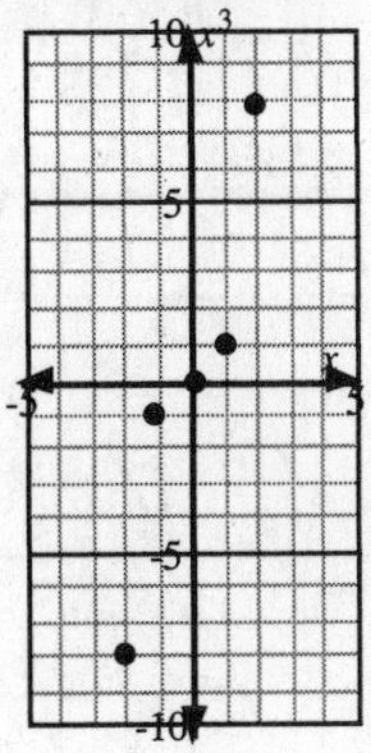

7. a) see table **b)** see grid **c)** see grid

Elements of Domain	3	2	1	–1	–2	–3
Elements of Range	5	0	–3	–3	0	5

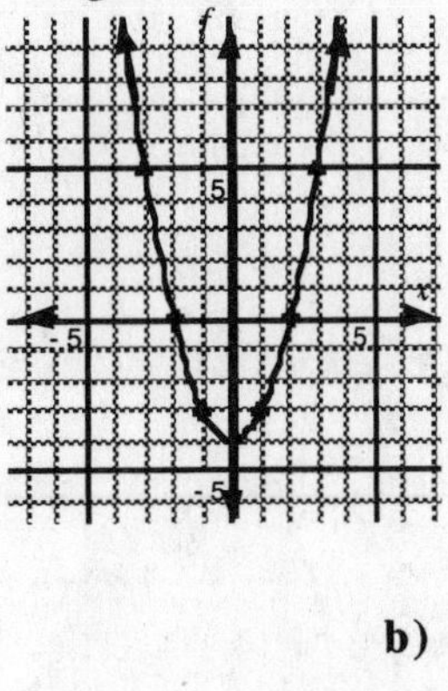

8. a) $\{(0, 6), (10, 6), (20, 6)\}$ **b)**

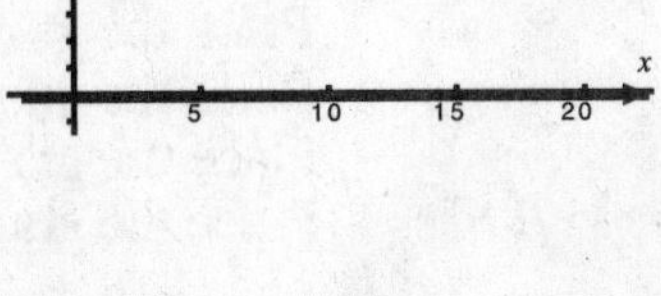

9. C **10.** C **11.** B **12.**

2	1	4	3

Relations and Functions Lesson #8:
Function Notation - Part One

Mapping Notation

In the previous lesson we discovered some ways in which functions can be represented:

- Graph
- Ordered pairs
- Table of Values
- Mapping
- Arrow Diagram

A function was defined in mapping notation as follows.

"A function from a set D, the domain, to a set R, the range, is a relation in which each element of D is related to exactly one element of R.
If the function f maps an element x in the domain to an element y in the range, we write $f: x \rightarrow y$."

Consider the function $f: x \rightarrow 2x + 3$ defined on the set of real numbers.

Under this function we know that $5 \rightarrow 2(5) + 3$ ie $5 \rightarrow 13$.
We say that under the function f, the **image** of 5 is 13.
We also say that the **value of the function** is 13 when $x = 5$.

Function Notation

In most math courses, function notation is used to replace the mapping notation $f: x \rightarrow 2x+3$.
Under a function f, the image of an element x in the domain is denoted by $f(x)$, which is read "f of x".

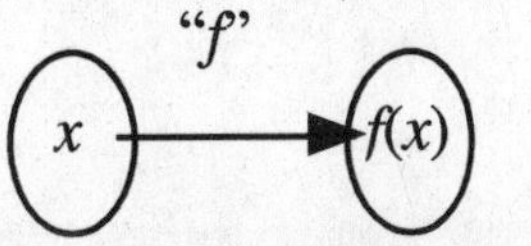

In the example above, the function f can be defined by the formula $f(x) = 2x + 3$.
The notation $f(x) = 2x + 3$ is called **function notation**.

We showed above, that, under the function f, the image of 5 is 13. We write $f(5) = 13$.

<u>mapping notation</u>	<u>function notation</u>	<u>equation of graph of function</u>
$f: x \rightarrow 2x+3$	$f(x) = 2x + 3$	$y = 2x + 3$
$f: 5 \rightarrow 2(5)+3$	$f(5) = 2(5) + 3$	$y = 2(5) + 3$
$f: 5 \rightarrow 13$	$f(5) = 13$	$y = 13$

The symbol $f(x)$ is read as "f at x" or "f of x".
$f(x)$ provides a formula for the function f, and also represents the <u>value</u> of the function for a given value of x.

In function notation:

- $f(x)$ does <u>not</u> mean f times x.
- The "name" of the function is f.
- Values of the independent variable represent the **inputs** of a function and are shown on the **horizontal axis**.
- Values of the dependent variable represent the **outputs** of a function and are shown on the **vertical axis**.

Class Ex. #1

Consider the function $f(x) = x^2 + 5$ and $g(x) = 4 - x$. Evaluate:

a) $f(3)$ **b)** $g(1)$ **c)** $f(-2)$

$f(3) = 3^2 + 5$
$f(3) = 14$

d) $g(-2)$ **e)** $f(0) - g(0)$

Class Ex. #2

Consider the function f defined by $f(x) = 5x^3 - 2x, x \in R$. Determine:

a) $f(-3)$ **b)** the value of f when $x = 2$. **c)** the image of 7 under f

e) an expression for $f(a)$ **f)** an expression for $f(2x)$

Class Ex. #3

If $P(x) = 4x^2 - 6x + 1$, determine a simplified expression for $P(x - 3)$.

Complete Assignment Questions #1 - #7

Class Ex. #4

Consider the function $f(x) = 10x - 3, x \in R$.

a) Determine the value of x if $f(x) = 47$.

b) Solve the equation $f(x) = -23$.

$f(x) = 47$
$y = 47$
$f(x) = 10x - 3$
$47 = 10x - 3$
$+3 \quad +3$
$\frac{50}{10} = \frac{10x}{10} \rightarrow 5 = x$

$-23 = 10x - 3$
$+3 \quad +3$
$\frac{-20}{10} = \frac{10x}{10} \rightarrow -2 = x$
$f(-2) = 10(-2) - 3 = -23$

Class Ex. #5

Consider the function $f(x) = x^2 - 5, x \in R$.

a) Evaluate $f(4)$

b) Solve the equation $f(x) = 4$.

c) Solve the equation $f(t) = 75$, where $t > 0$. Answer in simplest radical form.

Complete Assignment Questions #8 - #13

1-13

Assignment

1. Each statement refers to the function f whose graph has equation $y = f(x)$. Circle the correct choice.

a) f is the *name / value* of the function.

b) The values of x represent the *inputs / outputs* of the function.

c) The values of $f(x)$ represent the *inputs / outputs* of the function.

d) The values of y represent the *inputs / outputs* of the function.

e) x represents the *independent / dependent* variable of the function.

f) $f(x)$ represents the *independent / dependent* variable of the function.

g) y represents the *independent / dependent* variable of the function.

2. If $f(x) = 5x - 7$, determine:

a) $f(2)$

$f(2) = 5(2) - 7$

$f(2) = 3$

b) $f(-3)$

$f(-3) = 5(-3) - 7$

$f(-3) = -15 - 7$

$f(-3) = -22$

c) $f(0)$

$f(0) = 5(0) - 7$

$f(0) = -7$

3. Function g defined by $g(x) = 6 - x^2$. Evaluate:

 a) $g(4)$ **b)** $g(-6)$ **c)** $g(\sqrt{3})$ $\sqrt{3}^2 = 3$

$g(4) = 6 - 4^2$ *(16)* $g(-6) = 6 - (-6^2)$ *(36)* $g(\sqrt{3}) = 6 - 3$

$g(4) = -10$ $g(-6) = -30$ $g(\sqrt{3}) = 3$

4. A function f is defined by the formula $f(x) = x^3 + 1$. Find:
 a) the image of 2 under f **b)** the value of f at -7. **c)** an expression for $f(a)$

5. If $f(x) = x^3 - 2x^2 - x - 5$, evaluate:

 a) $f(5)$

 $f(5) = 5^3 - 2(5)^2 - 5 - 5$

 $f(5) = 125 + 100 - 10$

 $f(5) = 225 - 10$

 $f(5) = 215$

 b) $f(-3)$

 $f(-3) = -3^3 + 2(-3)^2 - 3 - 5$

 $f(-3) = -27 + 36 - 8$

 $f(-3) = 9 - 8$

 $f(-3) = 1$

6. Consider the function f defined by $f(x) = 8 - 2x, \ x \in R$. Determine:

 a) $f(4)$ **b)** the value of f when $x = -4$ **c)** the image of 0.5 under f

$f(4) = 8 - 2(4)$

 d) an expression for $f(2t)$. **e)** an expression for $f(a + 3)$.

7. If $F(x) = 3x^2 - 2x - 9$, determine a simplified expression for

 a) $F(-x)$ **b)** $F(x - 5)$

8. a) If $f(x) = 5x - 7$, then determine the value of x if $f(x) = 43$.

43 = 5x − 7
+7 +7
50 = 5x → 10 = x
5 5

b) If $g(x) = 6x + 3$, then determine the value of x if $g(x) = -24$.

−24 = 6x + 3
−3 −3
−27 = 6x → −4.5 = x
6 6

c) If $g(t) = 56 - 3t$, then determine the value of t if $g(t) = 11$.

11 = 56 − 3t
−56 −56
−45 = −3t 15 = t
−3 −3

d) If $h(x) = -3x + 1$, then determine the value of x if $h(x) = 22$.

22 = −3x + 1 → 21 = −3x → −7 = x
−1 −1 −3 −3

e) If $P(x) = 50 - 3x^2$, then determine the values of x if $P(x) = -25$.

−25 = 50 − 3x²
−50 −50
−75 = −3x² √25 = √x² = 5 = x
−3 −3

9. Consider the function f defined by $f(x) = 6x - 15$. Find:

a) $f(0)$ **b)** an expression for $f(2x + 1)$. **c)** the solution to the equation $f(x) = 27$

f(0) = −15

10. A function C is defined by $C(x) = \sqrt{x}$ where $x \geq 0$.

a) Evaluate:

i) $C(16)$ **ii)** $C\left(\frac{1}{36}\right)$ **iii)** $\frac{C(100)}{C(4)}$

b) If $C(x) = 9$, find x.

11. A function g is defined by the formula $g(t) = t + 12$.

a) Calculate the value of $g(4) + g(-2)$.

$g(4) = 4 + 12$ $g(-2) = -2 + 12$
$g(4) = 16$ $g(-2) = 10$

$16 + 10 = 26$

b) If $g(a^2) = 52$, determine the values of a in simplest radical form.

$52 = g(a^2)$

Multiple Choice **12.** If $f(x) = 3x - 1$ and $f(t) = 8$, then $t =$

A. $\frac{7}{3}$
B. 3
C. $\frac{11}{3}$
D. 23

Numerical Response **13.** A function f is defined by the formula $f(x) = 8\sqrt{x}$, $x \in R$. The value of $f(20)$ can be written in the form $k\sqrt{5}$. The value of k is _____.

(Record your answer in the numerical response box from left to right)

Note: Further assignment questions on Function Notation Part One will appear in the assignment of the next lesson, Function Notation Part Two.

Answer Key

1. a) name **b)** inputs **c)** outputs **d)** outputs
e) independent **f)** dependent **g)** dependent

2. a) 3 **b)** −22 **c)** −7 **3. a)** −10 **b)** −30 **c)** 3

4. a) 9 **b)** −342 **c)** $a^3 + 1$ **5. a)** 65 **b)** −47

6. a) 0 **b)** 16 **c)** 7 **d)** $8 - 4t$ **e)** $2 - 2a$

7. a) $3x^2 + 2x - 9$ **b)** $3x^2 - 32x + 76$

8. a) 10 **b)** $-\frac{9}{2}$ **c)** 15 **d)** −7 **e)** ±5

9. a) −15 **b)** $12x - 9$ **c)** $x = 7$ **10. a) i)** 4 **ii)** $\frac{1}{6}$ **iii)** 5 **b)** 81

11. a) 26 **b)** $a = \pm 2\sqrt{10}$ **12.** B **13.**

1	6		

Relations and Functions Lesson #9:
Function Notation - Part Two

Graphing a Function

Consider the function $f(x) = 3x + 1$. The values of x represent the inputs and make up the domain of the function. The values of $f(x)$ represent the outputs and make up the range of the function.

In previous lessons, we have used y to represent the outputs and the range of a relation. We can therefore write the function $f(x) = 3x + 1$ in x-y notation as $y = 3x + 1$.

The function $f(x) = 3x + 1$ can be written in x-y notation as shown.

Function notation	x-y notation
$f(x) = 3x + 1$	$y = 3x + 1$

Note

- Values of the independent variable represent the **inputs** of a function and are shown on the **horizontal axis**.
- Values of the dependent variable represent the **outputs** of a function and are shown on the **vertical axis**.

Class Ex. #1

Use a graphing calculator to sketch the graph of the function $f(x) = 3x + 1$.

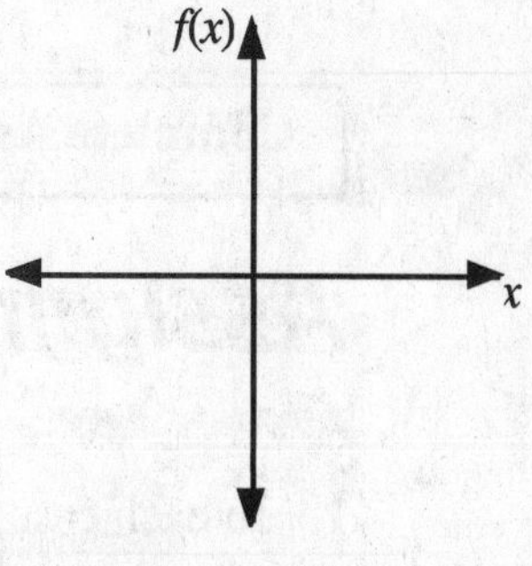

Class Ex. #2

a) In each case, express the relation given in function notation as an equation in two variables.

i) $f(x) = 7x - 23$ **ii)** $g(t) = t^2 - 2t + 35$

b) Express the relation $y = 11x - 15$ in function notation.

c) The graph of the function defined by $y = f(x)$ has equation $y = 4 - 3x$. Express the equation in function notation.

Class Ex. #3

The graph of a function f is shown.

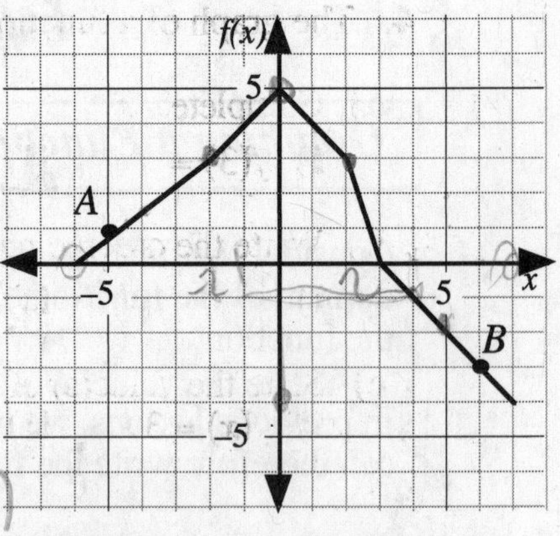

a) Complete:
i) $f(5) =$ -2 **ii)** $f(-2) =$ 3 **iii)** $f(4) =$ -1

b) Write the ordered pairs associated with i), ii), and iii).
i) (5, -2) **ii)** (-2, 3) **iii)** (4, -1)

c) State the value(s) of x if:
i) $f(x) = -1$ **ii)** $f(x) = 3$ **iii)** $f(x) = 4$

x = 4 (4, -1) x = -2 (-2, 3) x = -1 (-1, 4)

d) Use the notation in a) to make a statement about the points A and B on the graph.

(-5, 1) (6, -3) f(-5) = 1 f(6) = -3

e) Write the x- and y- intercepts of the graph using function notation.

f) Complete the following statements.
- The domain of f is $\{x \mid$ ____ $\leq x \leq$ ____ $, x \in R\}$
- The range of f is $\{f(x) \mid$ ____ $\leq f(x) \leq$ ____ $, f(x) \in R\}$

Complete Assignment Questions #1 - #12

Assignment

1. In each case express the relation given in function notation as an equation in two variables.
a) $f(x) = 10 - 3x$ **b)** $g(x) = 12x^2 - 5$ **c)** $P(t) = 2t + 9$

f(2) = 4 g(4) 2299 P(5) = 19

2. Express the following relations in function notation.
a) $y = 17x - 9$ **b)** $y = 4v + 25$ **c)** $x + 2y + 6 = 0$

3. **a)** The graph of the function defined by $y = f(x)$ has equation $y = 0.5x - 0.25$
Express the equation in function notation.

b) The graph of the velocity function defined by $v = f(t)$ has equation $v = 4.9t^2$.
Express the equation in function notation.

4. The graph of a function f is shown.

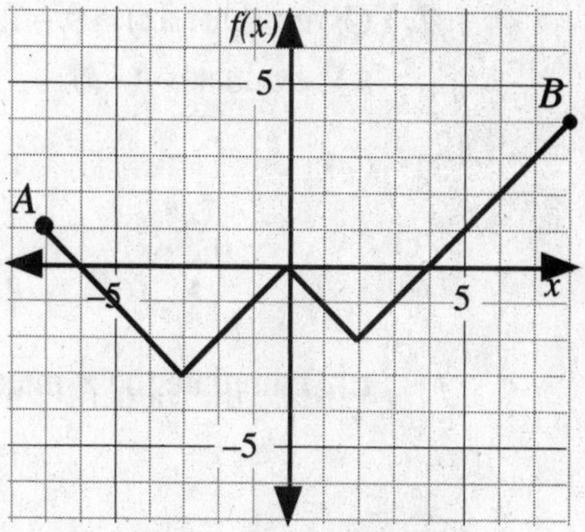

a) Complete:
i) $f(3) =$ **ii)** $f(-3) =$ **iii)** $f(-6) =$

b) Write the ordered pairs associated with i), ii), and iii).
i) **ii)** **iii)**

c) State the value(s) of x if:
i) $f(x) = 3$ **ii)** $f(x) = -2$ **iii)** $f(x) = -4$

d) Use the notation in a) to make a statement about the points A and B on the graph.

e) Write the x- and y- intercepts of the graph using function notation.

f) Complete the following statements.
- The domain of f is $\{x \mid$ _____ $\le x \le$ _____, $x \in R\}$
- The range of f is $\{f(x) \mid$ _____ $\le f(x) \le$ _____, $f(x) \in R\}$

5. The function $g(x) = 3x^2 - 4$ has a domain $\{-2, -1, 0, 1, 2\}$.
a) State the range of g. **b)** Solve the equation $g(x) = -1$.

6. Consider the graph of the function f shown below.

a) Complete the table.

b) Explain why the solution to the equation $f(x) = 4$ has an infinite number of solutions.

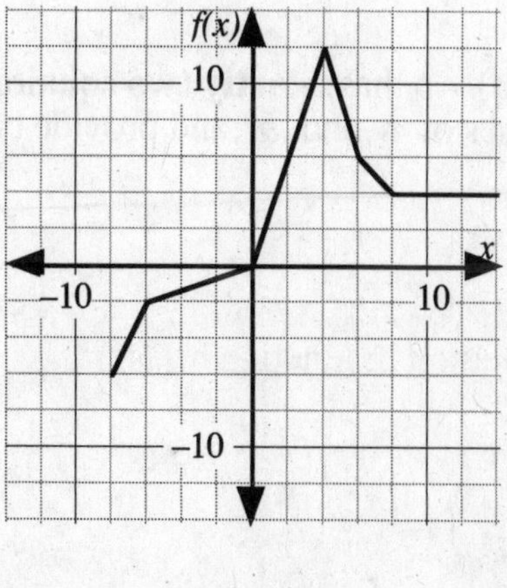

x	$f(x)$	Ordered Pair
2		(2,)
	0	
−6		
8		
	−6	
10		

7. Given that $f(x) = 9 - 2x$,

a) evaluate $f(-3)$

$f(-3) = 9 - 2(-3)$

$\hookrightarrow f(-3) = 9 - 6$

$\hookrightarrow f(-3) = 3$

b) find the value of $f(t) + f(-t)$

c) calculate the x-intercept and the y-intercept on the graph of f.

8. The graph of a function is shown.

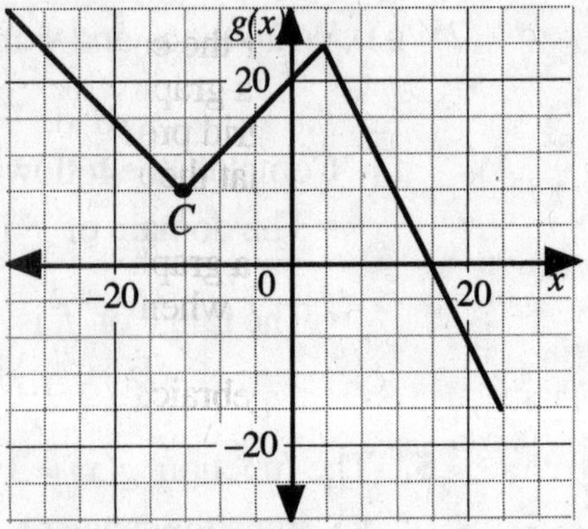

a) A student is asked to make a statement about point C on the graph. The student states that $f(-3) = 2$.

i) Explain **two** errors in the student's statement.

ii) Write a correct statement using function notation about point C.

b) Give the solution to the following equations.

i) $g(x) = -8$ **ii)** $g(x) = 16$.

c) State the value of: **i)** $g(-8)$ **ii)** $g(16)$

d) State the domain and range of the function.

e) The equation $g(a) = b$ has **exactly two** solutions. Explain clearly how to use the graph to determine values of a and b, and provide two sets of answers to the problem.

9. Consider the function $f(x) = 1 - x^2$, where x is an integer.

a) Evaluate $f(2) - f(-1)$ **b)** Given that $f(a^{\frac{1}{4}}) = -8$, calculate the value of a.

f(2) = 1 - 2²
f(2) = -3
f(1) = 1 - 1²
f(1) = 0
-3 + 0 = -3
f(2) - f(1) = -3

Multiple Choice **10.** The graph of the function $f(x) = 4^x$, $x \in R$, intersects the y-axis at

A. $(0,0)$
B. $(0,1)$
C. $(0,4)$
D. no point

11. Function P is such that $P(5) = -1$. Two students each make a statement about the function P.

Rose states "When the domain value is 5, the related range value is -1."
Susan states "The point $(-1,5)$ is on the graph of $y = P(x)$".

-1 = y not x

Which of the following is true?

A. Both statements are correct.
B. Both statements are incorrect.
C. Rose is correct and Susan is incorrect.
D. Susan is correct and Rose is incorrect.

5 = x (Domain) -1 = y (Range)

Numerical Response **12.** Consider the graph of the function $f(x) = 5x - 11$. The x-intercept of the graph of f is located at $(a, 0)$. The value of a is _____ .

(Record your answer in the numerical response box from left to right)

Answer Key

1. a) $y = 10 - 3x$ **b)** $y = 12x^2 - 5$ **c)** $y = 2t + 9$

2. a) $f(x) = 17x - 9$ **b)** $f(v) = 4v + 25$ **c)** $f(x) = -\frac{1}{2}x - 3$

3. a) $f(x) = 0.5x - 0.25$ **b)** $f(t) = 4.9t^2$

4. a) **i)** -1 **ii)** -3 **iii)** 0
b) **i)** $(3, -1)$ **ii)** $(-3, -3)$ **iii)** $(-6, 0)$
c) **i)** 7 **ii)** $-4, -2, 2$ **iii)** no solution **d)** A is $f(-7) = 1$, B is $f(8) = 4$
e) x-intercepts can be represented in function notation by; $f(-6) = 0, f(0) = 0, f(4) = 0$
y-intercept can be represented in function notation by $f(0) = 0$
f) $-7 \le x \le 8, \quad -3 \le f(x) \le 4$

5. a) Range = $\{-4, -1, 8\}$ **b)** $x = \pm 1$

6. See table below.

x	$f(x)$	Ordered Pair
2	6	(2, 6)
0	0	(0, 0)
−6	−2	(−6, −2)
8	4	(8, 4)
−8	−6	(−8, −6)
10	4	(10, 4)

b) The horizontal line where $f(x) = 4$ has an infinite number of input values between 8 and 14.

7. a) 15 **b)** 18 **c)** x-int = $\frac{9}{2}$, y-int = 9

8. a) **i)** The name of the function is g not f. The scale is 4 units per box, not 1 unit per box.
ii) $g(-12) = 8$
b) **i)** $x = 20$ **ii)** $x = -20, -4, 8$
c) **i)** 12 **ii)** 0
d) Domain = $\{x \mid -32 \le x \le 24, x \in R\}$, $\{g(x) \mid -16 \le g(x) \le 28\}, g(x) \in R$
e) A horizontal line must intersect the graph at exactly two points.
This occurs when $g(x) = 24$ and when $g(x) = 8$.
Solution 1: $b = 24$ when $a = -28$ or 4.
Solution 2: $b = 8$ when $a = -12$ or 12

9. a) -3 **b)** 81 **10.** B **11.** C **12.**

2	.	2	

Relations and Functions Lesson #10:
Function Notation and Problem Solving

Using Function Notation

In Lesson 2 and 3 we solved problems about relations defined by an equation. In this lesson we solve problems where function notation is used to define the relation.

In lesson 3, assignment question #6, we had the following scenario.

" A candle manufacturer found that their "Long-Last" candles melted according to the formula $h = -2t + 12$, where h is the height of the candle, in cm, after t hours."

The relation between height and time is described by an **equation.**

The relation is a function because for each input there is only one output, and so it can be described using the **function notation** below.

" A candle manufacturer found that their "Long-Last" candles melted according to the formula $h(t) = -2t + 12$, where h is the height of the candle, in cm, after t hours."

In this example, the notation $h(4)$ is a simplified way of representing the height of the candle after four hours.

Class Ex. #1

A candle manufacturer found that their "Long-Last" candles melted according to the formula $h(t) = -2t + 12$, where h is the height of the candle, in cm, after t hours.

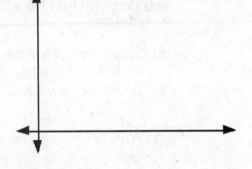

a) Use a graphing calculator to sketch the graph of the function and show the graph on the grid

b) Determine the value of $h(5)$.

c) Write in words the meaning of $h(5)$.

d) Evaluate the following, and explain each of their significance.

i) $h(0)$ **ii)** $h(6)$ **iii)** $h(8)$

e) How long will it take for the candle to burn down to a height of 7 cm?

f) Suggest an appropriate domain and range for the function.

Complete Assignment Questions #1 - #5

Assignment

1. Ivory the botanist treated a 2 cm plant with a special growth fertilizer. With this fertilizer, the plant grew at a rate modelled by the function $H(t) = \frac{5}{3}t + 2$, where $H(t)$ represents the height of the plant in cm after t days.

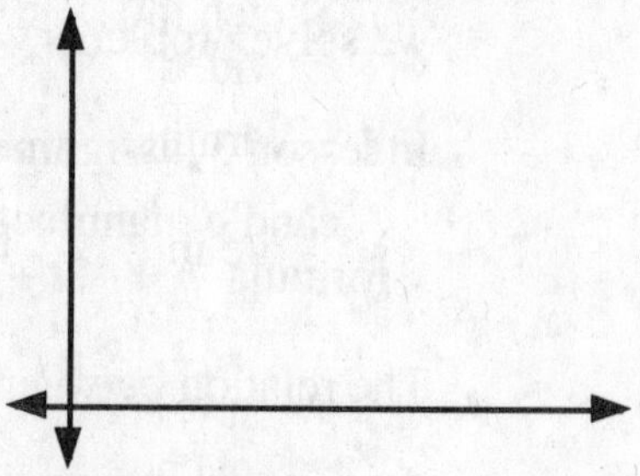

a) Use a graphing calculator to sketch the graph of the function and show the graph on the grid.

b) Determine the value of $H(3)$.

c) Write in words the meaning of $H(3)$.

d) Evaluate the following.

i) $H(0)$ **ii)** $H(6)$ **iii)** $H(21)$

e) How long will it take for the plant to reach a height of 21 cm?

f) It takes 27 days for the plant to mature (to reach maximum height). State the domain and range of the function $H(t)$.

2. The cost to Inner Technology of producing IT graphing calculators can be modelled by the function $C(n) = 11750 + 32n$, where $C(n)$ represents the cost in dollars of producing n calculators.

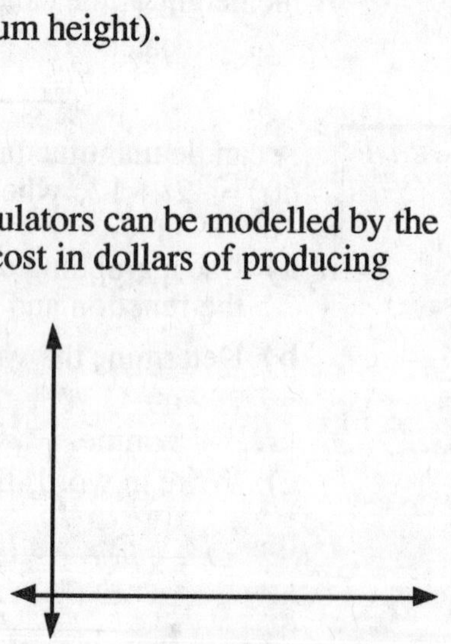

a) Sketch the graph of the function for a maximum of 4000 calculators.

b) Determine the value of $C(30)$.

c) Write in words the meaning of $C(30)$.

d) Evaluate $C(0)$ and explain its significance.

e) How many calculators can be produced for $31 270?

f) Last month IT produced 2 600 calculators and spent $14 000 on advertising. If there are other fixed monthly costs of $24 500, and each calculator sells for $165, how much profit would be made if all the calculators are sold?

3. Over the last 10 years, data was recorded for the number of cups of hot chocolate sold at BGB Senior High School. It was found from the data that the warmer the weather, the less cups of hot chocolate were sold. The data can be modelled by the formula $N(t) = 150 - 10t$, where $N(t)$ is the daily number of cups of hot chocolates sold when the average daily temperature is t °C.

a) Sketch the graph of the function on the grid provided.

b) Determine the value of $N(-5)$.

c) Write in words the meaning of $N(-5)$.

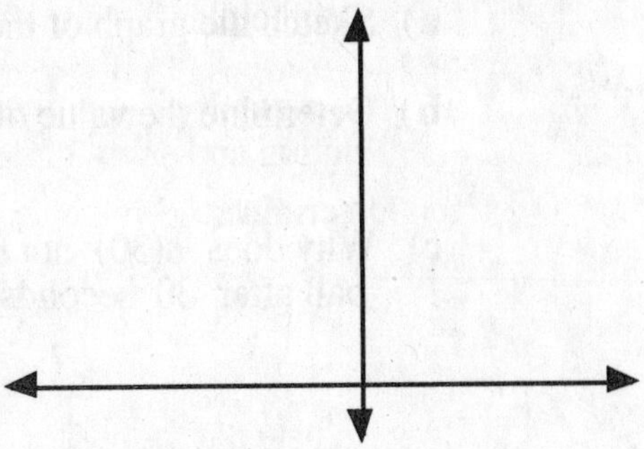

d) What was the average temperature if 190 cups of hot chocolate were sold?

e) Explain how to estimate the lower limit of the domain of the relation.

f) Suggest an appropriate domain and range for the function $N(t)$ if BGB High School is located in southern Alberta.

4. A special type of weather balloon follows a path which can be represented by the formula $h(t) = -9t^2 + 900t$, where $h(t)$ is the height in cm after t minutes.

a) Sketch the graph of the function on the grid.

b) Determine the value of $h(30)$ and $h(70)$.

c) Does $h(30) = h(70)$? Do they mean the same thing? Explain.

d) Evaluate the following, and explain their significance in the context of the question.

i) $h(0)$ **ii)** $h(100)$ **iii)** $h(110)$

e) What is the highest point the balloon will reach?

f) When will the balloon land?

g) Suggest appropriate domain and range for the function $h(t)$?

5. As part of an experiment, a 50 kg steel ball is dropped from a Canadian Air Force jet. The height of the steel ball above the ground can be described by part of the graph of the function $h(t) = 2575 - 4.9t^2$, where $h(t)$ is the height, in metres, of the steel ball after t seconds.

a) Sketch the graph of the function on the grid.

b) Determine the value of $h(30)$.

c) Why does $h(30)$ not represent the height of the ball after 30 seconds?

d) At what height is the ball dropped from the jet?

e) How long (to the nearest second) will it take the ball to make contact with the ground?

f) Suggest an appropriate domain and range for the function $h(t)$.

Answer Key

1. b) 7 **c)** After 3 days the height is 7 cm. **d)** i) 2 ii) 12 iii) 37 **e)** 11.4 days
f) domain $\{t \mid 0 \le t \le 27, t \in R\}$ range $\{H(t) \mid 2 \le H(t) \le 47, H(t) \in R\}$

2. b) 12710 **c)** It costs $12 710 to produce 30 calculators.
d) $C(0)$ = 11 750. There are fixed costs of $11750 before any calculators are produced.
e) 610 **f)** $295 550

3. b) 200 **c)** 200 cups are sold when the average temperature is –5°C. **d)** –4°C
e) Estimate the minimum average daily temperature.
f) Answers may vary. domain $\{t \mid -35 \le t \le 15, t \in R\}$ range $\{N(t) \mid 0 \le N(t) \le 500, N(t) \in W\}$

4. b) both = 18 900
c) They are equal but do not represent the same thing. $h(30)$ is the height after 30 minutes. and $h(70)$ is the height after 70 minutes
d) i) 0 Initial height = 0 m ii) 0 After 100 min the balloon has landed on the ground.
iii) –9900 this has no meaning since the balloon has already landed
e) 22 500 cm = 225 m **f)** after 100 min
g) domain $\{t \mid 0 \le t \le 100, t \in R\}$ range $\{h(t) \mid 0 \le h(t) \le 22\,500, h(t) \in R\}$

5. b) –1835
c) The ball has already hit the ground, so the function no longer represents the height of the ball.
d) 2575 m **e)** 23 seconds
f) domain $\{t \mid 0 \le t \le 23, t \in R\}$ range $\{h(t) \mid 0 \le h(t) \le 2575, h(t) \in R\}$

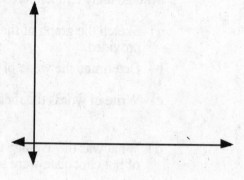

Relations and Functions Lesson #11:
Interpreting Graphs of Functions

Class Ex. #1

The Carter Family are driving to Yukon for a family vacation. The graph represents the amount of fuel (in litres) in the gas tank of their car on the first day of their journey.

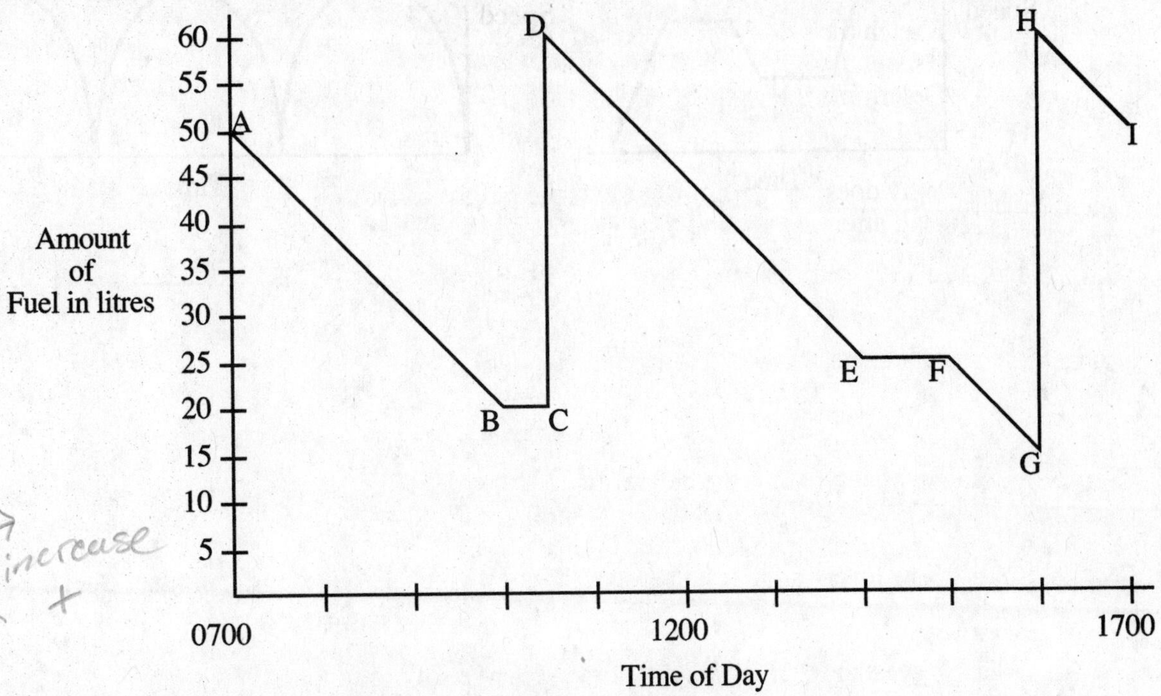

The graph of the journey is divided into eight line segments.

a) With reference to the journey, explain what is happening between:

i) A and B

ii) B and C

iii) C and D

b) What is the rate of fuel consumption (in litres per hour) between D and E?

c) Which line segment represents the car being refueled for the second time?

d) Calculate the total time when the car is being driven.

e) If fuel costs 85¢ per litre, calculate the cost of the fuel used for the first day of the journey?

Suggest a possible scenario for each of the following graphs:

a)

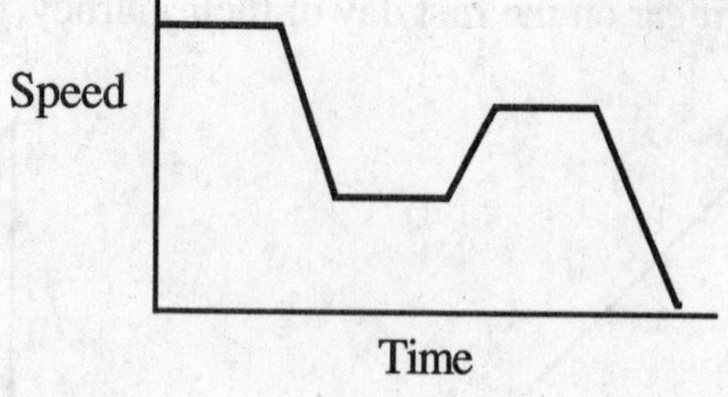

b)

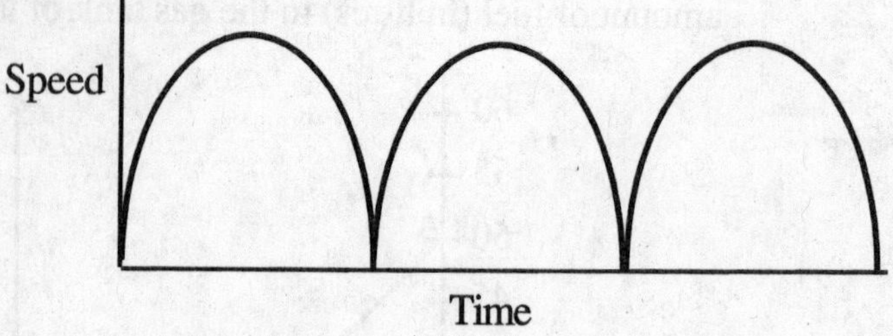

Sketching a Graph

Sketch a graph with no scale for each of the following:

a) the oven temperature when baking a pie.

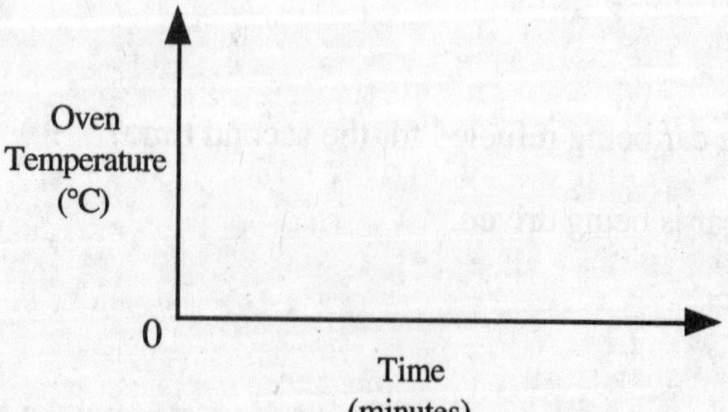

b) Ben taking part in a 100 m sprint.

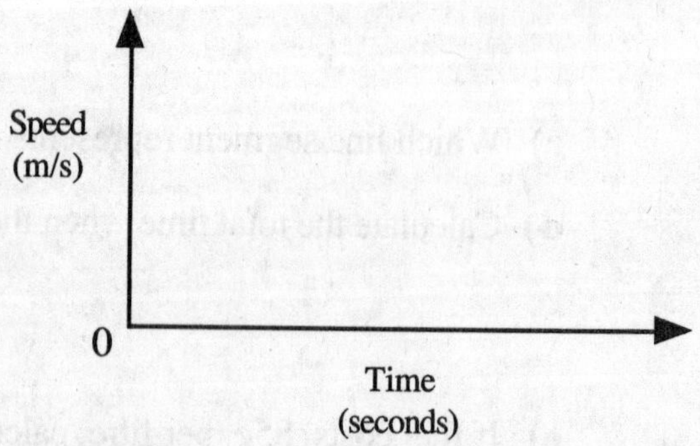

Complete Assignment Questions #1 - #13

Assignment

1. Three sisters, Amanda, Brittany, and Chelsea, each follow the same route to school. One morning Amanda cycles to school, Brittany walks to school, and Chelsea runs to school.
Lines 1, 2, and 3, on the graph represent the three routes.

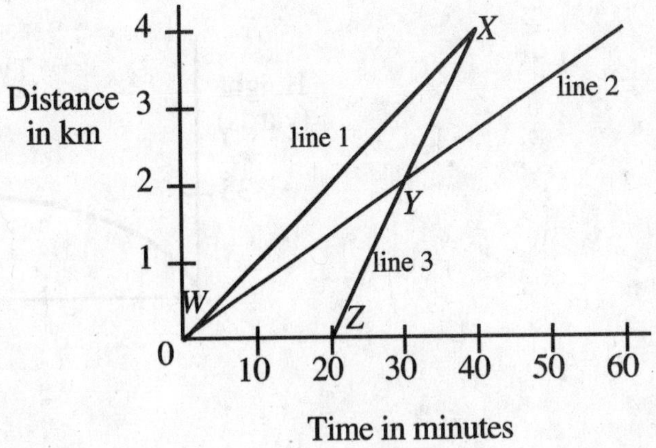

a) Complete the table below.

	Line 1	Line 2	Line 3
Distance (km)	4		
Time (hrs)	⅔		
Rate (km/hr)	6		
Student			

b) Explain what is happening at the following points.

i) *W*

ii) *X*

iii) *Y*

iv) *Z*

c) How can you tell from the steepness of the lines which line represents the route of each student?

2. Tyler, a member of St. Andrews High School golf team, hits a golf ball. The graph shows the path of the ball. Describe Tyler's golf shot.

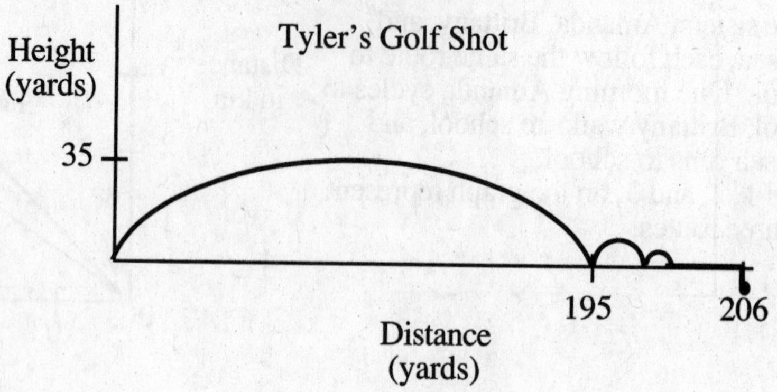

3. Dar sells medical supplies. The graph shows the amount of gasoline in his car during a particular day.

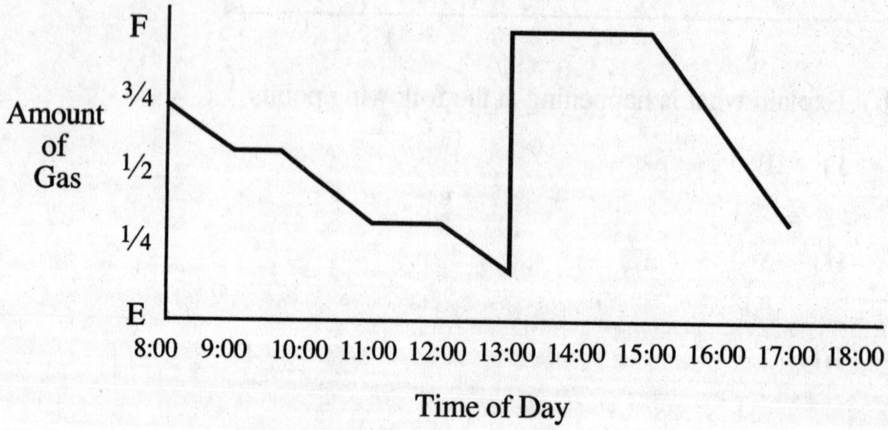

Describe how Dar may have spent the day.

4. The two graphs shown compare two yachts: the Yukon and the Territory. The first graph compares the yachts by age and cost. The second graph compares the boats by speed and length. Describe the comparison between the two yachts.

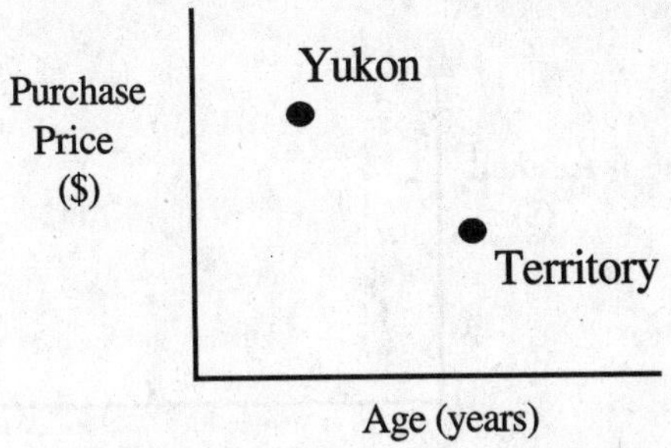

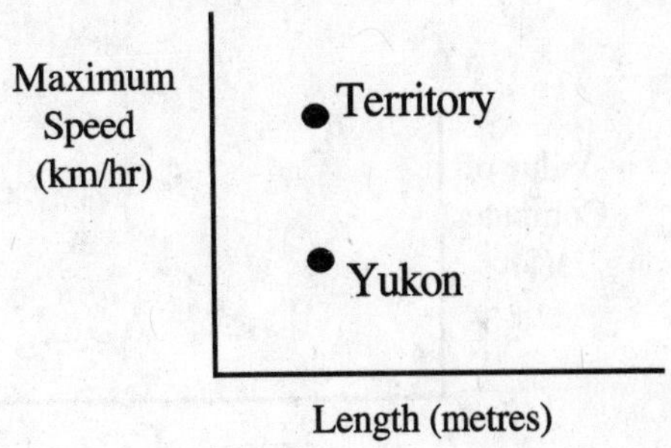

5. A super ball is dropped from a 10 m building. On each bounce, it bounces back to 80% of its previous height. Create a graph of height as a function of time.

6. Suggest a possible scenario for each of the following graphs.

a)

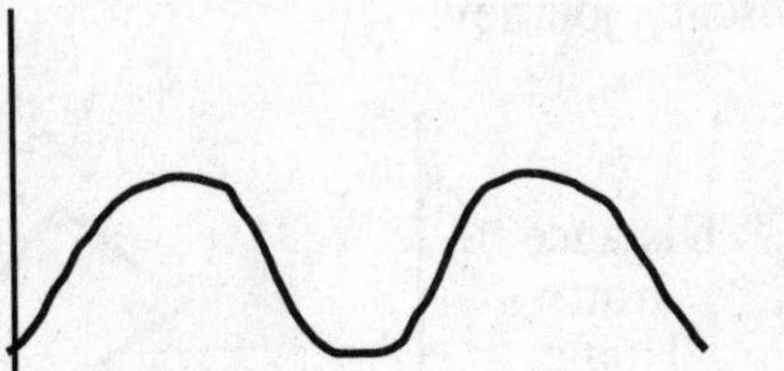

b)

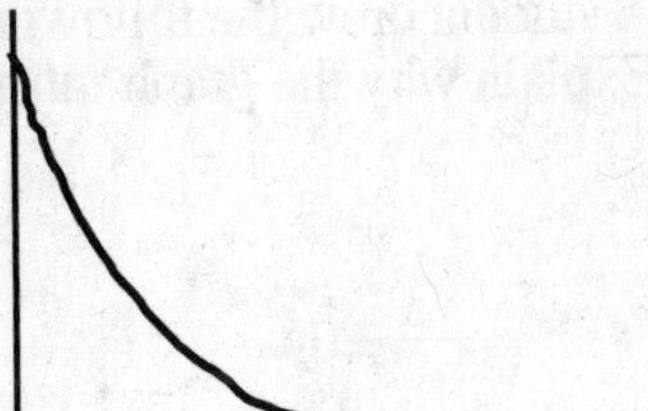

7. Sketch a graph with no scale to represent each of the following.

a) A computer's value compared to its age.

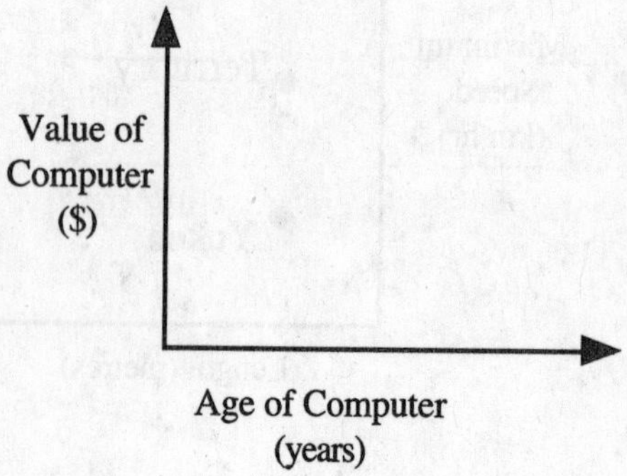

b) The amount of your savings if you save $10 every month for a period of six months.

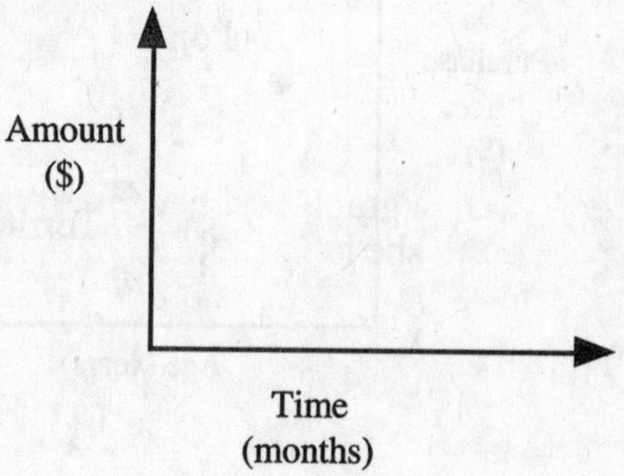

c) The air temperature during a spring day from 6:00 a.m. to 6:00 p.m.

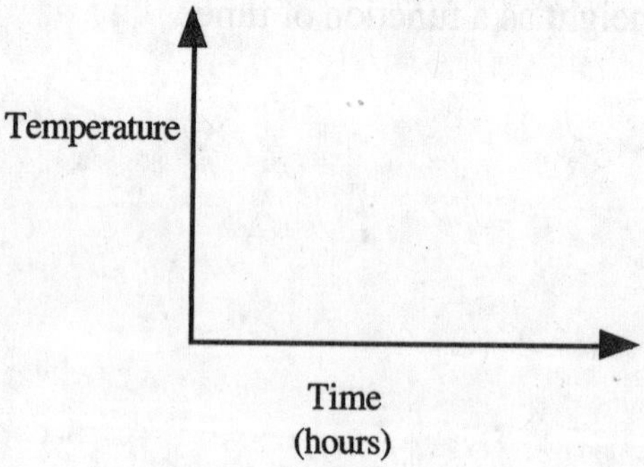

d) You are sitting in the bottom chair of a ferris wheel. Graph your height above the ground during two rotations of the wheel.

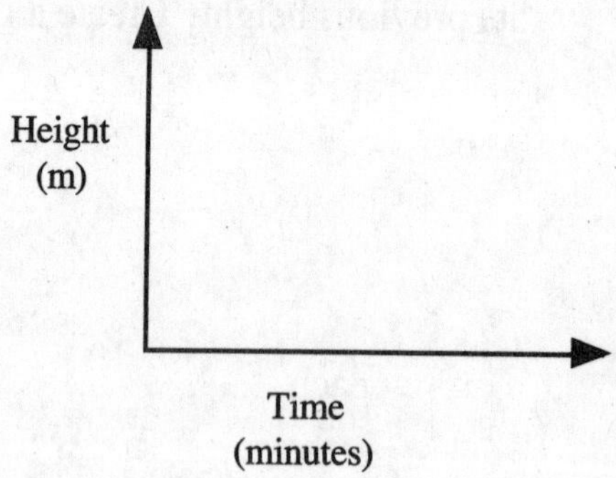

8. A student drew the following graph to represent a journey. Explain why the graph must be incorrect.

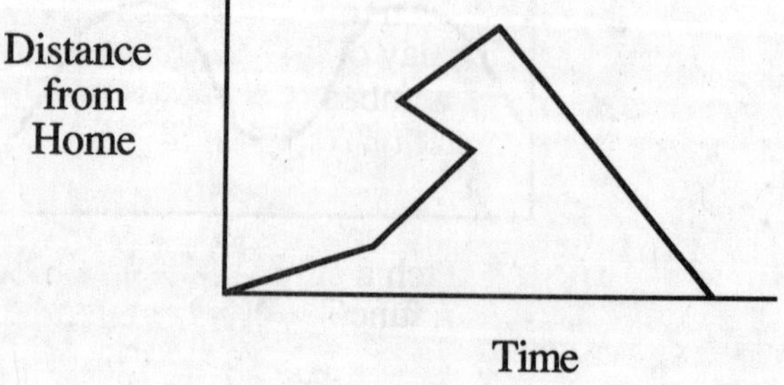

Use the following information to answer the next question.

Melanie leaves school and runs to the shop. She spends some time in the shop and walks home.

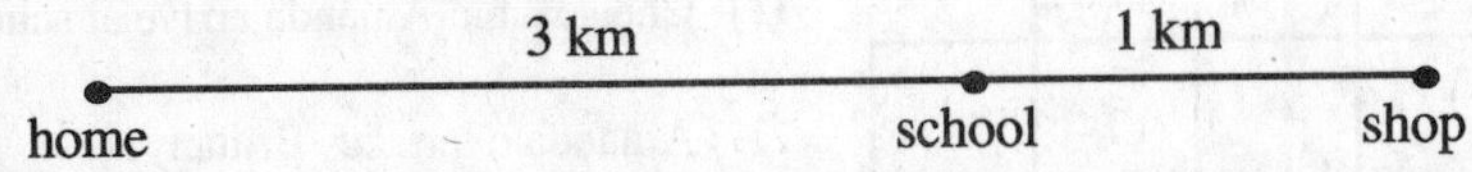

Multiple Choice **9.** Which graph best describes Melanie's distance from home starting from when she left school?

A.

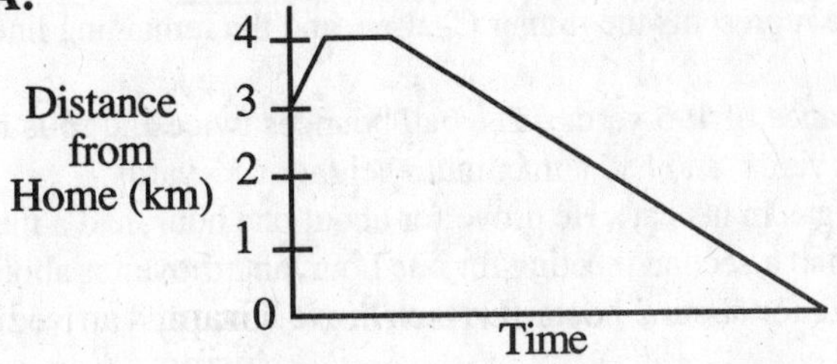

B.

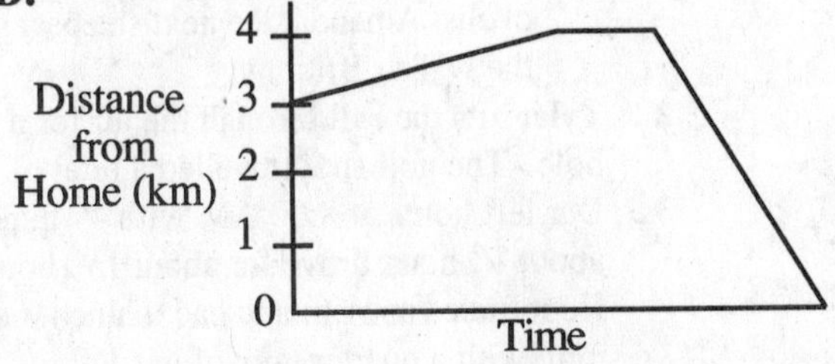

C.

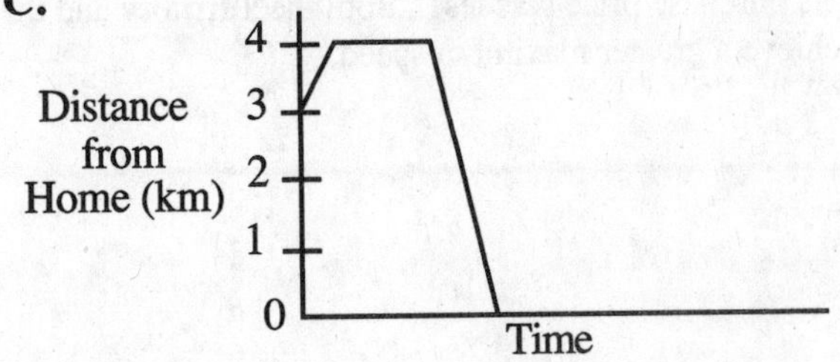

D.

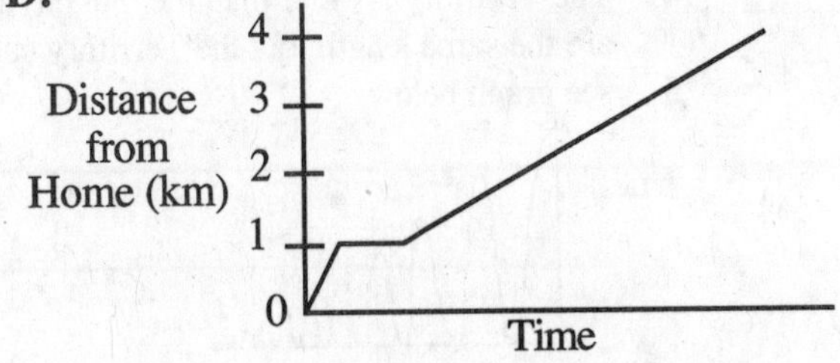

Matching Match each description on the left with the best graph on the right. Each graph may be used once, more than once, or not at all.

<u>Description</u>

10. Sketch a graph of a person's height as a function of their age.

11. The number of hours of daylight in a given town in Alberta depends on the day of the year. Sketch a graph of number of hours of daylight as a function of day of the year.

12. Sketch a graph of the area of a circle as a function of its radius.

13. You start driving at a constant speed with a full tank of gas. Sketch a graph of litres of gas in the tank as a function of distance travelled.

<u>Graph</u>

A.

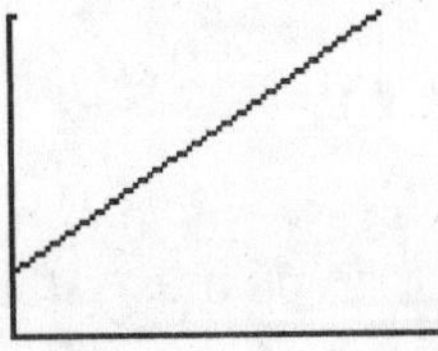

B.

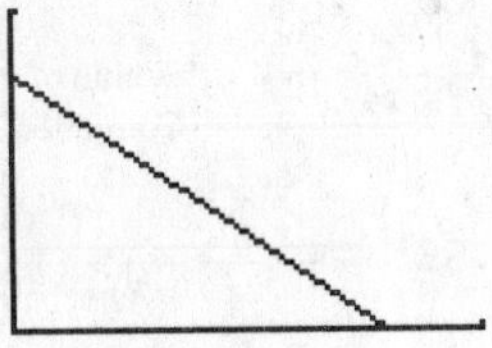

C.

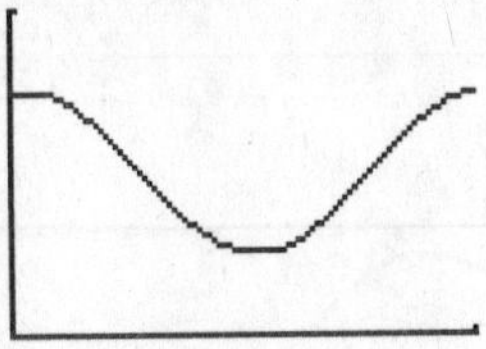

D.

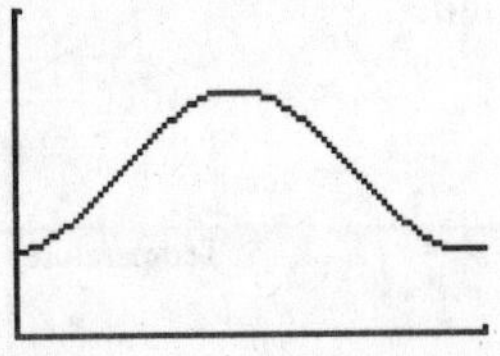

E.

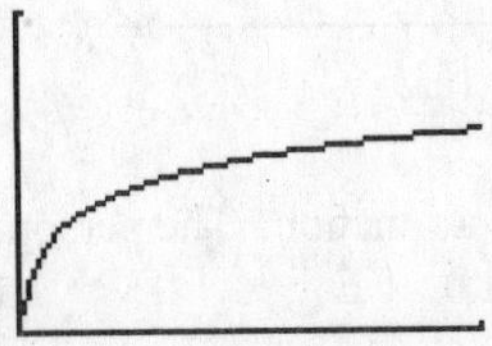

F.

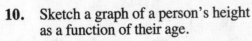

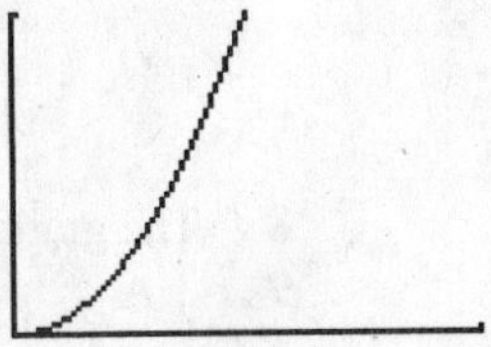

Answer Key (Answers may vary)

1. a) see table below

	Line 1	Line 2	Line 3
Distance (km)	4	4	4
Time (hrs)	$2/3$	1	$\frac{1}{3}$
Rate (km/hr)	6	4	12
Student	Chelsea	Brittany	Amanda

b) i) Chelsea and Brittany leave home at the same time.

ii) Chelsea and Amanda arrive at school.

iii) Amanda overtakes Brittany.

iv) Amanda leaves home 20 minutes after Brittany and Chelsea.

c) The steeper the graph, the less time is taken to travel to school. The steepest slope represents the cyclist Amanda, the next steepest slope represents the runner Chelsea, and the remaining line represents the walker Brittany.

2. Tyler hits the ball through the air for a distance of 195 yards. The ball bounces twice and rolls into the hole. The golf shot travelled a total of 206 yards, and had a maximum height of 35 yards.

3. Dar left home at 8:00 AM with $3/4$ tank of gas in his car. He drove for about one hour, had a meeting for about $1/2$ hour, drove for about $1\,1/2$ hours, had a second meeting for one hour, and drove for about one hour. He refueled at 1 pm and had a lunch meeting for about 2 hours. He then drove home and arrived about 5 p.m. with a quarter tank of gas left.

4. The Territory is older than the Yukon, and its purchase price was less. Both the Territory and the Yukon are the same length, but the Territory can achieve a greater maximum speed.

5. see graph below

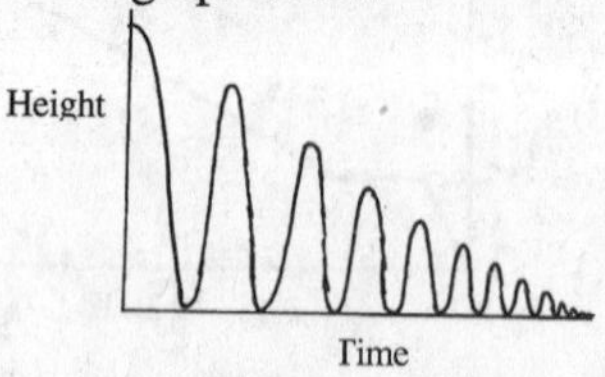

6. a) The number of hours of daylight per day over a period of two years for a location in the northern hemisphere.

b) The value of a car depreciating over time.

7. a)

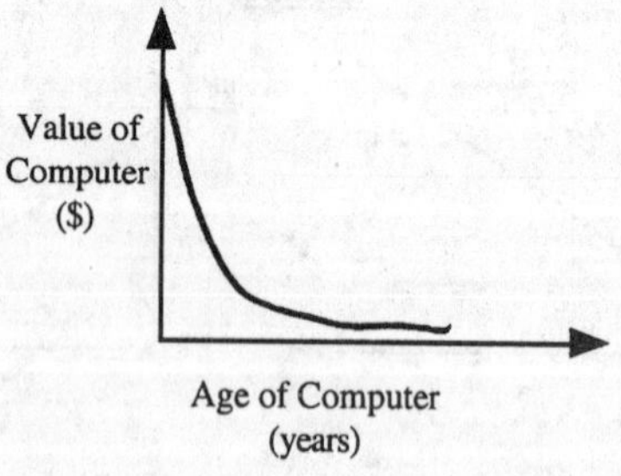

b)

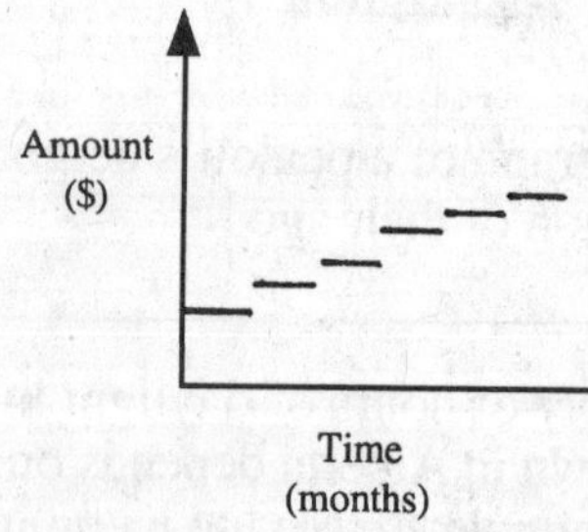

c)

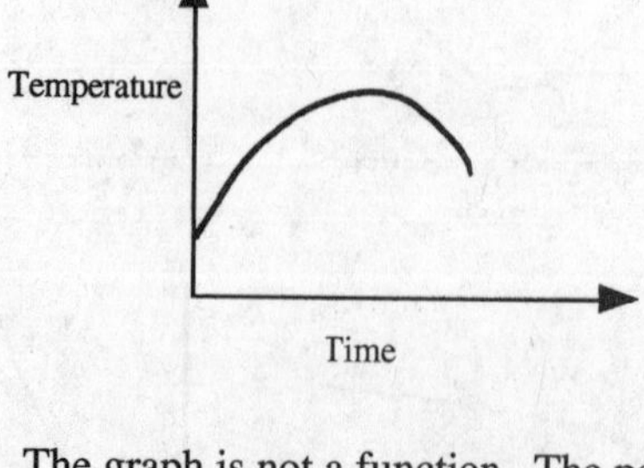

d)

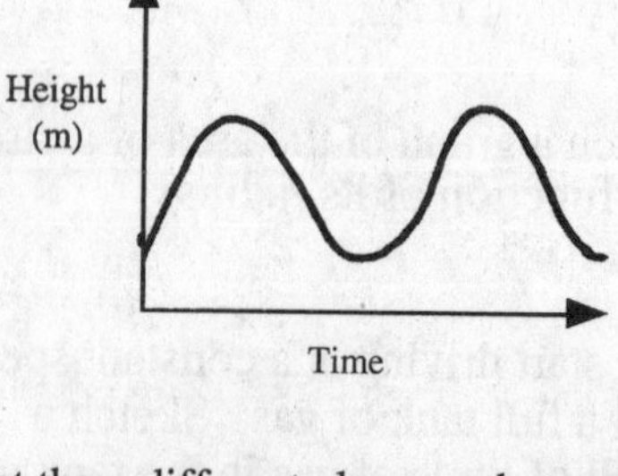

8. The graph is not a function. The person cannot be at three different places at the same time.

9. A 10. E 11. D 12. F 13. B

Relations and Functions Lesson #12: Practice Test

1. Which of the following variables is discrete?

   A. The time taken to run 50 metres.
   B. The distance travelled by a train.
   C. The number of animals in a zoo.
   D. The weight of a dog.

2. Which of the following statements is false?

   A. The domain of a relation is associated with values of the independent variable.
   B. The dependent variable is represented by the first coordinate of an ordered pair.
   C. The inputs of a relation are shown on the horizontal axis of a Cartesian Plane.
   D. The range of a relation is represented on the vertical axis of the graph of the relation.

Numerical Response 1. To the nearest hundredth, the positive x-intercept on the graph of the relation $2x^2 + 6y^2 = 7$ is _____ .
(Record your answer in the numerical response box from left to right)

Use the following information to answer the next question.

The graphs of two relations are shown.

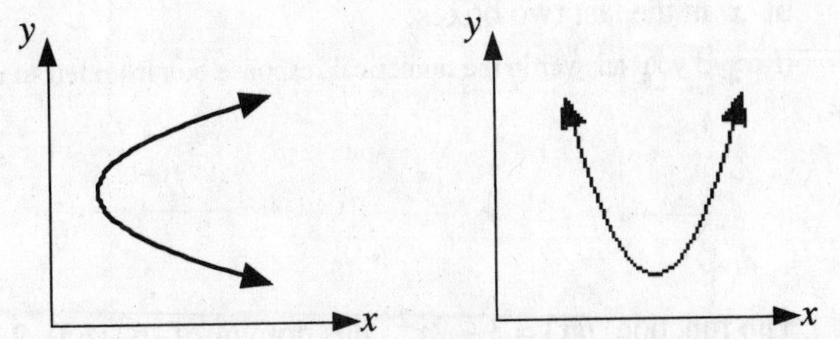

3. Which of the following statements is true?

   A. The domains are the same, but the ranges are different.
   B. The ranges are the same, but the domains are different.
   C. The domains are the same, and the ranges are the same.
   D. The domains are different, and the ranges are different.

Numerical Response

2. The graph of the relation $4x^2 - 3y = 12$ has x-intercepts a and b, and y-intercept c. The value of the product abc is _____ .

(Record your answer in the numerical response box from left to right)

Use the following information to answer the next two questions.

> The cost ($\$ C$) of publishing a school newspaper is partially fixed and partially depends on the number (n) of newspapers printed. The cost is given by the formula $C = 98 + 0.12n$.

4. The cost of publishing 780 newspapers is

   A. \$191.60
   B. \$773.76
   C. \$94.58
   D. \$9 458.00

Numerical Response

3. The domain of the relation can be expressed in the form $n \geq x$, and the range can be expressed in the form $C \geq y$. Write the value of y in the first two boxes, and the value of x in the last two boxes.

(Record your answer in the numerical response box from left to right)

5. The function $f(x) = 3 - 2x^2$, has domain $\{-6, -4, 0, 2, 5\}$. Which of the following is an element of the range of the function?

   A. 35
   B. 27
   C. 1
   D. −29

Use the following information to answer the next question.

The diagram shows the graph of the function $y = f(x)$.

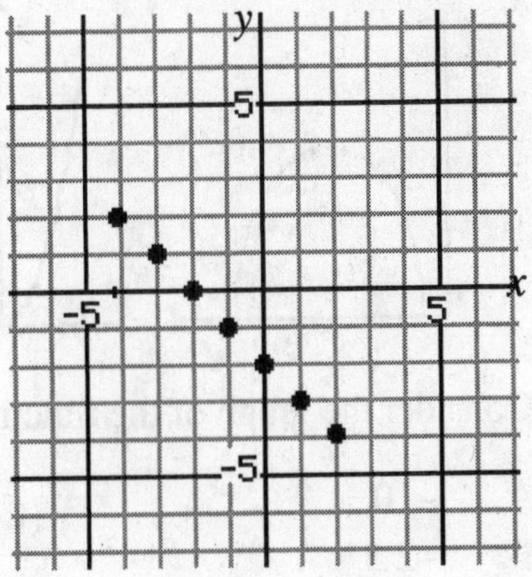

6. The diagram shows the graph of the function $y = f(x)$. The value of $f(-2) + f(2)$ is

A. –4
B. –2
C. 0
D. $f(0)$

Use the following information to answer questions #7 and #8.

Consider the function $P(x) = 5x + 2$.

7. The value of $P(6)$ is

A. $\frac{8}{5}$
B. $\frac{4}{5}$
C. 32
D. 58

8. If $P(b) = 6$, then $b =$

A. $\frac{8}{5}$
B. $\frac{4}{5}$
C. $\frac{5}{4}$
D. 32

9. Which of the following diagrams shows a relation which is not a function?

A.

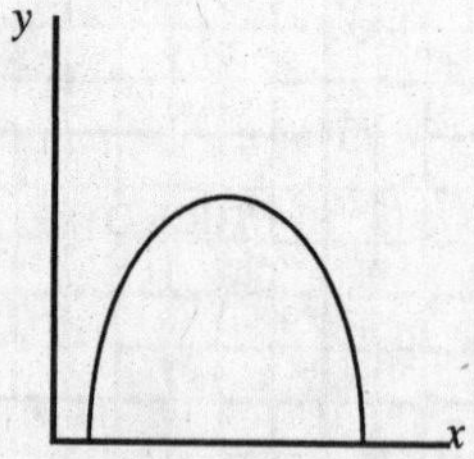

B.

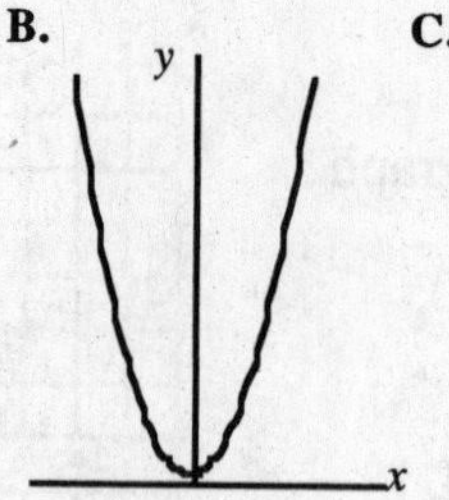

C.

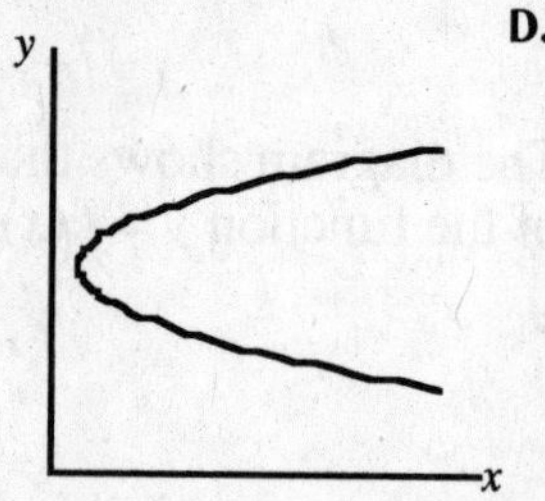

D.

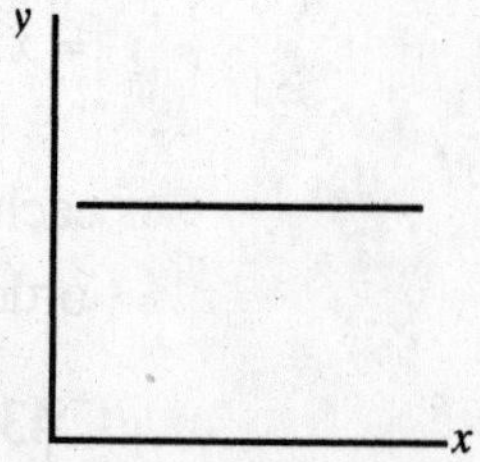

10. Consider the graph of the function $f(x) = 4x - 10$. The x-intercept of the graph of f is

A. -10
B. -2.5
C. 2.5
D. 10

11. Given a function g defined by $g(x) = px + q$ with $g(0) = 2$ and $g(1) = 3$ then

A. $p = 1,\ q = 0$
B. $p = 3,\ q = 2$
C. $p = 1,\ q = 2$
D. $p = 3,\ q = 0$

12. If $f(x) = 3^x$ and $f(-a) = \frac{1}{81}$, then $a =$

A. 4
B. -4
C. $-\frac{1}{4}$
D. $\frac{1}{4}$

13. If $g(x) = \frac{2}{3}x + 6$, an expression for $g(2x - 1)$ is

A. $\frac{4}{3}x + 5$
B. $\frac{4}{3}x + \frac{16}{3}$
C. $\frac{4}{3}x + 11$
D $\frac{8}{3}x + 5$

14. Consider the following functions:

1. $p(x) = x^2 - 4x - 2$ **2.** $p(x) = \frac{1}{3}x + 14$ **3.** $p(x) = 3x^2 + x$ **4.** $p(x) = 7 - 5x$

For each function evaluate $p(-3)$, and put the expressions in order from greatest to least. The order is

A. 4312
B. 3412
C. 3124
D. none of the above

Numerical Response **4.** If $f(x) = 1 - 2x - 5x^2$, and if $f(x + 2)$ is written in the form $ax^2 + bx + c$, the value of $a - b - c$ is ______ .

(Record your answer in the numerical response box from left to right)

Numerical Response **5.** $f(a) = \frac{a}{a+4}$. The exact value of $f(5) - f(5^{-1})$ written as a rational number in simplest form is $\frac{p}{q}$. The value of p is ______ .

(Record your answer in the numerical response box from left to right)

15. Which of the following cannot be used to represent a function?

A. Graph
B. Table of Values
C. Ordered Pairs
D. Coordinate

Written Response - 5 marks

1. During an airshow, the path of a stunt dive of a jet can be modelled by the equation $h = t^2 - 9t + 81$, where h is the height in metres after t seconds. The end of the stunt occurs when the plane achieves its starting height.

- How high is the jet at the start of the dive?

- How high is the jet above ground level at its lowest point?

- When does the jet reach its lowest point in the dive?

- How high is the jet two seconds into its dive?

- After how many seconds does this height occur again within the jet's stunt dive?

Assignment Key

1. C **2.** B **3.** D **4.** A **5.** D **6.** A **7.** C **8.** B
9. C **10.** C **11.** C **12.** A **13.** B **14.** B **15.** D

1.

1	.	8	7

2.

1	2		

3.

9	8	0	0

4.

4	0		

5.

3	2		

Written Response

1.
- 81 m

- 60.75 m

- 4.5 sec

- 67 m

- 7 sec

Characteristics of Linear Relations Lesson #1:
Line Segments on a Cartesian Plane

Unit Overview

A linear relation is a relation whose graph is represented by a straight line. The line can be infinite or finite depending the domain and range of the linear relation. In some cases we are only interested in a portion of a line. This portion is called a **line segment**.

We have already studied some of the characteristics of the graph of a linear relation: intercepts, domain, and range. In this unit we study some chartacteristics of line segments: namely, length, midpoint, and slope. We demonstrate an understanding of slope with respect to rise and run, the slope formula, and rate of change. We then discuss the slopes of parallel and perpendicular lines.

Line Segment

A line segment is the portion of a line between two points on the line.
If the endpoints of a line segment are A and B, we refer to it as line segment AB.
NOTE: Line segment AB may also be written as $\overline{AB}$.

Length of a Horizontal Line Segment

Consider the line segments shown on the grid.

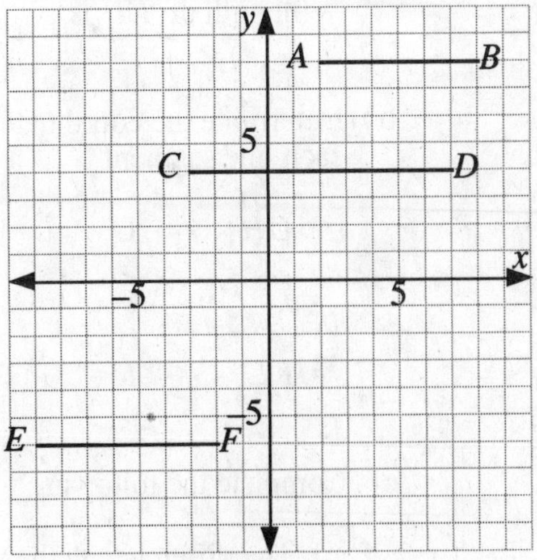

a) Find the length of each line segment by counting.

- length of AB is _____ units.
- length of CD is _____ units.
- length of EF is _____ units.

b) Determine the coordinates of the endpoints of each line segment.

- AB → A (,) B (,)
- CD → C (,) D (,)
- EF → E (,) F (,)

c) Complete the following.

- The difference in the x-coordinates, $x_B - x_A$, is _____ .
- The difference in the x-coordinates, $x_D - x_C$, is _____ .
- The difference in the x-coordinates, $x_F - x_E$, is _____ .

d) How can the coordinates of the end points of a horizontal line segment be used to find the length of the line segment?

a) Line segment AB has endpoints $A(2, 8)$ to $B(-5, 8)$. Determine the length of $\overline{AB}$.

b) Determine the length of the line segment from $P(a-2, b)$ to $Q(a+4, b)$.

Length of a Vertical Line Segment

Consider the line segments shown on the grid.

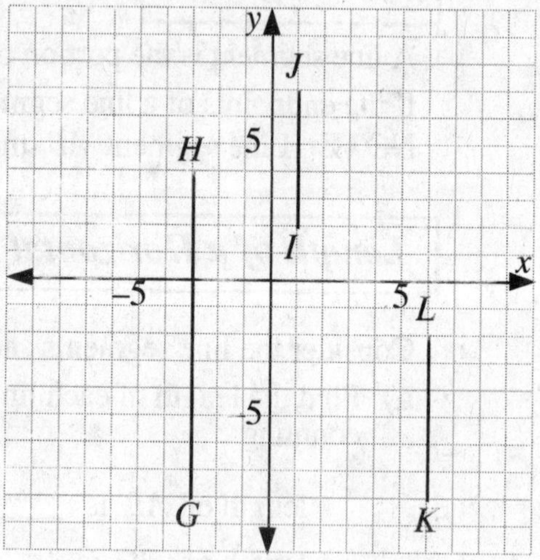

a) Find the lengths of each line segment by counting.

- length of GH is _____ units.
- length of IJ is _____ units.
- length of KL is _____ units.

b) Determine the coordinates of the endpoints of each line segment.

- GH → $G($, $)$ $H($, $)$
- IJ → $I($, $)$ $J($, $)$
- KL → $K($, $)$ $L($, $)$

c) Complete the following.

- The difference in the y-coordinates, $y_H - y_G$, is _____.
- The difference in the y-coordinates, $y_J - y_I$, is _____.
- The difference in the y-coordinates, $y_L - y_K$, is _____.

d) How can the coordinates of the end points of a vertical line segment be used to find the length of the line segment?

a) Line segment RS has endpoints $R(1,-4)$ to $S(1,-9)$. Determine the length of $\overline{RS}$.

b) Determine the length of the line segment from $P(a\,,b)$ to $Q(a, b+10)$.

Pythagorean Theorem Review

In a right triangle, the square of the length of the hypotenuse is equal to the sum of the squares of the lengths of the other two sides.

i.e. $a^2 + b^2 = c^2$

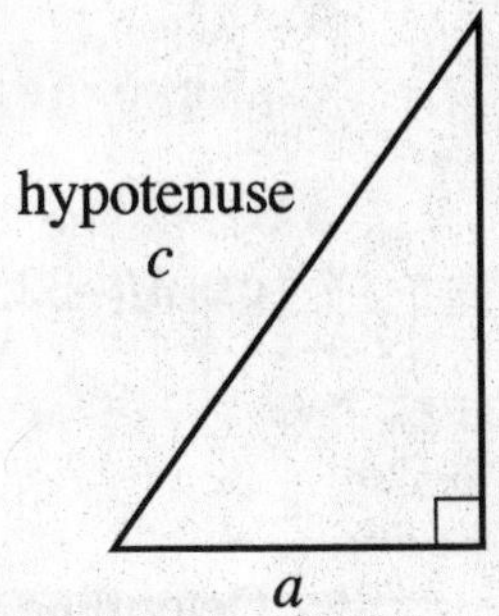

Use the Pythagorean theorem to determine the length of the line segments shown on the grid.

Answer as an exact value and as a decimal to the nearest tenth.

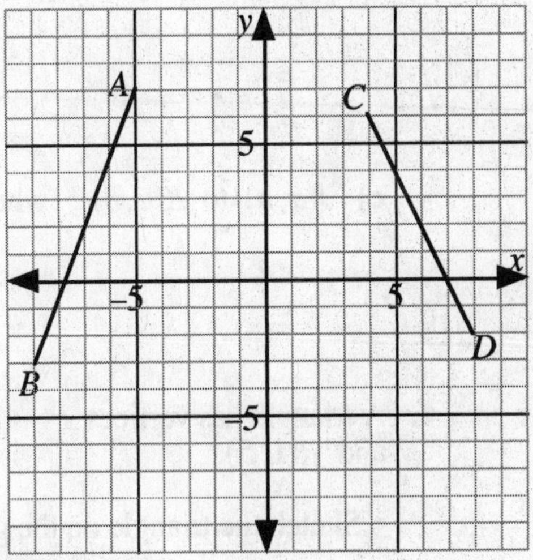

Complete Assignment Questions #1 - #11

Assignment

1. Determine the length of each line segment.

a) $A(2,7)$ to $B(5,7)$

b) $C(-5,3)$ to $D(-5,12)$

c) $E(2,-8)$ to $F(2,3)$

d) $G(8,-12)$ to $H(-5,-12)$

2. Determine the length of each line segment.

a) $I(-3,-8)$ to $J(-3,-3)$

b) $K(7,-10)$ to $L(-35,-10)$

c) $M(-325,-892)$ to $N(255,-892)$

d) $P(7251,-1286)$ to $Q(7251,1289)$

3. Determine whether each line segment is horizontal or vertical, and write an expression for its length.

a) $A(p,q)$ to $B(p-4,q)$

b) $C(m-3,n+5)$ to $D(m-3,n+12)$

c) $J(a,b)$ to $K(c,b)$ where $a > c$

d) $M(s,t)$ to $N(s,z)$, where $t > z$

4. A triangle has vertices $P(-4,-3)$, $Q(9,-3)$, and $R(1,5)$.

- Sketch the triangle on the grid.
- Calculate the area of the triangle.

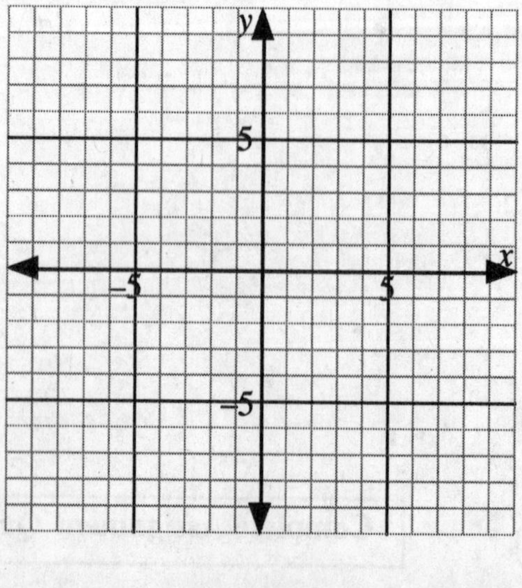

5. Use the Pythagorean theorem to determine the lengths of the line segments shown on the grid.

Give each answer as

i) a mixed radical in simplest form

ii) a decimal to the nearest hundredth

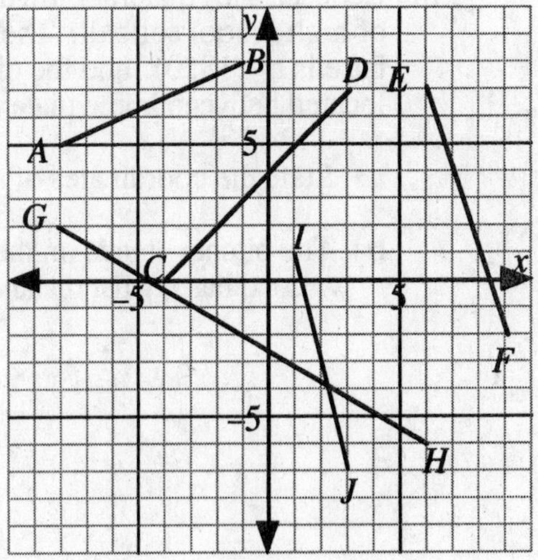

6. List the coordinates of A and B from question #5. How can they be used to find the length of AB?

7. On the grid, plot the points $P(-6, 6)$, $Q(-6, -10)$, and $R(8, -10)$.

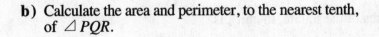

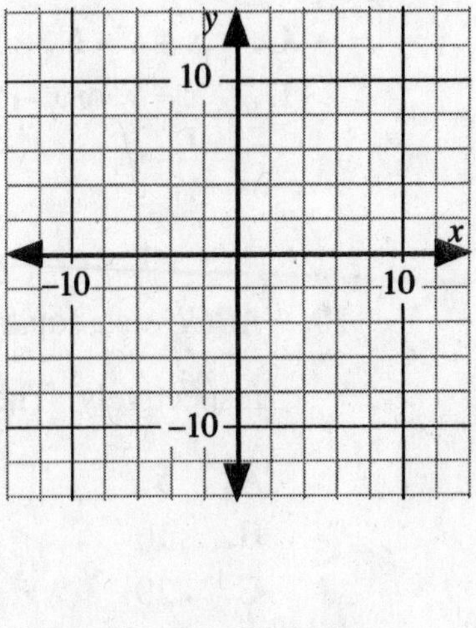

a) Determine, as an exact value, the distance from P to R.

b) Calculate the area and perimeter, to the nearest tenth, of $\triangle PQR$.

8. Rebecca uses quadrant I in a Cartesian plane to describe the location of the bases in a game of high school softball. The four bases form a square. The origin is at home plate. First base is at $(18, 0)$, and the distance between each base is 18 m. The pitcher's mound is located between home plate and second base.

a) State the coordinates of second base.

b) The pitcher stands on the mound 12 m from home plate. If she has to throw a ball to second base, what distance, to the nearest tenth of a metre, would she throw the ball?

c) Calculate the **exact** coordinates of the location of the pitcher.

Multiple Choice

9. Horizontal line segment EF, with endpoints $E(5,-1)$ and $F(x, y)$, has a length of 6 units. Which of the following must be true?

A. $x = 11$
B. $y = 5$ or -7
C. $x + y = 6$
D. $x = y$ or $x - y = 12$

10. $ABCD$ is a square with vertices $(\sqrt{5},0)$, $(0,\sqrt{5})$, $(-\sqrt{5},0)$, and $(0,-\sqrt{5})$ respectively. The area of the square, in unit^2, is

A. 5
B. 10
C. 20
D. 100

Numerical Response **11.** To the nearest tenth, the perimeter of $\triangle PQR$ with vertices, $P(3,8)$, $Q(3,0)$, and $R(-1,8)$ is ______.

(Record your answer in the numerical response box from left to right)

Answer Key

1. **a)** 3 **b)** 9 **c)** 11 **d)** 13

2. **a)** 5 **b)** 42 **c)** 580 **d)** 2575

3. **a)** horizontal, 4 **b)** vertical, 7 **c)** horizontal, $a - c$ **d)** vertical, $t - z$

4. 52 units^2

5. $AB = \sqrt{58} = 7.62$, $CD = 7\sqrt{2} = 9.90$, $EF = 3\sqrt{10} = 9.49$,
$GH = 2\sqrt{65} = 16.12$, $IJ = 2\sqrt{17} = 8.25$

6. $A(-8, 5)$, $B(-1, 8)$ $x_B - x_A = 7$, $y_B - y_A = 3$

$$AB^2 = (x_B - x_A)^2 + (y_B - y_A)^2$$
$$AB = \sqrt{(x_B - x_A)^2 + (y_B - y_A)^2}$$

7. **a)** $2\sqrt{113}$ units **b)** area = 112.0 units^2, perimeter = 51.3 units

8. **a)** (18,18) **b)** 13.5 m **c)** $(6\sqrt{2}, 6\sqrt{2})$

9. D **10.** B **11.**

2	0	.	9

Characteristics of Linear Relations Lesson #2: The Distance Formula

Investigation

Consider line segment AB shown on the grid.

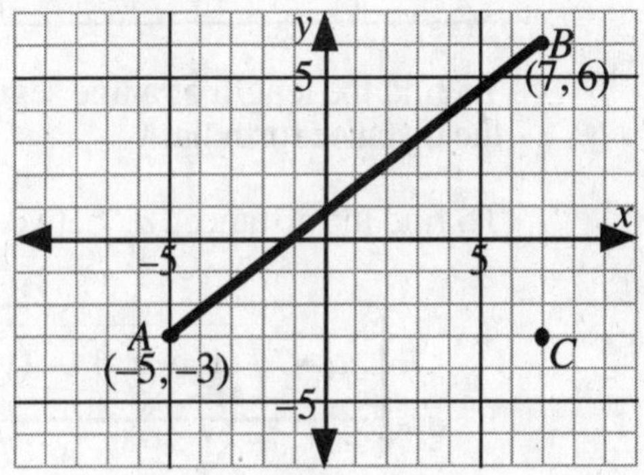

a) Use the Pythagorean theorem to show that the length of AB is 15 units.

b) Complete the following:

length of $AC = x_B - x_A = 7 - \_\_\_ = \_\_\_$

length of $CB = y_B - y_A = \_\_\_ - \_\_\_ = \_\_\_$

c) Complete the following to verify the length of AB.

$(\text{length of } AB)^2 = (\text{difference in } x\text{-coordinates of } B \text{ and } A)^2 + (\text{difference in } y\text{-coordinates of } B \text{ and } A)^2$

length of $AB = \sqrt{(\text{difference in } x\text{-coordinates of } B \text{ and } A)^2 + (\text{difference in } y\text{-coordinates of } B \text{ and } A)^2}$

length of $AB = \sqrt{(x_B - x_A)^2 + (y_B - y_A)^2}$

length of $AB = \sqrt{(7-(-5))^2 + (\qquad\qquad)^2}$

length of $AB = \sqrt{12^2 + \qquad}$

length of $AB = \sqrt{\qquad}$

length of $AB =$

d) Use the same procedure to make a rule for finding the distance between any two points $A(x_1, y_1)$ and $B(x_2, y_2)$.

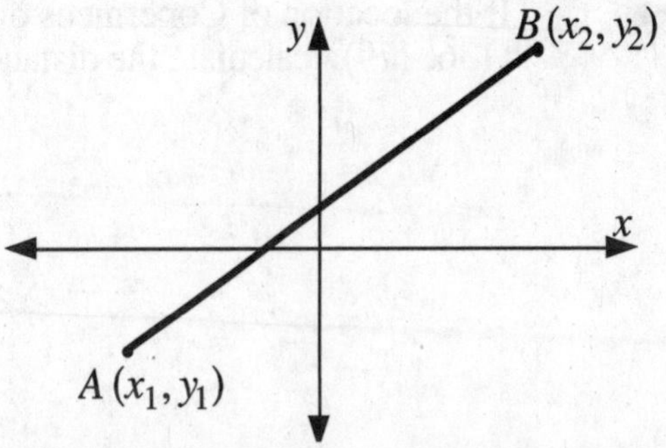

$(\text{length of } AB)^2 = (\text{difference in } x\text{-coordinates of } B \text{ and } A)^2 + (\text{difference in } y\text{-coordinates of } B \text{ and } A)^2$

length of $AB = \sqrt{(\text{difference in } x\text{-coordinates of } B \text{ and } A)^2 + (\text{difference in } y\text{-coordinates of } B \text{ and } A)^2}$

length of $AB = \sqrt{(x_2 - \qquad)^2 + (\qquad\qquad)^2}$

The Distance Formula

To find the length of a line segment on the graph of a linear relation, we can use the distance formula.

To find the distance, d, between points $P(x_1, y_1)$ and $Q(x_2, y_2)$, use

$$d = \sqrt{(x_2 - x_1)^2 + (y_2 - y_1)^2} \quad \text{or} \quad d_{PQ} = \sqrt{(x_Q - x_P)^2 + (y_Q - y_P)^2}$$

Find the exact length of the following line segments.

a) $P(2, 3)$ to $Q(10, -3)$

b) $G(-25, 3)$ to $H(-17, -5)$

Sometimes grids are superimposed on maps to find the distance between two locations. For example, to calculate the distance between two craters, Copernicus and Plato, on the Earth's moon, a coordinate system could be superimposed on a map of the moon. Ordered pairs would then be assigned to Copernicus and Plato to find the distance between the two craters. If the location of Copernicus on the coordinate grid is $(-89, 226)$ and the location of Plato is $(136, 179)$, calculate the distance between the two craters to the nearest unit.

Class Ex. #3

a) Explain how we can determine if a triangle is right angled if we know the length of each side.

b) L is the point $(0,1)$, M is $(-3,-3)$ and N is $(-7,0)$. Prove that $\triangle LMN$ is right angled.

Complete Assignment Questions #1 - #12

Assignment

1. Determine the distance between each pair of points.

a) $A(2,0)$ and $B(7,12)$ **b)** $C(3,7)$ and $D(6,11)$

2. Determine the distance, to the nearest hundredth, between each pair of points.

a) $P(4,0)$ and $Q(-2,-7)$ **b)** $R(-2.3, 8.9)$ and $S(-3.4,-6.8)$

3. Determine the exact distance between each pair of points. Answer in simplest radical form.

a) $E(6, 1)$ and $F(-2, -3)$

b) $K(-\frac{1}{2}, \frac{5}{2})$ and $L(1, 3)$

4. Consider the points $P(-2, 2)$, $Q(1, 6)$ and $R(7, 14)$.

a) Calculate the lengths of PQ, QR, and PR. What do you notice?

b) What does this mean with regard to the points P, Q, and R?

5. A is the point $(6, -2)$, B is $(4, 4)$ and C is $(-3, -5)$.

a) Calculate the exact lengths of AB, BC, and AC in entire radical form.

b) Show how you can use the answers in a) to prove that $\angle BAC$ is a right angle.

6. In a high school football game, the Chiefs' quarterback scrambles to the Chiefs' 7 yard line, 15 yards from the left sideline. From that position he throws the ball upfield. The pass is caught by a wide receiver who is on the Chiefs' 38 yard line, 4 yards from the left sideline.

The first quadrant of a coordinate grid is superimposed on the football field, with the origin located at the intersection of the Chiefs' goal line and the left side line.

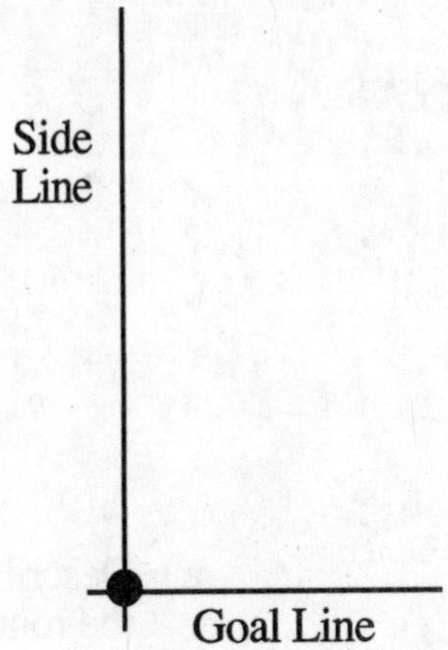

a) With reference to this origin, state ordered pairs for the location of the quarterback (when he throws the ball) and the wide receiver (when he catches the ball). Mark these points on the grid shown.

b) Determine the length of the pass (to the nearest yard).

7. At the end of a high school soccer game, Jonas walks 6 blocks west and 5 blocks north from the corner of the soccer field to his house. Beverly walks 3 blocks east and 4 blocks south to reach her house from the same corner of the soccer field.

a) Taking the corner of the soccer field as the origin, list the coordinates of each home.

b) If a block represents 135 metres, determine the direct distance, to the nearest metre, between their homes.

8. A family moves from Grand Forks, North Dakota, to Toronto, Ontario. The family's belongings were transported by van. The graph below shows part of the route taken by the van.

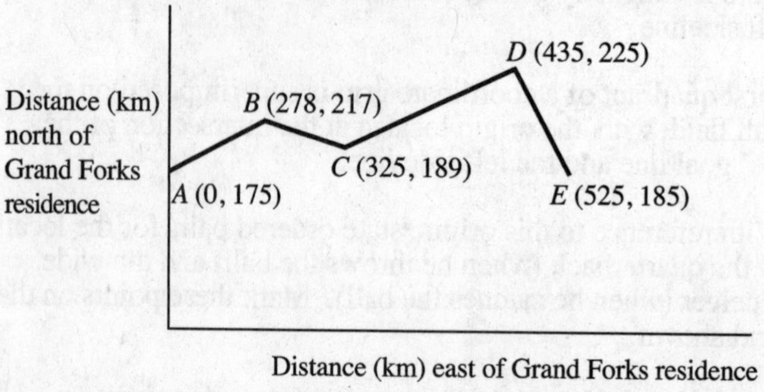

a) Describe the starting position relative to the family home in Grand Forks for the part of the route which is shown.

b) Calculate the distance, to the nearest km, travelled by the van from A to E.

c) The van used an average of one litre of gasoline for every 5 km travelled. If the average cost of gasoline for the trip was 95¢ per litre, calculate the amount spent on gasoline for the part of the route shown in a).

Multiple Choice

9. The distance between the points $(2,-1)$ and $(6,2)$ is

A. 5
B. $\sqrt{7}$
C. $\sqrt{17}$
D. 25

10. A circle with its centre at the origin passes through the point $(-6,-8)$. The radius of the circle is

A. 6
B. 8
C. 10
D. 100

11. Which of the following points is equidistant from $A(-2,7)$ and $B(-6,-5)$?

A. $(0,-4)$
B. $(7,-10)$
C. $(-1,0)$
D. $(4,-5)$

Numerical Response

12. The diameter, to the nearest tenth, of the circle with centre $(-5,9)$ which passes through $(4,-3)$ is _____.

(Record your answer in the numerical response box from left to right)

Answer Key

1. a) 13 **b)** 5 **2. a)** 9.22 **b)** 15.74 **3. a)** $4\sqrt{5}$ **b)** $\frac{1}{2}\sqrt{10}$

4. a) $PQ = 5, QR = 10, PR = 15.$ $PQ + QR = PR$ **b)** The points P,Q and R lie on a straight line.

5. a) $AB = \sqrt{40}$, $BC = \sqrt{130}$, $AC = \sqrt{90}$.
b) Since $BC^2 = AB^2 + AC^2$, triangle ABC must be right angled at A so angle BAC is a right angle.

6. a) $Q(15, 7)$ $W(4, 38)$ **b)** 33 yards

7. a) $J(-6, 5)$ $B(3, -4)$ **b)** $9\sqrt{2}$ blocks ~ 1718 m.

8. a) 175 kilometres north of Grand Forks. **b)** 550 km **c)** $104.50

9. A **10.** C **11.** C **12.**

3	0	.	0

Characteristics of Linear Relations Lesson #3: The Midpoint of a Line Segment

Midpoint

The **midpoint,** ***M*****,** of a line segment on the graph of a linear relation is the point at the centre of the line segment.

Midpoint of a Horizontal Line Segment

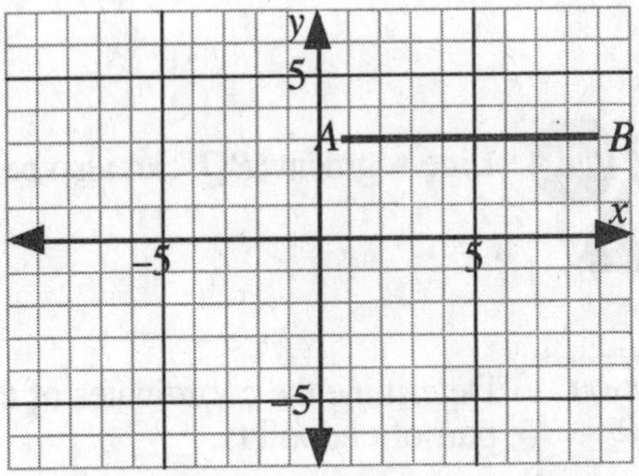

Consider the line segment AB shown on the grid.

a) Determine the coordinates of the midpoint by counting. Label the midpoint M, on the grid and list the coordinates beside it.

b) List the coordinates of point A and point B on the grid. How can the x-coordinates of points A and B be used to find the coordinates of the midpoint of a horizontal line?

Midpoint of a Vertical Line Segment

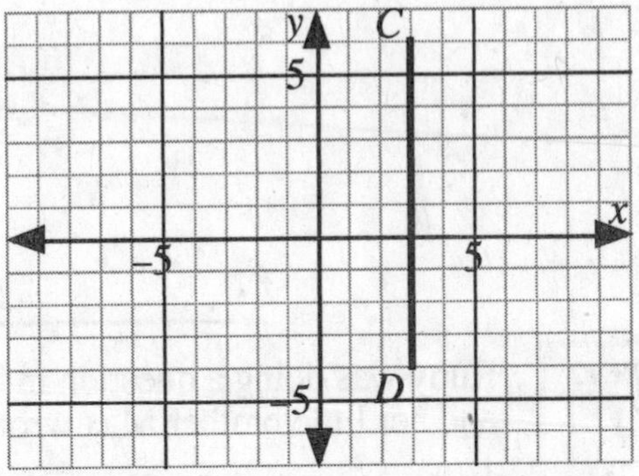

Consider the line segment CD shown on the grid.

a) Determine the coordinates of the midpoint by counting. Label the midpoint M, on the grid and list the coordinates beside it.

b) List the coordinates of point C and point D on the grid. How can the y-coordinates of points C and D be used to find the coordinates of the midpoint?

Midpoint of an Oblique (Diagonal) Line Segment

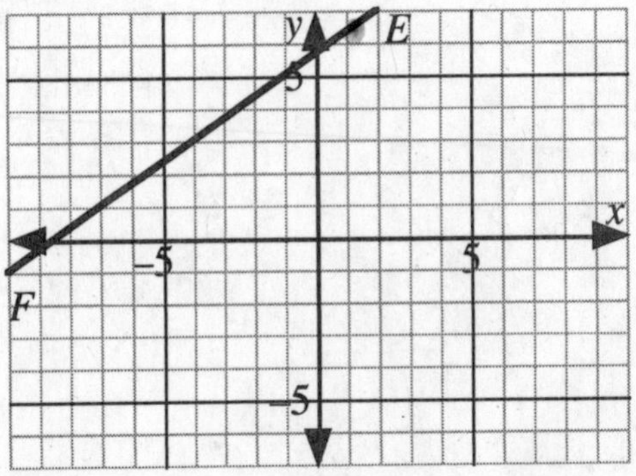

Consider the line segment EF shown on the grid.

a) Use the results from above to determine the midpoint of EF.

b) Express in words how to find the midpoint, M, of the line segment joining the points (x_1, y_1) and (x_2, y_2).

c) Complete the formula to express the relationship in b). $x_M =$ $y_M =$

Midpoint of a Line Segment

Consider line segment PQ with endpoints $P(x_1, y_1)$ and $Q(x_2, y_2)$.

The midpoint, M, of the line segment has coordinates.

$$M\left(\frac{x_1 + x_2}{2}, \frac{y_1 + y_2}{2}\right)$$

Line segment PQ can also be written as $\overline{PQ}$.

Determine the coordinates of the midpoint of the line segment with the given pair of endpoints.

a) $P(4, 7)$, $Q(12, 3)$ **b)** $E(-5, 7)$, $F(-11, -2)$ **c)** $A(w + 3, 2w)$, $C(5w - 1, 7w + 1)$

Ruby was doing a question in her coordinate geometry homework, and her little brother Max wrote over part of the question as a prank.

$P(5$  $Q(-11, -10)$

Midpoint $,-6)$

Calculate the missing coordinates.

Complete Assignment Questions #1 - #15

Assignment

1. Determine the coordinates of the midpoint of the line segment with the given pair of endpoints.

a) $A(2, 6)$, $C(4, 16)$ **b)** $X(-3, -8)$, $Y(-11, 0)$ **c)** $K(15, -17)$, $L(-11, 3)$

d) $A(-25, 56)$, $O(0, 0)$ **e)** $P(-2.5, 5.6), Q(1.5, -6.4)$ **f)** $E(-2, 7)$, $F(6, 2)$

2. Determine the coordinates of the midpoint of the line segment with the given pair of endpoints.

a) $C(3x, 8y)$, $D(7x, -4y)$ **b)** $S(a + b, a + 7b)$, $T(a + b, a - 3b)$

c) $A(p + 3, q - 2)$, $B(p - 1, q + 8)$, **d)** $U(m - 5n, m + n)$, $V(3n - m, m - n)$,

3. Otto was given two points: $A(-6, 4)$ and $B(12, -8)$. He was asked to divide $\overline{AB}$ into four equal parts. State the coordinates of the points which will divide $\overline{AB}$ into four equal parts.

4. In each case M is the midpoint of $\overline{AB}$. Determine the value of x.

a) $A(2,6)$, $B(6,x)$, $M(4,-1)$

b) $A(3,6)$, $B(x,0)$, $M(0,3)$

c) $A(x,2)$, $B(3x,18)$, $M(-8,10)$

d) $A(2,x+1)$, $B(-6,2x-7)$, $M(-2,x)$

5. A refinery is to be built halfway between the rural towns of Branton and Oilville. A railway is to be built connecting the towns to the refinery. On a Cartesian plane, Branton is located at $(1232, 3421)$ and Oilville is located at $(1548, 3753)$.

a) What are the coordinates of the refinery?

b) Determine the length of the railway, to the nearest kilometre, if the grid scale is 1 unit represents 100 metres.

6. Consider $\triangle ABC$ with vertices $A(-3,6)$, $B(1,-2)$, $C(-11,2)$.

a) Calculate the length of each side of the triangle and explain why the triangle is right angled.

b) Calculate the coordinates of the midpoint, M, of the hypotenuse.

c) Calculate the distance from M to each of the vertices of the triangle. What do you notice?

7. In a relay race, a team of four athletes runs across the diagonal, AC, of a rectangular sports field. On a coordinate grid, the vertices of the rectangle are $A(4,7)$, $B(240,7)$, $C(240,367)$ and $D(4,367)$. The four legs of the relay are of equal distance, and none of the athletes can start until they have received the relay baton.

Melanie runs the first leg from A to X, Alex runs from X to Y, Nick runs from Y to Z, and Rachel completes the race from Z to C.

a) Draw a diagram to represent the information.

b) Calculate the coordinates of X, Y, and Z.

c) Calculate the distance, to the nearest 0.1 m, that each athlete had to run if the units for the coordinate system are metres.

Multiple Choice

8. $P(4,-8)$ and $Q(-2,10)$ are the endpoints of a diameter of a circle. The coordinates of the centre of the circle are

A. $(-3,9)$
B. $(2,2)$
C. $(3,-9)$
D. $(1,1)$

9. AB is a diameter of a circle; the centre is C.
If $A(8,-6)$ and $C(5,-2)$ then B is the point

A. $(2,2)$
B. $(6.5,-4)$
C. $(11,-10)$
D. $(13,-8)$

10. $\overline{PQ}$ has endpoints $P(-4,9)$ and $Q(0,5)$. Which of the following points is equidistant from $S(-6,-5)$ and M, the midpoint of $\overline{PQ}$?

A. $(0,-4)$
B. $(7,-10)$
C. $(-1,0)$
D. $(4,-5)$

11. Which statement is always true?

A. Two line segments of equal length have the same midpoint.
B. Two line segments with the same midpoint are of equal length.
C. A point equidistant from the endpoints of a line segment is the midpoint.
D. None of the above statements is always true.

Numerical Response

12. The midpoint of line segment ST is $M\left(\frac{1}{2},-4\right)$. If the coordinates of T are $(-3,3)$, and the coordinates of S are (x,y), the value of x is _____.

(Record your answer in the numerical response box from left to right)

13. The point $M(a, 6)$ is the midpoint of $\overline{GH}$ with $G(22, b)$ and $H(6, -8)$. The value of $a + b$ is _____.

(Record your answer in the numerical response box from left to right)

14. The midpoint of line segment AB lies on the y-axis. A lies on the x-axis, and B has coordinates $(-4, 5)$. The length of AB, to the nearest tenth, is _____.

(Record your answer in the numerical response box from left to right)

15. A **median** in a triangle is a line drawn from a vertex to the midpoint of the opposite side. ΔABC has vertices $A(0, 8)$, $B(-6, 2)$, and $C(10, 4)$. To the nearest tenth, the length of median AD is _____.

(Record your answer in the numerical response box from left to right)

Answer Key

1. a) (3, 11) **b)** (−7, −4) **c)** (2, −7)

d) $\left(-\frac{25}{2}, 28\right)$ **e)** (−0.5, −0.4) **f)** $\left(2, \frac{9}{2}\right)$

2. a) $(5x, 2y)$ **b)** $(a + b, a + 2b)$ **c)** $(p + 1, q + 3)$ **d)** $(-n, m)$

3. $\left(-\frac{3}{2}, 1\right)$, $(3, -2)$, $\left(\frac{15}{2}, -5\right)$

4. a) −8 **b)** −3 **c)** −4 **d)** 6

5. a) (1390, 3587) **b)** 46 km

6. a) $AB = \sqrt{80} = 4\sqrt{5}$, $BC = \sqrt{160} = 4\sqrt{10}$, $AC = \sqrt{80} = 4\sqrt{5}$
Since $BC^2 = AB^2 + AC^2$, triangle ABC must be right angled at A.

b) $M(-5,0)$ **c)** $MA = MB = MC = \sqrt{40} = 2\sqrt{10}$. M is equidistant from A, B, and C.

7. b) $X(63, 97)$, $Y(122, 187)$, $Z(181, 277)$ **c)** 107.6 m

8. D **9.** A **10.** C **11.** D

12.

4			

13.

3	4		

14.

9	.	4	

15.

5	.	4	

Characteristics of Linear Relations Lesson #4: Slope of a Line Segment

A trucker driving up a hill with a heavy load may be concerned with the steepness of the hill. When building a roof, a builder may be concerned with the steepness (or pitch) of the roof. A skier going down a hill may be concerned with the steepness of the ski hill.

In mathematics, the term **slope** is used to describe the steepness of a line segment.

Slope of a Line Segment

The **slope** of a line segment is a measure of the steepness of the line segment.

It is the ratio of **rise** (the change in vertical height between the endpoints) over **run** (the change in horizontal length between the endpoints).

$$\textbf{Slope} = \frac{\textbf{rise}}{\textbf{run}}$$

- the **rise** is POSITIVE if we count UP, and NEGATIVE if we count DOWN.
- the **run** is POSITIVE if we count RIGHT, and NEGATIVE if we count LEFT.

Class Ex. #1

Each line segment on the grid has endpoints with integer coordinates.
Complete the table below.

Rise = ↑↓
Run = ←→

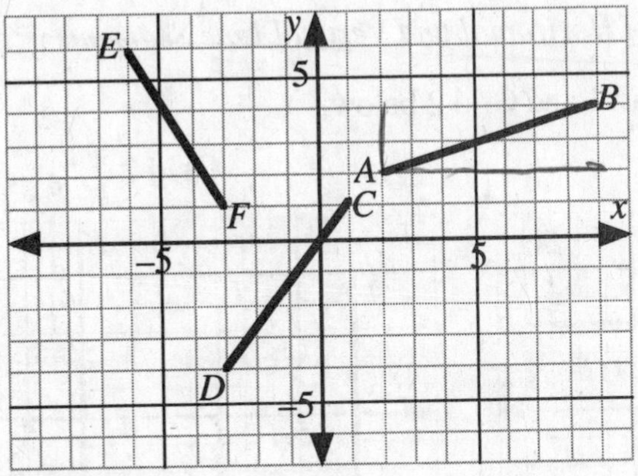

Line Segment	Rise	Run	Slope = $\frac{\text{Rise}}{\text{Run}}$
AB	2	7	0.29 $\frac{2}{7}$
CD	-5	-4	1.25 $-\frac{5}{4}$
EF	-5	3	-1.6 $-\frac{5}{3}$

Investigation #1

Investigating the Slope of Line Segments

a) Complete the chart. Write the slopes in simplest form.

Rate of Change

Line Segment	Rise	Run	Slope = $\frac{\text{Rise}}{\text{Run}}$
AB	2	3	$\frac{2}{3}$
AC	8	12	$\frac{8}{12} \to \frac{2}{3}$
AD	10	15	$\frac{10}{15} \to \frac{2}{3}$
BC	6	9	$\frac{6}{9} \to \frac{2}{3}$

All are =

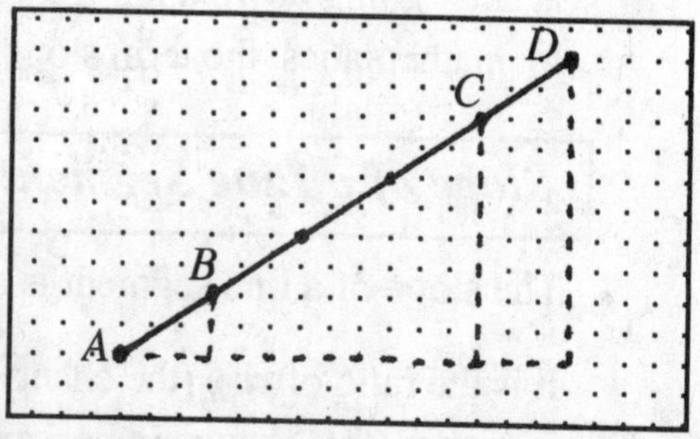

b) How are the slopes of the line segments related?

Same line segment = the same/Equal. can use any 2 point on the line (same line slope).

Slope of a Line

The slopes of all line segments on a line are equal.
The slope of a line representing the graph of a linear relation can be found using

$$\text{slope} = \frac{\text{rise}}{\text{run}} \text{ for any two points on the line.}$$

Investigation #2

Slopes of Horizontal and Vertical Line Segments

Horizontal → slope = 0, y = #
HOY VUX
verticle → undefined → x = #

Consider the line segments in Grid 1 and Grid 2 below.

Grid 1

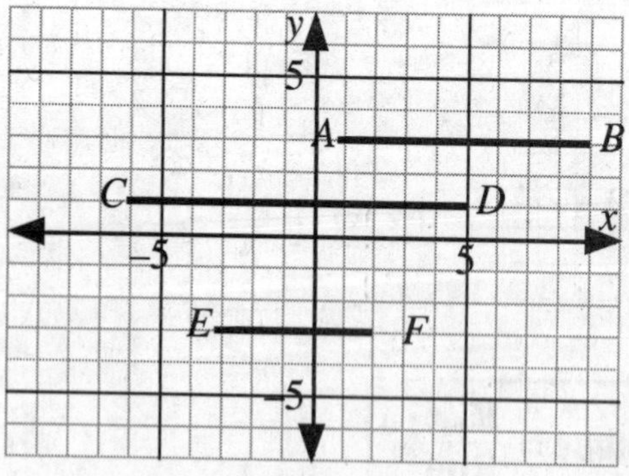

Grid 2

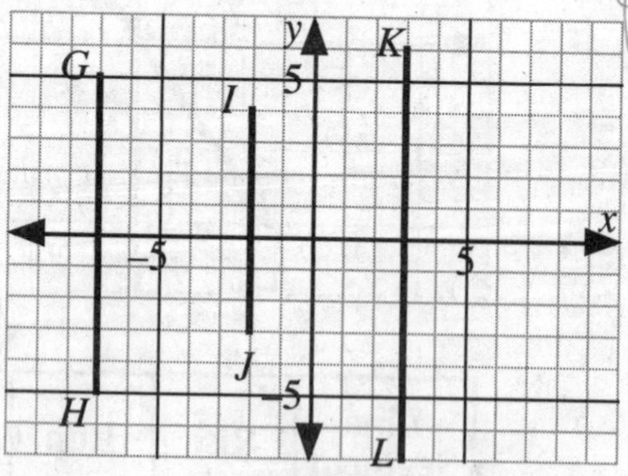

a) Determine the slopes of all the line segments in Grid 1. AB = 0 0/8 = 0, CD = 0 0/11 = 0, EF = 0 0/5 = 0

b) Determine the slopes of all the line segments in Grid 2. 10/0 = X Error, undefined (NOT POSSIBLE).

c) Complete the following statements.

- Horizontal line segments have a slope of ___0___ .
- Vertical line segments have an ___undefined___ slope.

Investigation #3 *Positive and Negative Slopes*

a) Each of the lines on the grids passes through at least two points with integer coordinates. Calculate the slope of each of the lines.

Remember: On a Cartesian Plane:
- the **rise** is POSITIVE if we count UP, and NEGATIVE if we count DOWN.
- the **run** is POSITIVE if we count RIGHT, and NEGATIVE if we count LEFT.

Grid 1

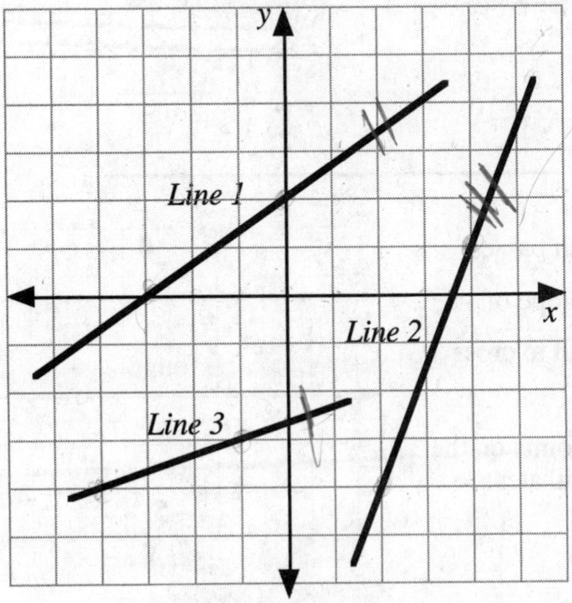

Grid 2

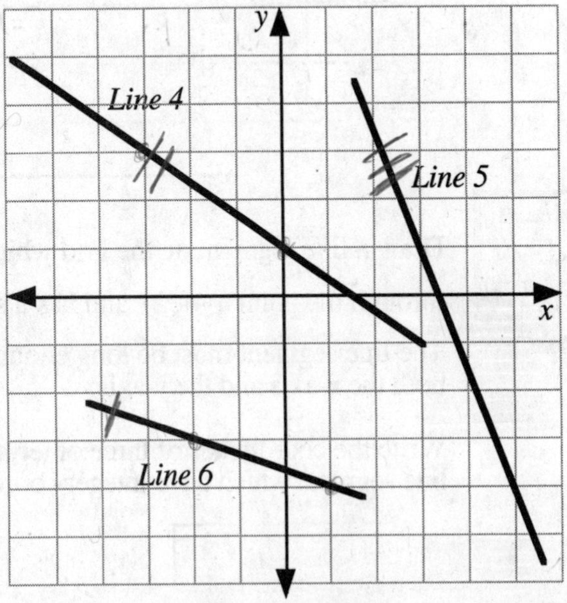

Table For Grid 1

Line	Slope
1	$\frac{2}{3}$
2	$+\frac{5}{2}$
3	$\frac{1}{3}$

Rise / Run

Left - Right

Table For Grid 2

Line	Slope
4	$-\frac{2}{+3}$
5	$-\frac{5}{+2}$
6	$-\frac{1}{+3}$

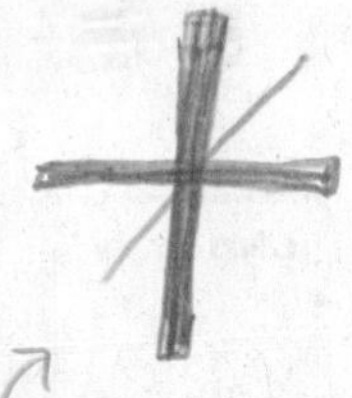

(slope =) Rise = (+) Run = (+).

b) Compare the slopes of:

- Line 1 and Line 4 — Equal
- Line 2 and Line 5 — Equal but positive/negaties
- Line 3 and Line 6 — Equal

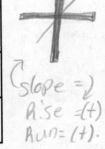

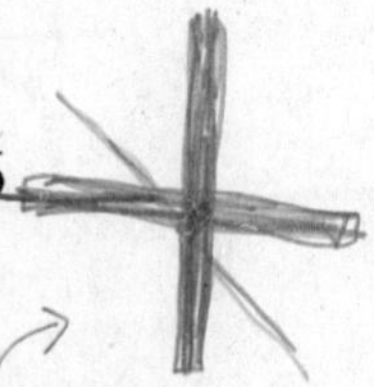

c) Complete the following statements.

- A line which rises from left to right has a Positive slope.
- A line which falls from left to right has a negative slope.

slope = Rise = (−) Run = (+)

Complete Assignment Questions #1 and #2

Class Ex. #2

A grid has been superimposed on the sketch.

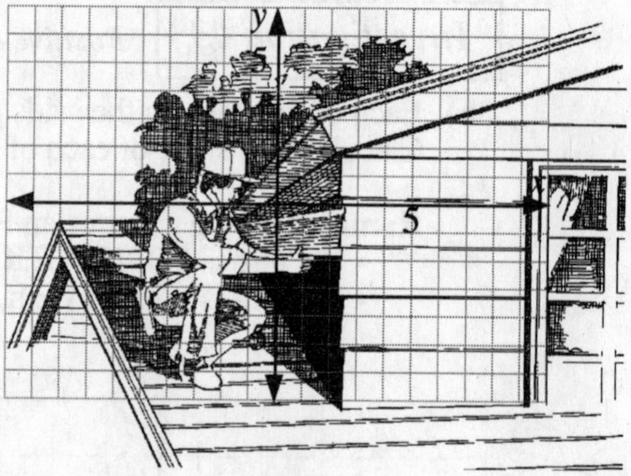

a) Estimate the pitch (slope) of the roof to the right of the worker's head.

$$\frac{1}{4}$$

b) Could the grid be used to estimate the pitch of the roof the worker is standing on? Explain.

no, must be on same plane.

$$\frac{-2}{3} \rightarrow -\frac{2}{3}$$

Class Ex. #3

Draw a line segment on the grid which passes through the point $(-4, 2)$ and has a slope of $-\frac{2}{3}$.

The line segment must be long enough to cross both the *x*-axis and the *y*-axis.

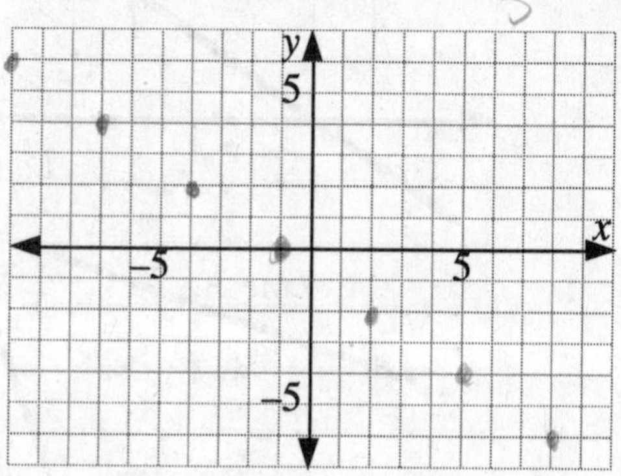

Write the coordinates of three other points on the line segment which have integer coordinates.

$$(-1, 0) \quad (-7, 4)$$

$$(x + 3, y \pm 2)$$

Class Ex. #4

A line segment has a slope of $-\frac{5}{7}$ and a rise of 12. Calculate the run as an exact value.

$$x \cdot \frac{-5}{7} = \frac{12}{x} x$$

$$\frac{-5x}{7} = 12 \cdot 7$$

$$\frac{-5x}{-5} = \frac{84}{-5} \rightarrow x = \frac{-84}{5}$$

$$\frac{-84}{5} \rightarrow 16.8$$

Complete Assignment Questions #3 - #13

Assignment

1. Each line segment on the grid has endpoints with integer coordinates. Complete the table.

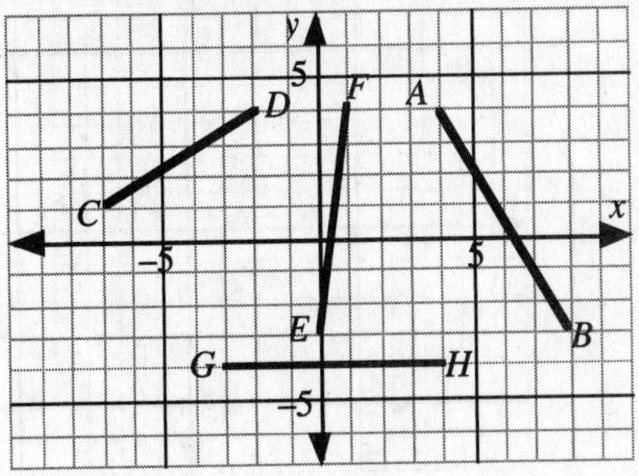

Line Segment	Rise	Run	Slope = $\frac{\text{Rise}}{\text{Run}}$
AB			
CD			
EF			
GH			

2. Each of the lines on the grid passes through at least two points with integer coordinates. Calculate the slope of each of the lines.

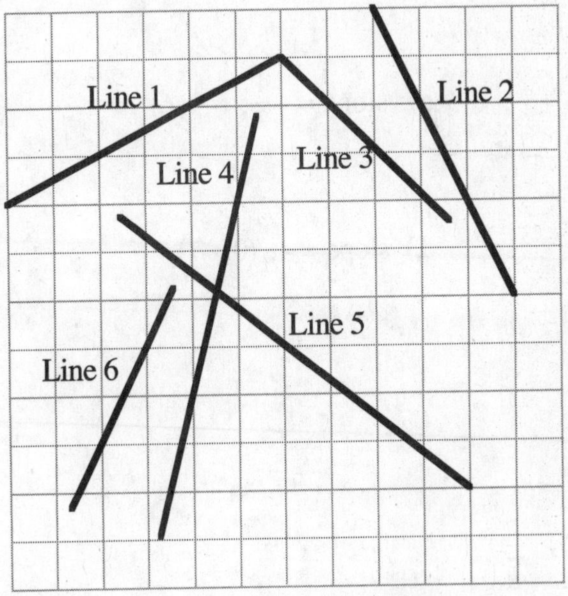

slope of Line 1 :

slope of Line 2:

slope of Line 3:

slope of Line 4:

slope of Line 5:

slope of Line 6:

3. Draw a line segment on the grid which passes through the point $(-5,-2)$ and has a slope of $\frac{2}{3}$. The line segment must be long enough to cross both the *x*-axis and the *y*-axis.

Write the coordinates of three other points on the line segment which have integer coordinates.

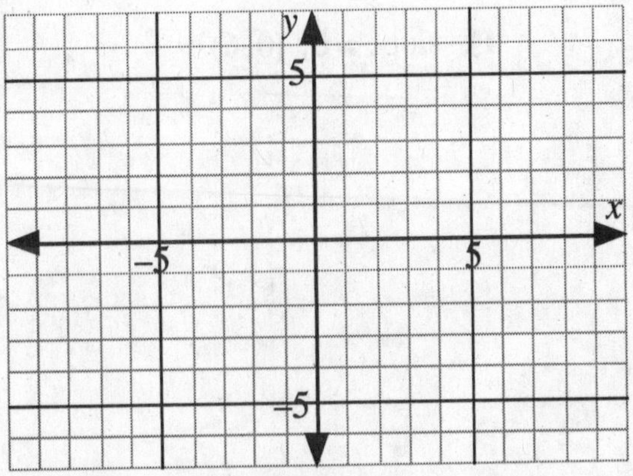

4. Repeat question #3 for line segments with the given slope passing through the given point.

a) slope = $\frac{2}{5}$, (2, 1)

b) slope = $-\frac{1}{3}$, (6, –3)

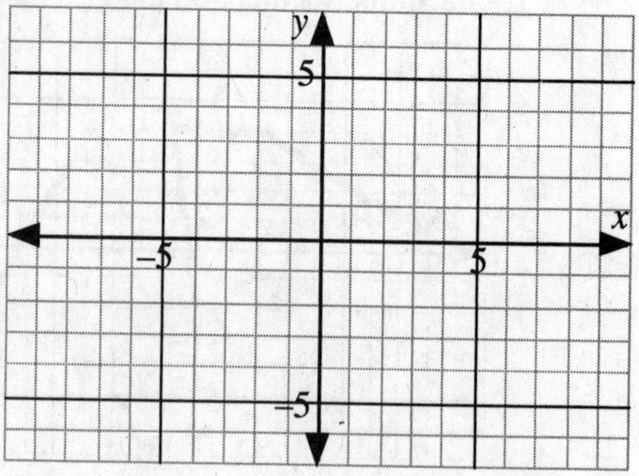

c) slope = $-\frac{4}{3}$, (–9, 6)

d) slope = 4, (0, –7)

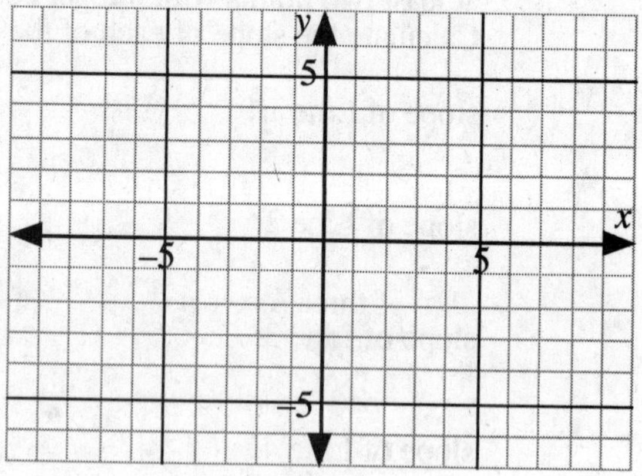

e) slope = –2, (4, –12)

f) slope = 0, (0, 6)

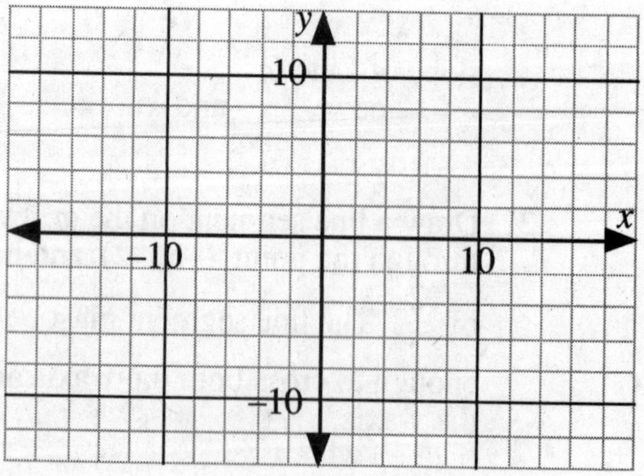

5. P has coordinates $(-1, 2)$. Find two positions for point Q so that the slope of PQ is

a) 2

b) -3

c) $\frac{1}{3}$

d) $-\frac{2}{5}$

e) 0

f) undefined

6. Two of three measures are given for rise, run, and slope.
Calculate the value of the third measure in each of the following.

a) slope $= \frac{5}{7}$ and run $= 49$

b) slope $= -\frac{3}{8}$ and rise $= 15$

c) slope $= -\frac{6}{11}$ and run $= 33$

d) slope $= \frac{3}{4}$ and rise $= 15$

7. A ramp which has been set up by skateboarders has a slope of $\frac{2}{3}$. Calculate the height of the ramp if the ramp has a base length of 1.5 metres.

8. Triangle ABC is isoceles with $AB = AC$ and $BC = 6.8$ cm. Calculate the area of the triangle if the slope of $AC = -\frac{5}{4}$.

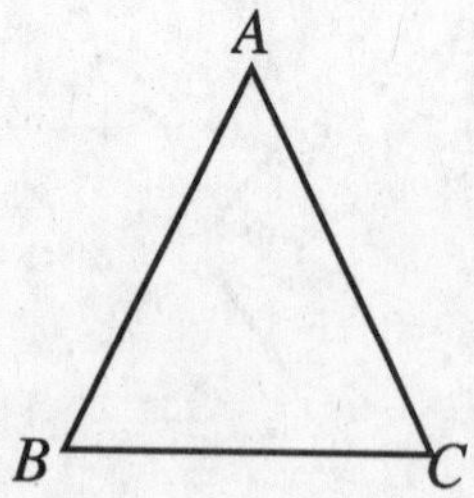

Multiple Choice **9.** The slope of $\overline{PQ}$ is

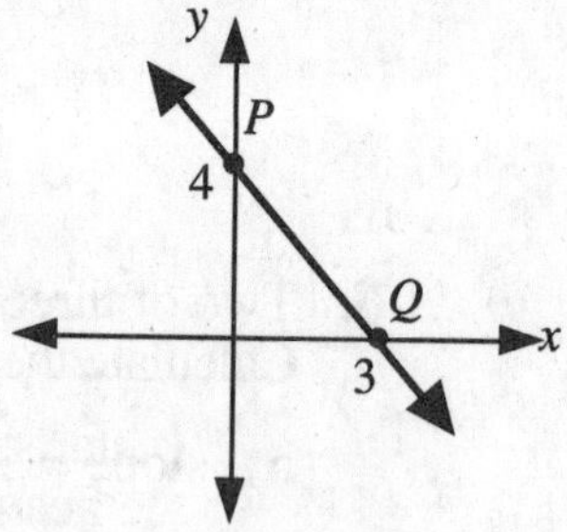

A. $\frac{3}{4}$
B. $-\frac{3}{4}$
C. $\frac{4}{3}$
D. $-\frac{4}{3}$

10. The point $(-4, 0)$ is on a line which has a slope of $-\frac{2}{5}$. The next point with integer coordinates on the line to the right of $(-4, 0)$ is

A. $(-9,-2)$
B. $(-9,2)$
C. $(1,-2)$
D. $(-2,-5)$

11. P is a point in quadrant I, Q is a point in quadrant II, R is a point in quadrant III, and S is a point in quadrant IV.

Which one of the following statements must be true?

A. Line segment PQ has a positive slope.
B. Line segment QR has a positive slope.
C. Line segment PR has a positive slope.
D. Line segment QS has a positive slope.

Use the following information to answer questions #12 and #13.

A pyramid has a square base of length 12 m and a vertical height of 15 m.

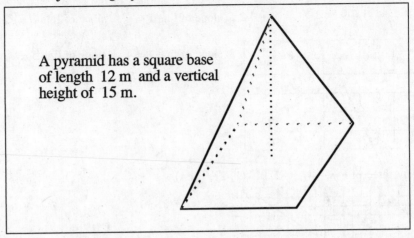

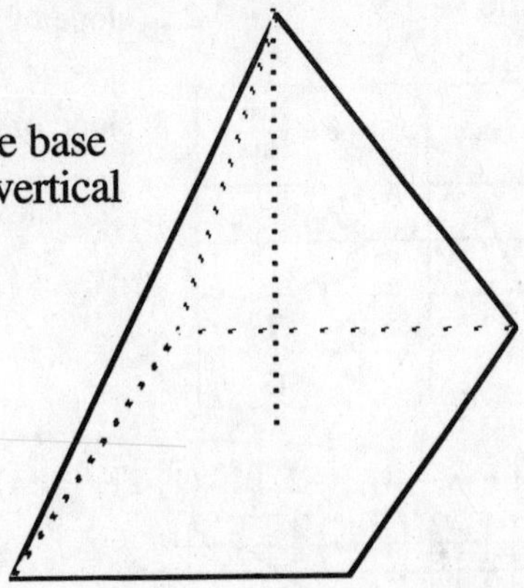

Numerical Response

12. A beetle starts to climb the pyramid starting from the midpoint of one of the faces. To the nearest tenth, the slope of the beetle's climb is _____.

(Record your answer in the numerical response box from left to right)

13. A fly starts to climb the pyramid along one of the edges. To the nearest tenth, the slope of the fly's climb is _____.

(Record your answer in the numerical response box from left to right)

Answer Key

1.

Line Segment	Rise	Run	Slope = $\frac{\text{Rise}}{\text{Run}}$
AB	−7	4	$-\frac{7}{4}$
CD	3	5	$\frac{3}{5}$
EF	7	1	$\frac{7}{1} = 7$
GH	0	7	$\frac{0}{7} = 0$

2. slope of line 1 = $\frac{1}{2}$, slope of line 2 = −2, slope of line 3 = −1

slope of line 4 = 4, slope of line 5 = $-\frac{3}{4}$, slope of line 6 = 2

3. Any three of (−8, −4), (−2, 0), (1, 2), (4, 4)

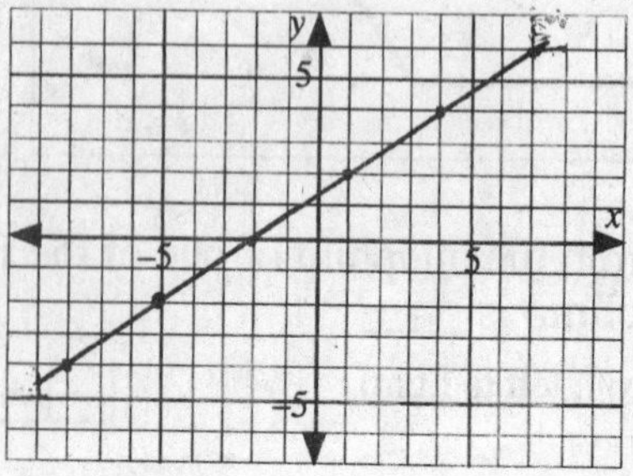

4.

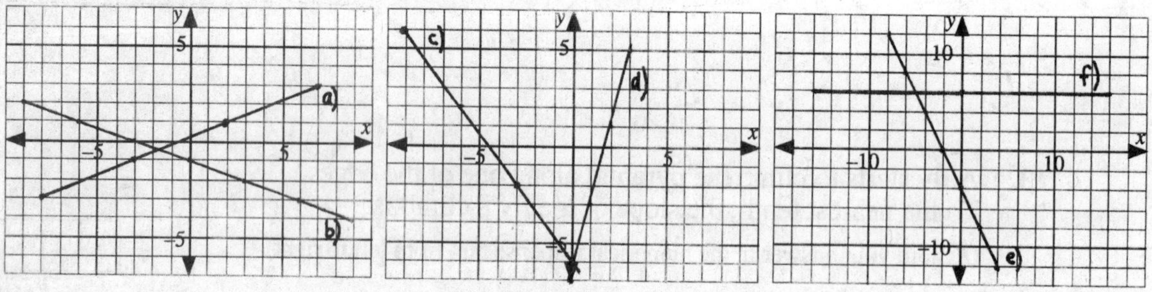

a) (−8, −3), (−3, −1), (7, 3)

b) Any 3 of (−9, 2), (−6, 1), (−3, 0) (0, −1), (3, −2), (9, −4)

c) (−6, 2), (−3, −2), (0, −6)

d) (1, −3), (2, 1), (3, 5)

e) Many possible answers including (2, −8), (0, −4), (−2, 0)

f) Many possible answers including (1, 6), (2, 6), (3, 6)

5. Many possible answers, including any two from:
a) (−3, −2), (−2, 0), (0, 4), (1, 6) **b)** (−3, 8), (−2, 5), (0, −1), (1, −4),
c) (2, 3), (5, 4), (−4, 1), (−7, 0) **d)** (−11, 6), (−6, 4), (4, 0), (9, −2)
e) (−3, 2), (−2, 2), (0, 2), (1, 2) **f)** (−1, 1), (−1, 0), (−1, −1), (−1, 3)

6. **a)** rise = 35 **b)** run = −40 **c)** rise = −18 **d)** run = 20

7. 1 metre **8.** 14.45 cm^2 **9.** D **10.** C **11.** C

12.

2	.	5	

13.

1	.	8	

Characteristics of Linear Relations Lesson #5:
The Slope Formula

Review

Complete the following statements.

a) Slope is the measure of the _______________ of a line.

b) Slope is the ratio of the vertical change (called the ___________) over the horizontal change (called the ___________).

c) A line segment which rises from left to right has a _______________ slope.

d) A line segment which falls from left to right has a _______________ slope.

e) A horizontal line segment has a slope of _____.

f) A vertical line segment has an _______________ slope.

g) The slopes of all line segments on a line are _________ .

Same slope = No same points

M = Slope.

$m = \frac{y_2 - y_1}{x_2 - x_1}$

Developing the Slope Formula

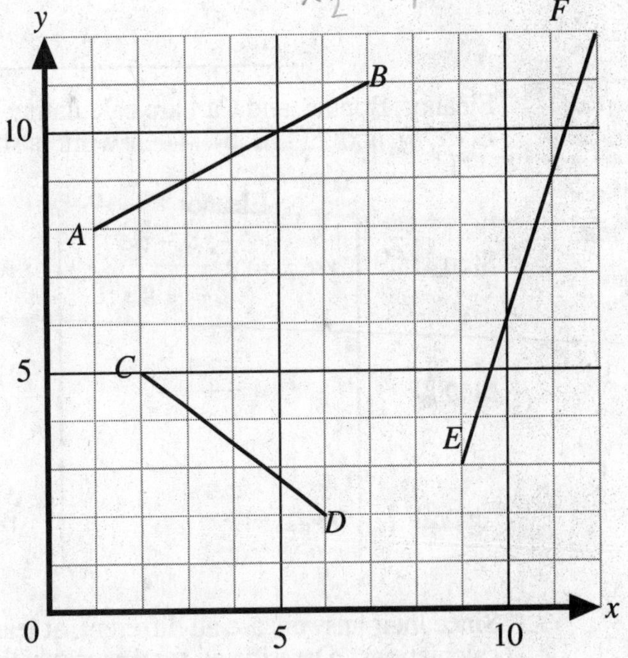

a) Calculate the slope of line segment AB using slope $= \frac{\text{rise}}{\text{run}}$.

b) List the coordinates of the endpoints of line segment AB.

$A($, $)$ $B($, $)$

c) How can the rise of line segment AB be determined using y_B and y_A?

d) How can the run of line segment AB be determined using x_A and x_B?

e) Use your results from c) and d) to write a formula which describes how the slope of line segment AB can be calculated using its endpoints.

f) Calculate the slope of line segment AB using the formula in e).

g) Calculate the slope of the line segments CD and EF using the method in a) and verify using the formula from e).

The Slope Formula

In mathematics the letter "m" is used to represent slope. If the graph of a linear relation passes through the points $P(x_1, y_1)$ and $Q(x_2, y_2)$, then the slope of this line can be calculated using

$$m = \frac{y_2 - y_1}{x_2 - x_1} \quad \text{or} \quad m_{PQ} = \frac{y_Q - y_P}{x_Q - x_P}$$

Class Ex. #1

Find the slope of a line which passes through the points $G(-3, 8)$ and $H(7, -2)$.

$$m_{GH} = \frac{y_H - y_G}{x_H - x_G} =$$

Class Ex. #2

Eleanor, Bonnie, and Carl are calculating the slope of a line segment with endpoints $E(15, 8)$ and $F(-10, 6)$. Their work is shown below.

	Eleanor	Bonnie	Carl
Step 1:	$m_{\overline{EF}} = \frac{-10 - 15}{6 - 8}$	$m_{\overline{EF}} = \frac{6 - 8}{15 - (-10)}$	$m_{\overline{EF}} = \frac{8 - 6}{15 - 10}$
Step 2:	$= \frac{-25}{-2}$	$= \frac{-2}{25}$	$= \frac{2}{5}$
Step 3:	$m_{\overline{EF}} = \frac{25}{2}$	$m_{\overline{EF}} = -\frac{2}{25}$	$m_{\overline{EF}} = \frac{2}{5}$

Since their answers are all different, at least two of the students have made errors in their calculations. Describe all the errors which have been made and determine the correct slope

Complete Assignment Questions #1 - #5

Collinear Points

Two lines in a plane can either be

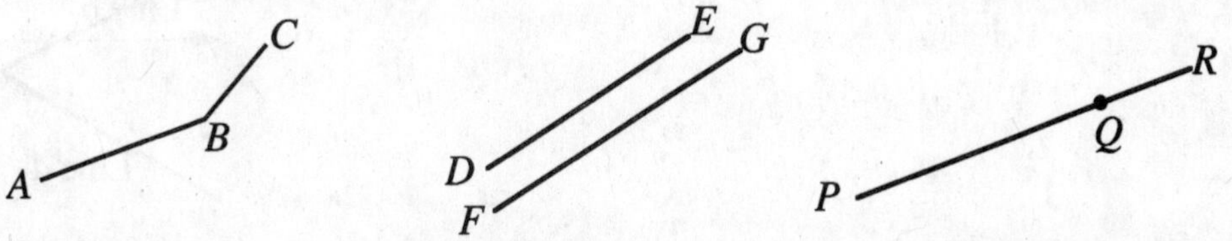

at an angle — parallel and distinct — parallel and form a straight line.

Points that lie on the same straight line are said to be **collinear**, i.e. P, Q, and R are collinear.

If three points P, Q, and R are collinear then $m_{PQ} = m_{QR} = m_{PR}$.
Proving that any two of these three slopes are equal is sufficient for the third to be equal and for the points to be collinear.

Consider points $A(5, -3)$, $B(2, 6)$, and $C(-7, 33)$.

a) Prove that the points A, B, and C are collinear.

b) Find the value of y if the point $D(-4, y)$ lies on line segment AC.

Complete Assignment Questions #6 - #12

Assignment

1. State whether the slope of each line is positive, negative, zero or undefined.

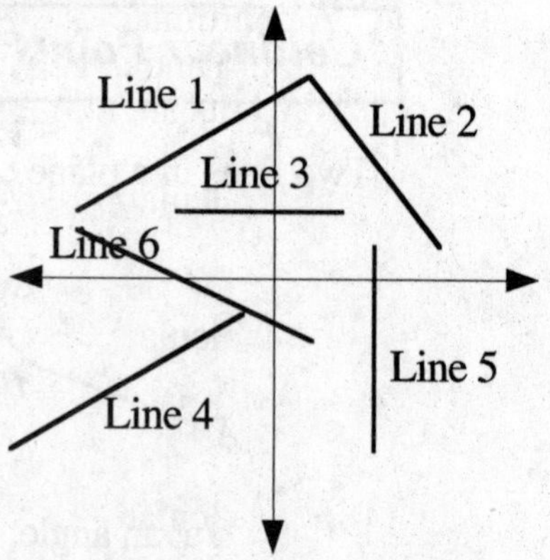

2. Use the slope formula to calculate the slope of the line segment with the given endpoints.

a) $A(12,-2)$ and $B(0,3)$

$m_{AB} = \dfrac{y_B - y_A}{x_B - x_A} =$

b) $C(-2,3)$ and $D(2,-2)$

c) $P(-15,-2)$ and $O(0,0)$

d) $S(36,-41)$ and $T(-20,-27)$

e) $U(-172,-56)$ and $V(-172,32)$

f) $K(8,-41)$ and $L(397,-41)$

3. Use the slope formula to calculate the slope of the line passing through the given points.

a) $(3,-6)$ and $(8,4)$

$m = \dfrac{y_2 - y_1}{x_2 - x_1} =$

b) $(-12,7)$ and $(0,-2)$

c) $(-3,-8)$ and $(1,5)$

d) $(21,1)$ and $(-4,-9)$

4. A coordinate grid is superimposed on a cross-section of a hill. The coordinates of the bottom and the top of a straight path up the hill are, respectively, $(3,2)$ and $(15,47)$, where the units are in metres.

a) Calculate the slope of the hill.

b) Calculate the coordinates of the midpoint of the path up the hill.

c) Calculate the length of the path to the nearest tenth of a metre.

5. The line segment joining each pair of points has the given slope. Determine each value of k and draw the line segment on the grid

a) $S(4,6)$ and $T(5,k)$ slope = 3

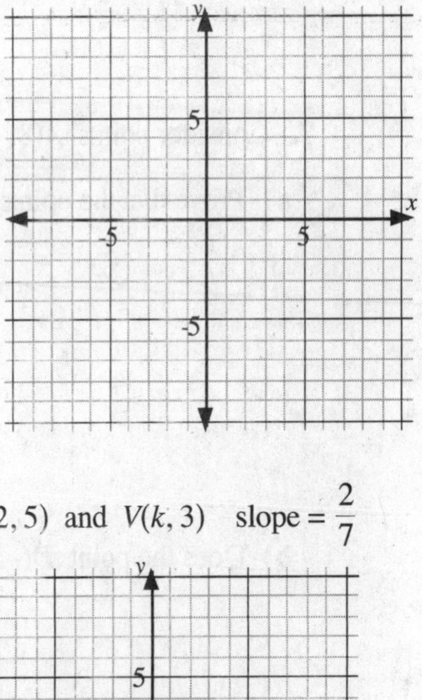

b) $L(k,-2)$ and $M(3,-7)$ slope $= -\frac{1}{2}$

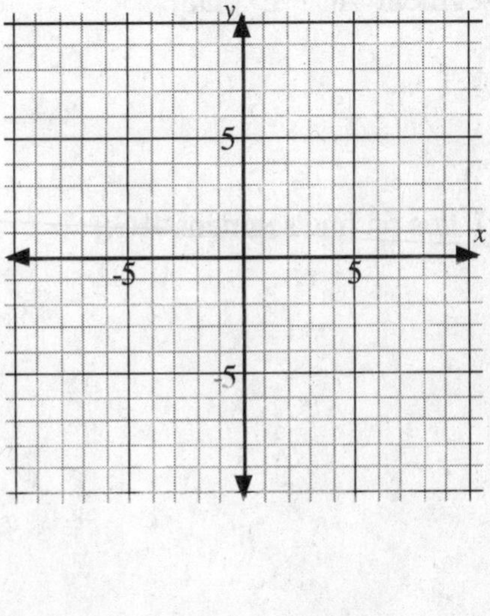

c) $U(2,5)$ and $V(k,3)$ slope $= \frac{2}{7}$

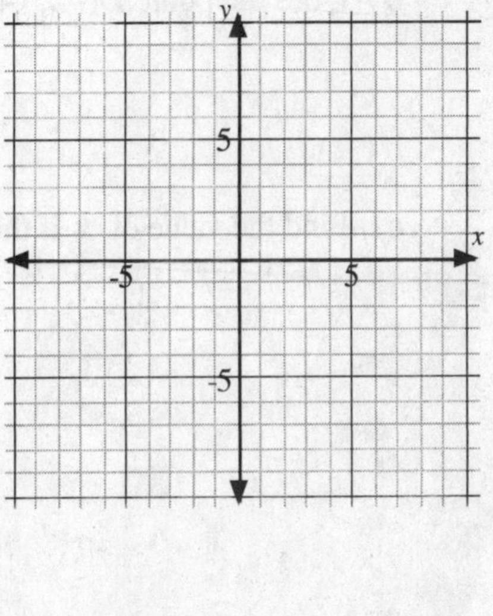

6. Consider points $P(4,-9)$, $Q(-1,-7)$, and $R(-11,-3)$.

a) Use the slope formula to prove that the points P, Q, and R are collinear.

b) Use the distance formula to prove that the points P, Q, and R are collinear.

7. Consider points $A(8,-7)$, $B(-8,-3)$, and $C(-24,1)$.

a) Prove that the points A, B, and C are collinear.

b) Does the point $D(-2,-4)$ lie on line segment AC? Explain.

c) Find the value of k if the point $E(k,k)$ lies on line segment AC.

8. A private jet has crashed in the desert at the point $P(-10, 17)$. A search party sets out in an all terrain vehicle from A_1 passing in a straight line through A_2. A helicopter sets out from B_1 and flies in a straight line through B_2.
If the search parties continue in these directions, will either of them discover the crashed plane?

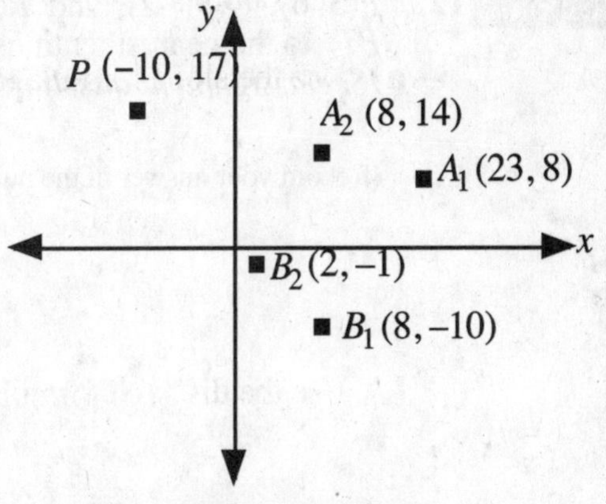

Diagram not to scale

Multiple Choice

9. The slope of the line segment joining $E(5,-1)$ and $F(3, 7)$, is

A. -3
B. -4
C. $-\frac{1}{3}$
D. $-\frac{1}{4}$

10. If the line segment joining $(2, 3)$ and $(8, k)$ has slope $-\frac{2}{3}$, then $k =$

A. -1
B. -3
C. -6
D. 7

11. One endpoint of a line segment is $(1, 6)$. The other endpoint is on the x-axis. If the slope of the line segment is -3, then the midpoint of the line segment is

A. $(4, 6)$
B. $(2, 3)$
C. $(-10, 3)$
D. $\left(\frac{1}{2}, \frac{15}{2}\right)$

Numerical Response

12. $P(3,6)$, $Q(8,-2)$, and $R(-6,0)$, are the vertices of a triangle. The slope of the median PT, to the nearest tenth, is ____.
(See assignment question #15 from Lesson 3 of this unit for the definition of a median).

(Record your answer in the numerical response box from left to right)

Answer Key

1. Line 1 - positive, Line 2 - negative, Line 3 - zero, Line 4 - positive, Line 5 - undefined, Line 6 - negative

2. a) $-\frac{5}{12}$ **b)** $-\frac{5}{4}$ **c)** $\frac{2}{15}$ **d)** $-\frac{1}{4}$ **e)** undefined **f)** 0

3. a) 2 **b)** $-\frac{3}{4}$ **c)** $\frac{13}{4}$ **d)** $\frac{2}{5}$

4. a) $\frac{15}{4}$ **b)** $\left(9, \frac{49}{2}\right)$ **c)** 46.6 m.

5. a) $k = 9$

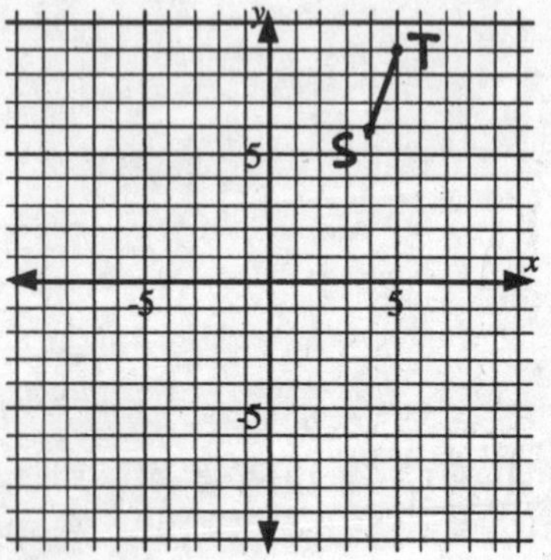

b) $k = -7$

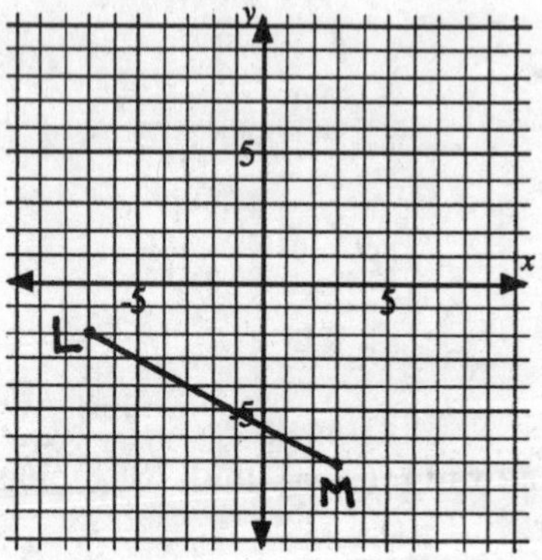

c) $k = -5$

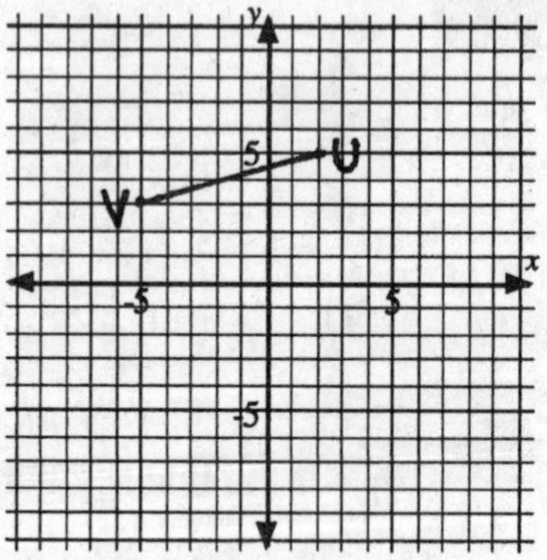

6. a) $m_{PQ} = -\frac{2}{5}$, $m_{QR} = -\frac{2}{5}$. Since $m_{PQ} = m_{QR}$, the points P, Q and R are collinear.

b) $PQ = \sqrt{29}$, $QR = 2\sqrt{29}$, $PR = 3\sqrt{29}$. Since $PQ + QR = PR$, the points P, Q and R are collinear.

7. a) $m_{AB} = -\frac{1}{4}$, $m_{BC} = -\frac{1}{4}$. Since $m_{AB} = m_{BC}$, the points A, B and C are collinear.

b) $m_{AD} = -\frac{3}{10}$ Since $m_{AD} \neq m_{AB}$, the point D does not lie on line segment AC. **c)** $k = -4$

8. $m_{A_1A_2} = -\frac{2}{5}$, $m_{A_2P} = -\frac{1}{6}$. Since $m_{A_1A_2} \neq m_{A_2P}$, the search party in the all terrain vehicle will not discover the plane.

$m_{B_1B_2} = -\frac{3}{2}$, $m_{B_2P} = -\frac{3}{2}$. Since $m_{B_1B_2} = m_{B_2P}$, the search party in the helicopter will discover the plane.

9. B **10.** A **11.** B **12.**

3	.	5	

Characteristics of Linear Relations Lesson #6: Parallel and Perpendicular Lines

Review of Transformations

In earlier mathematics courses we studied transformations: translations, reflections, and rotations. In order to investigate parallel and perpendicular line segments, we will review translations and rotations.

On the grid, show the image of the point $A(2,5)$ after the following transformations. In each case write the coordinates of the image.

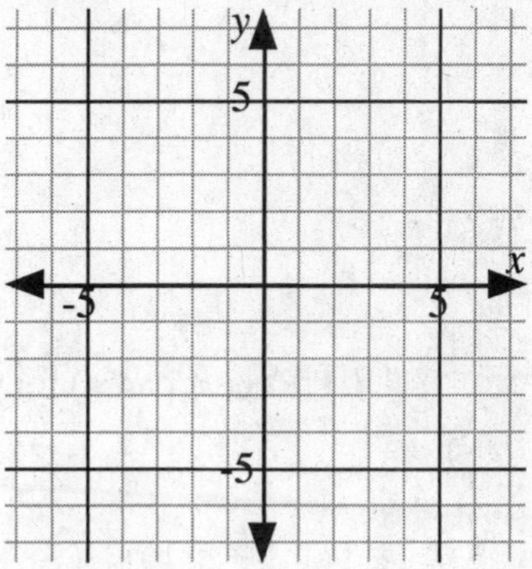

a) A translation 3 units right and 2 units up.

$A(2,5) \rightarrow \quad B(\quad , \quad)$

b) A 90° clockwise rotation about the origin.

$A(2,5) \rightarrow \quad C(\quad , \quad)$

c) A 90° counterclockwise rotation about the origin.

$A(2,5) \rightarrow \quad D(\quad , \quad)$

Investigating Parallel Line Segments

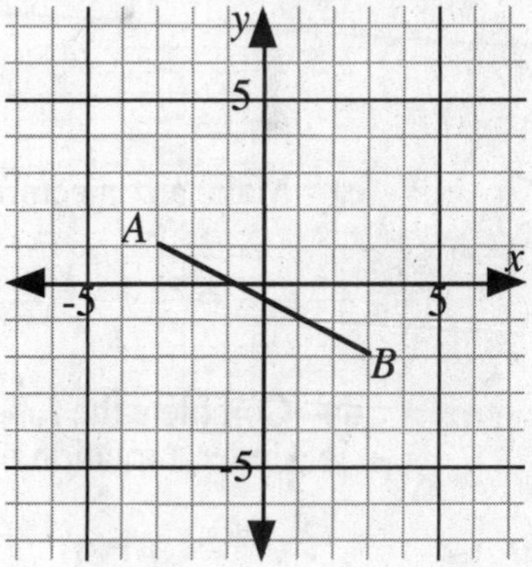

a) On the grid show the image of line segment AB after the following transformations.

i) A translation 4 units right and 1 unit down to form line segment CD.

ii) A translation 3 units left and 6 units up to form line segment EF.

iii) A translation 3 units down to form line segment GH.

b) Calculate the slope of each of the line segments.

c) The four line segments are parallel. Make a conjecture about the slopes of parallel line segments.

Investigating Perpendicular Line Segments

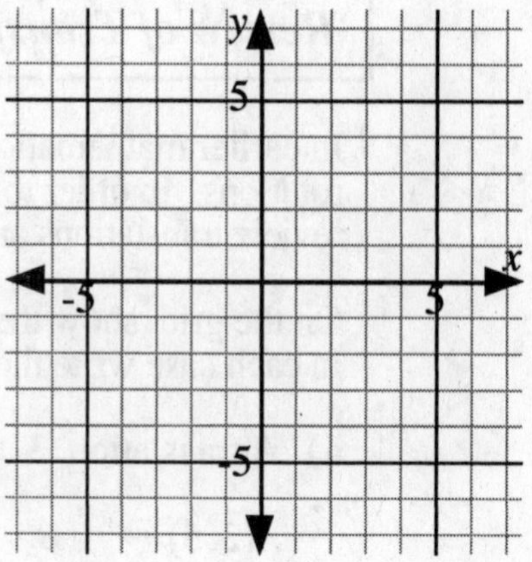

a) i) On the grid plot the point $A(5, 2)$ and draw the line joining the point to the origin, O.

ii) Rotate the line through an angle of 90° clockwise about O and show the image on the grid.

iii) Find the slopes of the two perpendicular lines and multiply them together.

b) Repeat part a) for the point $B(-6, 1)$.

c) Make a conjecture about the slopes of perpendicular line segments.

d) Complete the following to prove the conjecture in c).
Under a rotation of 90° clockwise about O, $P(a, b) \rightarrow Q(b, -a)$.

$$m_{OP} = \frac{y_P - y_O}{x_P - x_O} = \frac{b-0}{a-0} =$$

$$m_{OQ} = \frac{y_Q - y_O}{x_Q - x_O} = \frac{-a-0}{b-0} =$$

$$m_{OP} \times m_{OQ} =$$

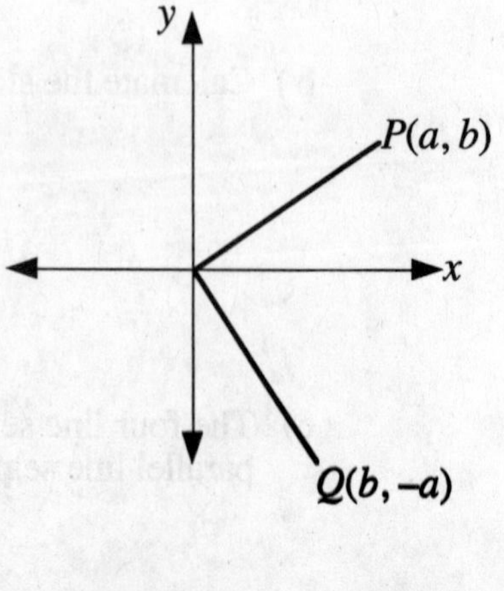

Parallel Lines and Perpendicular Lines

Recall that the slope of any line segment within a line represents the slope of the line.

Consider then two lines with slopes m_1 and m_2.

- The lines are **parallel** if they have the same slope, i.e. $m_1 = m_2$.
- The lines are **perpendicular** if the product of the slopes is -1,
  i.e. $m_1 \times m_2 = -1$ or $m_1 m_2 = -1$ or $m_1 = -\dfrac{1}{m_2}$
- For perpendicular lines, each slope is the negative reciprocal of the other, provided neither slope is equal to zero.

Consider line segment AC with a slope of $\frac{3}{4}$.

a) Write the slope of line segment GH which is parallel to AC.

b) Write the slope of line segment BF which is perpendicular to AC.

The slopes of two lines are given.
Determine if the lines are parallel, perpendicular, or neither.

a) $m_1 = \frac{1}{4}$, $m_2 = \frac{3}{12}$ **b)** $m_1 = \frac{5}{7}$, $m_2 = \frac{14}{10}$

Complete Assignment Questions #1 - #6

If P is the point $(4, 7)$ and Q is the point $(6, -2)$, find the slope of a line segment

a) parallel to line segment PQ **b)** perpendicular to line segment PQ

Class Ex. #4 $\triangle LMN$ has coordinates $L(-4,2)$, $M(-2,7)$, and $N(1,0)$. Use slopes to show that the triangle is right-angled at L.

$M_{LM} = \dfrac{+5}{+2}$

$M_{MN} = \dfrac{7}{3}$ *Perpendicular*

$M_{Ln} = \dfrac{-2}{-5}$

Class Ex. #5 Two lines have slopes of $-\dfrac{3}{4}$ and $\dfrac{k}{5}$ respectively. Find the value of k if the lines are

 a) parallel **b)** perpendicular

inverse

$\left(-\dfrac{3}{4}\right)\left(\dfrac{k}{5}\right)$ $-1 \cdot 20$

$\dfrac{3k}{-20} = \dfrac{-20}{-3}$

$k = \dfrac{20}{3}$ $\dfrac{20}{3} \cdot \dfrac{1}{5}$

$\dfrac{20}{3} \to \dfrac{4}{3}$
$\overline{15}$

Complete Assignment Questions #1 - #16

Assignment

1. AB is parallel to CD. EF is parallel to GH.

 a) Determine the slopes of the following pairs of parallel line segments using $m = \dfrac{\text{rise}}{\text{run}}$.

Line Segment	Slope
AB	
CD	

Line Segment	Slope
EF	
GH	

(-5, 4)

(3, 2)

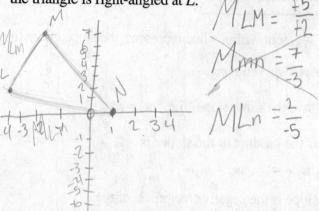

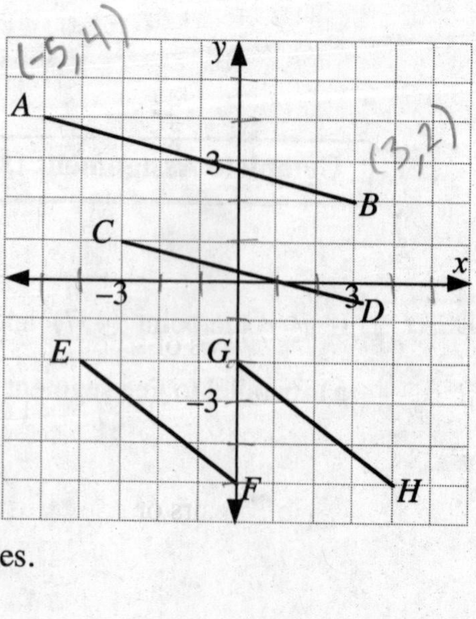

 b) Observe the slopes of the pairs of parallel lines in a).
 Write a rule in reference to the slopes of parallel lines.

2.a) Determine the slopes of the following pairs of perpendicular line segments using $m = \frac{\text{rise}}{\text{run}}$.

Line Segment	Slope
AB	
CD	

Line Segment	Slope
EF	
GH	

Line Segment	Slope
IJ	
JK	

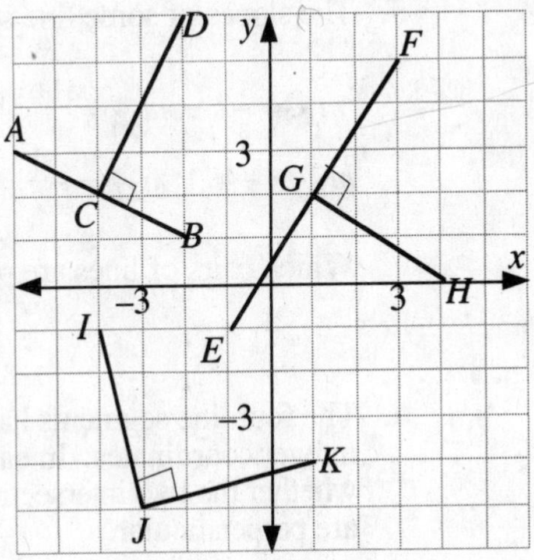

b) Multiply the slopes of the pairs of perpendicular line segments.

$m_{AB} \times m_{CD}$ | $m_{EF} \times m_{GH}$ | $m_{IJ} \times m_{JK}$

$-\frac{1}{2} \times 2 =$

c) Write a rule in reference to the slope of two lines which are perpendicular to each other.

3. The slopes of two line segments are given. Determine if the lines are parallel, perpendicular, or neither.

a) $m_{AB} = \frac{8}{20}$, $m_{PQ} = \frac{2}{5}$ **b)** $m_{AB} = \frac{3}{2}$, $m_{PQ} = -\frac{2}{3}$ **c)** $m_{AB} = \frac{1}{6}$, $m_{PQ} = \frac{2}{12}$

d) $m_{AB} = \frac{7}{8}$, $m_{PQ} = \frac{8}{7}$ **e)** $m_{AB} = \frac{9}{3}$, $m_{PQ} = -\frac{1}{3}$ **f)** $m_{AB} = -5$, $m_{PQ} = \frac{1}{5}$

g) $m_{AB} = \frac{4}{8}$, $m_{PQ} = 2$ **h)** $m_{AB} = -\frac{12}{2}$, $m_{PQ} = -6$ **i)** $m_{AB} = -\frac{5}{2}$, $m_{PQ} = -\frac{2}{5}$

4. The slopes of some line segments are given.

$m_{AB} = 6$ $m_{CD} = \frac{1}{6}$ $m_{EF} = -6$ $m_{GH} = 6$ $m_{IJ} = -6$ $m_{KL} = \frac{1}{6}$

Which pairs of lines are parallel to each other?

5. The slopes of some line segments are given.

$m_{RS} = -2 \quad m_{UV} = \frac{1}{4} \quad m_{EF} = 0.5 \quad m_{ZT} = 2$

$m_{PQ} = -4 \quad m_{KL} = -\frac{1}{2} \quad m_{MN} = 4 \quad m_{XY} = -\frac{1}{4}$

Which pairs of lines are perpendicular to each other?

6. The four line segments have endpoints with integer coordinates. In each case determine whether the two intersecting line segments are perpendicular.

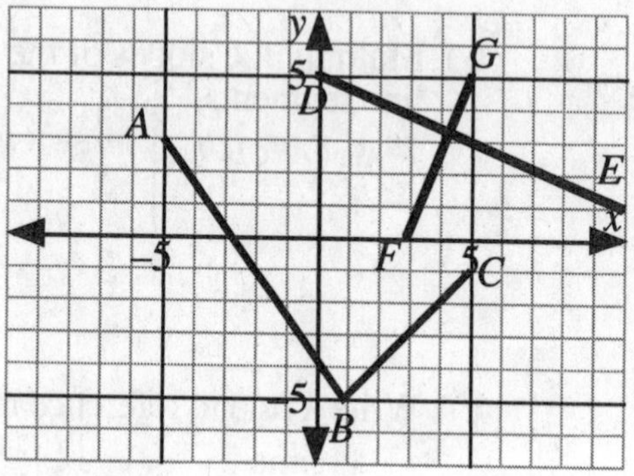

7. *A*, *B*, and *C* are the points $(0, 4)$, $(-3, 1)$, and $(5, -2)$ respectively. Determine the slope of a line

a) parallel to line segment *AB*

b) perpendicular to line segment *AB*

c) parallel to line segment *BC*

d) perpendicular to line segment *AC*

8. ΔABC has vertices $A(3, 5)$, $B(-2, -5)$, $C(-5, 1)$.

a) Explain how we can determine if $\triangle ABC$ is a right triangle.

b) Determine if $\triangle ABC$ is a right triangle.

9. The vertices of two triangles are given.
Determine if either of the triangles is right angled.

a) $\Delta PQR \rightarrow P(-3,3),\ Q(-1,1),\ R(-5,-1)$ **b)** $\Delta ABC \rightarrow A(-7,9),\ B(3,13),\ C(7,3)$

10. In each case the slopes of parallel lines are given.
Determine the value of the variable.

a) $4, \frac{k}{3}$ **b)** $-2, \frac{2}{n}$ **c)** $\frac{5}{6}, 3m$ **d)** $\frac{3}{4}, -\frac{w}{6}$

11. In each case the slopes of perpendicular lines are given.
Determine the value of the variable.

a) $\frac{1}{3}, 3h$ **b)** $4, \frac{8}{p}$ **c)** $-5, \frac{s}{2}$ **d)** $-\frac{3}{4}, -\frac{q}{6}$

12. $P(-4,0)$ and $R(1,-3)$ are opposite vertices of a rhombus $PQRS$. Find the slope of diagonal QS.

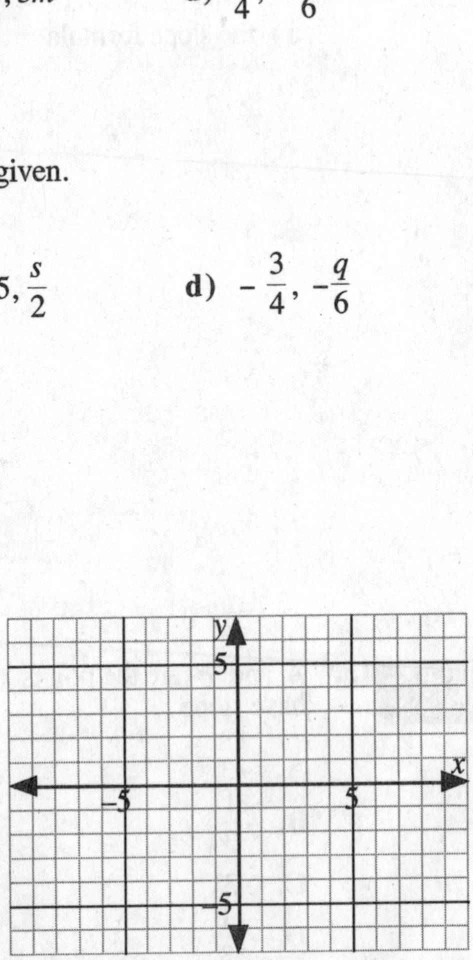

13. a) Show that when line segments JK and ML are extended until they intersect, they will not meet at right angles.

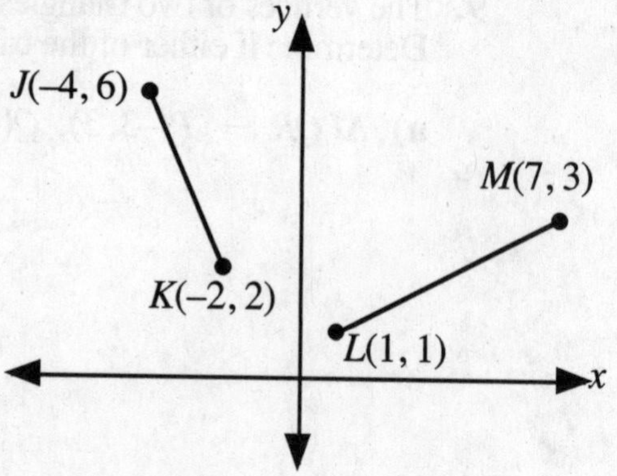

b) If the y-coordinate of M is changed, the line segments, when extended, will meet at right angles. To what value should the y-coordinate of M be changed?

14. Given that $A, B,$ and C are the points $(-3, 3)$, $(0, 6)$, and $(5, 1)$ respectively, prove that triangle ABC is right angled by using

a) the slope formula

b) the distance formula

Multiple Choice

15. A and B are the points $(1, 2)$ and $(-2, 3)$ respectively. A line perpendicular to AB will have slope

A. -3

B. $-\frac{1}{3}$

C. 3

D. $\frac{1}{3}$

Numerical Response **16.** The line segment joining $U(-3, p)$ and $V(-6, 5)$ is perpendicular to the line segment joining $X(4, 2)$ and $Y(9, 0)$. The value of p, to the nearest tenth, is _____.

(Record your answer in the numerical response box from left to right)

Answer Key

1. a) slope $AB = -\frac{1}{4}$ slope $CD = -\frac{1}{4}$ slope $EF = -\frac{3}{4}$ slope $GH = -\frac{3}{4}$

b) Lines which are parallel have the same slope

2. a) slope $AB = -\frac{1}{2}$ slope $EF = \frac{3}{2}$ slope $IJ = -4$

slope $CD = 2$ slope $GH = -\frac{2}{3}$ slope $JK = \frac{1}{4}$

b) All the products are -1. **c)** The product of the slopes is -1.

3. a) parallel **b)** perpendicular **c)** parallel

d) neither **e)** perpendicular **f)** perpendicular

g) neither **h)** parallel **i)** neither

4. AB and GH, CD and KL, EF and IJ.

5. RS and EF, UV and PQ, ZT and KL, MN and XY.

6. AB and BC are not perpendicular. DE and FG are perpendicular.

7. a) 1 **b)** -1 **c)** $-\frac{3}{8}$ **d)** $\frac{5}{6}$

8. a) Determine the slope of each side of the triangle. If two of the slopes are negative reciprocals of each, then the triangle is a right triangle.

b) $m_{BC} = -2$, $m_{AC} = \frac{1}{2}$. Since the slopes are negative reciprocals, the triangle is a right triangle.

9. a) ΔPQR is <u>not</u> a right triangle **b)** ΔABC is a right triangle

10.a) $k = 12$ **b)** $n = -1$ **c)** $m = \frac{5}{18}$ **d)** $w = -\frac{9}{2}$

11.a) $h = -1$ **b)** $p = -32$ **c)** $s = \frac{2}{5}$ **d)** $q = -8$

12. $m_{QS} = \frac{5}{3}$

13.a) $M_{JK} = -2$, $M_L = \frac{1}{3}$. The product of the slopes does not equal -1. **b)** $y_M = 4$

14.a) $m_{AB} = 1$, $m_{BC} = -1$ Since the product of the slopes = -1, AB and BC are perpendicular. Triangle ABC is right angled at B.

b) $AB = \sqrt{18}$, $BC = \sqrt{50}$, $AC = \sqrt{68}$. $AC^2 = 68$. $AB^2 + BC^2 = 68$.
$AC^2 = AB^2 + BC^2$ so the Pythagorean theorem is satisfied and the triangle is right angled at B.

15. C **16.**

1	2	.	5

Characteristics of Linear Relations Lesson #7: Practice Test

1. Which of the following horizontal or vertical line segments has the greatest length?
   A. PQ with $P(2,9)$ and $Q(7,9)$.
   B. RS with $R(4,11)$ and $S(4,4)$.
   C. TV with $T(-6,1)$ and $V(2,1)$.
   D. WZ with $W(-5,-5)$ and $Z(-5,-11)$.

2. The exact distance between the points $(8,3)$ and $(5,-2)$ is
   A. 5.83
   B. $\sqrt{34}$
   C. 8
   D. 34

Numerical Response 1. To the nearest hundredth, the distance between $A(-2,3)$ and $B(-5,-6)$ is _____.
(Record your answer in the numerical response box from left to right)

Use the following information to answer the next two questions.

> The points $A(4,2)$ and $B(-2,6)$ are on the circumference of a circle.
>
> The line segment AB passes through the centre of the circle.

3. The centre of the circle is the point
   A. $(2,8)$ **B.** $(3,-2)$
   C. $(1,4)$ **D.** $(6,-4)$

Numerical Response 2. The area of the circle, to the nearest whole number, is _____.
(Record your answer in the numerical response box from left to right)

Numerical Response 3. PQ is the diameter of a circle, the centre is R. If $Q(6.7,4.5)$ and $R(8.5,7.9)$ then the x–coordinate of P is _____.
(Record your answer in the numerical response box from left to right)

Use the following information to answer questions #4 - #6.

Nadine practiced for a math quiz by drawing line segments on a grid and then determining their slopes. Her line segments and grid are shown.

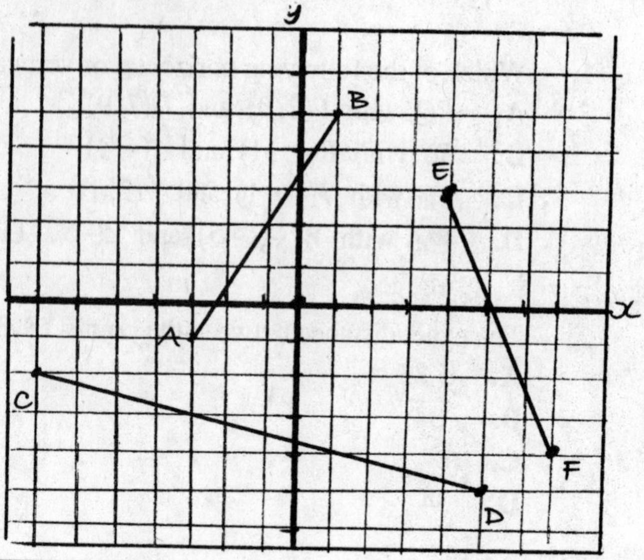

Matching Match each line segment on the left with the slope on the right. Each slope may be used once, more than once, or not at all.

Line Segment

Slope

4. *AB*

5. *CD*

6. *EF*

A. -4

B. $-\frac{3}{2}$

C. $-\frac{7}{3}$

D. $\frac{3}{7}$

E. $\frac{3}{2}$

F. $-\frac{1}{4}$

7. Consider $\overline{AB}$ joining $A(6,-4)$ and $B(-4,-4)$, and $\overline{CD}$ joining $C(1,-9)$ and $D(1,1)$. Which one of the following statements about these line segments is true?

A. $\overline{AB}$ and $\overline{CD}$ have the same slope and are equal in length.
B. $\overline{AB}$ and $\overline{CD}$ have the same slope and are unequal in length.
C. $\overline{CD}$ has a length of 10 units and a slope of zero.
D. $\overline{AB}$ and $\overline{CD}$ have the same midpoint and are equal in length.

Use the following information to answer questions #8 - #10.

Line Segment AB	Line Segment PQ
$A(-2,4)$ $B(2,-6)$	$P(7,1)$ $Q(-3,-3)$

8. Which of the following statements is correct about the line segments?

A. The length of line segment AB is greater than the length of line segment PQ.
B. The length of line segment AB is less than the length of line segment PQ.
C. The length of line segment AB is equal to the length of line segment PQ.
D. Not enough information is given to calculate the lengths of the line segments.

9. Which of the following statements is correct about the line segments?

A. The slope of line segment AB is positive and the slope of line segment PQ is negative.
B. The slope of line segment AB is positive and the slope of line segment PQ is positive.
C. Line segment AB is parallel to line segment PQ.
D. Line segment AB is perpendicular to line segment PQ.

10. Which of the following statements is correct about the line segments?

A. The midpoint of AB has an x-coordinate greater than the midpoint of PQ.
B. The midpoint of AB has an y-coordinate greater than the midpoint of PQ.
C. The midpoints of AB and PQ are the same point.
D. The line segment joining the midpoints is horizontal.

11. K and L are the points $(4, 7)$ and $(-1, -3)$ respectively. The slope of a line perpendicular to KL is

A. $\frac{1}{2}$
B. $-\frac{1}{2}$
C. 2
D. -2

Use the following information to answer questions #12–#15.

Quadrilateral $PQRS$ has vertices $P(-4,-6)$, $Q(-6,-2)$, $R(0, 1)$, and $S(2,-3)$.

12. The slope and length of line segment PQ are respectively

A. -2 and $2\sqrt{5}$
B. $-\frac{1}{2}$ and $2\sqrt{5}$
C. -2 and $2\sqrt{29}$
D. $-\frac{1}{2}$ and $2\sqrt{29}$

13. The slope and length of line segment QR are respectively

A. 2 and $\sqrt{37}$
B. $\frac{1}{2}$ and $\sqrt{37}$
C. 2 and $3\sqrt{5}$
D. $\frac{1}{2}$ and $3\sqrt{5}$

14. Consider the following statements:

I. PQ is parallel to SR.
II. QR is perpendicular to SR.
III. The lengths of PQ and SR are the same.

Which of the following is correct?

A. Statement **I** is false.
B. Statement **II** is false.
C. Statement **III** is false.
D. None of the above statements is false.

15. Which of the following most completely describes Quadrilateral $PQRS$?

A. rectangle **B.** square **C.** parallelogram **D.** rhombus

Numerical Response **4.** Two lines have slopes of $-\frac{2}{3}$ and $\frac{15}{t}$ respectively.
If the lines are perpendicular, then the value of t must be _____ .
(Record your answer in the numerical response box from left to right)

Numerical Response **5.** The line segment joining $K(-1, y)$ and $L(-2, 8)$ is parallel to the line segment joining $M(4, 4)$ and $N(0, 5)$. The value of y, to the nearest hundredth, is _____.

(Record your answer in the numerical response box from left to right)

Written Response - 5 marks

1. Consider the points $A(-2, 6)$, $B(2, 0)$, $C(0, 2)$, and $D(6, -6)$.

- Three of these points lie on the same straight line and one point does not. **Explain** how you could algebraically determine which of these points is not collinear with the other three.

- **Determine** algebraically which of the points $A(-2,6)$, $B(2,0)$, $C(0,2)$, and $D(6,-6)$ is not collinear with the other three.

- Without using the midpoint formula determine algebraically that B is the midpoint of line segment AD.

Assignment Key

1. C	2. B	3. C	4. E	5. F	6. C	7. D	8. C
9. D	10. D	11. B	12. A	13. D	14. D	15. A	

1. | 9 | . | 4 | 9 |

2. | 4 | 1 | | |

3. | 1 | 0 | . | 3 |

4. | 1 | 0 | | |

5. | 7 | . | 7 | 5 |

Written Response

1. • Use the slope formula to determine the slopes of AB, AC, AD. If the slopes are all different, then A is the point which is not collinear with the other three. If, on the other hand, only one of the slopes is different, then the point that is connected to A in the line segment with the different slope is the point that is not collinear with the other three.
   • C
   • Since we know that A, B, and D lie on the same straight line, B will be the midpoint of AD if we can show using the distance formula that $AB = BD$ in length.

Equations of Linear Relations Lesson #1: The Equation of a Line in Slope y-intercept Form → y = mx + b

Overview of Unit

In this unit we express the equation of a linear relation in three different forms: slope *y*-intercept form, point-slope form, and general form. We relate linear relations expressed in these forms to their graphs.

We also determine the linear relation given a graph, a point and the slope, two points, a point and the equation of a parallel or perpendicular line.

Investigating the Graphs of Linear and Non-Linear Relations

a) The equations of the graphs of some relations are given. In each case use a graphing calculator to sketch the graph of the relation and make a rough sketch of the graph on the grid provided. Do not list any *x*- or *y*-intercepts.

$y = 3x + 1$

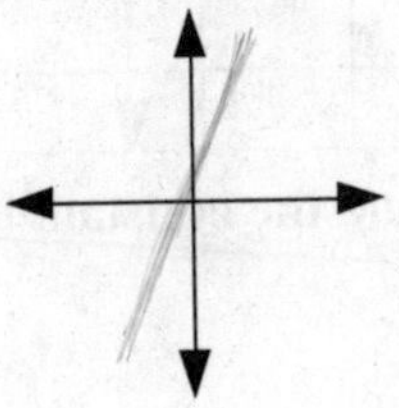

$y = -2x + 3$

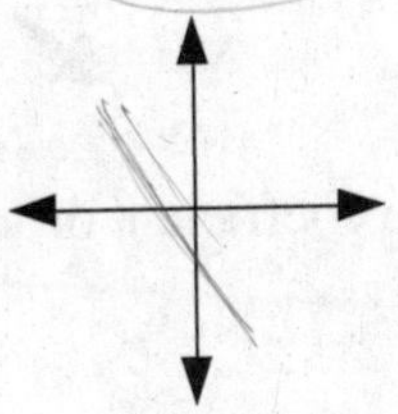

$y = -x^3 + 1$

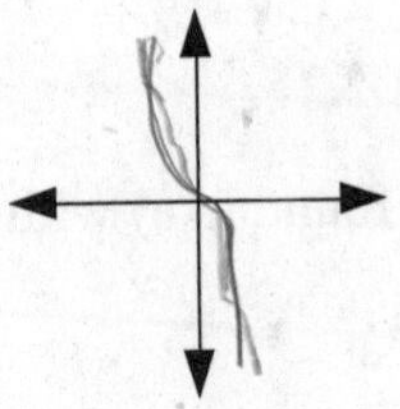

$y = x^2 - 3$

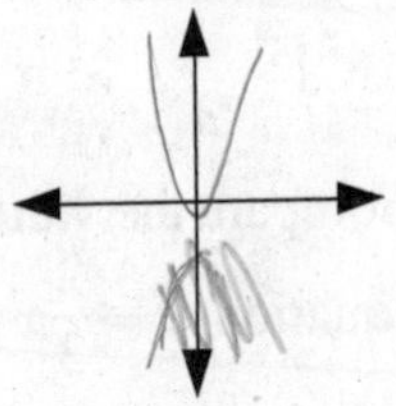

$y = \frac{1}{x}$

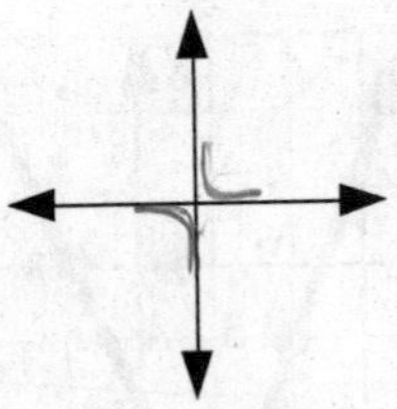

$y = \frac{1}{2}x - 2$

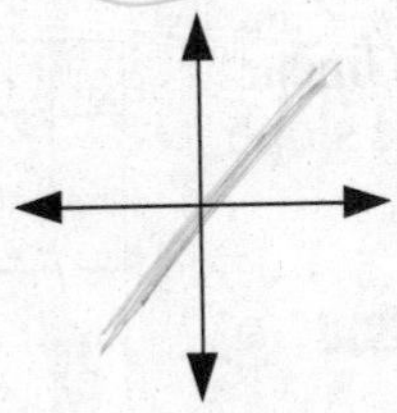

$y = 4x$

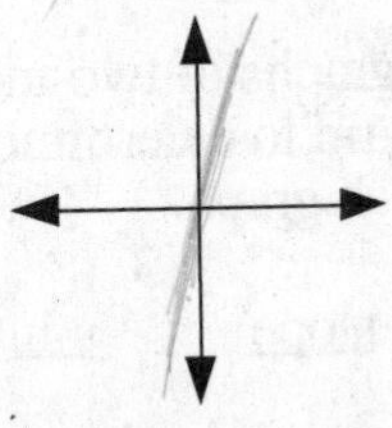

$y = 2^x$

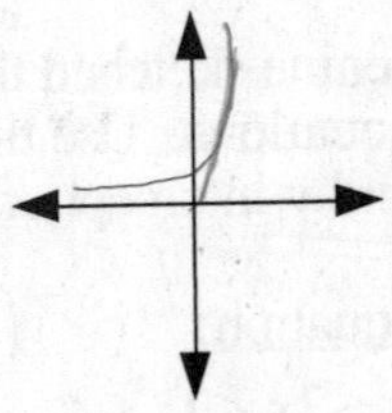

b) List the equations of the graphs in the appropriate row.

LINEAR: 3x + 1   -2x + 3   1/2 x - 2, 4x

NON-LINEAR: y = mx + b

c) Compare the lists. Write a rule from the equation which can be used to determine whether the graph is a straight line or not.

Linear Equation

A **linear equation** is an equation of the form $y = mx + b$, where $m, b \in R$. The graph of a linear equation is a straight line.

Investigating m and b in the equation $y = mx + b$

Part One

Jenine used a graphing calculator to sketch the graph of the linear equation $y = \frac{2}{3}x - 1$. Her sketch is shown on the grid.

$y = \frac{2}{3}x - 1$

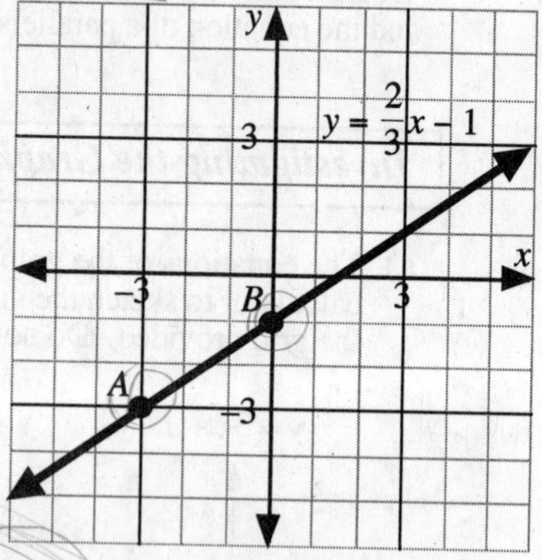

a) Use the sketch and points A and B to find the slope and y-intercept of the graph of $y = \frac{2}{3}x - 1$.

y-int (0,-1) $\frac{2}{3}$

b) Compare the values found in a) with the coefficient of x and the constant term in the equation $y = \frac{2}{3}x - 1$.

m slope Slope y-int

c) Jenine sketched the graphs of two more linear equations. Use the grid to determine the slope and y-intercept of each graph.

$y = 2x + 1$

$y = -\frac{5}{2}x - 3$

equation	slope	y-intercept
$y = 2x + 1$	$\frac{8}{4} = 2$	(0, 1)
$y = -\frac{5}{2}x - 3$	$\frac{-5}{1}$	(0, -3)

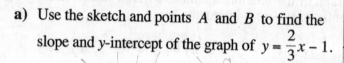

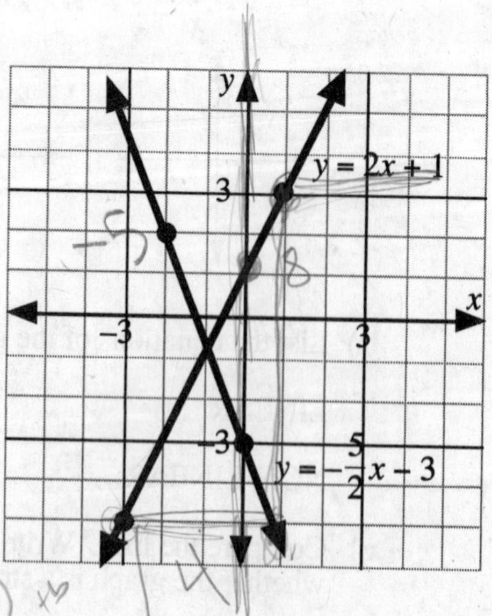

d) Make a conjecture about the slope and y-intercept of the graph of the linear equation $y = mx + b$.

m = slope b = y-intercept

$y = mx + b$

$y = m(0) + b$

$y = 0 + b$

$y = b$

Part Two

Hashib used a graphing calculator to graph the linear equation $2y = 5x + 8$.
The graph is shown on the grid.

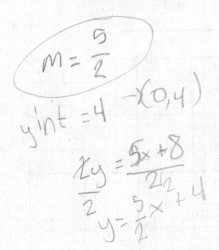

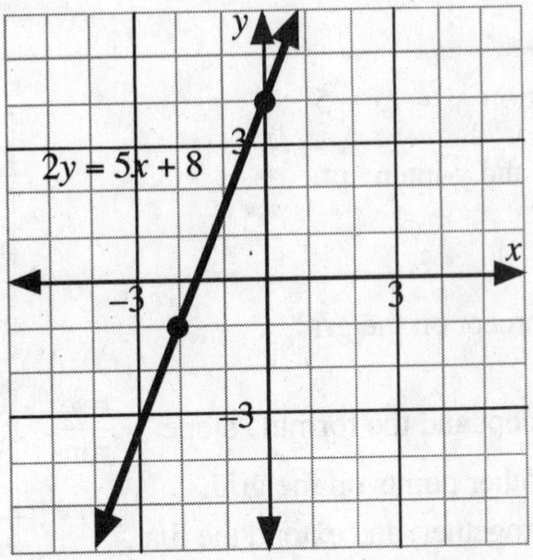

a) Use the sketch to determine the slope and y-intercept of the graph of $2y = 5x + 8$.

b) Explain why in this case the slope is not 5 (the coefficient of x) and the y-intercept is not 8 (the constant term).

Slope y-intercept Form of the Equation of a Line → y = mx + b

The graph of an equation in the form $y = mx + b$ (or a function in the form $f(x) = mx + b$) is a straight line with **slope** m and **y-intercept** b.

The equation $y = mx + b$ is known as the **slope y-intercept form** of the equation of a line.

The graph of an equation in this form can be drawn without making a table of values.

Determine the slope and y-intercept of the graph of each linear equation listed below:

a) $y = 3x + 2$ **b)** $y = 7 - \frac{2}{3}x$ **c)** $6y = 8x + 1$

by hand

Graphing an Equation of the Form $y = mx + b$

In this section we will look at two ways of sketching the graph of a linear equation without using a graphing calculator or a table of values.

Class Ex. #2

Consider the equation $y = 2x - 5$.

a) State the slope and y-intercept.

$m = 2$ $yint = -5 \rightarrow (0, -5)$

b) Mark the y-intercept on the grid.

c) Use the y-intercept and the formula slope $= \dfrac{\text{rise}}{\text{run}}$
to mark three other points on the grid.
Join the points together, and extend the line.

d) Verify the graph using a graphing calculator.

throw it in to check

switch

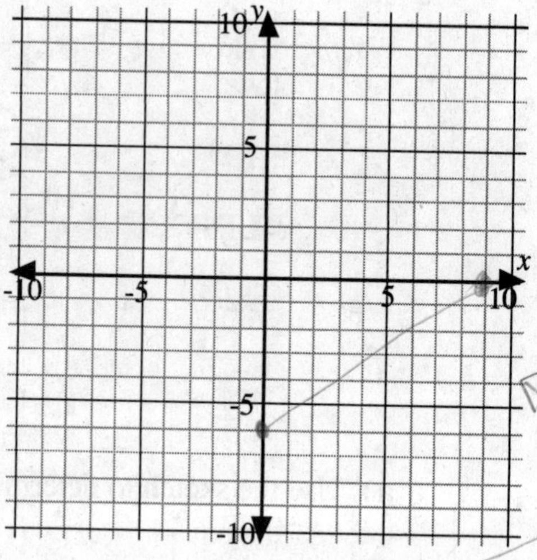

Class Ex. #3

Consider the equation $y = \dfrac{2}{3}x - 6$.

a) State the y-intercept.

$-6 \; (0, -6)$

b) Determine the x-intercept algebraically.

$y = 0$

$0 = \frac{2}{3}x - 6$

$+6 \; (+6 = \frac{2}{3}x$

$\frac{18}{2} = \frac{2x}{2}$

$9 = x$

c) Mark the x- and y-intercepts on the grid.
Join the points together, and extend the line.

d) Verify the graph and the intercepts using a
graphing calculator.

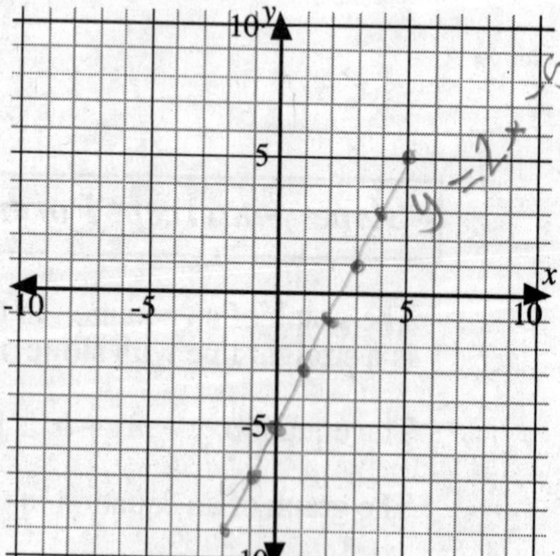

Complete Assignment Questions #1 - #14

Assignment

1. Each equation represents a relation.

 a) $y = 6x + 1$ **b)** $y = x^2$ **c)** $y = 3x^4 + 5$ **d)** $y = -\dfrac{1}{4}x - 8$

 e) $y = 1 - x$ **f)** $y = \dfrac{2}{1-x}$ **g)** $y = 4x$ **h)** $y = 4^x$

 Without sketching the graph of the relation, place the letters a) through h) in the appropriate row below.

 LINEAR: a, e, g

 NON-LINEAR: b, c, d, f, h

2. State the slope and y-intercept of the graph of each linear equation. $-4y = 6x$

 a) $y = 7x - 2$ **b)** $y = \dfrac{4}{3}x + 3$ **c)** $y = 6 - \dfrac{1}{6}x$ **d)** $4y = 6x + 8$ **e)** $y = ax + b$

 $m = 7$ $m = \dfrac{4}{3}$ $m = -\dfrac{1}{6}$ $m = ?$ $m =$

 $y\,int = -2 \to (0,2)$ $y\,int = (0,3)$ $y\,int = (0,6)$ $y\,int = (0,1)$ $y\,int = (0,)$

3. Write the equation of each line with the given slope and y-intercept.

 a) slope = 4 **b)** slope = $\dfrac{1}{5}$ **c)** slope = –3 **d)** slope = m

 y-intercept = –9 y-intercept = $\dfrac{1}{2}$ y-intercept = 0 y-intercept = b

4. For each line, state the slope and the y-intercept. Graph the equation without using a graphing calculator.

 a) $y = \dfrac{1}{4}x + 2$ **b)** $y = -x - 1$ **c)** $y = -\dfrac{4}{3}x$ **d)** $y = 5$

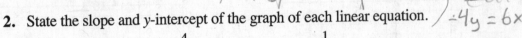

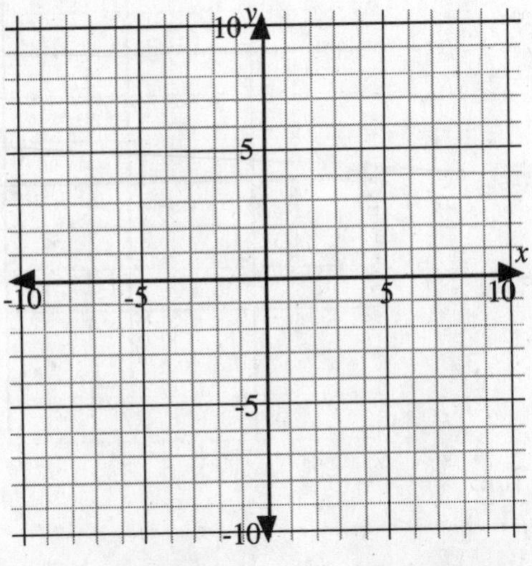

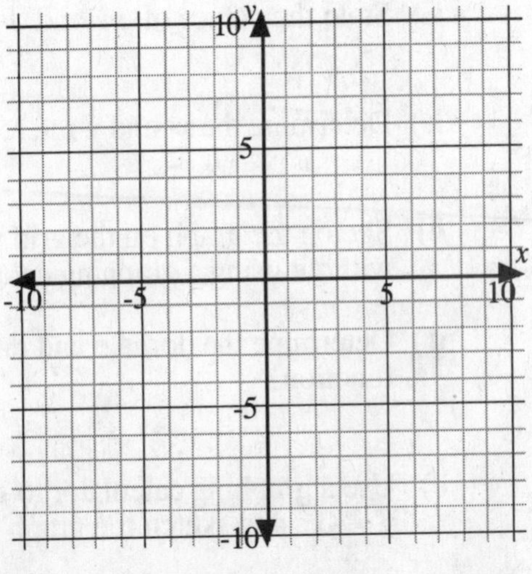

5. For each line, state the y-intercept. Determine the x-intercept algebraically, and graph the equation without using a graphing calculator.

a) $y = 2x + 6$ **b)** $y = -x - 4$ **c)** $y = \frac{6}{7}x - 6$ **d)** $y = -\frac{1}{2}x + 1$

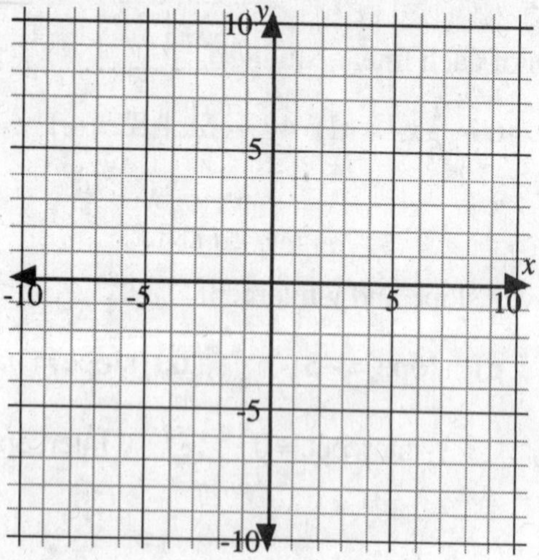

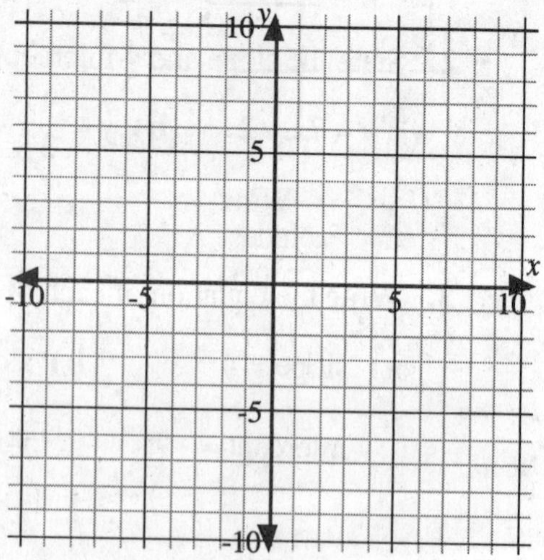

6. Explain why the linear equation $y = 5x$ can be graphed using the method in question 4 but not by the method in question 5.

7. Consider the graph of the function with equation $y = x$.

a) State the values of m and b.

b) Determine the x- and y-intercepts.

c) Sketch the graph on the grid provided without using a graphing calculator.

d) Determine the domain and range of the function.

e) Use a graphing calculator to graph the line $y = -x$, and sketch the graph on the grid.

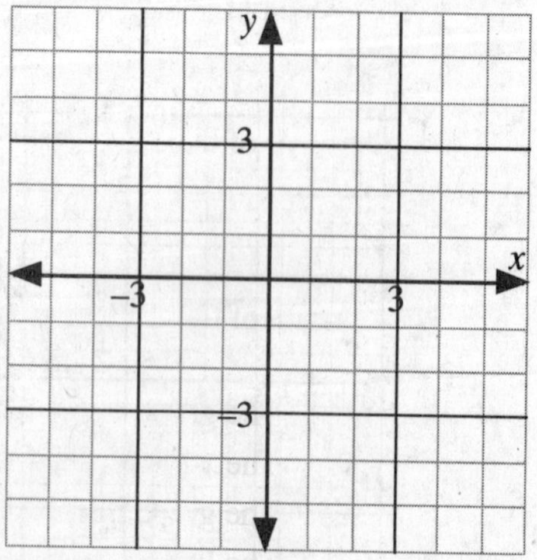

8. Use a graphing calculator to sketch the graph of each of the following linear equations. Complete the table giving the x-intercept to the nearest hundredth.

i) $y = 7x - 8$

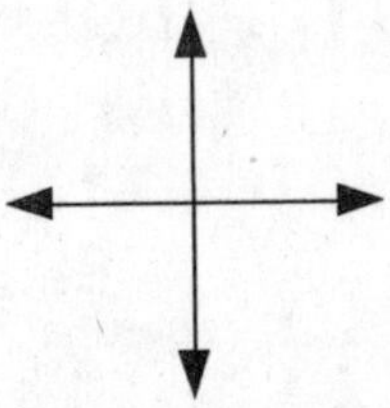

slope	
x-intercept	
y-intercept	

Graphing Window which includes both intercepts:

```
WINDOW
 Xmin=
 Xmax=
 Xscl=
 Ymin=
 Ymax=
 Yscl=
 Xres=1
```

ii) $y = -\frac{31}{2}x - 25$

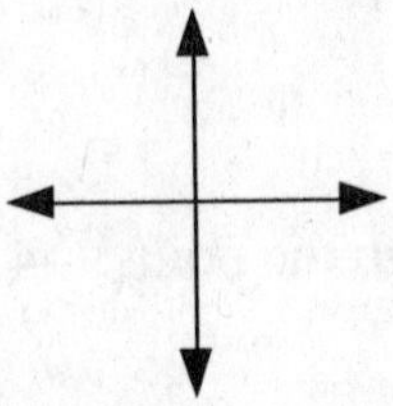

slope	
x-intercept	
y-intercept	

Graphing Window which includes both intercepts:

```
WINDOW
 Xmin=
 Xmax=
 Xscl=
 Ymin=
 Ymax=
 Yscl=
 Xres=1
```

iii) $y = 75 - \frac{5}{3}x$

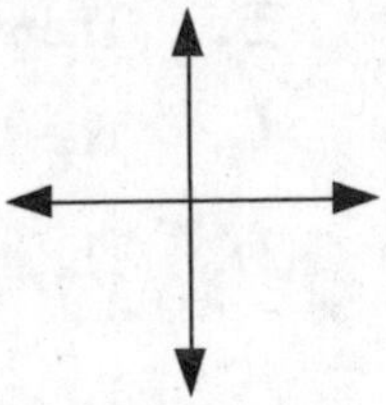

slope	
x-intercept	
y-intercept	

Graphing Window which includes both intercepts:

```
WINDOW
 Xmin=
 Xmax=
 Xscl=
 Ymin=
 Ymax=
 Yscl=
 Xres=1
```

Multiple Choice

9. Which of the following does not represent the equation of a straight line?

A. $y = 3x$
B. $y = 11 - 3x$
C. $y = \frac{x}{3}$
D. All of the above represent the equation of a straight line.

10. Which of the following statements is false for the line $y = -\frac{1}{2}x + 1$?

A. The graph of the line falls from left to right.
B. The x-intercept is 2.
C. The graph passes through the point $(8, -3)$.
D. The line is perpendicular to the line $y = -2x + 4$.

11. Which of the following statements is true for the line $2y = \frac{1}{4}x + 6$?

A. The x-intercept is 24.
B. The y-intercept is 6.
C. The slope is $\frac{1}{8}$.
D. The graph passes through the point $(-4, 5)$.

12. The lines $y = ax$, $y = bx$, and $y = cx$ are shown. Which of the following statements is true?

A. $a < b < c$
B. $a < c < b$
C. $c < a < b$
D. $c < b < a$

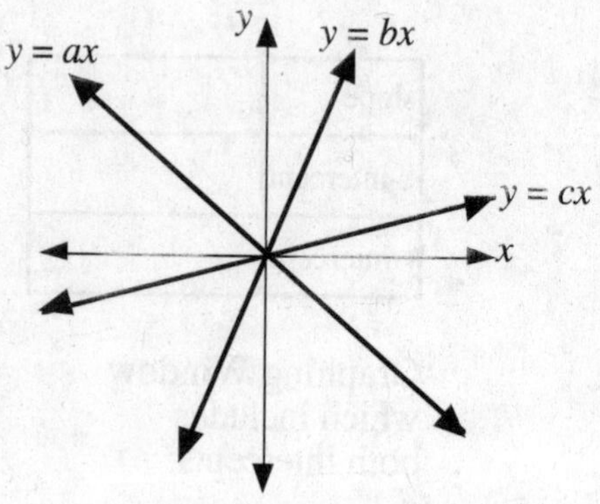

Use the following information to answer questions 13 and 14.

Consider the line with equation $y = 3x + 5$. The line intersects the x-axis at P and the y-axis at Q. Triangle POQ is formed, where O is the origin.

Numerical Response

13. The area of $\triangle POQ$, in square units, to the nearest tenth, is ____.

(Record your answer in the numerical response box from left to right)

14. To the nearest tenth, the perimeter of $\triangle POQ$ is ____.

(Record your answer in the numerical response box from left to right)

Answer Key

1. LINEAR a), d), e), g). NON-LINEAR b), c), f), h).

2. **a.** slope = 7, y-int = –2 **b)** slope = $\frac{4}{3}$, y-int = 3

c) slope = $-\frac{1}{6}$, y-int = 6 **d)** slope = $\frac{3}{2}$, y-int = 2 **e)** slope = a, y-int = b

3. **a)** $y = 4x - 9$ **b)** $y = \frac{1}{5}x + \frac{1}{2}$ **c)** $y = -3x$ **d)** $y = mx + b$

4. **a)** slope = $\frac{1}{4}$, y-int = 2 **b)** slope = –1, y-int = –1

c) slope = $-\frac{4}{3}$, y-int = 0 **d)** slope = 0, y-int = 5

5. **a)** y-int = 6, x-int = –3 **b)** y-int = –4, x-int = –4 **c)** y-int = –6, x-int = 7 **d)** y-int = 1, x-int = 2

6. The method in #4 needs a point and a slope. We have point (0, 0) and slope = 5. The method in #5 needs two points to be joined. Since the x- and y-intercepts are the same point, the line cannot be drawn.

7. **a)** $m = 1$, $b = 0$ **b)** x-int = 0 and y-int = 0. **d)** $D = x \in R$ $R = y \in R$

8.

i) $y = 7x - 8$

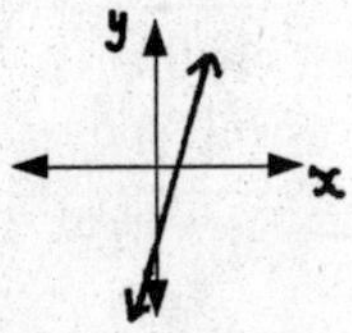

slope	7
x-intercept	1.14
y-intercept	−8

Graphing Window which includes both intercepts:

```
WINDOW
 Xmin= -4
 Xmax= 4
 Xscl= 1
 Ymin= -10
 Ymax= 5
 Yscl= 2
 Xres=1
```

ii) $y = -\frac{31}{2}x - 25$

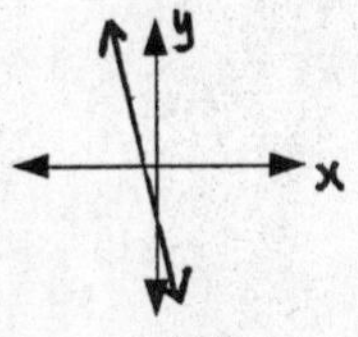

slope	$-\frac{31}{2}$
x-intercept	−1.61
y-intercept	−25

Graphing Window which includes both intercepts:

```
WINDOW
 Xmin= -4
 Xmax= 4
 Xscl= 1
 Ymin= -40
 Ymax= 10
 Yscl= 10
 Xres=1
```

iii) $y = 75 - \frac{5}{3}x$

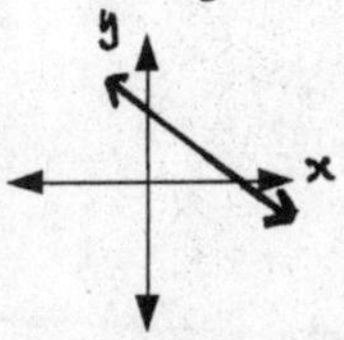

slope	$-5/3$
x-intercept	45
y-intercept	75

Graphing Window which includes both intercepts:

```
WINDOW
 Xmin= -10
 Xmax= 60
 Xscl= 10
 Ymin= -20
 Ymax= 100
 Yscl= 10
 Xres=1
```

9. D **10.** D **11.** C **12.** B

13.

4	.	2	

14.

1	1	.	9

Equations of Linear Relations Lesson #2:
Writing Equations Using y = mx + b

Review

We have learned that the graph of an equation in the form $y = mx + b$ is a straight line with slope m and y-intercept b.

Using the Form $y = mx + b$ to Write the Equation of a Line

The form $y = mx + b$ can be used to determine the equation of a line when the following information is given:
- the slope of the line
- the y-intercept of the line.

Class Ex. #1

Write the equation of a line passing through the point $(0, 2)$ with slope $\dfrac{5}{2}$.

$y = \frac{5}{2}x + 2$ y-int

Class Ex. #2

Each line on the grid passes through points with integer coordinates. In each case, state the slope and y-intercept of the line, and determine the equation of the line.

y-int $= -4$
slope $= \frac{1}{3}$ $y = \frac{1}{3}x - 4$

y-int $= 2$
$m = \frac{-3}{2}$ $y = \frac{-3}{2}x + 2$

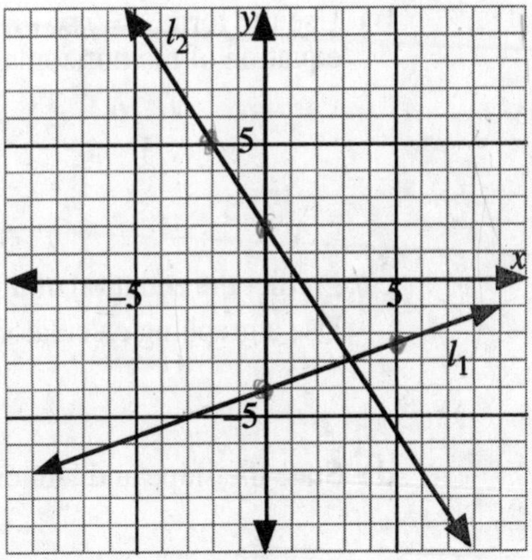

Class Ex. #3

Determine the equation of the following lines:

a) the line parallel to $y = \dfrac{1}{3}x + 4$, and with the same y-intercept as $y = 6x - 7$

b) the line passing through $(0, 9)$, and perpendicular to the line joining $(2, -6)$ and $(-5, 0)$

y-int

$y = \frac{7}{6}x + 9$

$m = \frac{-6 - 0}{2 - (-5)}$ $m = \frac{-6}{7} = \frac{7}{6}$

Class Ex. #4

The diagram shows the display from a graphing calculator screen. The intercepts are integers. Determine the equation of the line shown.

```
WINDOW
 Xmin=-5
 Xmax=30
 Xscl=5
 Ymin=-5
 Ymax=20
 Yscl=7
 Xres=1
```

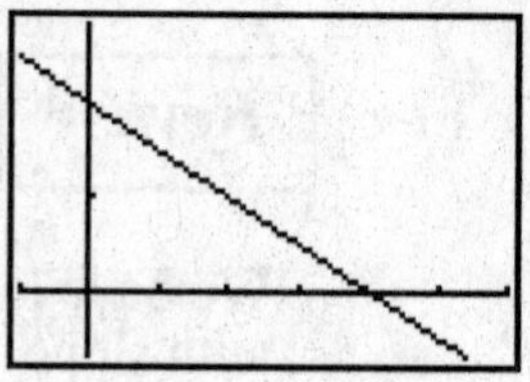

Complete Assignment Questions #1 - #5

HOY VUX

Horizontal and Vertical Lines

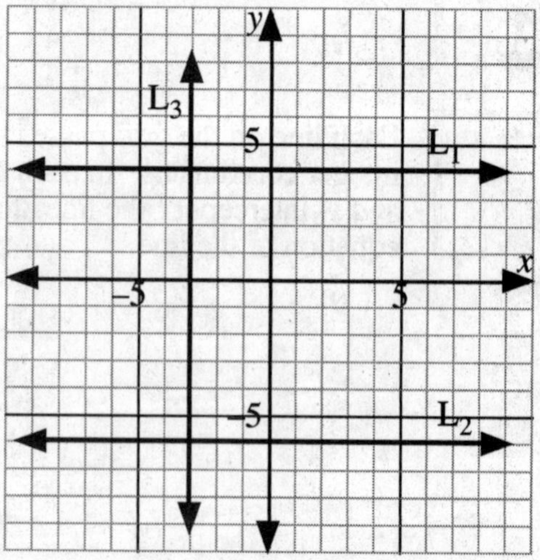

a) State the slope and *y*-intercept of the horizontal line L_1 shown on the grid.

b) Use the form $y = mx + b$ to determine the equation of the horizontal line L_1 .

y = 0x + b

y = 4

c) Predict the equation of the horizontal line L_2 . Use a graphing calculator to verify.

d) State the slope and *y*-intercept of the vertical line L_3 shown on the grid.

e) Why can we not use the form $y = mx + b$ to determine the equation of the vertical line L_3?

f) Predict the equation of the vertical line L_3 . Why can we not use a graphing calculator to verify?

The equation $y = k$ represents a horizontal line through $(0, k)$.
The equation $x = k$ represents a vertical line through $(k, 0)$.

Class Ex. #5

Determine the equation of the line through the point $(-2, 8)$ and

a) parallel to the y-axis.

b) parallel to the x-axis

Complete Assignment Questions #6 - #15

Assignment

1. Write the equation of each line

a) with slope 4 and y-intercept -6

$y = 4x - 6$

b) with a y-intercept of 3 and a slope of $-\frac{4}{3}$

c) passing through the origin with a slope of $-\frac{3}{5}$

d) with y-intercept -5 and parallel to $y = x$

e) with a y-intercept of -9 and perpendicular to $y = -\frac{2}{3}x + 7$

f) with the same y-intercept as $y = x + 2$ and parallel to $y = \frac{1}{4}x - 6$

g) through the point $(0, 1)$ and perpendicular to $y = 4x - 2$

h) through the point $(0, 4)$ and parallel to $y = \frac{1}{10}x + 24$

i) with the same y-intercept as $y = 2x - 3$ and perpendicular to $y = \frac{7}{3}x - 2$

j) with the same y-intercept as $y = ax + b$ and perpendicular to $y = cx + d$

2. Each of the lines on the grid passes through points with integer coordinates.
Determine the equation of each line.

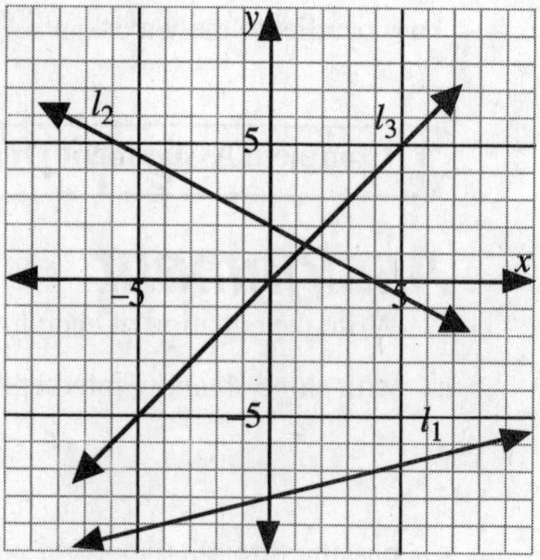

3. Each diagram represents the image from the display of a graphing calculator together with the window setting used to graph a linear equation. The *x*- and *y*-intercepts of each graph are integers.

In each case complete the table.

a)
```
WINDOW
 Xmin=-5
 Xmax=12
 Xscl=1
 Ymin=-10
 Ymax=5
 Yscl=1
 Xres=1
```

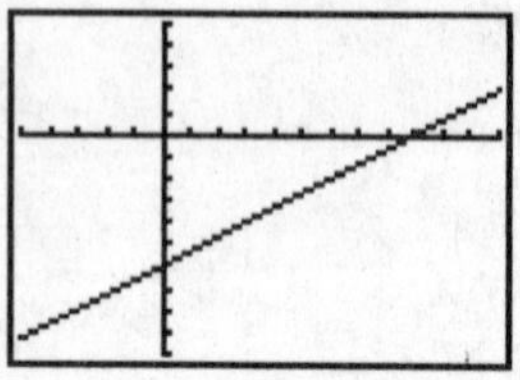

x-intercept	
y-intercept	
slope	
equation	

b)
```
WINDOW
 Xmin=-6
 Xmax=6
 Xscl=2
 Ymin=-36
 Ymax=16
 Yscl=4
 Xres=1
```

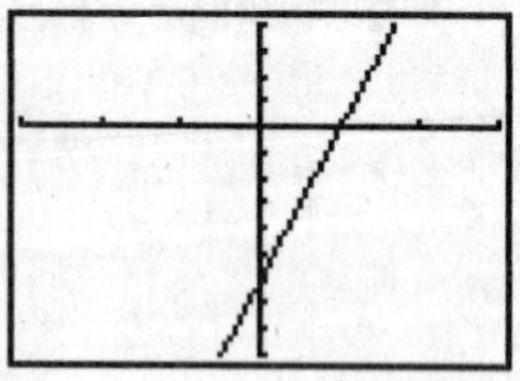

x-intercept	
y-intercept	
slope	
equation	

c)
```
WINDOW
 Xmin=-6
 Xmax=6
 Xscl=1
 Ymin=-10
 Ymax=10
 Yscl=3
 Xres=1
```

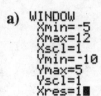

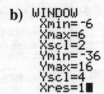

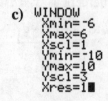

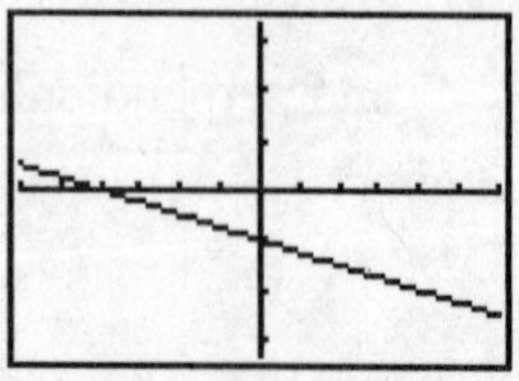

x-intercept	
y-intercept	
slope	
equation	

4. Determine the equation of the line which passes through the point $(0, 16)$ and is parallel to the line which passes through $(1, 3)$ and $(4, -6)$.

5. Determine the equation of the line which passes through the point $(0, -1)$ and is perpendicular to the line which passes through $(7, -2)$ and $(12, -3)$.

6. State the equations of the following lines:

a) through the point $(-5, 3)$ and parallel to the y-axis

b) through the point $(-5, 3)$ and parallel to the x-axis

c) through the point $(1, -1)$ and parallel to the x-axis

d) through the point (a, b) and parallel to the y-axis

7. Consider the graph of the function with equation $y = 2$.

a) State the values of m and b.

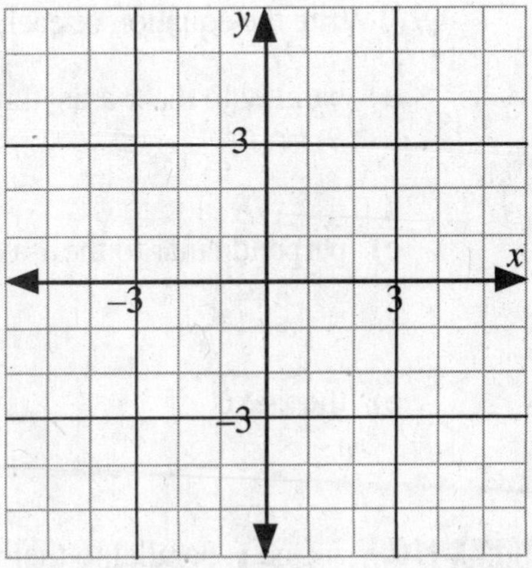

b) Sketch the graph on the grid provided.

c) State the x- and y-intercepts of the graph.

d) Determine the domain and range of the function.

e) On the same grid draw the line with equation $y = 2x - 4$ without using a graphing calculator.

f) State the coordinates of the point of intersection of the two lines.

g) On the grid draw the line with equation $y = -5$.

8. Consider the graph of the relation with equation $x = -4$.

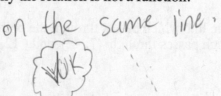

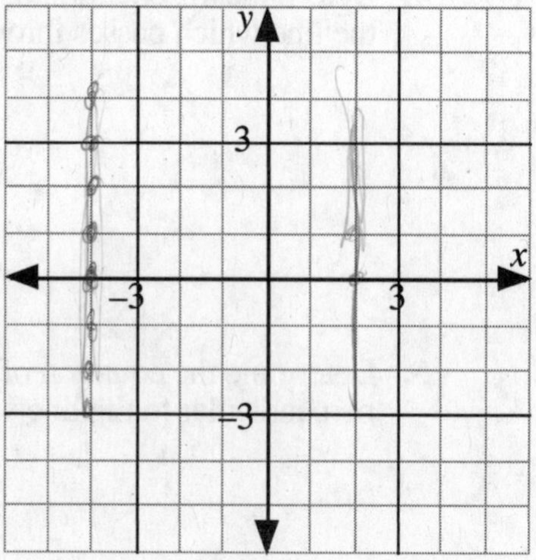

a) Sketch the graph on the grid provided.

b) State the x- and y-intercepts of the graph.

c) Explain why the relation is not a function.

on the same line

d) Explain why the [Y =] editor key cannot be used to graph $x = -4$.

e) Determine the domain and range of the relation with equation $x = -4$.

f) On the grid draw the line with equation $x = 2$.

9. Write the equation of each line

a) parallel to the x-axis through $(3, -9)$

b) parallel to the y-axis through $(3, -9)$

c) perpendicular to the x-axis through $(1, 4)$

d) perpendicular to the y-axis through $(1, 4)$

e) the x-axis

f) the y-axis

Multiple Choice

10. A line is parallel to the y-axis and passes through the point $(2, -7)$. The equation of the line is

A. $x = 2$
B. $x = -7$
C. $y = 2$
D. $y = -7$

11. A line is parallel to the x-axis and passes through the point $(-6, 10)$. The equation of the line is

A. $x = 10$
B. $x = -6$
C. $y = 10$
D. $y = -6$

12. The line through the origin, perpendicular to the line with equation $y = \frac{2}{3}x$, has equation

A. $y = \frac{2}{3}x$

B. $y = \frac{3}{2}x$

C. $y = -\frac{2}{3}x$

D. $y = -\frac{3}{2}x$

13. The point $(2, -1)$ lies on a line with slope 3. The y- intercept of the line is

A. -7
B. -5
C. 5
D. 7

Numerical Response

14. Consider the line which is perpendicular to the line $y = \frac{1}{3}x + 4$ and has the same y-intercept as $y = 6x - 7$. If the equation of this line is written in the form $y = mx + b$, then the exact value of $m - b$ is _____.

(Record your answer in the numerical response box from left to right)

15. Two perpendicular lines intersect on the y-axis. One line has equation $y = 4x + 6$. If the equation of the other line is $y = mx + b$, then the exact value of $m + b$ is _____.

(Record your answer in the numerical response box from left to right)

Answer Key

1. a) $y = 4x - 6$ **b)** $y = -\frac{4}{3}x + 3$ **c)** $y = -\frac{3}{5}x$ **d)** $y = x - 5$ **e)** $y = \frac{3}{2}x - 9$

f) $y = \frac{1}{4}x + 2$ **g)** $y = -\frac{1}{4}x + 1$ **h)** $y = \frac{1}{10}x + 4$ **i)** $y = -\frac{3}{7}x - 3$ **j)** $y = -\frac{1}{c}x + b$

2. l_1: $y = \frac{1}{4}x - 8$ l_2: $y = -\frac{1}{2}x + 2$ l_3: $y = x$

3. a)

x-intercept	9
y-intercept	−6
slope	2/3
equation	$y = \frac{2}{3}x - 6$

b)

x-intercept	2
y-intercept	−24
slope	12
equation	$y = 12x - 24$

c)

x-intercept	−4
y-intercept	−3
slope	−3/4
equation	$y = -\frac{3}{4}x - 3$

4. $y = -3x + 16$ **5.** $y = 5x - 1$ **6. a)** $x = -5$ **b)** $y = 3$ **c)** $y = -1$ **d)** $x = a$

7. a) $m = 0, b = 2$

b), e), g) see graph below

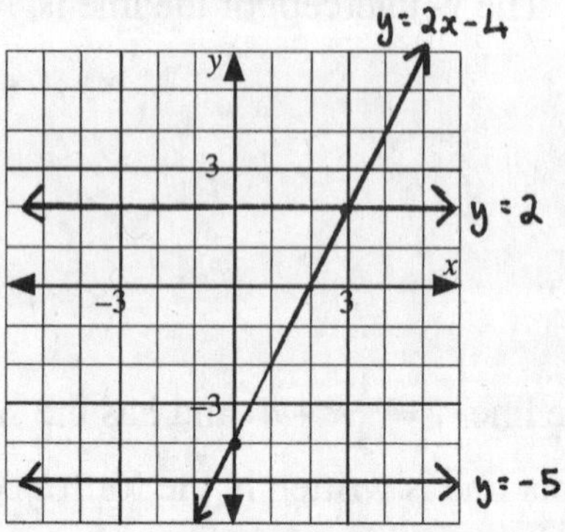

c) no *x*-intercept, *y*-intercept = 2

d) domain $x \in R$, range $y = 2$ **f)** (3, 2)

8. a), f) see graph below

b) *x*-intercept = −4, no *y*-intercept

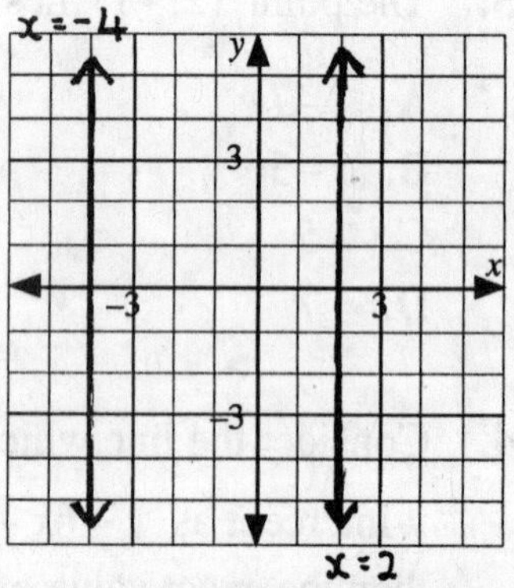

c) When the input = −4, there are multiple values for the output. The graph of the relation does not pass the vertical line test.

d) The equation $x = -4$ cannot be written in the form y= . . . .

e) domain $x = -4$, range $y \in R$

9. a) $y = -9$ **b)** $x = 3$ **c)** $x = 1$ **d)** $y = 4$ **e)** $y = 0$ **f)** $x = 0$

10. A **11.** C **12.** D **13.** A

14.

4			

15.

5		7	5

Equations of Linear Relations Lesson #3:
The General Form Equation Ax + By + C = 0

In lesson #2 we used the form $y = mx + b$ to determine the equation of a line when given the slope of the line and the y-intercept.

A linear equation written in the form $y = mx + b$ has slope m and y-intercept b.

General Form of the Equation of a Line → $Ax + By + C = 0$

The **general form** of the equation of a line is an equation where all the terms are collected to the left side of the equation.

The general form of an equation is written as $Ax + By + C = 0$, where A, B, and C are expressed as **integers** if possible, and A is usually positive.

The general form of the equation of a line allows us to write equations for oblique lines, horizontal lines, and vertical lines.

In some texts, the form $Ax + By + C = 0$ is referred to as **standard form**.

Class Ex. #1 Convert the following equations from slope y-intercept form, $y = mx + b$, to general form $Ax + By + C = 0$, where A, B, and C are integers.

a) $y = 5x - 8$

$\frac{-y \quad -y}{}$

$\boxed{0 = 5x - y - 8}$

b) $y = \frac{2}{3}x + 7$

$(3) \quad (3)$

$3y = \frac{6}{3}x + 21$

$3y = 2x + 21$

$\boxed{0 = 2x - 3y + 21}$

c) $y = \left(-\frac{1}{4}x + \frac{3}{5}\right)$

20

$20y = -1x + 3$

$\frac{-20y \qquad -20y}{}$

$(-1) \qquad (-1)$

$0 = (1x - 20y)$

$\boxed{0 = x + 20y - 3}$

Determining the Slope and y-intercept from $Ax + By + C = 0$

Given the equation of a line in general form $Ax + By + C = 0$, the slope and y-intercept can be found by converting the equation into slope y-intercept form $y = mx + b$.

Class Ex. #2 Determine the slope and y-intercept of the graph of the following lines.

 fractions

a) $2x - 5y + 25 = 0$

$-25 \quad -25$

b) $6x + 2y - 15 = 0$

$+15 \quad +15$

$6x + 2y = 15$

$\frac{-6x \qquad -6x}{}$

$\frac{2y}{2} = \frac{-6x + 15}{}$ → $\boxed{y = -3x + \frac{15}{2}}$

Class Ex. #3 The lines $3x - 4y + 8 = 0$ and $5x - ky - 6 = 0$ have the same y-intercept. Determine the value of k.

- y alone
- break down } same thing
- ~~Anything~~ just y

$\dfrac{6}{k}$

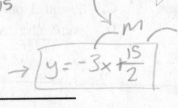

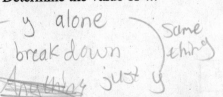

Class Ex. #4

Which of the following lines is/are perpendicular to the line $4x - 2y + 9 = 0$?

i) $6x + 3y - 1 = 0$ **ii)** $x + 2y - 12 = 0$ **iii)** $5x + 10y = 0$

$6x + 3y - 1 = 0$
$+1 \quad +1$

$6x + 3y = 1$

Class Ex. #5

Write the equation of a line which is perpendicular to $2x + 5y - 7 = 0$ and has the same *y*-intercept as $2x + y - 6 = 0$.
Answer in slope *y*-intercept form and in general form.

Use the following information to answer Class Ex. #6.

A student made the following statements about the line with equation $2y = 5x + 12$.

Statement 1: The line has a slope of 5.
Statement 2: The line is parallel to $10x - 4y + 13 = 0$.
Statement 3: The line passes through $(-2, 1)$.

Class Ex. #6

Which of the above statement(s) is/are true?

A. 1 and 2 only
B. 1 and 3 only
C. 2 and 3 only
D. some other combination of statements 1, 2, and 3

Complete Assignment Questions #1 - #16

Assignment

1. Convert the following equations from slope y-intercept form $(y = mx + b)$ to general form $(Ax + By + C = 0)$, where A, B, and C are integers.

a) $y = 7x - 3$ **b)** $y = -2x + 9$ **c)** $y = mx + b$

d) $y = -\frac{3}{4}x + 5$ **e)** $y = \frac{2}{3}x + \frac{1}{6}$ **f)** $y = \frac{5}{3}x - \frac{1}{4}$

2. Determine the slope and y-intercept of the graph of the following lines.

a) $x + y - 11 = 0$ **b)** $3x - 2y + 30 = 0$ **c)** $8x - 3y - 3 = 0$

d) $3x + 6y - 7 = 0$ **e)** $8y = 4x + 32$ **f)** $4x + 3y = 12$

3. Determine the slope, y-intercept, and x-intercept of the graph of the following lines.

a) $2x + y - 6 = 0$ **b)** $5x - 2y + 20 = 0$ **c)** $4x - 5y - 3 = 0$

4. Write the equation, in general form, of a line parallel to $2x - 3y + 9 = 0$ and with the same y-intercept as $22x - 3y - 18 = 0$.

5. Write the equation, in general form, of a line perpendicular to $3x - 2y + 5 = 0$ and with the same y-intercept as $3x - y + 18 = 0$.

6. Consider the lines $x - 2y + 1 = 0$ and $4x + ky - 8 = 0$.

a) Determine the value of k if the lines have the same slope.

b) Determine the value of k if the lines have the same y-intercept.

7. Consider the lines $3x - 5y - 15 = 0$ and $ax + 2y - 6 = 0$.

a) Determine the value of a if the lines have the same slope.

b) Determine the value of a if the lines have the same x-intercept.

8. Match each equation on the left with the correct characteristic of the graph of the equation on the right. Each characteristic may be used once, more than once, or not at all.

Equation		Characteristic	
i)	$6x - 2y + 5 = 0$	**A.**	Slope $= -\frac{1}{3}$
ii)	$2x - 5y = 0$	**B.**	y-intercept $= -\frac{5}{2}$
iii)	$x + 3y + 6 = 0$	**C.**	Passes through $(-10, -4)$
iv)	$x - 4y + 10 = 0$	**D.**	Slope $= 0$
v)	$2x - y - 5 = 0$	**E.**	y-intercept $= \frac{5}{2}$
		F.	Perpendicular to $y = \frac{5}{2}x - 3$
		G.	x-intercept $= \frac{5}{2}$

Multiple Choice

9. The slope of the line with equation $6x + 5y - 1 = 0$ is

A. $-\frac{6}{5}$

B. $-\frac{5}{6}$

C. $\frac{6}{5}$

D. $\frac{1}{5}$

10. Which line has a y-intercept of 1?

A. $x + 5y + 1 = 0$

B. $x + 3y + 3 = 0$

C. $x - 2y + 2 = 0$

D. $2y = 3x + 1$

11. The slope of a line perpendicular to the line $x + 3y + 8 = 0$ is

A. -8

B. $-\frac{1}{3}$

C. $\frac{1}{3}$

D. 3

12. The line $2y + 3x + 6 = 0$ intersects the y-axis at P. The slope of the line joining P to $Q(6, -2)$ is

A. $-\frac{5}{6}$

B. $\frac{1}{6}$

C. $-\frac{1}{6}$

D. $-\frac{2}{3}$

13. The lines with equations $ay = 4x + 9$ and $y = 5x - 7$ are perpendicular. The value of a is

A. $\frac{4}{5}$

B. $-\frac{4}{5}$

C. $-\frac{5}{4}$

D. -20

Use the following information to answer the next question.

Consider the following statements about all the lines in the form $kx + 4y - 8 = 0$, where $k \in R$.

Statement 1: The lines have the same slope.
Statement 2: The lines have the same y-intercept.
Statement 3: The lines have the same x-intercept.

14. Which of the above statement(s) is/are true?

A. 1, 2, and 3
B. 1 only
C. 2 only
D. 3 only

15. Line L has equation $5x - 3y + 21 = 0$. A is the point $(-6, -3)$, B is $(3, -2)$, and C is $(-3, 2)$. Which of these points lie on line L?

A. A only
B. A and B only
C. A and C only
D. B and C only

Numerical Response

16. Given that the line joining the points $(2, 3)$ and $(8, -q)$, where $q \in W$, is perpendicular to the line $3x - 2y - 5 = 0$, then the value of q is ________ .

(Record your answer in the numerical response box from left to right)

Answer Key

1. **a)** $7x - y - 3 = 0$ **b)** $2x + y - 9 = 0$ **c)** $mx - y + b = 0$
d) $3x + 4y - 20 = 0$ **e)** $4x - 6y + 1 = 0$ **f)** $20x - 12y - 3 = 0$

2. **a)** slope = -1, y–int = 11 **b)** slope = $\frac{3}{2}$, y–int = 15 **c)** slope = $\frac{8}{3}$, y–int = -1
d) slope = $-\frac{1}{2}$, y–int = $\frac{7}{6}$ **e)** slope = $\frac{1}{2}$, y–int = 4 **f)** slope = $-\frac{4}{3}$, y–int = 4

3. **a)** slope = -2, y–int = 6, x–int = 3
b) slope = $\frac{5}{2}$, y–int = 10, x–int = -4
c) slope = $\frac{4}{5}$, y–int = $-\frac{3}{5}$, x–int = $\frac{3}{4}$

4. $2x - 3y - 18 = 0$ **5.** $2x + 3y - 54 = 0$

6. **a)** -8 **b)** 16 **7.** **a)** $-\frac{6}{5}$ **b)** $\frac{6}{5}$

8. **i)** E **ii)** C **iii)** A **iv)** E **v)** G

9. A **10.** C **11.** D **12.** B

13. D **14.** C **15.** C **16.**

1			

Equations of Linear Relations Lesson #4: Slope-Point Form → $y - y_1 = m(x - x_1)$

Review

Complete the following:

a) The general form of an equation of a line is ____________________ .

b) The slope y-intercept form of the equation of a line is ____________________ .

Investigation *Slope-Point Form*

The graph of $y + 3 = 2(x - 1)$ is shown on the grid.

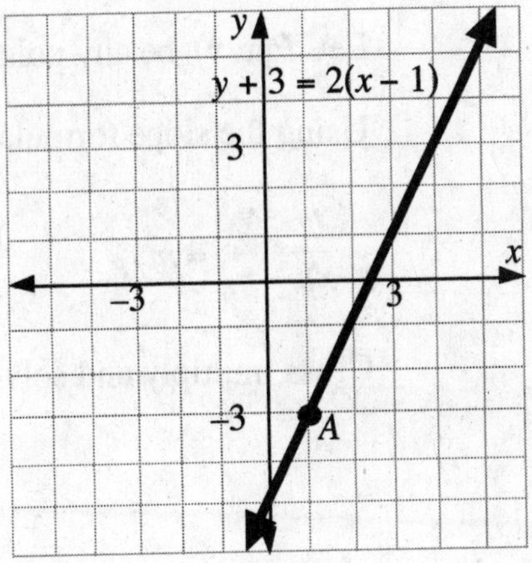

a) Determine the slope of the graph of $y + 3 = 2(x - 1)$.

b) List the coordinates of point A on the line.

c) Compare your answers in a) and b) with the numbers in the equation.

The graph of $y - 1 = -\frac{2}{3}(x + 4)$ is shown on the grid.

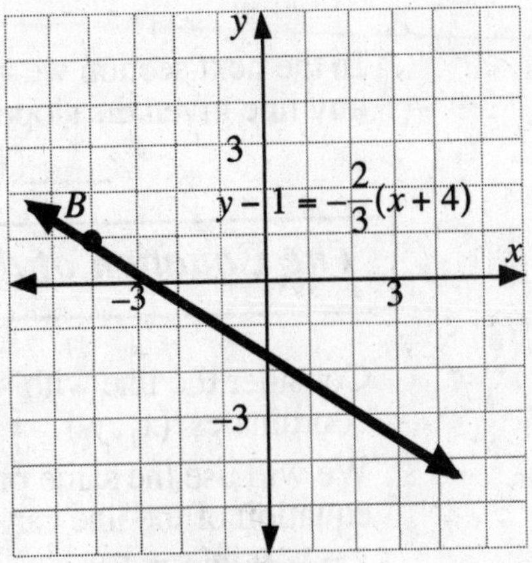

d) Determine the slope of the graph of $y - 1 = -\frac{2}{3}(x + 4)$.

e) List the coordinates of point B on the line.

f) Compare your answers in e) and f) with the numbers in the equation.

g) Consider the graph of the linear equation $y - y_1 = m(x - x_1)$. Based on your observations in c) and g), state the slope of the line, and write the coordinates of one point on the line.

Equation of a Line Given the Slope of the Line and a Point on the Line

Consider the line with slope 2 passing through the point $A(1,-3)$. The line is shown on the grid.

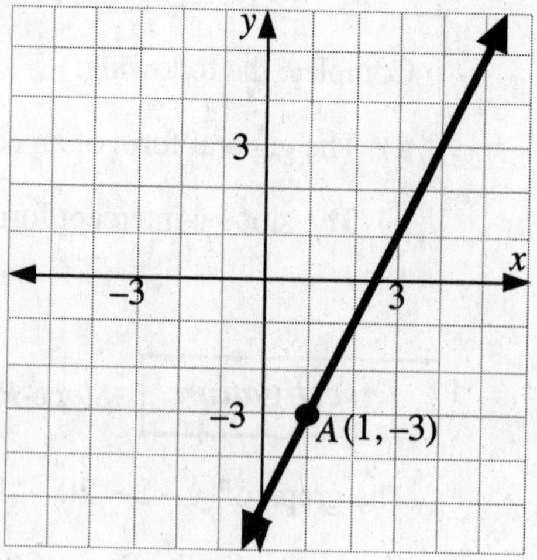

Our objective is to determine the equation of the line. In other words, to find a relation between x and y which is satisfied by every point (x, y) on the line.

Let $P(x, y)$ be any point on the line except A.

Using the slope formula we have

$$\frac{y_P - y_A}{x_P - x_A} = m_{AP} \qquad \frac{y-(-3)}{x-1} = 2$$

Cross multiply and solve for y to determine the equation of the line in the form $y = mx + b$.

At this point in the exploration, the equation above is valid for all points on the line except A.

Note that the coordinates of A also satisfy the equation, so that it is the equation of all points on the line.

In the next section we will use the same procedure to develop a formula for the equation of any line given the slope of the line and the point on the line.

The Equation of the Line with slope m through the point (x_1, y_1)

Consider the line with slope m passing through the point with coordinates (x_1, y_1).
We will use the same procedure as above to show that the equation of the line can be expressed in the form $y - y_1 = m(x - x_1)$.

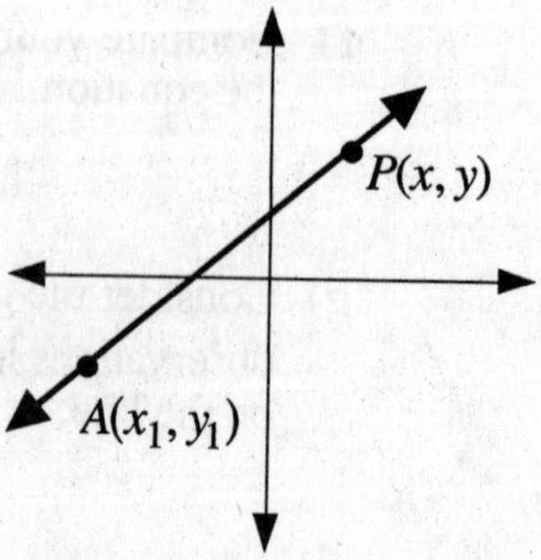

Let $P(x, y)$ be any point on the line distinct from A.

Using the slope formula we have

$$m_{AP} = \frac{y_P - y_A}{x_P - x_A} \qquad \text{so} \qquad m = \frac{y - \quad}{x - \quad}$$

Slope-Point Equation of a Line → $y - y_1 = m(x - x_1)$

- The point-slope form of the equation of a line is $y - y_1 = m(x - x_1)$ where m is the slope of the line, and (x_1, y_1) represents a point on the line.
- To determine the equation of a line in higher grade math courses, the point-slope equation, $y - y_1 = m(x - x_1)$, is used more frequently than the slope-y-intercept equation, $y = mx + b$.
- Note that the slope-point equation is used when we have the slope of a line and the coordinates of any point on the line. When using this method to determine the equation of a line, it is usual to give the final equation in general form, $Ax + By + C = 0$, or in slope-y-intercept form, $y = mx + b$.

State the equation, in slope-point form, of the line through the given point and with the given slope.

a) $(6, 5)$, 3 **b)** $(1, -1)$, -4 **c)** $(-9, -8)$, $\frac{1}{2}$

In each case the slope of a line and a point on the line are given. Determine the equation of the line in slope y-intercept form, $y = mx + b$.

a) $m = 5$, point $(-5, 2)$ **b)** $m = -7$, point $(-3, 4)$

John and Nicki were solving the following quiz question:

" Determine the equation, in general form, of a line with slope -2 passing through the point $(3, -5)$".

John could only remember the slope y-intercept form $y = mx + b$, but Nicki remembered the slope-point form $y - y_1 = m(x - x_1)$. Complete their work which is started below.

John's work	Nicki's work
$y = mx + b$	$y - y_1 = m(x - x_1)$
$y = -2x + b$	$y - y_1 = -2(x - x_1)$
$-5 = -2(3) + b$	$y - (-5) = -2(x - 3)$

Class Ex. #4

The line on the grid passes through at least two points with integer coordinates. Determine the equation of the line in general form.

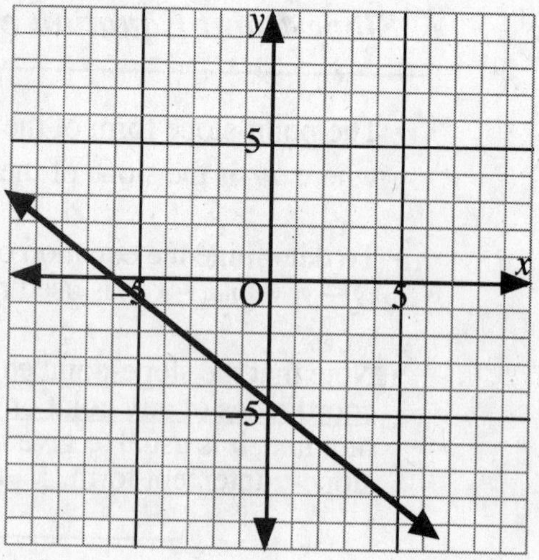

Class Ex. #5

In each case state the slope of the line, and write the coordinates of a point on the line.

a) $y + 11 = \frac{1}{7}(x - 4)$

b) $y - 9 = -\frac{5}{3}(x - 7)$

c) $y = -3(x - 6)$

d) $y = -3x - 6$

Complete Assignment Questions #1 - #10

Assignment

1. State the equation, in slope-point form, of the line through the given point and with the given slope.

a) $(9, 3)$, 4

b) $(8, -2)$, -3

c) $(-5, 7)$, 1

d) $(0, 3)$, $\frac{1}{2}$

e) $(-7, 0)$, $\frac{1}{4}$

f) $(-\frac{1}{2}, -\frac{5}{4})$, $\frac{6}{5}$

2. Write the following equations in slope y-intercept form $y = mx + b$.

a) $y + 1 = 8(x - 2)$

b) $y - 3 = -2(x - 7)$

c) $y - 9 = -11(x + 3)$

d) $y + 3 = 7(x + 12)$

3. Find the equation, in slope y-intercept form, of the line through the given point and with the given slope.

a) $(2, 4)$, 6

b) $(2, -1)$, 2

c) $(0, 4)$, -2

d) $(-6, 2)$, $\frac{1}{2}$

e) $(-7, -7)$, 1

f) $(0, b)$, m

4. Find the equation, in general form, of the line through the given point and with the given slope.

a) $(6, 1)$, 3

b) $(2, -5)$, $\frac{1}{4}$

c) $(-4, 2)$, $-\frac{1}{3}$

d) $(-9, -2)$, $\frac{2}{5}$

e) $(0, -8)$, $-\frac{3}{4}$

f) $(0, 0)$, $\frac{4}{3}$

5. The slope-point equation of a line is given. State the slope and the coordinates of the point which was used to write the equation.

a) $y - 9 = -\frac{11}{3}(x + 3)$ **b)** $y + 3 = \frac{1}{2}x$ **c)** $y - 8 = -2(x - 6)$

d) $y = 3(x + 12)$ **e)** $y - 9 = -\frac{5}{3}x$ **f)** $y = \frac{2}{5}x$

6. Two lines have been drawn on the grid. Each line passes through at least two points with integer coordinates.

Determine the equation of each line.

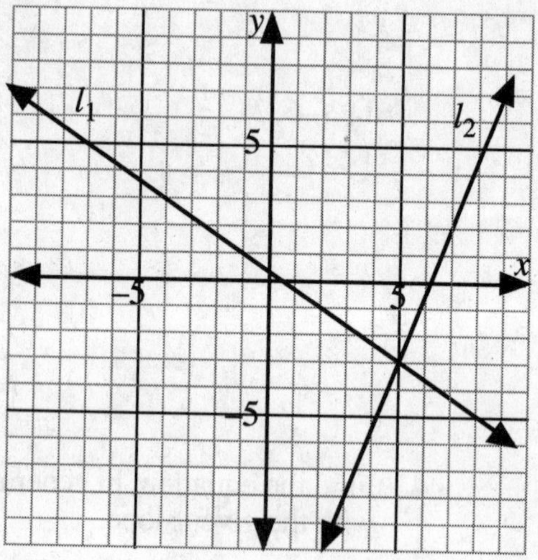

Multiple Choice

7. The equation of the line passing through the point $(4, 2)$ with slope -3 is

A. $3x + y - 14 = 0$
B. $3x + y + 10 = 0$
C. $3x + y - 10 = 0$
D. $3x + y + 14 = 0$

8. The equation of the line passing through the origin with slope $-\frac{1}{2}$ is

A. $x + 2y = 0$
B. $x - 2y = 0$
C. $2x + y = 0$
D. $2x - y = 0$

9. Which of the following linear equations is equivalent to $y - 3 = -\frac{3}{4}(x + 7)$?

A. $3x - 4y + 33 = 0$
B. $3x + 4y + 9 = 0$
C. $3x + 4y - 33 = 0$
D. $3x + 4y + 18 = 0$

Numerical Response

10. The equation of the line with an x-intercept of -2 and slope 12 can be written in general form $12x + By + C = 0$. The value of $B + C$ is _____.

(Record your answer in the numerical response box from left to right)

Answer Key

1. a) $y - 3 = 4(x - 9)$ **b)** $y + 2 = -3(x - 8)$ **c)** $y - 7 = 1(x + 5)$
d) $y - 3 = \frac{1}{2}x$ **e)** $y = \frac{1}{4}(x + 7)$ **f)** $y + \frac{5}{4} = \frac{6}{5}\left(x + \frac{1}{2}\right)$

2. a) $y = 8x - 17$ **b)** $y = -2x + 17$ **c)** $y = -11x - 24$ **d)** $y = 7x + 81$

3. a) $y = 6x - 8$ **b)** $y = 2x - 5$ **c)** $y = -2x + 4$ **d)** $y = \frac{1}{2}x + 5$ **e)** $y = x$ **f)** $y = mx + b$

4. a) $3x - y - 17 = 0$ **b)** $x - 4y - 22 = 0$ **c)** $x + 3y - 2 = 0$
d) $2x - 5y + 8 = 0$ **e)** $3x + 4y + 32 = 0$ **f)** $4x - 3y = 0$

5. a) $m = -\frac{11}{3}$, $P(-3, 9)$ **b)** $m = \frac{1}{2}$, $P(0, -3)$ **c)** $m = -2$, $P(6, 8)$ **d)** $m = 3$, $P(-12, 0)$
e) $m = -\frac{5}{3}$, $P(0, 9)$ **f)** $m = \frac{2}{5}$, $P(0, 0)$

6. $l_1 \Rightarrow 2x + 3y - 1 = 0$ or $y = -\frac{2}{3}x + \frac{1}{3}$ $l_2 \Rightarrow 5x - 2y - 31 = 0$ or $y = \frac{5}{2}x - \frac{31}{2}$

7. A **8.** A **9.** B **10.**

2	3		

Equations of Linear Relations Lesson #5: Further Practice with Linear Equations

Writing Linear Equations

Linear equations can be written in different forms:

$Ax + By + C = 0$ → General form of a linear equation.

$y = mx + b$ → Slope y-intercept form of a linear equation.

$y - y_1 = m(x - x_1)$ → Slope-point form of a linear equation.

The slope y-intercept form is used when we are given the slope of a line and the y-intercept. The slope-point form is used when we are given the slope of a line and <u>any</u> point on the line. In many cases, either the point or the slope of the line has to be determined from the information given before the equation can be used.

Given $P(3,-1)$ and $Q(-2,-6)$, determine the equation, in general form, of a line passing through the two points.

Determine the equation, in general form, of a line through the point $(5,0)$ and perpendicular to the line with equation $3x - 5y + 17 = 0$.

Class Ex. #3

Find the equation, in general form, of the line perpendicular to the line $5x - 7y - 10 = 0$ and with the same x-intercept as $x - 2y - 12 = 0$.

Complete Assignment Questions #1 - #14

Assignment

1. Find the equation, in general form, of the line through each pair of points.

a) $(7, 5)$ and $(6, 1)$ **b)** $(3, -7)$ and $(-5, 9)$ **c)** $(-3, 4)$ and $(11, 25)$

d) $(10, -15)$ and $(-2, -12)$ **e)** $(4, -7)$ and $(3, -7)$ **f)** $(-5, -8)$ and $(-4, -10)$

2. Identify the lines in #1 which are
i) parallel
ii) perpendicular

3. Write the equation of each line in general form:

a) with slope $\frac{2}{7}$ and an x-intercept of -6

b) with a y-intercept of $-\frac{8}{3}$ and a slope of 7

c) through the point $(2, 0)$ and perpendicular to $3x - 5y + 19 = 0$

d) through the point $(3, -6)$ and parallel to $5x + 3y + 9 = 0$

4. Write the equation of each line in general form:
a) perpendicular to $y = x$ and with the same x-intercept as $y = 2x + 10$

b) parallel to $2x - 3y + 7 = 0$ and with the same y-intercept as $5x - 3y - 12 = 0$

5. Write the equation of each line in general form:

a) perpendicular to $6x - 2y + 5 = 0$ and with the same y-intercept as $x - y + 8 = 0$

b) with the same x-intercept as $9x - 2y + 18 = 0$ and through the point $(4, -5)$

6. Line l contains the point $A(7, 9)$ and is parallel to a line which contains the points $B(-4, 5)$ and $C(8, -1)$. Determine the equation of line l in the form $y = mx + b$.

7. A Cartesian plane is placed on a plan of a farm. The farmhouse is at the origin, and $ABCD$ represents a rectangular field of wheat. A farm road, with equation $y = 3x$, runs from the farmhouse along one side of the field.

a) If the point A has coordinates $(2, 4)$, determine the equation of AD.

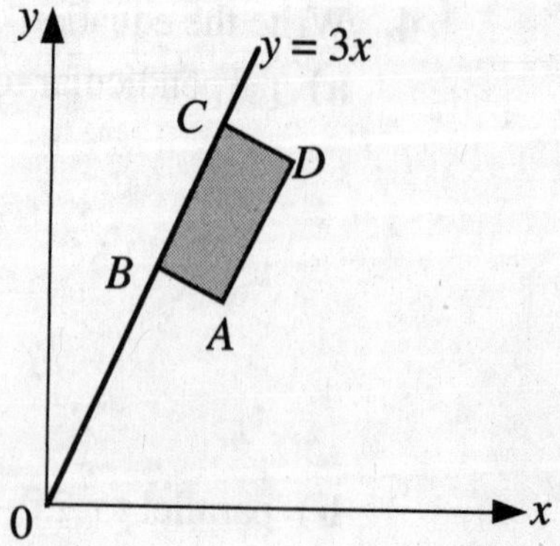

b) Determine the equation of AB.

8. A child with a fixed amount of money can buy 2 bags of chips and 5 cans of pop, or 3 bags of chips and 2 cans of pop. A linear relationship exists between the number of bags of chips, x, and the number of cans of pop, y, which can be bought.

a) Write the coordinates of two points which lie on the graph of this linear relationship.

b) Determine the equation of the linear relationship.

Multiple Choice

9. The equation of the line through the point $(7, -4)$ and perpendicular to the line with equation $5x - 4y + 13 = 0$ can be written in the form

A. $y + 4 = \frac{5}{4}(x - 7)$

B. $y = -\frac{4}{5}(x + 7)$

C. $y + 4 = -\frac{4}{5}(x - 7)$

D. $y + 4 = \frac{4}{5}(x - 7)$

10. A line passing through the point $(0, 3)$ is perpendicular to the line $x - 2y - 5 = 0$. The equation of the line is

A. $2x + y - 3 = 0$
B. $2x + y + 3 = 0$
C. $x - 2y + 6 = 0$
D. $2x - y + 3 = 0$

11. Which of the following linear relations is not equivalent to the other three?

A. $y - 4 = -\frac{1}{3}(x + 6)$

B. $x + 3y + 2 = 0$

C. the line passing through $(0, 2)$ and $(6, 0)$

D. $y = -\frac{1}{3}x + 2$

12. A line passing through the point $(0, 3)$ is parallel to the line $x - 2y - 5 = 0$. The equation of the line is

A. $2x + y - 3 = 0$
B. $2x + y + 3 = 0$
C. $x - 2y + 6 = 0$
D. $2x - y + 3 = 0$

13. The image of $y = 2x + 7$ after a counterclockwise rotation of $90°$ about the origin is

A. $y = -\frac{1}{2}x + \frac{7}{2}$
B. $y = \frac{1}{2}x - \frac{7}{2}$
C. $y = -\frac{1}{2}x - \frac{7}{2}$
D. $y = -2x - 7$

Numerical Response

14. The line through the points $(-3, 4)$ and $(-1, -2)$ has equation $y + ax + b = 0$, where a and b are integers. The value of $a + b$ is _____.
(Record your answer in the numerical response box from left to right)

Answer Key

1. a) $4x - y - 23 = 0$ **b)** $2x + y + 1 = 0$ **c)** $3x - 2y + 17 = 0$
d) $x + 4y + 50 = 0$ **e)** $y + 7 = 0$ **f)** $2x + y + 18 = 0$
2. i) b and f **ii)** a and d
3. a) $2x - 7y + 12 = 0$ **b)** $21x - 3y - 8 = 0$ **c)** $5x + 3y - 10 = 0$ **d)** $5x + 3y + 3 = 0$
4. a) $x + y + 5 = 0$ **b)** $2x - 3y - 12 = 0$
5. a) $x + 3y - 24 = 0$ **b)** $5x + 6y + 10 = 0$ **6.** $y = -\frac{1}{2}x + \frac{25}{2}$
7. a) $y = 3x - 2$ or $3x - y - 2 = 0$ **b)** $y = -\frac{1}{3}x + \frac{14}{3}$ or $x + 3y - 14 = 0$
8. a) (2, 5) and (3, 2) **b)** $3x + y - 11 = 0$
9. C **10.** A **11.** B **12.** C **13.** C **14.**

8			

Equations of Linear Relations Lesson #6: Graphing Linear Equations

Graphing Linear Equations Without Technology

Linear equations can be written in different forms:

$Ax + By + C = 0$ → General form of a linear equation.

$y = mx + b$ → Slope y-intercept form of a linear equation.

$y - y_1 = m(x - x_1)$ → Slope-point form of a linear equation.

The method used to graph a linear relation without technology depends on the form in which the linear equation is written.

Without altering the form in which the linear equation is written, explain the different strategies used to graph (without technology) each of the following linear relations. Draw the graph of each linear relation on the grid provided.

a) $y = 2x + 4$

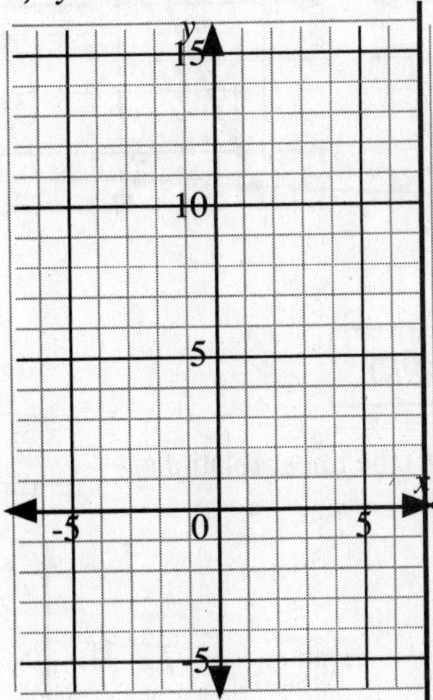

b) $y - 2 = 2(x + 1)$

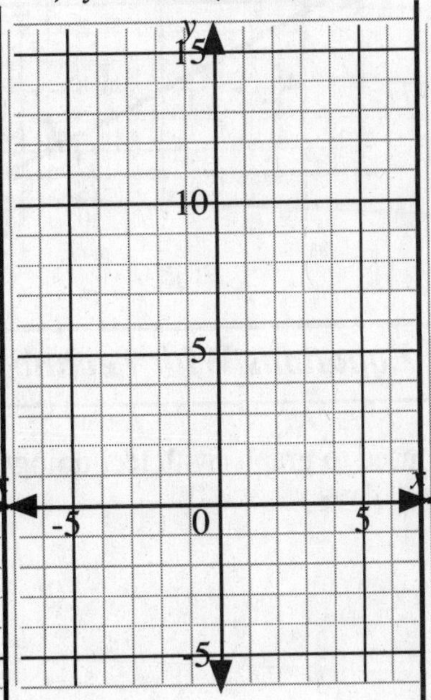

c) $2x - y + 4 = 0$

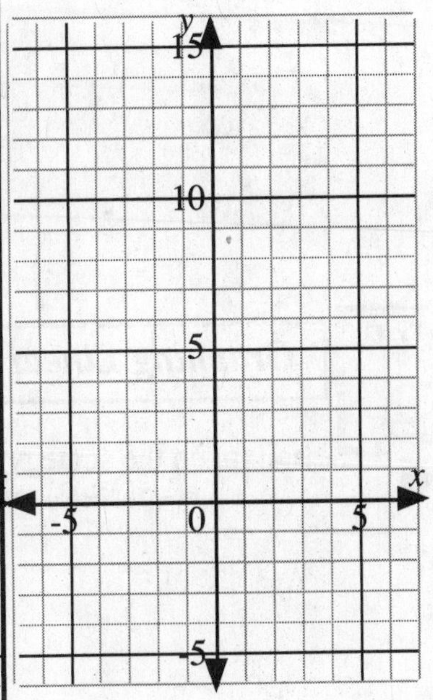

Match each linear relation to its graph.

Equation 1:

$2x - y + 3 = 0$

Equation 2:

$y = -2x + 3$

Equation 3:

$y + 1 = -\frac{1}{2}(x + 4)$

Equation 4:

$2y - x - 6 = 0$

Graph A

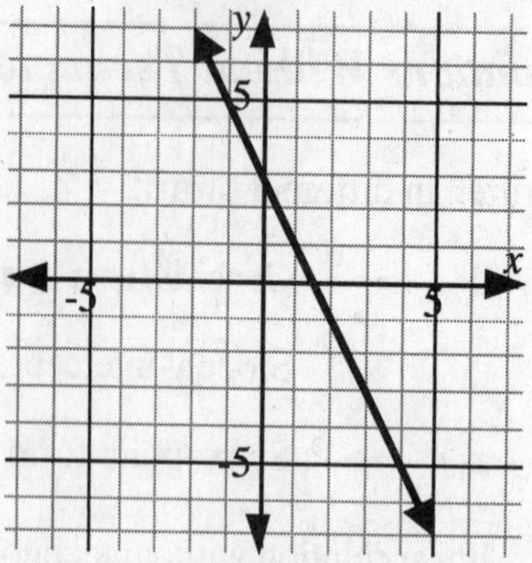

Graph B

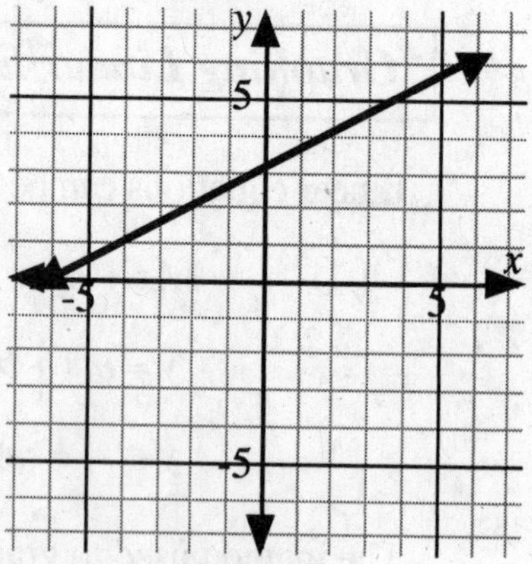

Graph C

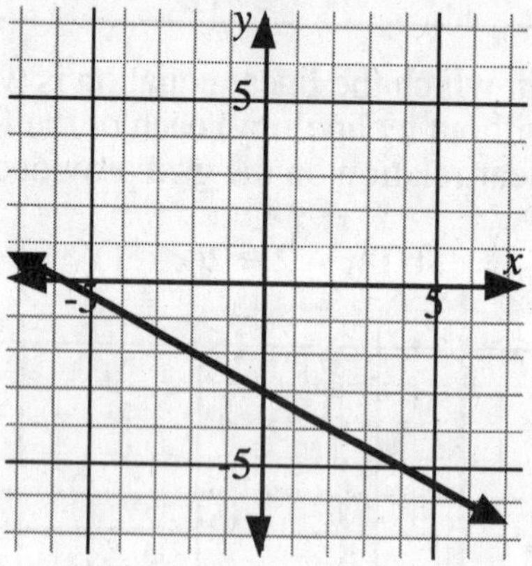

Graph D

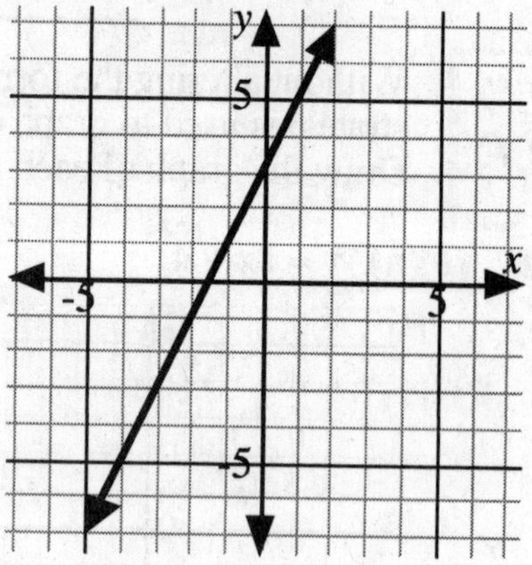

Graphing Linear Equations With Technology

- <u>Explain</u> the strategy used to graph (with technology) the linear relations. $y + 8 = -5(x - 2)$ and $4x - y + 9 = 0$

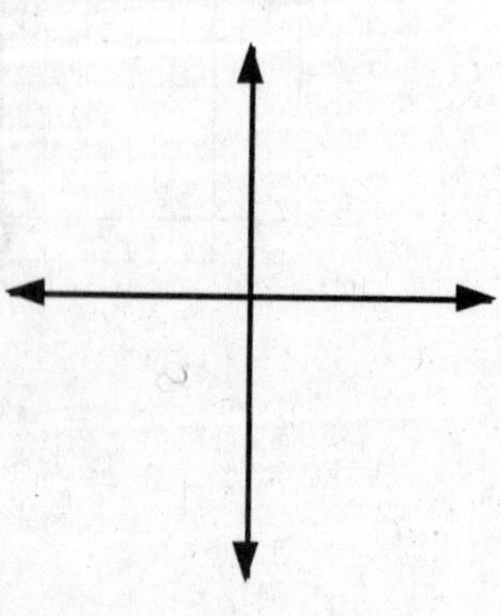

- State an appropriate window to show x- and y-intercepts, and draw the graph of both linear relations on the same grid.

- Determine the x and y-intercepts of $4x - y + 9 = 0$.

Complete Assignment Questions #1 - #7

Assignment

1. Without using technology and without altering the form in which the linear equation is written, <u>explain</u> how to graph $y = -3x - 6$ on a grid.
Draw the graph on the grid provided.

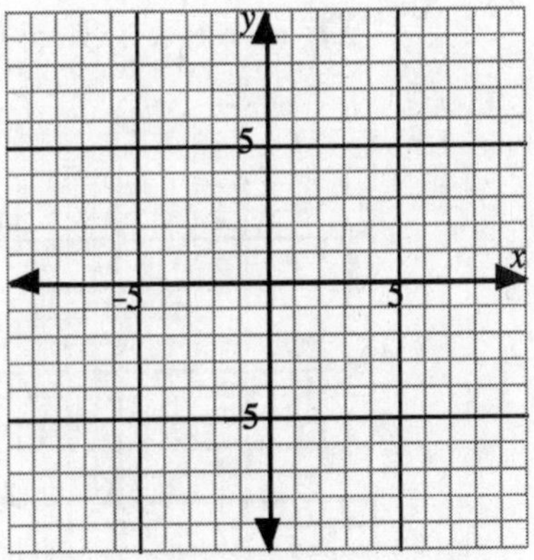

2. Without using technology and without altering the form in which the linear equation is written, <u>explain</u> how to graph $2x - 5y + 20 = 0$ on a grid.
Draw the graph on the grid provided.

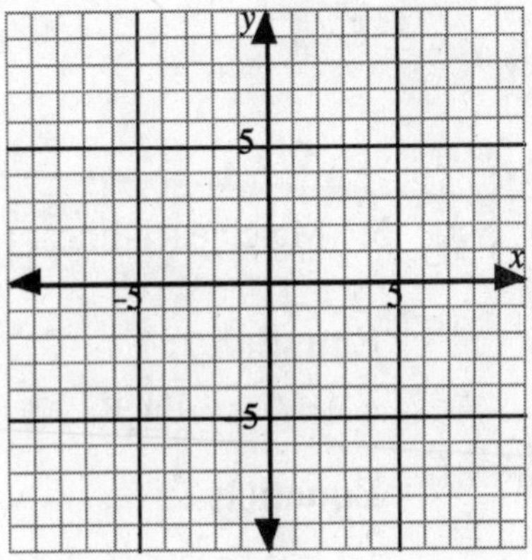

3. Without using technology and without altering the form in which the linear equation is written, <u>explain</u> how to graph $y + 4 = \frac{1}{2}(x - 2)$ on a grid.
Draw the graph on the grid provided.

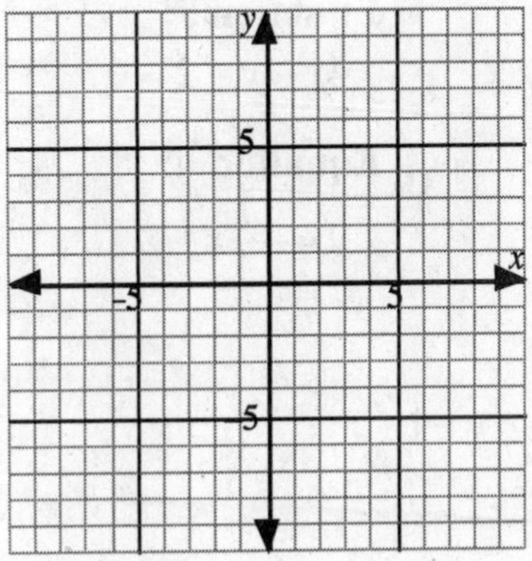

4. Without altering the form in which the linear equation is written, draw the graph (without technology) of each of the following linear relations on the grid provided.

a) $y = -\frac{1}{3}x + 3$

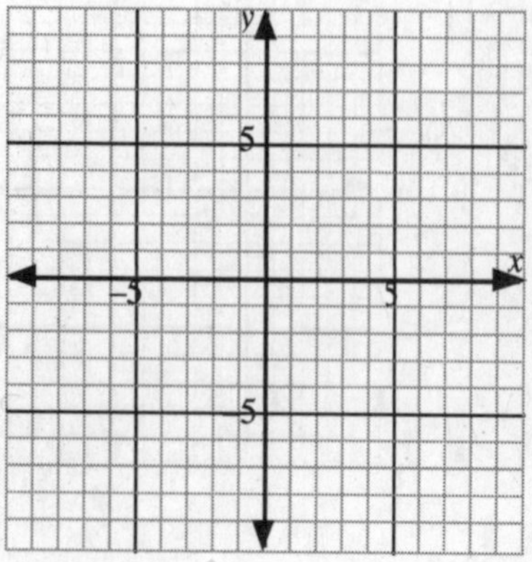

b) $y - 5 = -2(x + 6)$

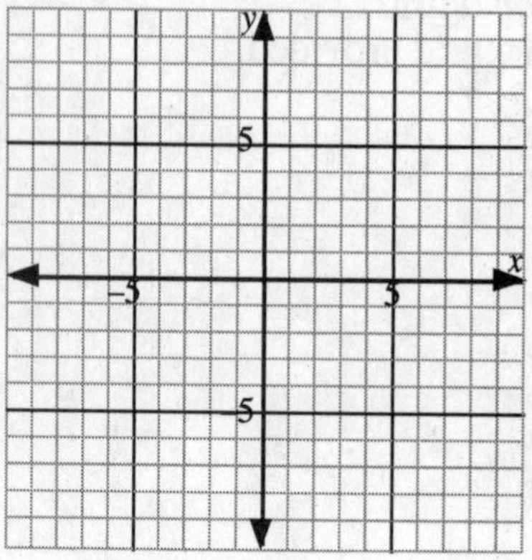

c) $x - 4y - 8 = 0$

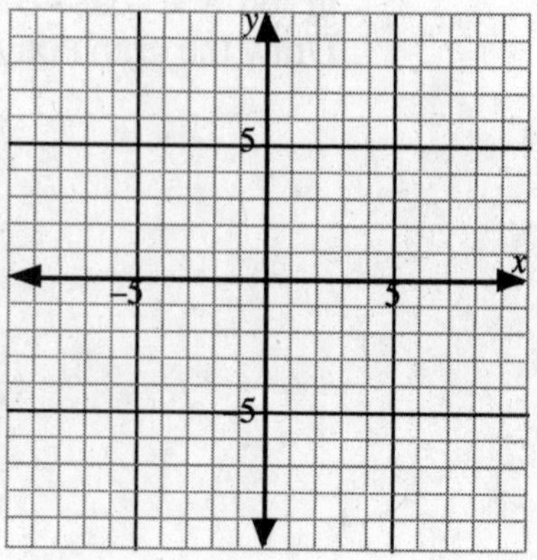

5. Match each linear relation to its graph.

Equation 1:
$y - 6 = -4(x + 1)$

Equation 2:
$x - 4y - 8 = 0$

Equation 3:
$4x - y - 2 = 0$

Equation 4:
$y = -\frac{1}{4}x + 2$

Graph A

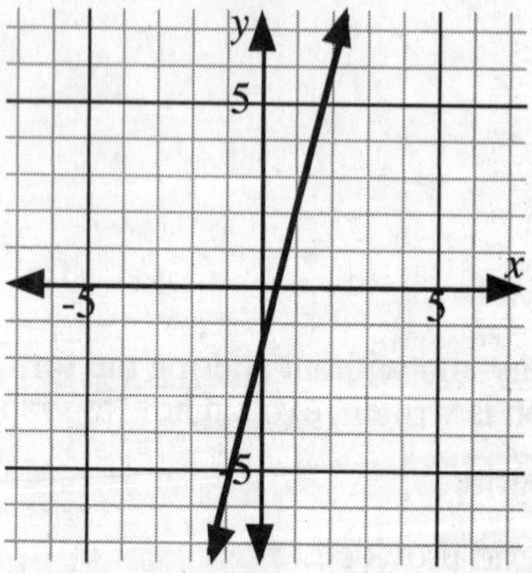

Graph B

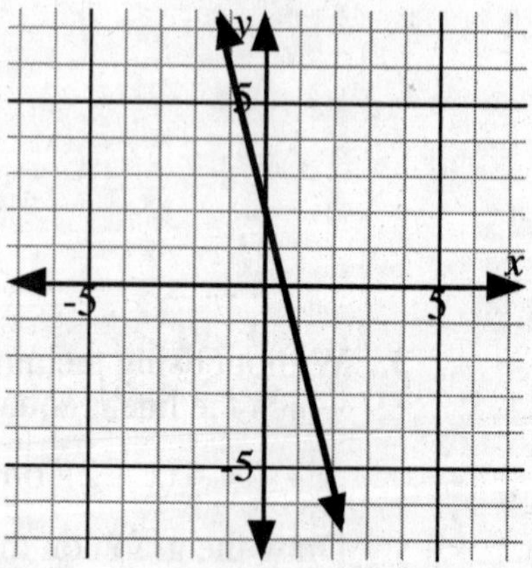

Graph C

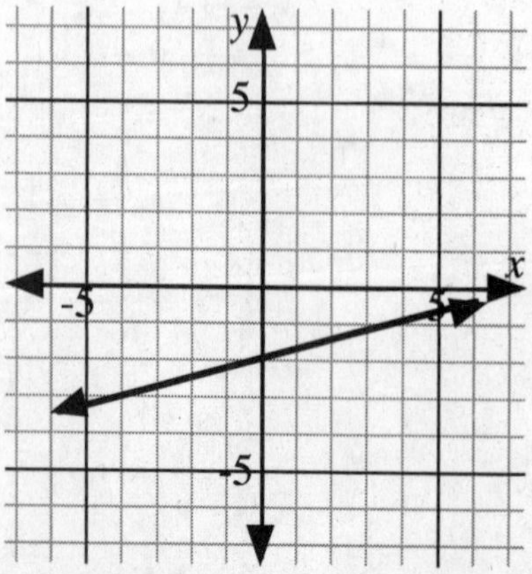

Graph D

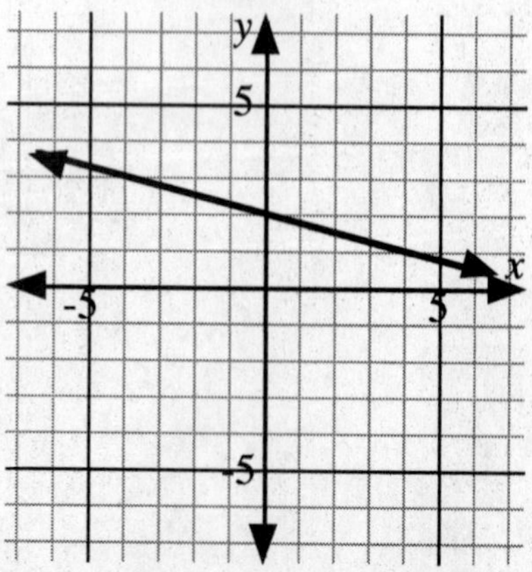

6. The following data is taken from a continuous linear relationship involving two quantities x and y.

x	32	41	50	59	68	77	86	95
y	0	5	10	15	20	25	30	35

a) Plot the data on the grid and obtain, in general form, the equation of the linear relation which is represented by the data.

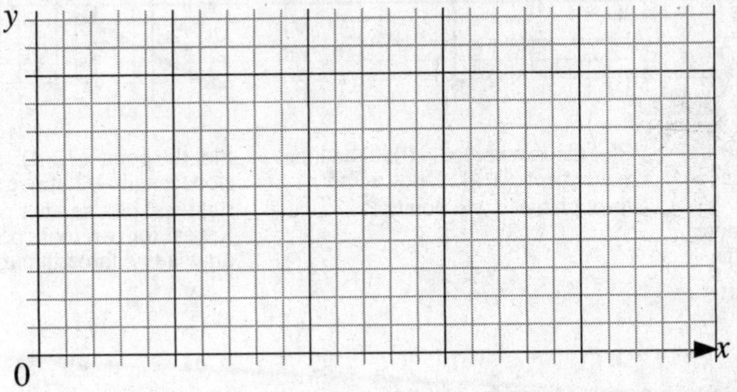

b) Rewrite the equation of the linear relation

i) in terms of x (i.e. $y = ...$)

ii) in terms of y (i.e. $x = ...$)

c) The formulas in b) are well known in the scientific field. Can you suggest what scientific variables are represented by x and y?

7. a) Explain the strategy used to graph (with technology) the linear relations $x + 5y + 10 = 0$ and $y - 3 = \frac{1}{3}(x + 6)$.

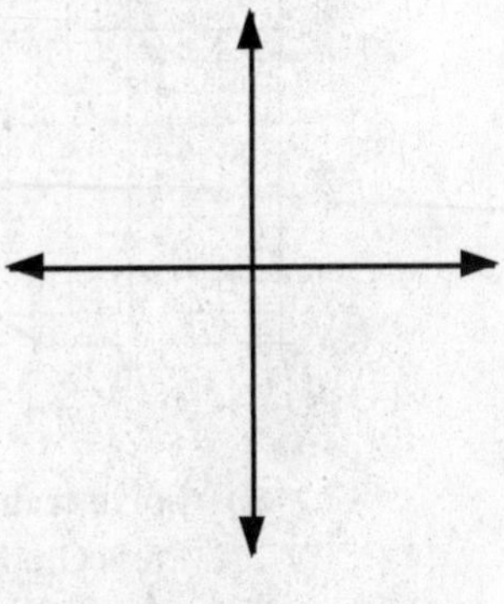

b) State an appropriate window to show x- and y-intercepts, and draw the graph of both linear relations on the grid.

c) Determine the x- and y-intercepts of each graph.

Answer Key

1.

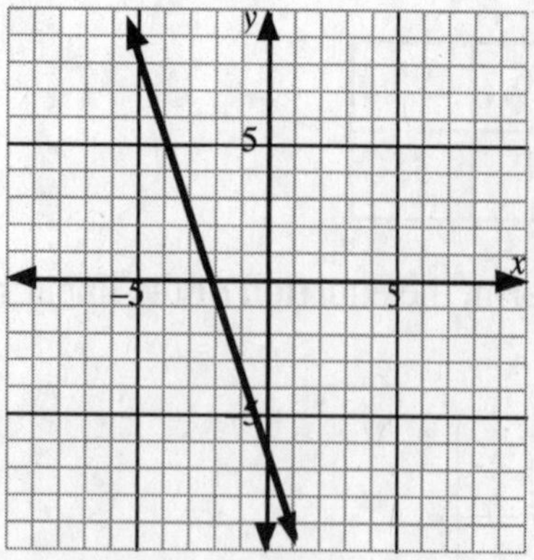

Plot the y-intercept $(0, -6)$. Since the slope, -3, equals rise over run, move 3 up and 1 left and plot another point. Repeat for two more points and draw a line through the points.

2.

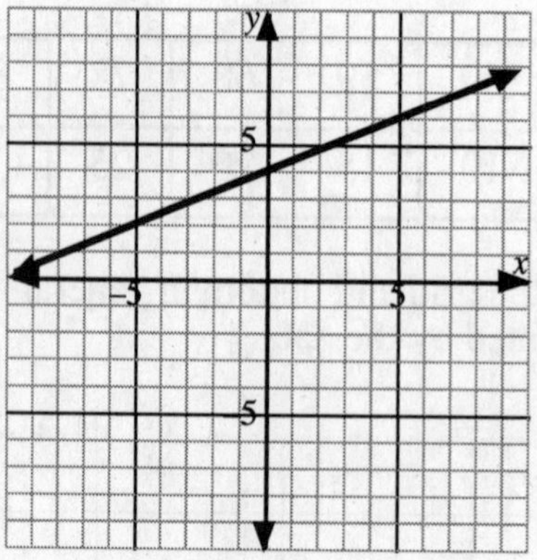

Plot the x-intercept $(-10, 0)$ and the y-intercept $(0, 4)$. Draw a line through these two points.

3.

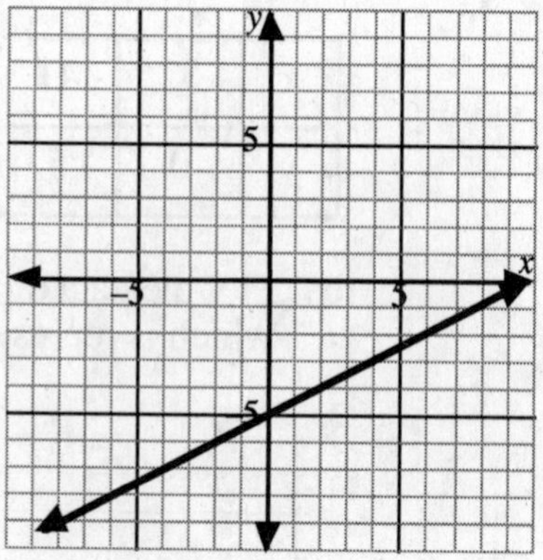

Plot the point $(2, -4)$. Since the slope equals $1/2$, move 1 up and 2 right and plot another point. Repeat for two more points and draw a line through the points.

4. a)

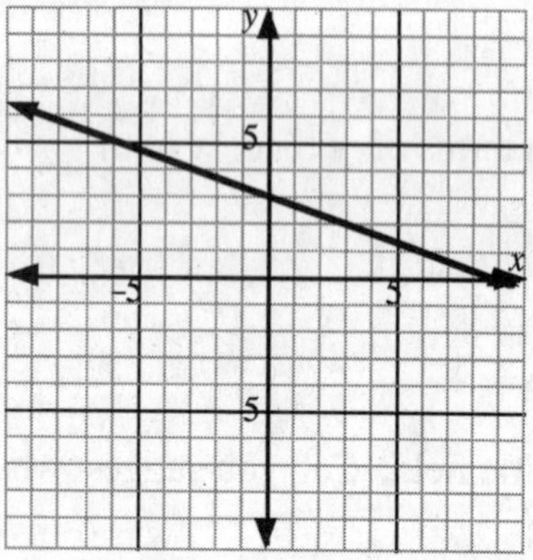

b)

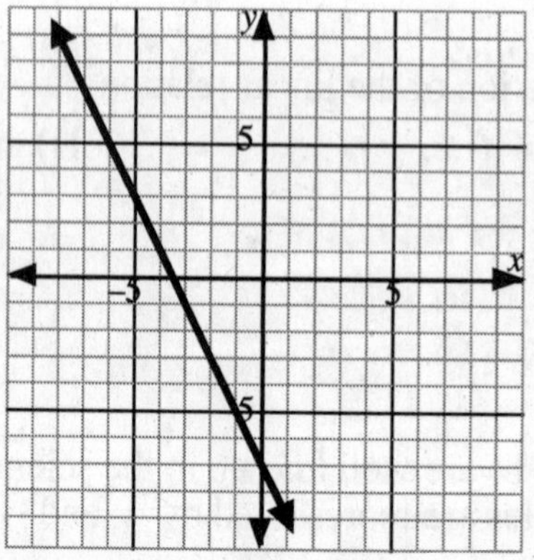

c)

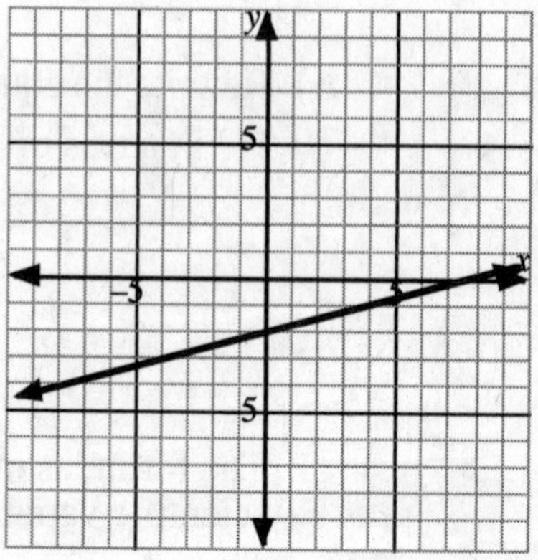

5. 1B, 2C, 3A, 4D.

6. a) $5x - 9y - 160 = 0$

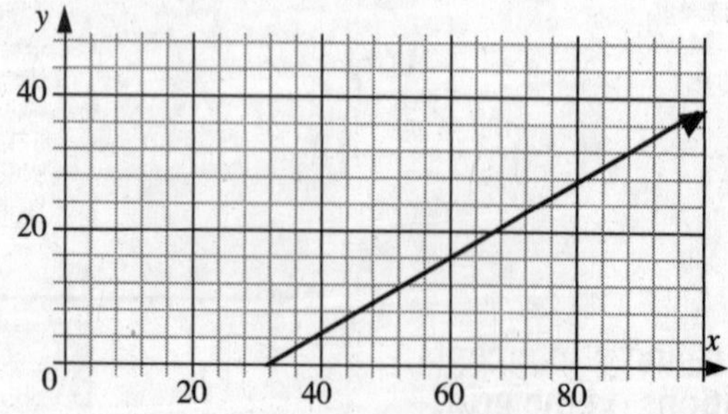

b) i) $y = \frac{5}{9}x - \frac{160}{9}$, or $y = \frac{5}{9}(x - 32)$

ii) $x = \frac{9}{5}y + 32$

c) x is temperature in °F, and y is temperature in °C.

7. a) Solve each equation for y. Then input Y_1 and Y_2 into the equation editor of the graphing calculator. Press Graph.

b) x:[−20, 10, 5] y:[−6, 10, 2], answers may vary.

c) For $x + 5y + 10 = 0$, x-int $= -10$, y-int $= -2$, and for $y - 3 = \frac{1}{3}(x + 6)$, x-int $= -15$, and y-int $= 5$.

Equations of Linear Relations Lesson #7: Slope as a Rate of Change

Rate of Change

Part One

The graph shown represents the distance travelled by a car as a linear function of time.

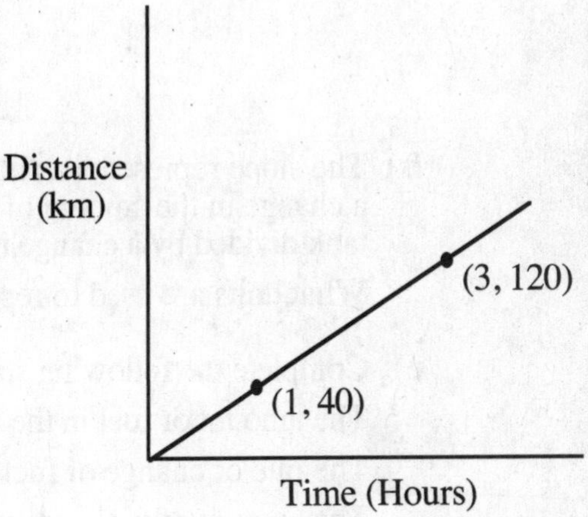

a) Complete the following to calculate the slope of the line.

$$m = \frac{\text{rise}}{\text{run}} = \frac{y_2 - y_1}{x_2 - x_1} =$$

b) The slope represents a **rate of change**: a change in distance divided by a change in time.

Complete the following statement by choosing the correct alternative and filling in the blank.

The distance is (increasing/decreasing) at the rate of ______ km per hour.

Part Two

The graph shown represents the temperature of an oven as a linear function of time.

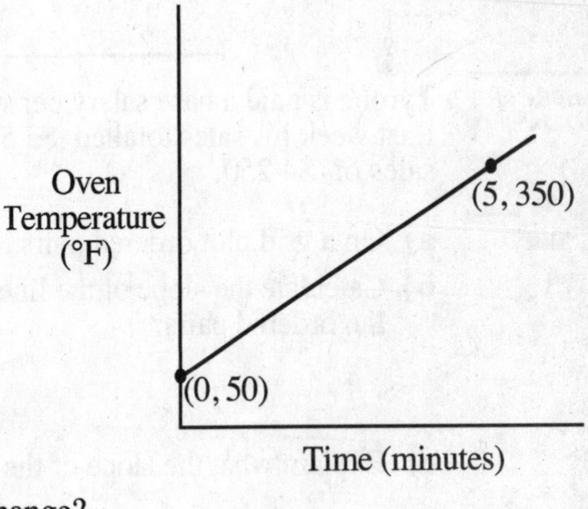

a) Calculate the slope of the line.

b) The slope represents a **rate of change**: a change in temperature divided by a change in time.

What units are used to represent this rate of change?

c) Complete the following statement.

The temperature is (increasing/decreasing) at the rate of ______ ____ per ______ .

Part Three

The graph shown represents the amount of fuel in the gas tank of a car as a function of the distance travelled.

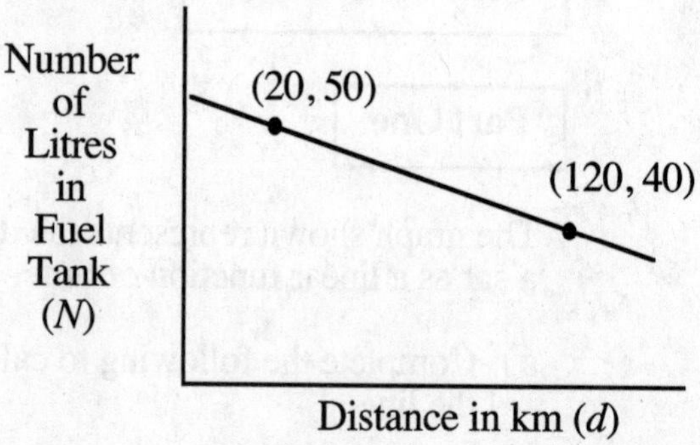

a) Calculate the slope of the line.

b) The slope represents a **rate of change**: a change in the amount of fuel in the fuel tank divided by a change in distance.
What units are used to represent this rate of change?

c) Complete the following statements.
The amount of fuel in the tank is (increasing/decreasing). Circle one.
The rate of change of fuel in the fuel tank is ______ ____ per ______ .
The amount of fuel is decreasing at the rate of __________ per ________ .

d) Determine the equation of the line in the form $N = mD + b$.

Tyrone is paid a base salary per week plus commission for selling electrical appliances. Last week his sales totalled $3 500, and he earned $620. This week he earned $680 for sales of $4 250.

a) On a grid plot ordered pairs to represent this information.

b) Calculate the slope of the line segment joining the ordered pairs.

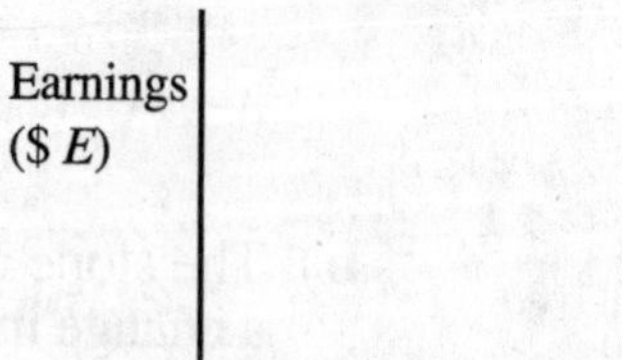

c) Explain what the slope of the graph represents.

d) State as a percent, the rate of commission which Tyrone is paid.

e) Calculate his weekly base salary.

f) How does the answer to e) relate to the graph?

g) Write the equation in the form $E = mS + b$.

h) Two weeks ago Tyrone earned $486. Calculate his sales for that week.

Average Speed

John is taking part in a long distance car race. After 3 hours he had travelled 270 km, and after 6 hours he had travelled 630 km.

a) On a grid, plot ordered pairs to represent this information.

b) Calculate the slope of the line segment joining the ordered pairs.

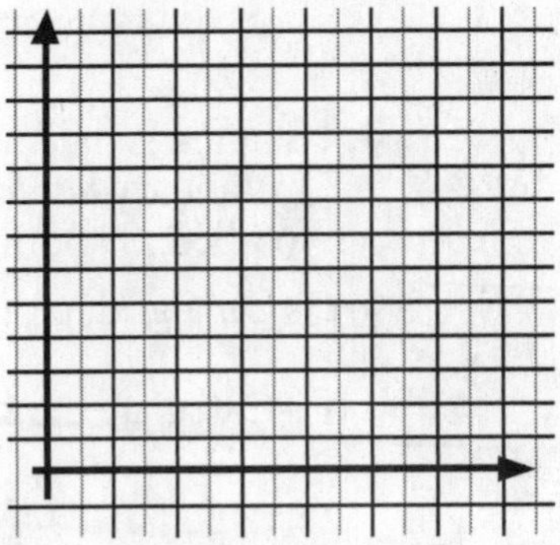

c) The slope of the line segment represents a rate of change: **a change in distance divided by a change in time.** This rate is the **average speed** between the two points. State the average speed of the car from 3 h to 6 h using appropriate units.

d) On the grid, plot the point (0, 0) and determine the average speed of the car during the first 3 h of the race.

e) By looking at the grid and without doing any calculations, how can we tell that the average speed during the first 3 h was less than the average speed during the next 3 h?

On a graph of distance as a function of time, the slope of a line segment joining two points represents the average speed between the two points.

Complete Assignment Questions #1 - #10

Assignment

1. The distances and times are recorded at certain points on a journey. Calculate the average speed

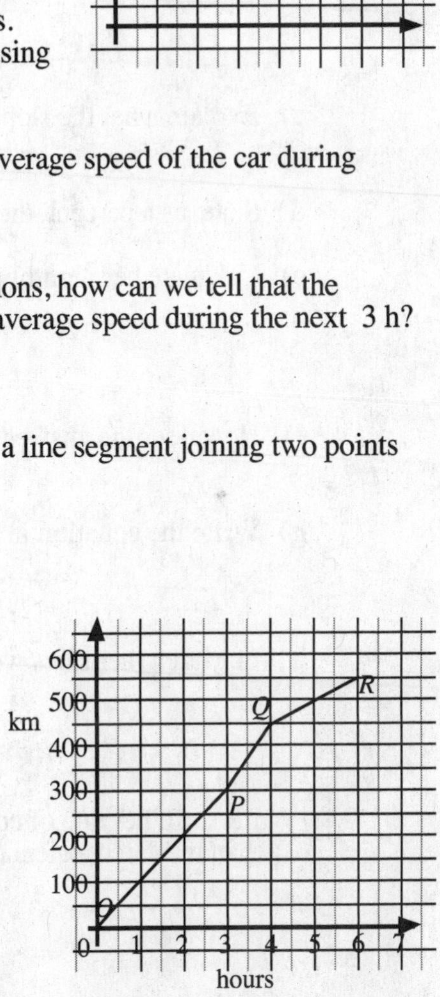

a) between O and P

b) between P and Q

c) between Q and R

d) for the whole journey

2. Absolute Value Computer Company was formed in 2002. By Jan 2004, the company had sold 520 000 computers and by July 2004, the company had sold 610 000 computers. Calculate the average rate of change stating appropriate units.

3. In 2003, the transit authority in a large city reported 17 678 465 passenger journeys. In 1998, the number of passenger journeys was 21 520 075. Calculate the average rate of change stating appropriate units.

4. Shanna is paid a base salary per month plus commission for working in a clothing store. In January her sales totalled \$10 500 and she earned \$2 460. In February her sales totalled \$9 350, and she earned \$2 322.

a) On a grid, plot ordered pairs to represent this information.

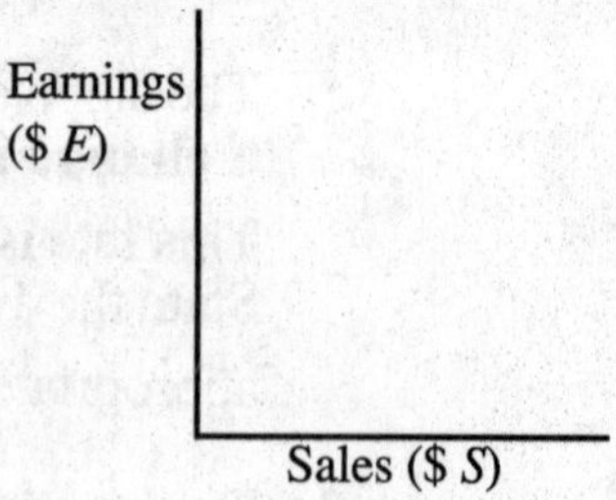

b) Calculate the slope of the line segment joining the ordered pairs.

c) Explain what the slope of the graph represents.

d) State, as a percent, the rate of commission which Shanna is paid.

e) Calculate her monthly base salary.

f) How does the answer to e) relate to the graph?

g) Write the equation in the form $E = mS + b$.

h) In March, her sales were \$11 200. Calculate her earnings for March.

i) In April, her rate of commission was increased by 1%. If her earnings were \$70 less than in March, calculate the value of her sales in April.

5. Water is leaking out of the bottom of a barrel at a constant rate. After 3 min the water level is 58 cm and after 8 min the water level is 23 cm.

a) On a grid, plot ordered pairs (time, water level) to represent this information.

b) Calculate the slope of the line segment joining the ordered pairs.

c) Explain what the slope of the graph represents.

d) Complete the following.
The water level is changing at the rate of ______ ____ per ______.

e) Determine an equation to represent this information in the form $W = mt + b$, where W represents the water level in cm and t represents the time in minutes.

f) After how many minutes will the barrel be empty?

g) What was the water level in the barrel when it started leaking?

h) The barrel is cylindrical in shape with a radius of 20 cm.

i) Calculate the volume (in terms of π) of water in the barrel after 3 min and after 8 min.

ii) Calculate the rate (in terms of π) at which water is leaking out of the barrel.

6. Jack rented a car from Absolute Value Rent-a-Car Company. After driving for two hours, the odometer reading was 21 328 and after five hours the odometer reading was 21 604. His journey was completed after six hours.

a) On a grid, plot ordered pairs to represent this information.

b) Calculate the slope of the line segment joining the ordered pairs.

c) Explain what the slope of the graph represents.

d) Assuming a constant rate of driving for the whole journey, determine the odometer reading at the start of the journey.

e) Determine an equation to represent this information in the form $f(t) = mt + b$, where $f(t)$ represents the odometer reading after t hours.

f) State an appropriate domain and range for f.

7. To test the gas consumption of a new SUV, Jana filled up the gas tank of 58 L and drove the SUV until it was empty. She drove the SUV for 464 km.

a) Sketch the graph on the grid provided with distance travelled on the horizontal axis.

b) Write an equation in the form $y = mx + b$ which represents the volume of fuel in the tank as a function of distance.

c) State the slope of the graph, and explain what it represents.

d) Determine the distance travelled on 12 litres of gas.

e) How many litres of gas are used by the SUV when it has travelled 200 km?

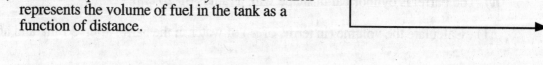

8. After 7 days of heavy rainstorms, the water level in a river peaked at 2.85 m above the regular level. Four days later the water dropped to 2.25 m above the regular level.

a) Assuming the water level falls at a constant rate, determine a function $h(t)$ which describes the height of the river above regular level as a function of time. Take $t = 0$ at peak water level.

b) State the slope of the graph of the function, and explain what it represents.

c) Determine an appropriate domain and range for h.

Multiple Choice

9. A repair company charges a fixed call-out fee for any service call, plus a fixed rate per hour for the length of the repair. A three hour repair costs \$155, and a four and a half hour repair costs \$215. The fixed call-out fee and the cost of a seven hour repair are respectively

A. \$35 and \$285
B. \$40 and \$285
C. \$35 and \$315
D. \$40 and \$315

Numerical Response

10. The temperature at the top of a mine shaft is 18° C. 250 metres below the surface, the temperature is 18.8° C. To the nearest tenth, the rate of temperature increase in ° C per km is _____ .

(Record your answer in the numerical response box from left to right)

Answer Key

1. a) 100 km/h b) 150 km/h c) 50 km/h d) $91\frac{2}{3}$ km/h

2. 15 000 computers per month

3. –768 322 passenger journeys per year

4. b) 0.12 c) the rate of commission (earnings per sales)
   d) 12% e) $1200
   f) it is the intercept on the vertical axis g) $E = 0.12S + 1200$ h) $2544 i) $9800

5. b) –7
   c) the rate at which the water level is changing in cm/min
   d) –7 cm/min e) $W = -7t + 79$ f) $11\frac{2}{7}$ min
   g) 79 cm h) i) 23200π cm^3, 9200π cm^3 ii) 2800π cm^3/min

6. b) 92
   c) the average speed between 2h and 5h is 92 km/h
   d) 21144 e) $f(t) = 92t + 21144$
   f) domain $0 \le t \le 6, t \in R$, range $21144 \le f(t) \le 21696, f(t) \in R$

7. b) $y = -\frac{1}{8}x + 58$
   c) slope $= -\frac{1}{8}$, the volume of fuel in the gas tank is decreasing at the rate of $\frac{1}{8}$ L/km
   d) 96 km e) 25 litres

8. a) $h(t) = -0.15t + 2.85$
   b) slope = –0.15, it represents the rate at which the water level is changing in metres per day
   c) domain $0 \le t \le 19, t \in R$, range $0 \le h(t) \le 2.85, h(t) \in R$

9. C 10.

3	.	2	

Equations of Linear Relations Lesson #8: Practice Test

1. The slope of the line with equation $3y = 2x - 12$ is

A. 2
B. $\frac{2}{3}$
C. -4
D. -12

2. The y-intercept of the graph of the line with equation $y = 5x - 10$ is

A. 2
B. 5
C. 10
D. -10

3. Which equation represents a line with a slope of 3 and a y-intercept of -4?

A. $y = -4x + 3$
B. $y = -\frac{1}{3}x - 4$
C. $y = 3x - 4$
D. $y = 3x + 4$

4. Which of the following is the equation of a line perpendicular to $5y + x + 6 = 0$?

A. $y = 5x$
B. $y = x$
C. $y = \frac{1}{5}x$
D. $y = -\frac{1}{5}x$

5. Which of these ordered pairs can be found on the graph of the line $3x - 5y - 4 = 0$?

i) $(8, 4)$ **ii)** $(-3, 1)$ **iii)** $(0, -0.8)$ **iv)** $(-2, 2)$

A. **i)** and **ii)** only
B. **i)** and **iii)** only
C. **i)**, **ii)**, and **iii)** only
D. some other combination of **i)**, **ii)**, **iii)**, and **iv)**

6. The point of intersection of the line $9x - 3y + 9 = 0$ and the y-axis is

A. $(0, 9)$
B. $(0, 3)$
C. $(0, -1)$
D. $(0, -3)$

*Use the following information to answer the next **two** questions.*

The x- and y-intercepts of the graph shown are integers.

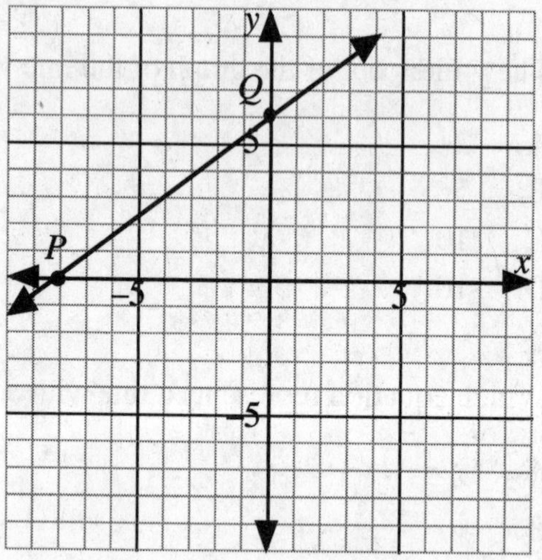

7. The equation of the line PQ is

A. $3x + 4y + 24 = 0$
B. $3x + 4y + 32 = 0$
C. $3x - 4y + 24 = 0$
D. $3x - 4y + 32 = 0$

Numerical Response **1.** Given that the line above passes through $(7.2, k)$, the value of k, to the nearest tenth, is ______ .

(Record your answer in the numerical response box from left to right)

8. If the lines $ax + by + c = 0$ and $dx + ey + f = 0$ are parallel, then

A. $ae - bd = 0$
B. $ae + bd = 0$
C. $ad - be = 0$
D. $ad + be = 0$

Numerical Response **2.** Given that the line joining the points $(2, 3)$ and $(8, -q)$, where $q \in W$, is perpendicular to the line $3x - 2y - 5 = 0$, then the value of q is ________ .

(Record your answer in the numerical response box from left to right)

9. The equations of four straight lines are
1) $7x - y = 0$ **2)** $7x + y - 6 = 0$ **3)** $x - 7y + 4 = 0$ **4)** $x + 7y - 2 = 0$

Which pairs of lines are perpendicular?

A. 1) and 2) only
B. 1) and 4) only
C. both 1) and 4) and 2) and 3)
D. both 1) and 2) and 2) and 3)

10. The line passing through the points $(-5, -2)$ and $(-2, -1)$ has equation

A. $x + y + 3 = 0$
B. $x + 3y + 5 = 0$
C. $x - 3y + 1 = 0$
D. $x - 3y - 1 = 0$

Numerical Response **3.** The lines $3x - y + 2 = 0$ and $5x - By + 26 = 0$, where $B \in W$, intersect on the y-axis. The value of B is ______.
(Record your answer in the numerical response box from left to right)

11. Which equation represents a line which is perpendicular to line l_1 and has the same x-intercept as line l_2?

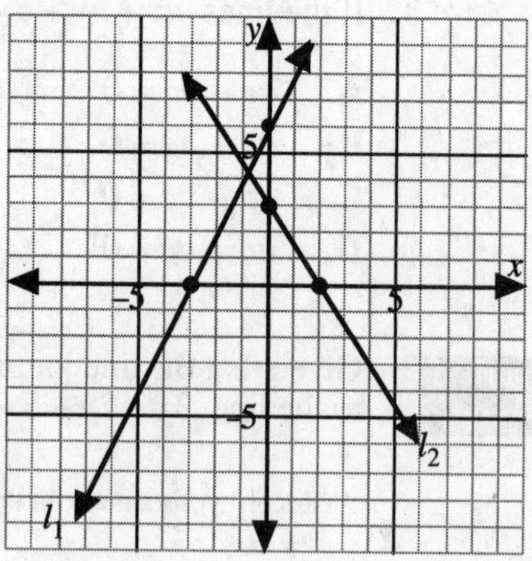

A. $x + 2y - 2 = 0$
B. $x + 2y + 2 = 0$
C. $2x + y - 4 = 0$
D. $2x + y + 4 = 0$

Numerical Response

4. The equation of the line shown in the diagram is $Ax + 2y + C = 0$. The value of $\frac{A}{C}$, to the nearest hundredth, is ______.

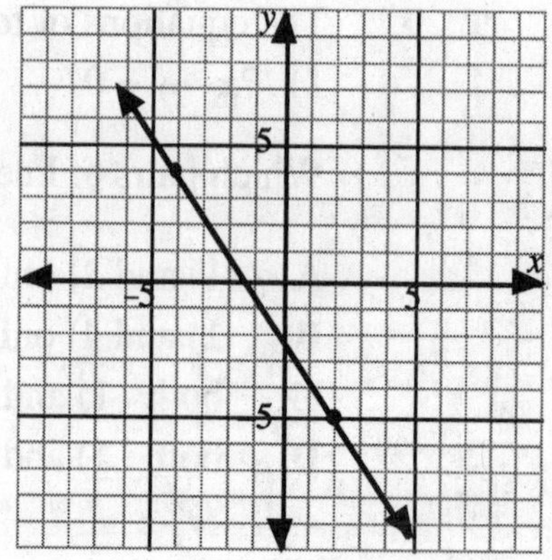

(Record your answer in the numerical response box from left to right)

12. The equation of AB is $x - 2y + 4 = 0$.
AB cuts the y-axis at C.
CD is perpendicular to AB.

The equation of CD is

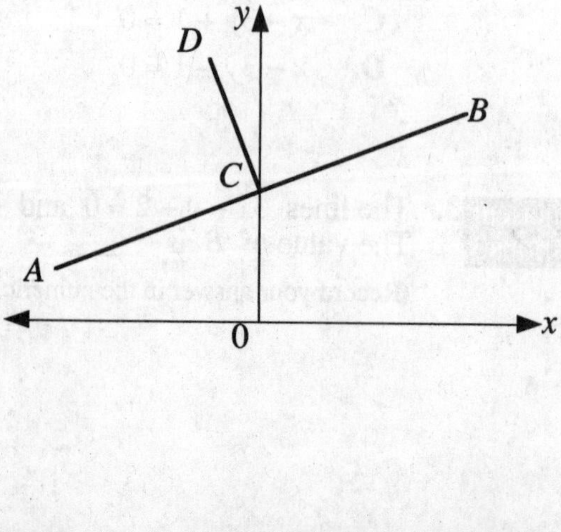

A. $x + 2y - 2 = 0$
B. $2x + y - 2 = 0$
C. $2x - y + 2 = 0$
D. $2x + y - 4 = 0$

13. Consider $\triangle PQR$ in which side PQ has slope $\frac{1}{3}$ and R has coordinates $(-4, 7)$.

The equation of the altitude from R to PQ (the line drawn from R to PQ, perpendicular to PQ), is

A. $x + 3y = 25$
B. $3x + y = 19$
C. $3x + y = -5$
D. $3x + y = -19$

14. Which of the following lines is/are perpendicular to the line $9x + y + 2 = 0$?

i) $9y + x = 2$ **ii)** $9y - x = 2$ **iii)** $y = 9x + 2$ **iv)** $9y = x - 2$

A. i) and iii) only
B. ii) only
C. iv) only
D. some other combination of i), ii), iii), and iv)

15. The line l_1 passes through the points $(-3, 5)$ and $(-2, -1)$.

Which of the following statements is true?

i) l_1 passes through $(4, -37)$.

ii) l_1 has an x–intercept of $-\frac{13}{6}$.

iii) l_1 is perpendicular to $y = \frac{1}{6}x + 2$.

A. i) and ii) only
B. i) and iii) only
C. ii) and iii) only
D. i), ii), and iii)

Numerical Response

5. The temperature at sea level is 12.1 °C. At the top of a mountain, 6 400 m above sea level, the temperature is −29.5 °C. To the nearest tenth, the rate of temperature decrease, in °C per km, is _____ .

(Record your answer in the numerical response box from left to right)

Written Response - 5 marks

1. Consider the points $P(-7,-2)$, $Q(2,1)$, $R(-2,-7)$, and $S(8,3)$.

- Show that the equation of the line, L_1, through S and perpendicular to PQ is $y = -3x + 27$.

- Determine the equation of the line, L_2, through R and parallel to PQ. Give the answer in in slope y-intercept form.

- Draw both lines on the grid, and state a suitable window which shows x- and y-intercepts for each graph.

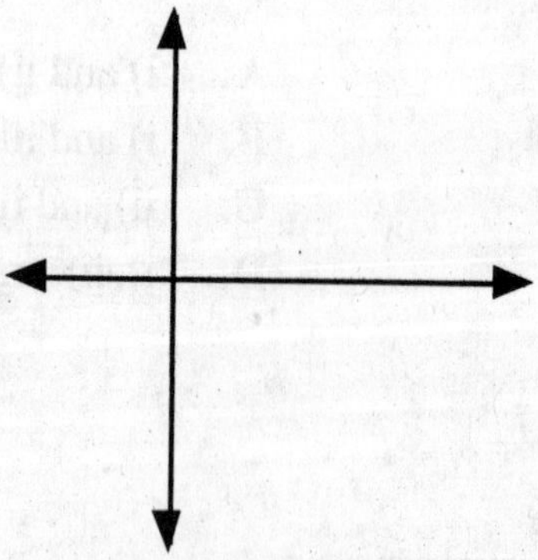

Answer Key

1. B	**2.** D	**3.** C	**4.** A	**5.** B
6. B	**7.** C	**8.** A	**9.** C	**10.** D
11. A	**12.** B	**13.** C	**14.** D	**15.** D

NR 1.

1	1	.	4

NR 2.

1			

NR 3.

1	3		

NR 4.

0	.	7	5

NR 5.

6	.	5	

Written Response

- $y = -3x + 27$
- $y = \frac{1}{3}x - \frac{19}{3}$
- x:[−5, 25, 5] and y:[−10, 35, 5]

Systems of Linear Equations Lesson #1: Solving Systems of Linear Equations by Graphing

Overview of Unit

In this unit, we solve problems that involve systems of linear equations in two variables, graphically, and algebraically using the method of substitution and the method of elimination.

Exploration

The Smith family and the Harper family are going to a book fair raising money for charity. Mr. Smith pays entry fees of \$11 for three adults and one child. Mrs. Harper pays entry fees of \$12 for two adults and three children.

We can determine the cost of an adult ticket and the cost of a child ticket by forming two linear equations and graphing them.

Let \$$x$ be the entry fee for an adult ticket and let \$$y$ be the entry fee for a child. The information about the Smith family can be modelled by the equation $3x + y = 11$, and the information about the Harper family can be modelled by the equation $2x + 3y = 12$.

a) Draw the graphs of the equations $3x + y = 11$ (A) and $2x + 3y = 12$ (B) on the grid without using technology.

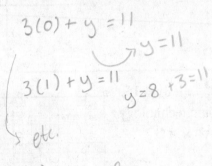

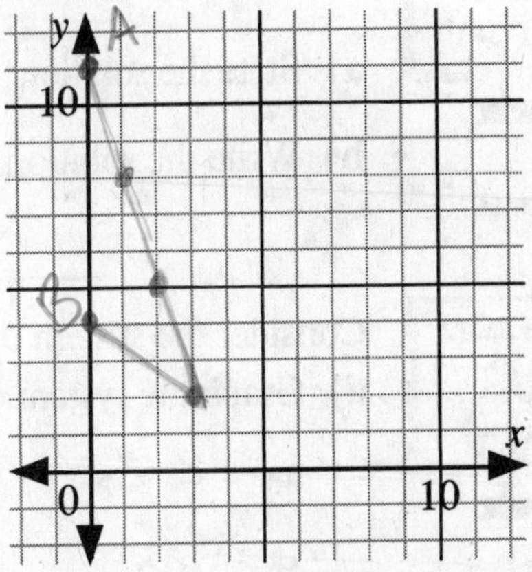

$3(0) + y = 11$ → $y = 11$

$3(1) + y = 11$ $y = 8$ $+3 = 11$

etc.

$2(0) + 3y = 12$

$3 \cdot y = 12$

$y = 4$

etc.

$2(3) + 3y = 12$

$6 + 3y = 12$

$y = 2$ → $6 + 3(2) = 12$, where $3(2) = 6$

b) The graphs of the equations intersect at a point. State the coordinates of this point and explain what the coordinates represent in the context of the question.

(3,2) is the point where the equations intersect.

Systems of Equations

In the exploration on the previous page, we worked with the equation $3x + y = 11$. There are many values for x and y which satisfy this equation, e.g. $x = 1$ and $y = 8$, or $x = 2$ and $y = 5$, or $x = 3$ and $y = 2$, etc.

We also worked with the equation $2x + 3y = 12$. There are also many values for x and y which satisfy this equation, e.g. $x = 0$ and $y = 4$, or $x = 3$ and $y = 2$, or $x = 4.5$ and $y = 1$, etc.

If we consider both of these equations at the same time, there is only one solution, $x = 3$ and $y = 2$.

The equations $3x + y = 11$ and $2x + 3y = 12$, considered at the same time, are called a **system of equations**.

The **solution** to this system of equations is $x = 3$ and $y = 2$. This is because $x = 3$ and $y = 2$ **satisfy** each equation in the system.

Graphically, the solution to the system is the point of intersection of the two lines.

Class Ex. #1

A system of equations has been represented on the grid. The system has an integral solution.

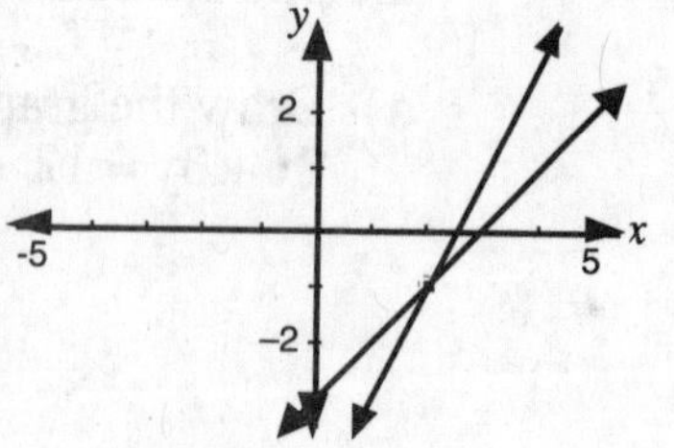

a) State the solution $x =$ _____, $y =$ _____ .

b) Write the solution as an ordered pair.

Class Ex. #2

Consider the system of equations $2x + y = 2$, $x - 3y = 15$.

a) Graph the system of equations without using technology.

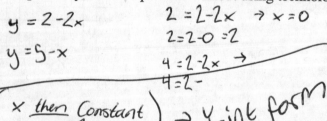

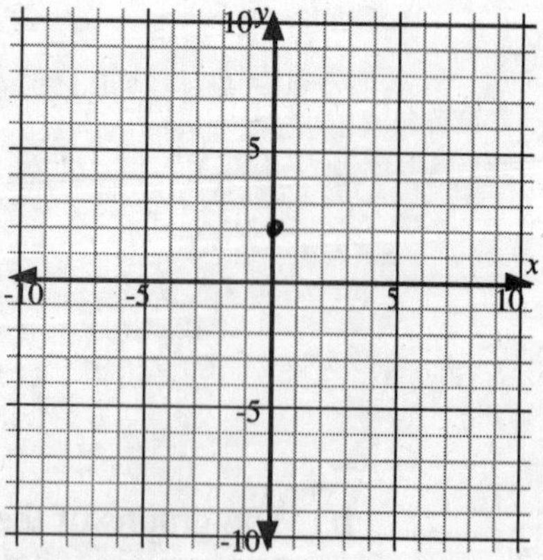

y = 2 − 2x   2 = 2 − 2x → x = 0
2 = 2 − 0 = 2
y = 5 − x   4 = 2 − 2x →
4 = 2 −
x − 3y = 15
−3y = 15 − x
y = 5 − x
(x then constant) → y-int form

b) State the solution to the system of equations (−3, 8)

c) Algebraically verify the solution by replacing the values in the original equations.

8 = 2 − 2(−3)   8 = 5 − −3 → 5 + 3 = 8 ✓
8 = 2 + 6 ✓

Conplete Assignement Questions #1 and #2

Solving a System of Equations using a TI Graphing Calculator

Check that the calculator is in "Function" mode.

Use the following procedure to find the solution to a system of equations.

1. Write each equation in terms of y.
2. Access the "Y= editor" by pressing the **Y=** key.
3. Enter one equation in **Y_1**.
4. Enter the other equation in **Y_2**.
5. Press the **GRAPH** key to display the graphs.
6. Access the intersect command by pressing **2nd** then **TRACE** and scroll down to "**intersect**". The calculator will return to the display window with the graphs.
7. The calculator will display "**First curve?**". Use the cursor key, if necessary, to select the first graph and then press **ENTER**.
8. The calculator will display "**Second curve?**". Use the cursor key, if necessary, to select the second graph and then press **ENTER**.
9. The calculator will display "**Guess?**". Press **ENTER**.

Consider the system of equations from the exploration at the beginning of this lesson.

$$3x + y = 11$$
$$2x + 3y = 12.$$

a) Rewrite each equation in slope y-intercept form.

$3x + y = 11$ ($-3x$, $-3x$) → $y = -3x + 11$ | $2x + 3y = 12$ ($-2x$, $-2x$) → $\frac{3y}{3} = -2x + \frac{12}{3}$ ↓ $y = -2x + 4$

b) Use a graphing calculator to graph each equation.

$y = -3x + 11$ $y = -2x + 4$

c) State a suitable window which shows both sets of x- and y-intercepts and the point of intersection.

Bruh....

d) Solve the system of equations using the features of the graphing calculator. Confirm the amount of the entry fees established in the exploration.

If a decimal value appears for the x and/or y coordinates, then the x and/or y value can be converted to an exact value (as long as it is not irrational and within the limitations of the calculator) by using the following procedure.

For the *x*-coordinate

1. Exit the graphing screen by pressing [CLEAR] twice.
2. Press [X,T, θ, *n*] key, then press [ENTER] to import the *x*-coordinate.
3. To display the exact value,

   Press [MATH], select "**Frac** ", then press [ENTER].

For the *y*-coordinate

Except for step 2, the instructions to import the *y*-coordinate are the same as above.
For step 2, press [ALPHA] [1] [ENTER] to import the *y*-coordinate value.
Then proceed to step 3 above.

a) Solve the following system of equations using a graphing calculator.

$$6a + 7b = 5$$
$$3a = 14b$$

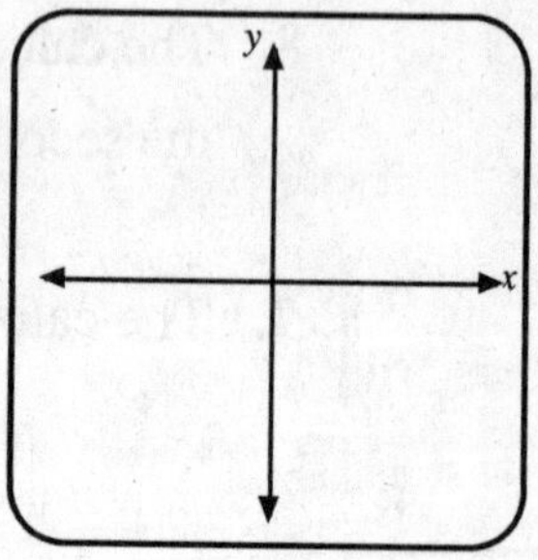

b) List the answers as exact values using the technique above.

c) Algebraically verify the solution.

Complete Assignment Questions #3 - #7

Assignment

1. Consider the system of equations $x - 2y = 3,\ x + y = 0$.

a) Write each equation in slope y-intercept form.

b) Complete the table of values for each equation.

$x - 2y = 3$

x	y
–3	-3
–1	-2
1	-1
3	0
5	1

$x + y = 0$

x	y
–4	4
–2	2
0	0
2	-2
4	-4

c) Draw the lines on the grid and state the solution to the system.

forget about this.... haha, oops.

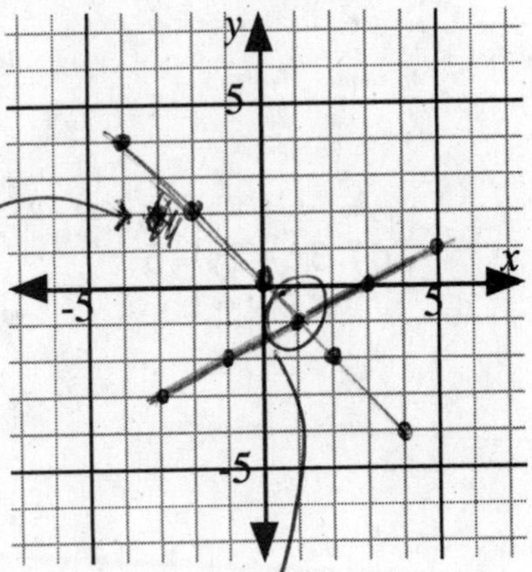

d) Verify the solution.

(1, -1)

$x + 5y = -5$ → $y = -1 - x$

2. The following system of equations is given: $x - y = 7,\ x + 5y = -5$

a) Without using technology, graph each equation and hence solve the system.

$x - y = 7 \rightarrow y = 7 - x$

$x + 5y = -5 \rightarrow y = -1 - x$

x	y
1	6
2	5
3	4
4	3
5	2
6	1

x	y
1	-2
2	-3
3	-4
4	-5
5	-6
6	-7

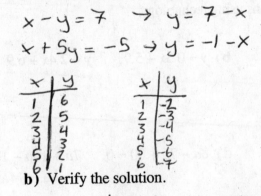

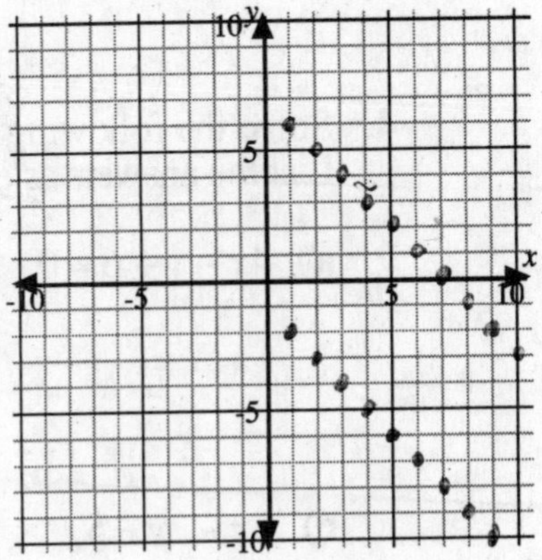

b) Verify the solution.

There is no solution because the lines are paralell, meaning they'll never touch.

HA HA!

3. In each case, solve the system of equations by using technology. Verify the solution by replacing the values in the original equations.

a) $y = 3x - 7$
$y = -x + 9$

(4,5)

b) $y = -x$
$y = -\frac{1}{3}x + 3$

c) $y = x - 2$
$y = \frac{3}{4}x - 4$

d) $3x + 2y = 5$
$x - y = 1$

e) $4a - b = 6$
$3a + b = 1$

f) $0.6p - 0.8q = 2.6$
$5p + 6q = 9$

4. Solve the following systems of equations using technology.
List the answers as exact values.

a) $4x - y + 6 = 0, \quad y = x + 2$

b) $y = 0.3x - 5.9, \quad y = 2.4x + 6.9$

c) $8x - 3y = 5, \quad 5x + 3y = 2$

d) $8a - 7b + 80 = 0, \quad 7a + 14b - 177 = 0$

Multiple Choice **5.** The ordered pair (x, y) which satisfies the system of equations $x - 2y = 6,\ x + 6y = 22$ is

A. $(-10, 2)$

B. $(2, 10)$

C. $(10, -2)$

D. $(10, 2)$

Numerical Response **6.** If $7x - 5y = 19$ and $2x + 3y = 17$, then the value of x, to the nearest tenth, is ______ .

(Record your answer in the numerical response box from left to right)

7. A pear costs 24 cents less than two apples. Four apples cost the same as three pears. In order to determine the cost of each piece of fruit, Courtney graphs the equations $y = 2x - 24$ and $4x = 3y$. The cost of a pear, in cents, is ______ .

!! This is fun haha !!

(Record your answer in the numerical response box from left to right)

2 Apples − 24? = 1 pear (Alright then)

x = Apples # y = Pears #

4A = 3P

(36, 48)

$\frac{4x}{3} = \frac{3y}{3}$ $\frac{4x}{3} = y$

1 Apple = 36 cents

1 pear = 48 cents

Answer Key

1. a) $y = \frac{1}{2}x - \frac{3}{2},\ y = -x$ **b)**

x	y
-3	-3
-1	-2
1	-1
3	0
5	1

x	y
-4	4
-2	2
0	0
2	-2
4	-4

c) $x = 1,\ y = -1$

2. a) $x = 5, y = -2$

3. a) $x = 4, y = 5$ **b)** $x = -4.5, y = 4.5$ **c)** $x = -8, y = -10$
d) $x = 1.4, y = 0.4$ **e)** $a = 1, b = -2$ **f)** $p = 3, q = -1$

4. a) $x = -\frac{4}{3}, y = \frac{2}{3}$ **b)** $x = -\frac{128}{21}, y = -\frac{541}{70}$ **c)** $x = \frac{7}{13}, y = -\frac{3}{13}$ **d)** $a = \frac{17}{23}, b = \frac{1976}{161}$

5. D **6.**

4	.	6	

7.

4	8		

(1) 2nd
(2) Calc
(3) intersect
(4) "Enter" until shown

Systems of Linear Equations Lesson #2:
Determining the Number of Solutions to a System of Linear Equations

Exploration ***Determining the Number of Solutions to a System of Linear Equations***

As part of a high school work experience course, three students have been placed in three different burger restaurants. Deja has been placed at Burger Shack, Shelly has been placed at Big's Burgers, and John has been placed at The Burger Haven.

Detailed below are the first two orders taken by each student and the total cost calculated by the student for each order.

Burger Shack	For the first order Deja charges \$28 for 4 burgers and 2 salads. For the second order she charges \$34 for 6 burgers and a salad.
Big's Burgers	Shelly charges \$18 for a burger and 3 salads, and \$54 for 3 burgers and 9 salads.
The Burger Haven	John charges \$32 for 2 burgers and 4 salads, and \$42 for 3 burgers and 6 salads.

a) Let x dollars be the cost of a burger and y dollars be the cost of a salad. Write a system of equations for each scenario.

Burger Shack　　Big's Burgers　　The Burger Haven

b) Consider the equations for the Burger Shack. Write each equation in terms of y and use a graphing calculator to determine the cost of a burger and the cost of a salad.

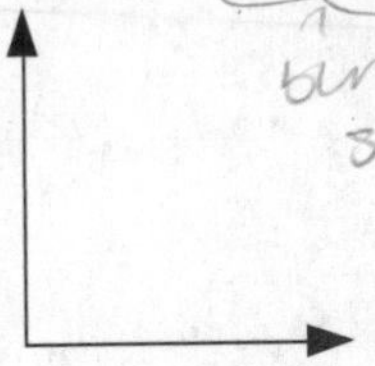

c) Repeat part b) for Big's Burgers. Can you determine the cost of a burger and the cost of a salad? Explain.

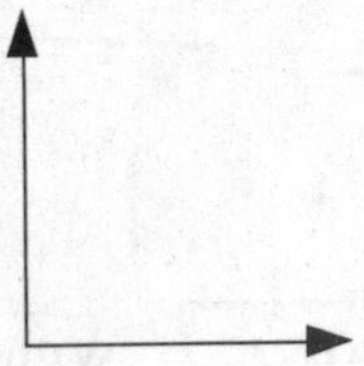

d) Repeat part b) for The Burger Haven. Can you determine the cost of a burger and the cost of a salad? Explain how you can tell that the student must have made an error in at least one of the calculations.

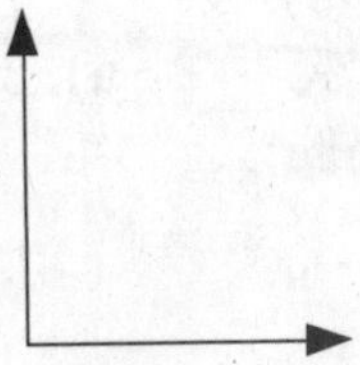

Number of Solutions to a System of Equations

In all of the examples in lesson #1, each system of equations had one unique solution. However, we have seen on the previous page that a system of two linear equations may have no solution, only one solution or an infinite number of solutions.

Graph each system of equations on the grid provided. State the number of solutions for each system.

a) $y = x + 5$
$y = -x + 1$

b) $y = 2x - 8$
$y = 2x + 6$

c) $y = 3x - 2$
$6x - 2y - 4 = 0$

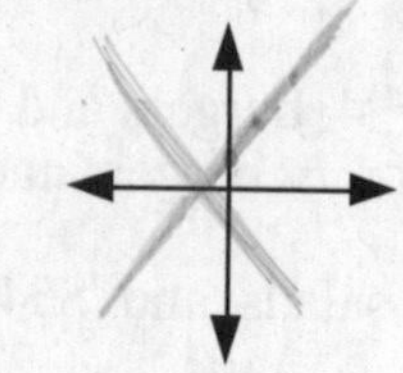

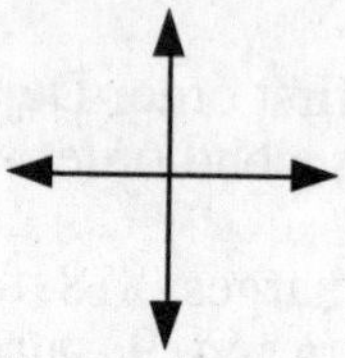

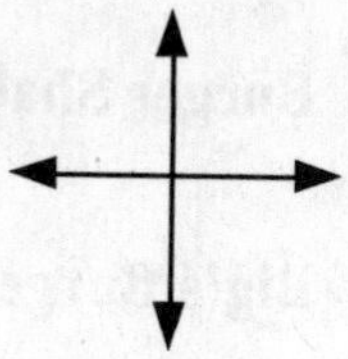

The number of solutions can be determined from the graph as above or directly from the equations if they are expressed in slope *y*-intercept form.

d) Complete the following chart.

Number of Solutions			infinitely many
Graphical Example	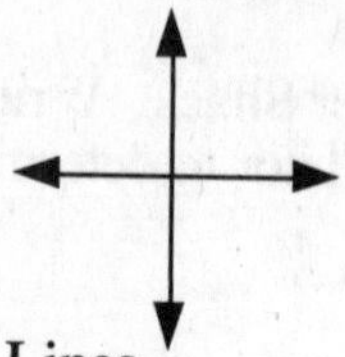 Lines intersect at one point	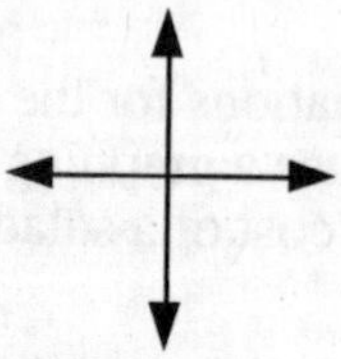 Lines are parallel	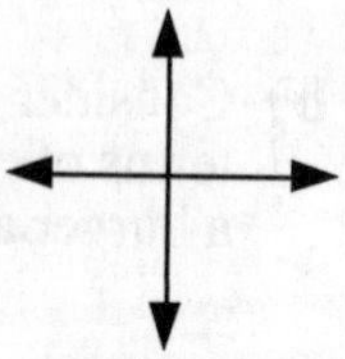 Lines are coincident
Slopes and Intercepts		Slopes are equal and intercepts are different	

Without graphing, analyze each system to determine whether the system has one solution, no solution, or infinitely many solutions.

a) $3x + 5y = 15, \ y = -\frac{3}{5}x$ **b)** $x - 4y + 8 = 0, \ y = \frac{1}{4}x + 2$ **c)** $7x + y = 12, \ x - 6y = 5$

Complete Assignment Questions #1 - #5

Solving a System Graphically by Changing the Calculator Window

Often, the solution to a system of equations will not be visible using the default window of the graphing calculator. When this occurs, the window requires to be changed.

We use the following graphing calculator window format:

$$x:[x_{min}, x_{max}, x_{scl}] \qquad y:[y_{min}, y_{max}, y_{scl}]$$

Class Ex. #3

At a local High School the Students' Council decided to sell sweaters to students. The cost of designing the sweaters included a fixed cost of $600 plus $5 per sweater. *600 + 5n*

The Students' Council planned to sell the sweaters for $25 each. The cost and revenue can be represented by the following system of equations where d represents the dollar cost and n represents the number of sweaters sold.

Cost of sweaters in dollars $d = 600 + 5n$
Revenue of sweaters in dollars $d = 25n$

n = # → sweaters

inter =
x = 30
y = 750

30 → n = $750

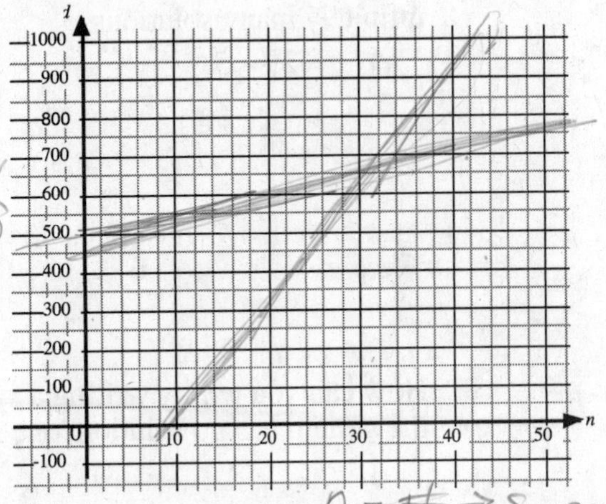

a) Use a graphing calculator to graph each equation and sketch each graph on the grid provided.

b) How much profit or loss is made if
 i) twenty sweaters are sold? **ii)** fifty sweaters are sold?
 $700 *$850*

c) The break even point is the point where no profit or loss is made.
 Mark the break even point on the grid.

d) Use a graphing calculator to determine the number of sweaters which must be sold in order to break even.

e) If all 850 students in the school purchased a sweater, how much profit would the Students' Council make?

Complete Assignment Questions #6 - #11

Assignment

1. How can you tell by graphing a system of linear equations whether the system has no solution, one solution, or infinitely many solutions?

Crossed points = One Solution → the Intersected point only/ where they meet.
Paralell = never meet/touch, meaning no solutions
Same line (collinear) = Every point is a solution if on the same line. (infinite).

(two in one deal haha.)

2. Graph each system and determine whether the system has no solution, one solution, or infinitely many solutions.

a) $x = 2y - 5$
$y = \frac{1}{2}(x + 5)$

b) $6x - y = 5$
$y = 6x + 7$

c) $2x - 5y = 10$
$3x - 4y = 24$

3. How can you tell by writing a system of linear equations in the form $y = mx + b$ whether the system has no solution, one solution, or infinitely many solutions?

— If the x and y are equal in 2 equations, the solutions are infinite.
— If the x is equal but y-int is different, there is no solution being the lines are paralell to one another.
— If lines = perpendicular or cross, there is only one solution. (points that meet).

4. Rearrange each equation into the form $y = mx + b$ and state whether the system has no solution, one solution, or infinitely many solutions.

a) $6x - y = 1$
$y = 6x + 1$

b) $8x - y = 13$
$x - 8y = 13$

c) $5y + x - 10 = 0$
$y = -\frac{1}{5}x + 2$

6x - y = 1 → +y +y → 6x = 1 + y → -1 -1 → 6x - 1 = y
6x - 1 = y → 4y = 6x + 1 (1) → y = 6x + 1

8x - y = 13 → +y +y → 8x = 13 + y → -13 -13 → 8x - 13 = y

5. Write an equation which forms a system with the equation $3x - y = 9$ so that the system has:

a) no solution **b)** one solution **c)** an infinite number of solutions

6. All 480 tickets for a school concert were sold. Seats in the front part of the hall cost $6 each, and seats in the back part of the hall cost $4 each. The total receipts were $2 530.

The information from the number of tickets can be represented by $f + b = 480$.

a) State an equation which can be formed from the costs of the tickets.

$$6f + 4b = 2530 \quad \rightarrow \text{rearange.}$$

b) Graph the system to determine the number of tickets sold for each part of the hall.

intersect = Answer

c) State the graphing window used.

d) Verify the solution.

7. Six pencils and four crayons cost $3.40. Three similar pencils and ten similar crayons cost $4.90. **Describe** a method to determine how much you would expect to pay for a set of eight pencils and twelve crayons and then calculate the cost.

ELIMINATION

let x = pencils cost (per)
let y = crayons cost (per)

$$6x + 4y = 3.40 \quad \rightarrow \quad y = .40$$
$$2(3x + 10y = 4.90)$$

flip so its easier habit

$$6x + 4y = 3.40$$
$$6x + 20y = 9.80$$
$$\frac{16y}{16} = \frac{6.40}{16}$$

$$6x + 4(.4) = 3.40$$
$$-1.6 \quad 1.6 \qquad -1.6$$
$$\frac{6x}{6} = \frac{1.8}{6}$$
$$x = 0.30$$

check:
$$6(.3) + 4(.4) = 3.40$$
$$1.8 + 1.6 = 3.4 ✓$$
$$3(.3) + 10(.4) = 4.90$$
$$.90 + 4 = 4.90 ✓$$

8. The solution to the system $\begin{cases} 4x - 3y = 9 \\ 8x - 6y = 81 \end{cases}$ has

$$4x - 3y = 9 \rightarrow y = 3 - 4x$$
$$8x - 6y = 81 \rightarrow y = \frac{81}{6} - 8x$$

A. no solution

B. one solution $\rightarrow (2.625, -7.5)$

C. two solutions

D. infinitely many solutions

Numerical Response

9. If $3x + 2y = 48$ and $2x + 3y = 12$, then the value of $x - 2y$, to the nearest tenth, is _____ .

(Record your answer in the numerical response box from left to right)

10. The value of k, $k \in N$, for which the system of equations $10x + ky = -8$ and $-15x - 6y = 12$ has an infinite number of solutions, is _____ .

(Record your answer in the numerical response box from left to right)

11. The value of a, $a \in N$, for which the system of equations $ax + 5y = 10$ and $6x + 2y = 7$ has no solution, is _____ .

(Record your answer in the numerical response box from left to right)

Answer Key

1. If the lines are parallel, there is no solution.
If the lines intersect, there is one solution.
If the lines are coincident, there are infinitely many solutions.

2. **a)** infinitely many solutions **b)** no solution **c)** one solution

3. If the values of m are identical but the values of b are different, there is no solution.
If the values of m are different, there is one solution.
If the values of m are identical and the values of b are identical, there are infinitely many solutions.

4. **a)** no solution **b)** one solution **c)** infinitely many solutions

5. **a)** e.g. $3x - y = 4$ **b)** e.g. $7x - 3y = 6$ **c)** e.g. $6x - 2y = 18$

6. **a)** $6f + 4b = 2530$ **b)** Front 305 tickets, Back 175 tickets **c)** x:[–100, 500, 100] y:[–100, 700, 100]

7. Let \$$x$ be the cost of a pencil and \$$y$ be the cost of a crayon. Form two equations from the given information. These are $6x + 4y = 3.4$ $3x + 10y = 4.9$ Write each equation in slope y-intercept form. Graph the system of equations and determine the coordinates (x, y) of the intersection point. The answer is $8x + 12y = 8(0.3) + 12(0.4) = 7.2$ *Answer* = \$7.20

8. A

9.

4	8	.	0

10.

4			

11.

1	5		

Systems of Linear Equations Lesson #3:
Solving Systems of Linear Equations by Substitution

Using graphing to solve a system of equations is an excellent visual tool. An alternative approach is to solve the system algebraically. There are two algebraic methods - substitution and elimination.

Method of Substitution

In using the method of substitution, there are four general steps which are shown in the flowchart below.

Step 1	Step 2	Step 3	Step 4
Choose the simpler equation and express one variable in terms of the other.	Substitute the expression from step 1 into the other equation.	Solve the single variable equation.	Substitute the solution from step 3 into the equation in step 1 to find the value of the other variable.

Class Ex. #1

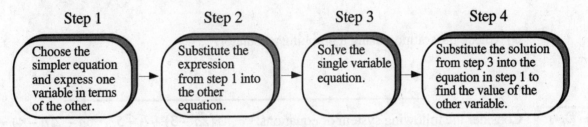

Consider the following system of equations
$$x + 4y = 17$$
$$2x - y = 7$$

a) Solve the system using the method of substitution by rewriting the first equation in the form $x = \ldots$

$(5, 3)$

$x + 4y = 17$

$\underline{x = 17 - 4y}$

$2x - y = 7$

$2(17 - 4y) - y = 7$

$34 - 8y - y = 7$

$34 - 9y = 7 \quad -34$

-34

$y = 3$

$x + 4y = 17$

$x + 4(3) = 17$

$-9y = -27$

$x + 12 = 17$

$x = 5$

b/c

x are ≠ parallel

(there is a solution)

b) Solve the system using the method of substitution by rewriting the first equation in the form $y = \ldots$

$x + 4y = 17$

$5 + 4y = 17 \quad -5$

-5

$\dfrac{4y}{4} = \dfrac{12}{4} \quad y = 3$

$2(5) - y = 7$

$10 - y = 7$

$10 - 3 = 7$

c) Verify that the solution satisfies both equations.

$x = 5$

$y = 3$

$x + 4y = 17$ $2x - y = 7$

$5 + 4(3) = 17$ $2(5) - 3 = 7$

$5 + 12 = 17$ $10 - 3 = 7$

d) Check the solution using a graphing calculator.

Class Ex. #2 Consider the following system of equations: $4x + 3y = 0, \ 8x - 9y = 5.$

a) Solve and verify the system using the method of substitution.

$$\frac{4x + 3y}{3} = \frac{0}{3}$$

$$4x + \cancel{y} = 0$$
$$\ \ \ -y$$

$$y = 4x$$

$$\frac{3y}{3} = \frac{4x}{3}$$

$$\frac{-4x}{3} \ ?$$

$$8x + \frac{36x}{3} = 5$$

$$8x + 12x = 5$$

$$\frac{20x}{20} = 5$$

$$x = \frac{5}{20} \rightarrow x = \frac{1}{4}$$

$$4\left(\frac{1}{4}\right) + 3y = 0$$

$$1 + 3y = 0$$

$$3y = -1$$

$$y = \frac{-1}{3}$$

$$\left(\frac{1}{4}, \frac{-1}{3}\right)$$

$$int$$

b) Check the solution using a graphing calculator.

Class Ex. #3 Consider the following system of equations: $5(2a - 3) + b = 5, \quad 6a - 2(b - 4) = 20.$

a) Solve the system using the method of substitution.

$$\underline{5(2a - 3) + b = 5}$$

$$10a - 15 + b = 5 \qquad a = 2 - b$$
$$\ \ +15 \qquad\quad +15$$

$$\frac{10a + b}{10} = \frac{20}{10}$$

$$a + b = 2$$
$$-b \quad\ -b$$

$$\underline{6(2 + b) - 2(b - 4) = 20}$$

$$(12 + 6b - 2b + 8) = (20)$$
$$\qquad\qquad\qquad\qquad -20$$

$$6b - 2b = 0$$

$$\frac{4b}{4} = \frac{0}{4} \qquad b = 0$$

b) Verify algebraically that the solution satisfies both equations.

$$5(2(2 - 0) - 3) + 0 = 5$$

$$\underline{5(4 - 3)}$$

$$\underline{5(1)}$$

$$5 + 0 = 5$$

$$6(2 + 0) - 2(0 - 4) = 20$$

$$12 \ + \ 8$$

$$20 = 20$$

Enrichment

Solve the following system using substitution.
$$\begin{array}{l} 4x - 3y - 5z = 6 \\ z = 2x \\ -2x + 5y - 14 = 0 \end{array}$$

Complete Assignment Questions #1 - #8

Assignment

1. In each of the following systems:
 - solve the system using the method of substitution
 - verify the solution satisfies both equations
 - check the solution by graphing

a) $y = x + 2, \quad 3x + 4y = 1$

$3x + \dfrac{4y}{4} = \dfrac{1}{4}$

$\dfrac{3x}{3x} + y = \dfrac{1}{4} - 3x$

$y = \dfrac{1}{4} - 3x$

$\dfrac{1}{4} - 3x = x + 2$
$\quad +3x \qquad +3x$

$(4) \ \dfrac{1}{4} = 4x + 2 \ (4)$

$\dfrac{1}{4} = \dfrac{4x}{4} + 8$

$\dfrac{1}{4} = x + 8$
$\quad -8 \qquad -8$
-8

b) $x - 2y = 10, \quad x + 5y + 4 = 0$

$x - 2y = 10$
$\underset{-x}{} \qquad \underset{-x}{}$

$\dfrac{-2y}{2} = \dfrac{10 - x}{2}$

$y = 5 - x$

$4 \ -29 \rightarrow y = -24$

check!

$-29 + 5(-24) + 4 = 0$
$-29 - 120 + 4 = 0$
$-149 + 4 = 0 \ ?$

$x + 5(5 - x) + 4 = 0$
$x + 25 - 5x + 4 = 0$

$-4x + 25 + 4 = 0$
$-4x + 29 = 0$
$\dfrac{}{-4} \qquad \dfrac{}{-4}$

$x + 29 = 0 \longrightarrow x = -29$
$\quad -29 \quad -29$

c) $4p + q = 0, \quad 7p + 4q = 3$

d) $6u - 3v + 4 = 0, \quad 3u = 3v - 5$

$6u - 3v + 4 = 0$
$\qquad -4 \ -4$

$\dfrac{6u - 3v}{3} = \dfrac{-4}{-3}$

$2u - v = -\dfrac{4}{3}$
$-6u \qquad \qquad -6u$

$v = -\dfrac{4}{3} - 6u$

$\dfrac{3u}{3} = \dfrac{3v}{3} - 5$

$u = v - 5$

2. Solve each of the following systems by substitution. Check each solution.

a) $2x - 5y = -7$

$\frac{1}{2}x - y = 3$

Handwritten work:

(2)

$\left(\frac{1}{2}x - \frac{7}{5} - 2x\right) = (3)$ (2)

$2x - \frac{5y}{-5} = \frac{-7}{-5}$

$x - \frac{7}{5} - 2x = 6$

$2x - y = -\frac{7}{5} - 2x$

$+\frac{7}{5}$ $+\frac{7}{5}$

$-2x$

$y = -\frac{7}{5} - 2x$

$x - 2x = 6 + \frac{7}{5}$

$x = 6 + \frac{7}{5}$

$2\left(6 + \frac{7}{5}\right) - \frac{7}{5} - 2x = -7$ $7 - 2$

$12 + \frac{14}{5} - \frac{7}{5} - 2x = -7$ -12 (LATER)

-12

$(5)\left(\frac{7}{5} - 2x\right) = +19^{(5)}$

b) $2(x + 2) + y = 8$

$7x - 2(y - 3) + 24 = 0$

Handwritten work:

$2(x + 2) + y = 8$

$2x + 4 + y = 8$

$-y$ $-y$

$2x + y = 8 - y$

-4 -4

$\frac{2x}{2} = \frac{4 - y}{2}$

$x = 2 - y$

$7x - 2(y - 3) +$

$7(2 - y) - 2(y - 3) = -24$

$(14 + 7y - 2y + 6) = +2$

-20

$7y - 2y = -44$

$\frac{5y}{5} = \frac{-44}{5}$

$y = \frac{-44}{5}$

c) $4(x - 5) + 2(y + 7) = 5$
$6x - 4(y + 1) = 16$

d) $4(2x + 3) - (y - 7) = -5$
$5(1 - 4x) - 4(4 - 2y) = 49$

3. The straight line $px + qy + 14 = 0$ passes through the points $(-3, 1)$ and $(-4, 6)$.

a) Substitute the x a nd y-coordinates of the two points into the equation of the line to form two equations in p and q.

b) Solve this system of equations by substitution to determine the values of p and q and write the equation of the line.

c) Verify the equation in b) using the slope formula and the point-slope equation of a line formula.

4. Solve the following systems by substitution. Explain the results.

a) $y = 3x - 7$
$6x - 2y = 14$

b) $x = 3y + 2$
$2x - 6y = 5$

Multiple Choice

5. If $x + 2y = 10$ and $x - 2y = 2$, then $x + y$ is equal to

A. 8
B. 12
C. 13
D. -2

6. When solving a system of equations, one of which is $\frac{x}{2} - \frac{y}{3} = 1$, a substitution which can be made is

A. $x = \frac{1}{3}(2y + 1)$
B. $y = \frac{1}{2}(3x - 1)$
C. $x = \frac{1}{2}(3y + 6)$
D. $y = \frac{1}{2}(3x - 6)$

Numerical Response **7.** If $s - 8t + 20 = 5s - 7t + 1 = 0$, then the value of $s + t$, to the nearest tenth, is _____ .

(Record your answer in the numerical response box from left to right)

Enrichment **8.** Solve each of the following systems using substitution.

a) $y = 3x$
$2x - y = -4$
$x - 5z = 4$

b) $x = 2y + 1$
$y + 3z + 5 = 0$
$x - 3z = 0$

Answer Key

1. a) $x = -1, y = 1$ **b)** $x = 6, y = -2$ **c)** $p = -\frac{1}{3}, q = \frac{4}{3}$ **d)** $u = \frac{1}{3}, v = 2$

2. a) $x = 44, y = 19$ **b)** $x = -2, y = 8$ **c)** $x = 3, y = -\frac{1}{2}$ **d)** $x = -3, y = 0$

3. a) $-3p + q + 14 = 0$, $-4p + 6q + 14 = 0$ **b)** $p = 5, q = 1$ $5x + y + 14 = 0$

4. a) There are an infinite number of solutions of the form $x = a, y = 3a - 7, a \in R$ because the equations are identical, (the resulting equation reduces to $0 = 0$).

b) There are no solutions since the graphs of the equations are parallel lines, (the resulting equation reduces to $4 = 5$).

5. A **6.** D **7.**

7	.	0	

8. a) $x = 4, y = 12, z = 0$ **b)** $x = -3, y = -2, z = -1$

Systems of Linear Equations Lesson #4:
Solving Systems of Linear Equations by Elimination

So far we have used two methods to solve systems of equations - graphing and substitution. In this lesson we will learn another algebraic technique - the method of elimination. This method is particularly useful when the equations involve fractions.

Method of Elimination

In using the method of elimination, there are four general steps which are shown below.

Step 1: If necessary, multiply each equation by a constant to obtain coefficients for x (or y) that are identical (except perhaps for the sign). →

Step 2: Add or subtract the two equations to eliminate one of the variables. →

Step 3: Solve the resulting equation to determine the value of one of the variables. →

Step 4: Substitute the solution into either of the original equations to determine the value of the other variable.

Consider the system of equations:

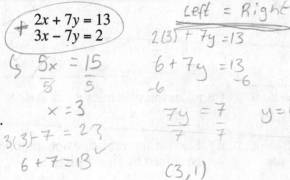

$$2x + 7y = 13$$
$$3x - 7y = 2$$

a) Add the two equations. This will eliminate the variable y.

b) Use the equation in a) to determine the value of x and hence solve the system.

c) Verify the solution satisfies both equations.

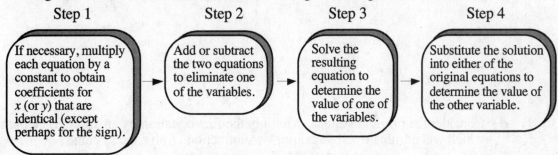

Consider the system of equations:

$$2x + 6y = 6$$
$$2x + 3y = 4.5$$

a) Subtract the two equations. This will eliminate the variable x.

b) Use the equation in a) to determine the value of y and hence solve the system.

c) Verify the solution satisfies both equations.

Complete Assignment Questions #1 - #3

Class Ex. #3

Consider the system of equations: (2) $\left\{ \begin{array}{l} 2x + 3y = 4 \\ 4x - y = 22 \end{array} \right.$ → $4x + 6y = 8$ (−) $5y = 14$ $y = -\frac{14}{5}$

a) Does adding or subtracting the equations eliminate either of the variables?

b) Multiply the second equation by 3 and then add the two equations.

$2x + 3y = 4$

$(4x - y = 22)(3)$

c) Solve and verify the system.

$2x + 3y = 4$

$+\ 12x - 3y = 66$

$\frac{14x}{14} = \frac{70}{14}$ → $x = \frac{70}{14}$ → $\frac{35}{7} = 5$

d) Consider the original system. Multiply the first equation by an appropriate number which will eliminate x by addition or subtraction. Solve the system.

Class Ex. #4

Consider the system of equations: $\left\{ \begin{array}{l} 5a + 3b = 3 \\ 3a - 7b = 81 \end{array} \right.$ (3), (5) → $15a + 9b = 9$, $-\ 15a - 35b = 405$, $\frac{-26b}{-26} = \frac{-396}{-26}$, $b = -\frac{198}{13}$

a) Choose appropriate whole numbers to multiply each equation so that the system can be solved by eliminating b.

b) Solve and verify the system by eliminating b.

$7(5a + 3b = 3)$

$3(3a - 7b = 81)$

$35a + 21b = 21$

$+\ 9a - 21b = 243$

$41a = 264$

$a = 6$

c) Choose appropriate whole numbers to multiply each equation so that the system can be solved by eliminating a.

d) Solve the system by eliminating a.

Class Ex. #5 Solve the following system using elimination. $4x + 2y - 13 = 0,$ $3x = 5y + 26$

$\left\{\begin{array}{l} 4x + 2y - 13 = 0 \\ 26 + 5y = \dfrac{3x}{-3x} \\ -3x \end{array}\right.$

$\left\{\begin{array}{l}(4x + 2y - 13 = 0)5 \\ 2(-3x + 5y + 26 = 0)\end{array}\right\}$

$\rightarrow \begin{array}{r} 20x + 10y - 65 = 0 \\ -6x + 10y + 52 = 0 \\ \hline 26x - 117 = 0 \\ +117 \end{array}$

$\left\{ \dfrac{26x}{26} = \dfrac{117}{26} \right.$

$x = 4.5$

$\boxed{(4.5, -2.5)}$

$\begin{array}{l} 4(4.5) + 2y - 13 = 0 \\ 18 + 2y - 13 = 0 \\ \quad\quad\quad\quad -18 \\ -18 \quad\quad +13 \quad +13 \\ \dfrac{2y}{2} = \dfrac{-5}{2} \quad y = -2.5 \end{array}$

check!

$3(4.5) = 5(-2.5) + 26$

$13.5 = -12.5 + 26$

$13.5 = 13.5$

$4(4.5) + 2(-2.5) - 13 = 0$

$18 - 5 - 13 = 0$

$18 - 18 = 0$

Class Ex. #6 Solve the following system using elimination.

$$\dfrac{x-2}{3} - \dfrac{y+2}{5} = 2, \qquad \dfrac{3}{5}(x+1) - \dfrac{4}{5}(y-3) = \dfrac{21}{2}$$

$15\left(\dfrac{x-2}{3} - \dfrac{y+2}{5}\right) = 2$ (15)

$x - 2 - y + 2 = 2$

$x - y = 2$

$\left(\dfrac{3}{5}(x+1) - \dfrac{4}{5}(y-3)\right) = \dfrac{21}{2}$ (25)

$(1)3(x+1) - 4(y-3) = \left(\dfrac{525}{2}\right)$

$6x + 6 - 8y + 12 = 525$

$6x - 8y = 507$

$\left.\begin{array}{l}(x - y = 2)(8) \\ 6x - 8y = 507\end{array}\right\}$ $\begin{array}{r} 8x - 8y = 16 \\ -6x - 8y = 507 \\ \hline \dfrac{2x}{2} = \dfrac{491}{2} \quad x = 245.5 \end{array}$

$245.5 - y = 2$

$y = 243.5$

check! $\dfrac{245.5 - 243.5 = 2}{6(245.5) - 8(243.5)}$

$1473 - (-1948) = ?$

not $\dfrac{a}{b}$, just seprate.

Complete Assignment Questions #4 - #12

Assignment

1. In each of the following systems:
- solve the system using the method of elimination by adding the equations.
- verify the solution satisfies both equations.

a) $8x - y = 10$
$\quad\quad 4x + y = 14$

$\left\{ 12x = 24 \right.$

$\left\{ x = 2 \right.$

$8(2) - y = 10$
$16 - y = 10$

$y = 6$

$8(2) - 6 = 10$ ✓
$16 - 6 = 10$

b) $x + 3y = 10$
$\quad\quad 5x - 3y = 14$

$\left\{ 6x = 24 \right.$

$\left\{ x = 4 \right.$

$4 + 3y = 10$
$y = 2$

$4 + 3(2) = 10$
$4 + 6 = 10$ ✓

$4(2) + 6 = 14$
$8 + 6 = 14$

$5(4) - 3(2) = 14$
$20 - 6 = 14$ ✓

c) $x + 2y = 3$
$\quad\quad -x + 3y = 2$

$5y = 5$

$y = 1$

$x + 2(1) = 3$
$x + 2 = 3$

$x = 1$

$1 + 2 = 3$ ✓
$-1 + 3(1) = 2$
$-1 + 3 = 2$

d) $4a - 3b = 2$
$\quad\quad -4a - b = 6$

$-4b = 8$

$b = -2$

$4a - 3(-2) = 2$
$4a + 6 = 2$

$a = -1$

$4(-1) - 3(-2) = 2$
$\left\{ -4 + 6 = 2 \right.$ ✓

$-4(-1) - (-2) = 6$
$4 - (-2) = 6$ ✓

$4(-1) + 6 = 2$
$-4 + 6 = 2$ ✓

2. In each of the following systems:

- solve the system using the method of elimination by subtracting the equations.
- verify the solution satisfies both equations.

a) $7x + y = 15$
$3x + y = 3$

b) $5m + 3n = 10$
$5m - 2n = -15$

c) $-x - 10y = 6$
$-x + y = 0$

d) $4a - 3b = -18$
$-2a - 3b = -9$

3. Solve and verify each of the following systems using the method of elimination.

a) $-10p + 10q = 3$
$10p + 5q = 6$

b) $x + 4y = -0.5$
$5x + 4y = 2.3$

c) $4x + 2y - 31 = 0$
$-4x + 6y - 13 = 0$

4. Solve each of the following systems by elimination. Check each solution.

a) $2a + 5b = 16$
$a - b = 1$

b) $4x - 3y = 9$
$2x - 5y = 1$

c) $5x - 2y = 0.6$
$2x + y = 1.5$

5. Solve each of the following systems by elimination. Check each solution.

a) $2x + 4y = 7, \ 4x - 3y = 3$

b) $5x = 8y, \ 4x - 3y + 17 = 0$

c) $7e + 4f - 1 = 0, \ 5e + 3f + 1 = 0$

d) $3x + 2y - 6 = 0, \ 9x = 5y + 18$

6. Consider the system of equations $x - 2y + 1 = 0, \ 2x + 3y = 12$. Solve the system by:

a) elimination

b) substitution.

Which method do you prefer?

7. Consider the system of equations: $11x + 3y + 2 = 0$, $11x - 5y - 62 = 0$.

Solve the system by:

a) elimination

b) substitution.

Which method do you prefer?

8. Solve each of the following systems by elimination. Explain the results.

a) $-2x + 6y - 1 = 0$, $5x - 15y + 2.5 = 0$

b) $2x - 4y = 7$, $-7x + 14y = -21$

9. Solve each of the following systems by elimination.

a) $3x - \frac{1}{2}y = 5$
$\frac{1}{3}x + \frac{1}{4}y = 3$

b) $\frac{m}{2} - \frac{n-4}{4} = 2$
$\frac{3m}{4} - \frac{n}{5} = 5$

c) $\frac{1}{2}(2x - y) + \frac{3}{4}x = 6$
$\frac{1}{2}x - \frac{1}{3}y = \frac{2}{3}$

Multiple Choice **10.** When b is eliminated from the equations $2x + b = 8$ and $5x + 2b = 2$, we obtain

A. $7x = 10$
B. $9x = 18$
C. $x = -14$
D. $3x = -6$

11. The solution to the systems of equations $x + y = 0$, $\frac{1}{2}x + \frac{1}{3}y = 1$ is

A. $x = 6, y = -6$
B. $x = 1, y = -1$
C. $x = 0, y = -0$
D. $x = -6, y = 6$

Numerical Response

12. If $\frac{1}{3}x + 5 = \frac{2}{3}y$ and $\frac{1}{2}x + \frac{1}{3}y = \frac{1}{3}$, then the value of $y - \frac{1}{2}x$, to the nearest tenth, is ______ .

(Record your answer in the numerical response box from left to right)

Answer Key

1. a) $x = 2,\ y = 6$ **b)** $x = 4,\ y = 2$ **c)** $x = 1,\ y = 1$ **d)** $a = -1,\ b = -2$

2. a) $x = 3,\ y = -6$ **b)** $m = -1,\ n = 5$ **c)** $x = -\frac{6}{11},\ y = -\frac{6}{11}$ **d)** $a = -\frac{3}{2},\ b = 4$

3. a) $p = \frac{3}{10},\ q = \frac{3}{5}$ **b)** $x = 0.7,\ y = -0.3$ **c)** $x = 5,\ y = \frac{11}{2}$

4. a) $a = 3,\ b = 2$ **b)** $x = 3,\ y = 1$ **c)** $x = 0.4,\ y = 0.7$

5. a) $x = \frac{3}{2},\ y = 1$ **b)** $x = -8,\ y = -5$ **c)** $e = 7,\ f = -12$ **d)** $x = 2,\ y = 0$

6. $x = 3,\ y = 2$ **7.** $x = 2,\ y = -8$

8. a) There are an infinite number of solutions of the form $x = a,\ y = \frac{1}{6}(2a + 1),\ a \in R$ because the equations are identical (the resulting equation reduces to $0 = 0$).

b) There are no solutions since the graphs of the equations are parallel lines (the resulting equation reduces to e.g. $0 = 7$).

9. a) $x = 3,\ y = 8$ **b)** $m = 12,\ n = 20$ **c)** $x = 5,\ y = \frac{11}{2}$

10. C **11.** A **12.**

7	.	5	

Systems Of Linear Equations Lesson #5:
Applications of Systems of Linear Equations - Part One

We have discussed three different methods for solving systems of equations.

**Methods for
Solving Systems of Equations**

*y = mx + b
intersection (x, y)*

Graphing **Substitution** **Elimination**

*Solve for 1
(x or y) =*

*eliminate x or y
by (+) or (-)
the equations*

In this lesson we apply these methods in problem solving.

Problem Solving

We can solve a variety of types of problems using a system of equations. There are four general steps to problem solving which are shown in the flowchart below.

Step 1 **Step 2** **Step 3** **Step 4**

Solve for

| Introduce variables to represent the unknown values. | → | Form a system of equations involving the variables. | → | Solve the system. | → | Answer the problem and check the solution. |

Number Applications

(-) x - y = 9

Class Ex. #1

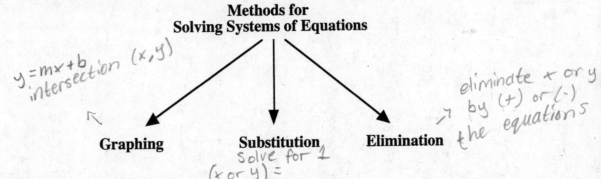

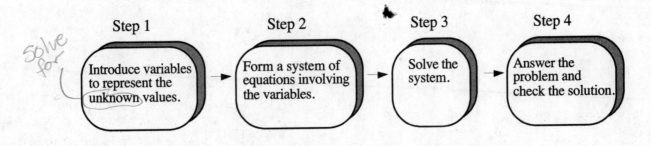

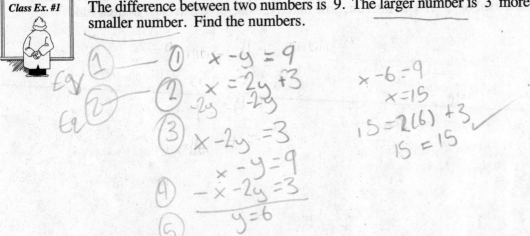

The difference between two numbers is 9. The larger number is 3 more than twice the smaller number. Find the numbers.

Eq ① — ① x - y = 9

Eq ② — ② x = 2y + 3
* -2y -2y*

③ x - 2y = 3

* x - y = 9*
④ -x - 2y = 3
* ─────────────*
* y = 6*

⑤

x - 6 = 9
x = 15

15 = 2(6) + 3 ✓

Class Ex. #2
The perimeter of a rectangle is 40 metres. The width is 4 metres less than the length. Find the dimensions of the rectangle.

let L = length let w = width.

$w = L - 4$

① $w = L - 4$

② $40 = 2L + 2(w)$

Substitution

$40 = 2L + 2(L-4)$
$40 = 2L + 2L - 8$
$40 = 4L - 8$ (+8)

$\frac{48}{4} = \frac{4L}{4}$
$12 = L$

$w = L - 4$
$w = 12 - 4$
$w = 8$

Money Applications

Class Ex. #3
Gary had a total of $260 in five-dollar bills and ten-dollar bills.
If he has 33 bills in total, how many of each denomination does he have?

$x = \#$ of $5 bills
$y = \#$ of $10 bills

$10(x + y = 33)$
$5x + 10y = 260$

$10x + 10y = 330$
$-5x + 10y = 260$

$\frac{5x}{5} = \frac{70}{5}$
$x = 14$

$5(14) + 10y = 260$
$70 + 10y = 260 - 70$
-70

$\frac{10y}{10} = \frac{190}{10}$
$y = 19$

check: $14 + 19 = 33$
$5(14) + 10(19) = 260$
$70 + 190 = 260$ ✓

Class Ex. #4
Lora invested her inheritance of $48 000 in two different mutual funds. At the end of one year one fund had earned 10.5% interest and the other fund had earned 12% interest. If she received a total of $5520 in interest, how much did she invest in each mutual fund?

$x =$ How much invested in first fund {sub}
$y =$ second fund

① $(x + y = 48 000)(0.12)$
② $0.105x + 0.12y = 5520$

$0.12x + 0.12y = 5760$
$-0.105x + 0.12y = 5520$

$\frac{0.015x}{0.015} = \frac{240}{0.015}$
$x = 16000$

$0.105(16 000) + 0.12y = 5520$
$1680 + 0.12y = 5520$
-1680 -1680

$\frac{0.12y}{0.12} = \frac{3840}{0.12}$
$y = 32000$

check: ① $16000 + 32000 = 4800$
② $0.105(16000) + 0.12(3200)$
$= 5520$
$1680 + 3840 = 5520$

Complete Assignment questions #1 - #13

Assignment

In problems #1 - #10 use the following procedure:

a) Introduce variables to represent the unknown values.
b) Form a system of equations involving the variables.
c) Solve the system.
d) Answer the problem and check the solution.

1. A rectangle is to be drawn with perimeter 64 cm. If the length is to be 14 cm more than the width, determine the area of the rectangle.

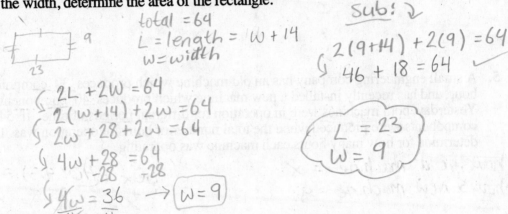

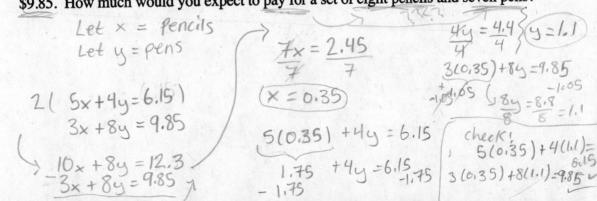

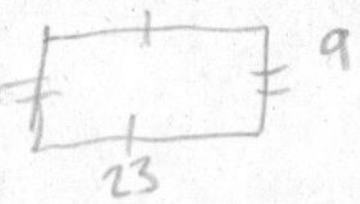

total = 64
L = length = w + 14
w = width

2L + 2W = 64
2(w + 14) + 2w = 64
2w + 28 + 2w = 64
4w + 28 = 64
−28 −28
4w/4 = 36/4 → w = 9

Sub:
2(9+14) + 2(9) = 64
46 + 18 = 64 ✓

L = 23
W = 9

2. The sum of two numbers is 3, and twice the larger number is 36 more than three times the smaller number. Find the numbers.

36 ÷ 2 = 18

Larger # = 18
Smaller # = x

3 = 18 ÷ x
x = 6 → 18/6 = 3

3. Five pencils and four pens cost $6.15. Three similar pencils and eight similar pens cost $9.85. How much would you expect to pay for a set of eight pencils and seven pens?

Let x = pencils
Let y = pens

2(5x + 4y = 6.15)
3x + 8y = 9.85

10x + 8y = 12.3
−3x + 8y = 9.85

7x/7 = 2.45/7
x = 0.35

5(0.35) + 4y = 6.15
1.75 + 4y = 6.15
−1.75 −1.75

4y/4 = 4.4/4 y = 1.1

3(0.35) + 8y = 9.85
1.05
−1.05 −1.05
8y/8 = 8.8/8 = 1.1

check!
5(0.35) + 4(1.1) = 6.15
3(0.35) + 8(1.1) = 9.85 ✓

4. The perimeter of a rectangle is 40 cm. If the length were doubled and the width halved, the perimeter would be increased by 16 cm. Find the dimensions of the original rectangle.

$2L + 2w = 40$ $40 + 16 = 56$

$(2)\ \frac{2L}{2} + \frac{w}{2} = 16$

$L + W = 16$

$4L + W = 56$

$4L = 56 - w$ $\quad \frac{4L}{4} = \frac{56 - w}{4}$

$L = 14 - w$

$2(14 - w) + 2w = 40$

$28 - 2w + 2w = 40$

$28 = 40$

5. A small engineering company has an old machine which produces 30 components per hour, and has recently installed a new machine which produces 40 components per hour. Yesterday, both machines were in operation for different periods of time. If 545 components were produced when the total number of hours of operation was 15 hours, determine for how many hours each machine was operating.

\# of hours old machine = x
\# of hours New machine = y

$30x + 40y = 545$

$30(x + y = 15)$

$30x + 40y = 545$
$-\ 30x + 30y = 450$

$\frac{10y}{10} = \frac{95}{10} \rightarrow y = 9.5$

$30x + 40(9.5) = 545$

$30x + 380 = 545$
$-380 \quad -380$

$\frac{30x}{30} = \frac{165}{30} \rightarrow x = 5.5$

Check!

$30(5.5) + 40(9.5) = 545$

$165 + 380 = 545$ ✓

$x + y = 545 \rightarrow 5.5 + 9.5 = 15$ ✓

6. In a hockey arena, a seat at rink level costs three times as much as a seat in the upper level. If five seats at rink level cost $112 more than eight seats in the upper level, find the cost of a seat at rink level.

x = Rink level seats cost
y = Upper level seats cost

$3x = y$

$5x - 112 = 8y$

$5x - 112 = 8(3x)$
$+112 \quad +112$

$5x$

0.25 0.10

7. Rachel had been saving quarters and dimes to buy a new toy. She had 103 coins and had saved $21.40. How many coins of each type had she saved?

Let x = quarters #
Let y = dimes #

$0.25x + 0.10y = 21.40$
$0.10(x + y = 103)$

$0.25x + 0.10y = 21.40$
$-\ 0.10x + 0.10y = 10.3$
$\frac{0.15x}{0.15} = \frac{11.1}{0.15} \rightarrow \boxed{x = 74}$

$0.25(74) + 0.10y = 21.40$
$18.5 + 0.10y = 21.40$
$-18.5 \qquad -18.5$
$\frac{0.10y}{0.10} = \frac{2.9}{0.10} \rightarrow \boxed{y = 29}$

Check: $0.25(74) + 0.10(29) = 21.40$
$18.5 + 2.9 = 21.4$ ✓ | $x + y = 103$, $74 + 29 = 103$ ✓

8. One year a man saved $5000. Next year his income increased by 10% and his expenditure decreased by 16%. He was able to save $14 600. Calculate his income in the second year.

x = Salary y = Expenses

1y = 5000
2nd y = 0.10

Re-Arrange

$x - y = 5000$
$(x + x(0.1)) - (y - y(0.16)) = 14\,600$

$x = 5000 + y$
$(5000 + y) + (5000 + y)(0.1) - (y - y(0.16)) = 14600$
$(5000 + y) + (500 + 0.1y) - (y - y(0.16)) = 14600$

9. Chad invested $\frac{3}{4}$ of his $56 000 lottery winnings in two different mutual funds. At the end of the year the *Balanced Fund* had earned 6.5% interest, but the *Emerging Markets Fund* had lost 3%. If the value of Chad's funds had increased by $1 590, determine the amount invested in each fund.

10. Shoji invested \$7 000, part at 9% interest and part at 6% interest. The interest obtained from the 6% investment was half of the interest obtained from the 9% investment. How much was invested at each rate?

7000

11. The heights, in metres, of the vertical rods of a suspension bridge, as you move out from the centre of the bridge, form the sequence,

1.1, 1.4, 1.9, 2.6, . . .

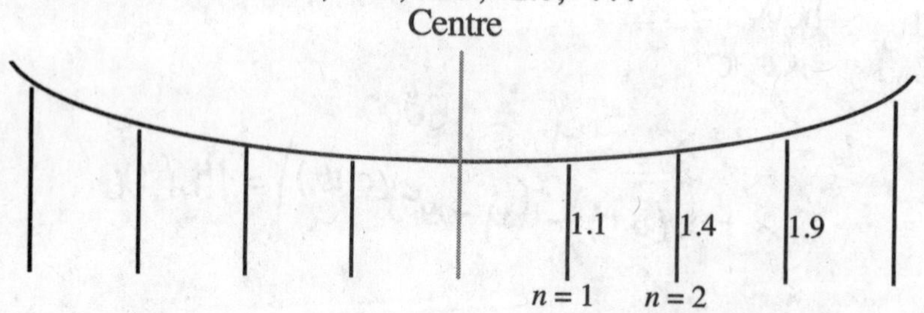

a) Without a calculator determine the next two terms in the sequence.

b) The height, h metres, of the nth rod is given by the formula $h = a + bn^2$. Using the terms of the sequence given to form a system of equations, determine the values of a and b and state the formula.

c) Use this formula to verify the answers in a).

Numerical Response **12.** The diagram shows two parallel lines and a transversal.

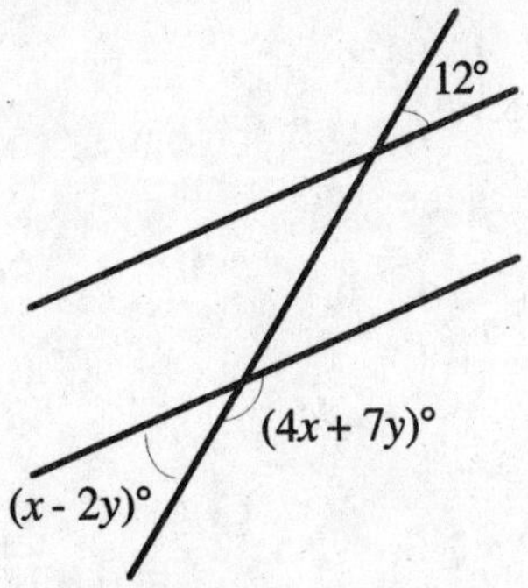

The value of $x + y$, to the nearest whole number, is _____.

(Record your answer in the numerical response box from left to right)

13. A number consists of two digits whose sum is 11. If the digits are reversed, the original number is increased by 27. The original number is _____.

(Record your answer in the numerical response box from left to right)

Answer Key

1. 207 cm^2 **2.** 9, –6 **3.** \$10.50 **4.** 12 cm by 8 cm

5. $5\frac{1}{2}$ hours old and $9\frac{1}{2}$ hours new **6.** \$48 **7.** 74 quarters, 29 dimes

8. \$44 000 **9.** \$30 000, \$12 000 **10.** \$3000 at 6% and \$4000 at 9%

11.a) 3.5, 4.6, **b)** $a = 1$, $b = 0.1$, $h = 1 + 0.1n^2$

12.

3	6		

13.

4	7		

Systems of Linear Equations Lesson #6:
Applications of Systems of Linear Equations - Part Two

Mixture Applications

Cashew nuts costing $22/kg are mixed with Brazil nuts costing $16/kg.
The mixture weighs 50 kg and sells for $18/kg.
How many kilograms of each type of nut were used in the mixture?

Earl the chemist has to make 180 mL of 60% hydrochloric acid (HCl) solution . He has available a one litre bottle of 45% HCl solution and a one litre bottle of 70% HCl solution by volume. How many mL of each solution are mixed to make the 60% HCl solution?

Distance, Speed, and Time Problems

A student drove the 1245 km from Edmonton to Vancouver in $16\frac{1}{2}$ hours. This included a one hour stop in Golden and a 30 minute stop in Kamloops. She averaged 100 km/h on the divided highways and 75 km/h on the non-divided mountainous roads. How much time did she spend on the divided highways?

A small cruise boat took 3 hours to travel 36 km down a river with the current. On the return trip it took 4 hours against the current. Find the speed of the current and the speed of the small cruise boat in still water.

Complete Assignment questions #1 - #9

Assignment

In problems #1 - #8 use the following procedure.

a) Introduce variables to represent the unknown values.
b) Form a system of equations involving the variables.
c) Solve the system.
d) Answer the problem and check the solution.

1. Candy costing $6 per kg is mixed with candy costing $4.50 per kg to produce 112 kg of candy worth $ 612. How many kg of each type of candy were used?

2. 300 grams of Type A Raisin Bran is mixed with 500 grams of Type B Raisin Bran to produce a mixture which is 11% raisins. Type A Raisin Bran has twice as many raisins per kilogram as Type B. What percentage of raisins are in each type of Raisin Bran?

3. A scientist has to make 800 ml of 61% sulfuric acid solution. He has available a one litre bottle of 40% sulfuric acid solution and a one litre bottle of 75% sulfuric acid solution by volume.

a) How many ml of each solution are mixed to make the 61% sulfuric acid solution?

b) What is the maximum volume, rounded down to the nearest ml, of 61% sulfuric acid solution which the scientist could mix with the original bottles of sulfuric acid?

4. Pure gold is often mixed with other metals to produce jewellery. Pure gold is 24 carat. 12 carat gold is $\frac{12}{24}$ or 50% gold, 6 carat gold is $\frac{6}{24}$ or 25% gold, etc. A jeweller has some 12 carat gold and some 21 carat gold and wants to produce 90 grams of 75% gold.

a) What percentage of gold is 21 carat?

b) How many grams of 12 carat gold and of 21 carat gold are needed to produce the mixture?

5. A train travels 315 km in the same time that a car travels 265 km. If the train travels on average 20 km/h faster than the car, find the average speed of the car and the time taken to travel 265 km.

6. A small plane flying into a wind takes 3h to travel the 780 km journey from Lethbridge to Fort McMurray. At the same time, a similar plane leaves Fort McMurray and reaches Lethbridge in $2\frac{1}{2}$h. If the planes have the same cruising speed in windless conditions, determine the speed of the wind.

7. A cyclist leaves home at 7:30 am to cycle to school 7 km away. He cycles at 10 km/h until he has a puncture; then he has to push his bicycle the rest of the way at 3 km/h. He arrives at school at 8:40 am. How far did he have to push his bicycle?

Multiple Choice

8. A shopkeeper wishes to mix two types of tea together. One type sells at \$8 per kg and the second type sells at \$12 per kg. He wishes to make 100 kg of the mixture to sell at \$11 per kg. The number of kg of the first type of tea in this mixture should be

A. 25
B. $33\frac{1}{3}$
C. 50
D. 75

Numerical Response

9. Raj left home at 1 pm to travel 675 km to visit his sister. He averaged 110km/h for the first part of the trip during which he had a 1 hour rest, and 90 km/h for the second part of the trip during which he had a 30 minute rest. He reached his destination at 9 pm. The number of minutes taken for the first part of the trip, to the nearest minute, was _____ .

(Record your answer in the numerical response box from left to right)

Answer Key

1. 72 kg of \$6/kg candy, 40 kg of \$4.50/kg candy

2. 16% in type A, 8% in type B

3. a) 320 ml of 40% solution, 480 ml of 75% solution **b)** 1666 ml

4. a) 87.5% **b)** 30 g of 12 carat gold, 60 g of 21 carat gold

5. 106 km/h, $2\frac{1}{2}$ h

6. 26 km/h **7.** 2 km **8.** A **9.**

2	7	0	

Systems of Linear Equations Lesson #7: Practice Test

Numerical Response **1.** Two students worked together to solve a system of equations which had integer solutions. Tara made a table of values for the first equation and Jorge made a table of values for the second equation.

Tara

x	y
−2	−6
0	−2
2	2
4	6

Jorge

x	y
−3	−2
−1	0
1	2
3	4
5	6

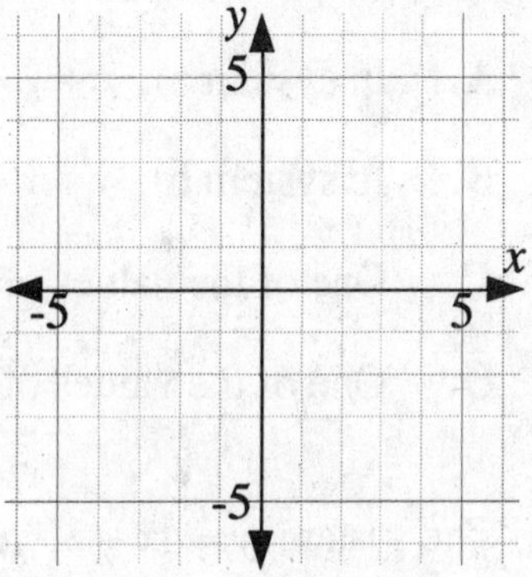

Using the students' results to determine the solution to the system, the value of $x + y$ is _____ .

(Record your answer in the numerical response box from left to right)

1. The ordered pair (x, y) which satisfies the system of equations $x - 3y = 8,\ x + 4y = -13$, is

A. $(-1, 3)$

B. $(3, -1)$

C. $(-1, -3)$

D. $(3, 1)$

2. The number of solutions to the system of equations $6x - 2y = 24,\ 5y = 15x - 64$, is

A. zero

B. one

C. two

D. infinite

Numerical Response **2.** Alyssa graphs the equations $x - y = -4$ and $x + 2y = 4$. The y-coordinate, to the nearest hundredth, of the point of intersection is _____ .

(Record your answer in the numerical response box from left to right)

3. Consider the following two systems of equations.

a) $y = \frac{2}{3}x + 1, \quad y = \frac{1}{2}x - 2$ **b)** $4x + 5y = 18, \quad 2x + 3y = 1$

Solve the above systems of equations using a graphing calculator and determine which one of the following statements is true.

A. In system a), $x + y = 29$.

B. In system b), $x + y = 40.5$.

C. One of the values of x is 42.5 more than the other.

D. One of the values of y is 42.5 more than the other.

4. The system $y = 4x - 8, \; x = by + c,$ has an infinite number of solutions if

A. $b = 0.25$ and $c = -2$

B. $b = 0.25$ and $c = 2$

C. $b = 0$ and $c = 0$

D. $b = 4$ and $c = -8$

5. The graphs of $y = ax + b$ and $y = cx + d$ are parallel.
The number of solutions to the system $y = ax + b, \; y = cx + d$ is

A. zero **B.** one **C.** two **D.** infinite

6. For which system of equations graphed on a grid is the point $(-2, -1)$ a solution?

A. $x - 2y = 3, \quad x + 5y = -11$

B. $3x - 3y = -9, \quad x - 4y = -6$

C. $2x - 10y = 6, \quad x + 5y = -3$

D. $x + y = -3, \quad -2x + 5y = -1$

7. When solving a system of equations, one of which is $\frac{x}{4} - \frac{y}{3} = 2$, a substitution which can be made is

A. $x = \frac{1}{4}(3y + 2)$

B. $x = \frac{1}{3}(4y + 6)$

C. $x = \frac{1}{4}(3y + 24)$

D. $x = \frac{1}{3}(4y + 24)$

8. In solving the system $3a - 2b = 14,\ 2a + b = 7$ by elimination, an equation which arises could be

A. $-7b = 49$

B. $-b = 7$

C. $5a = 21$

D. $7a = 28$

9. If $x + y = 12$ and $x - y = 2$, then $x + 2y$ is equal to

A. 10

B. 17

C. 19

D. 34

10. If $3(x - 2) + y = 7$ and $4x - 3(y - 1) = 16$, then y is equal to

A. $-\frac{15}{13}$

B. $-\frac{5}{13}$

C. 1

D. 4

11. Solve the following system using elimination.

$$\frac{2p}{3} - \frac{3q}{4} = \frac{11}{2}, \quad \frac{5p}{9} + \frac{q}{6} = 3$$

The value of p is

A. 6

B. $\frac{75}{38}$

C. $\frac{48}{11}$

D. $\frac{7}{24}$

Numerical Response **3.** If $m - 2n - 30 = 2m - n - 39 = 0$, then the value of $m - n$, to the nearest tenth, is _____ .

(Record your answer in the numerical response box from left to right)

12. If $\frac{2x + y}{3} - 5 = 0$ and $\frac{3x - y}{5} = 1$, then the value of y is

A. 4

B. 7

C. $\frac{13}{5}$

D. $\frac{23}{25}$

Numerical Response **4.** The straight line $ax + y = b$ passes through the points $(-1, 1)$ and $(-5, 4)$. The value of ab, to the nearest hundredth, is ______.

(Record your answer in the numerical response box from left to right)

Use the following information to answer the next two questions.

> Lisbeth cycled 100 km from Calgary to Canmore. On the uphill sections her average speed was 12 km/h, and on the rest of the trip her average speed was 28 km/h.
>
> She cycled for a total of 5 hours on the journey.

13. If x km represents the distance travelled uphill and y km represents the distance travelled on the rest of the trip, which of the following systems could be used to determine the values of x and y?

A. $x + y = 100,\quad 12x + 28y = 5$

B. $x + y = 100,\quad \dfrac{x}{12} + \dfrac{y}{28} = 5$

C. $x + y = 5,\quad 12x + 28y = 100$

D. $x + y = 5,\quad \dfrac{x}{12} + \dfrac{y}{28} = 100$

Numerical Response **5.** The distance travelled uphill, to the nearest km, is _____.

(Record your answer in the numerical response box from left to right)

14. Susan solves the system of equations $\frac{2}{x} + \frac{3}{y} = 2,\ \frac{8}{x} - \frac{9}{y} = 1$

by first substituting a for $\frac{1}{x}$ and b for $\frac{1}{y}$. The value of xy is

A. 6

B. $\frac{1}{6}$

C. $-\frac{49}{720}$

D. $-\frac{720}{49}$

15. Chris walks at 8 km/h and runs at 12 km/h.
One day he walks and runs on the way from his house to the library.
It takes him 20 minutes.
On his way back from the library he again walks and runs, but he runs twice as far as he did on the way to the library. The journey home takes $17\frac{1}{2}$ minutes.
The distance between his house and the library is

A. 3 km

B. 4 km

C. 5 km

D. 6 km

Written Response - 5 marks

1. Erika plans to set up an internet connection with *Y2K Internet Company*. There are three plans to choose from.

   - Plan 1 costs \$20 per month and includes a user fee of 40¢ per hour.
   - Plan 2 costs \$15 per month and includes a user fee of 80¢ per hour.
   - Plan 3 costs \$60 per month for unlimited use.

- What factor would determine which plan is most economical?

- Let y = total cost per month in dollars and x = number of hours of use per month. Write a linear equation for each of the three plans.

- Use a graphical method to determine when plans 1 and 2 are equally economical to use. State the graphing window used.

- Verify the solution in the bullet above algebraically.

- For each of plans 1 and 2 determine the number of hours of use which could be obtained for \$60.

- Devise a simple rule which would determine which plan is most economical depending on the expected number of hours of internet use per month.

Answer Key

1. C **2.** A **3.** C **4.** B **5.** A **6.** D **7.** D **8.** D

9. B **10.** C **11.** A **12.** B **13.** B **14.** A **15.** A

Numerical Response

1.

7			

2.

2	.	6	7

3.

2	3		

4.

0	.	1	9

5.

3	0		

Written Response

1.
- The expected number of hours of internet use per month.
- $y = 20 + 0.4x$, $y = 15 + 0.8x$, $y = 60$.
- 12.5 hours, eg. x:[0, 50, 10], y:[0, 50, 10].
- 12.5 hours.
- 100 hours, $56\frac{1}{4}$ hours
- Plan 2 for up to 12.5 hours, Plan 1 for between 12.5 and 100 hours, Plan 3 for more than 100 hours.

Notes Page 1

Notes Page 2